MEASURES FOR PROGRESS

A HISTORY OF THE NATIONAL BUREAU OF STANDARDS

REXMOND C. COCHRANE

Editorial consultant—James R. Newman

First printing: 1966
Second printing: 1974

NATIONAL BUREAU OF STANDARDS

U. S. DEPARTMENT OF COMMERCE

For sale by the Superintendent of Documents, U.S. Government Printing Office, Washington, D.C. 20402
(Order by SD Catalog No. C13.10:275.) Price $8.50

Grateful acknowledgment is made to the Prints and Photographs Division of the Library of Congress for the illustrations on pages 4, 10, and 113, the latter from the Herbert French collection; to the National Archives for those on pages 22, 40 (Public Buildings Service collection), and 230 (Bureau of Reclamation collection); to the Coast and Geodetic Survey for those on pages 25, 56, 516; to the Smithsonian Institution for those on pages 6 (Transportation Section) and 205 (National Air Museum collection); to the National Geographic Society for the copyright photograph used as the front end paper and that on page 481; to the Archives Library of M.I.T. for the portraits on page 652; to the Baltimore Sunpapers for the illustration on page 85; to Harris & Ewing for that on page 292; and to Charles B. Kipps of NBS for that on page 168.

Library of Congress Catalog Card Number: 65–62472

FOREWORD

If men are to accomplish together anything useful whatever they must, above all, be able to understand one another. That is the basic reason for a National Bureau of Standards.

True, men may get together themselves and agree on terms and definitions. Those who make screws may, for example, agree to avoid confusion by manufacturing a common range of sizes and thread numbers. But in broad areas the only possible way of securing agreement is by authoritative action by an agency of the Federal Government. The early history of the confusion in this country demonstrates this clearly.

There is also a genuine difference between the setting of fundamental standards and the practice of standardization as conducted in industry. The former has to do with definitions, with specifying clearly and exactly what technical words mean, in a fundamental and scientific sense. The latter may be concerned with commercial definitions, but it is primarily involved with the task of agreeing on limiting ranges of sizes and forms which shall be manufactured in large numbers.

The former may sometimes go too fast, but it can never go too far. As applied science ramifies there are always new terms appearing, where ambiguity or inaccuracy can hold up progress, where undue delay in forming exact specifications can slow down accomplishment. Yet too much speed can sometimes pin matters down in ways that are later found to be clumsy or expensive. It requires good judgment, and this can be applied only when there is sound comprehension not only of the science involved, but also of the ways in which it is being applied, and, more subtly, of the ways in which it is likely to be applied in the future. Sound fixing of standards can hardly occur in an ivory tower.

The latter can indeed go too far. The subject does not need treatment here. We have all witnessed commercial situations in which premature freezing of performance has throttled progress.

Now there is a popular fallacy about this business of setting standards. It is the belief that it is inherently a dull business. One of the reasons that I am glad to see the present history appear is that I believe it will help to dissipate this misunderstanding. Properly conceived the setting of standards can be, not only a challenging task, but an exciting one.

There are many examples of this as the history is traced. Let me mention just one. How long is a second? Certainly we ought to know that. Do we just take the time for the earth to revolve on its axis, and divide this by 86,400? The earth does not turn uniformly. Shall we use the time for the earth to complete a path around the sun? This depends, to a slight degree, on what other planets are doing in the meantime. How about the time for light to travel a measured distance? This would be in a vacuum no doubt, and the technique is difficult. There is even a possibility of becoming involved with questions of special relativity. Shall we use the time necessary for some specified atom to emit a certain number of vibrations? Now we are on sounder ground, but not entirely out of the woods. We have to be sure we have the right atom, and that we can count correctly. I am not of course attempting in this example to really explore this problem. I merely wish to indicate how deep an apparently simple question can lead.

Should an agency that is committed to the duty of setting standards also do research? I believe the answer is clear. Those who would set scientific standards wisely cannot limit themselves to working with science, they needs must work in science. Only those who are practicing scientists can grasp clearly where need for definition lies, and what constitutes useful definition.

The National Bureau of Standards has had a good history of accomplishment, and has contributed much to the scientific and technical progress of this country, to its security and well being. It is well that the story should be told. I assure you that the story will not be dull.

Vannevar Bush

VANNEVAR BUSH

PREFACE

This book is designed to provide a better understanding of a highly specialized Federal agency among the community of scientists and engineers that the agency serves directly, among the general public whose taxes support it but who are usually only indirectly aware of its existence, and among Government officials who depend on it for services or whose policy actions control its destiny.

The need for a definitive history of the National Bureau of Standards became apparent about the time of its 50th anniversary in 1951. This need developed primarily from the very rapid expansion of the role of Government in the scientific and technological progress of the Nation and the evolution of the Bureau's uniquely critical role in this expansion. A properly documented history would serve to clarify the dynamic nature of the Bureau's mission by recording its responses to the changing needs of the increasingly complex scientific activities within the Federal Government and throughout the Nation as a whole. Because of the intimate relationship of progress in measurement to progress in science, a history of the Bureau contributes to a better understanding of the extraordinary development of science and technology in this century.

A comprehensive and easily accessible record of the experience and goals of those whose achievements made the National Bureau of Standards what it is today should help significantly in making the organization even more effective in the future. The cumulative experience of those who managed the Bureau's affairs in the past would be of great value to those responsible for its future.

Initial efforts to produce an objective history from within the Bureau's own staff were unsuccessful. It was finally concluded that the task should be done by professional historians and writers. After an extensive survey of various alternatives, in 1960 we succeeded in obtaining the assistance of the distinguished scientific editor, James R. Newman, and of Dr. Rexmond C. Cochrane, an experienced and talented historian. Mr. Newman consented to provide general supervision for the production of the history, and Dr. Cochrane agreed to undertake the exacting professional task of research and writing. It is also most fortunate, and especially fitting, that Dr.

Vannevar Bush, architect of so much of the Nation's scientific and technological structure and a member of the Bureau's Visiting Committee from 1942 to 1946, should provide the history with a foreword.

Actual work on the history began in 1961, the same year that construction began on the Bureau's new laboratories at Gaithersburg, Md. It was hoped that the history would appear about the time that the new laboratories were ready. Although both projects have been delayed, publication of the history in 1966 will coincide with the expected move of the great majority of the Bureau's staff to the new site.

An important and planned byproduct of providing a history of the Bureau's development has been to bring together for ready reference the major documents bearing on important policy decisions and technical achievements. Extensive footnotes throughout the history identify these documents. Copies of all these, either in full size or microfilm, will be available in the Bureau's Gaithersburg Library.

The Bureau's first 50 years coincide almost exactly with the terms of service of its first four Directors. The history has been limited to this period, although a final chapter provides a brief résumé of major events since 1951, particularly the relocation plan. A detailed examination of the period of my own administration as the fifth Director will be left to later historians.

ALLEN V. ASTIN
Director
National Bureau of Standards

AUTHOR'S INTRODUCTION

This is the history of the origins and development of a key scientific agency in our Federal establishment. It is also a study of the long-debated role of science in government, of science as an activity of the Federal Government, illustrated by focusing a magnifying glass, as it were, on a single such agency. By choice I have written the history from the point of view of the men who sought the establishment of a central agency dedicated to providing standards of measurement for the Nation, and of those who accomplished the first 50 years of that history.

In the early months of the undertaking some among the staff seniors questioned whether the history of the Bureau could be written. There was no possible way to cover in a single work, let alone do justice to, the thousands of research and investigative projects that have occupied the Bureau over a half century. And the flavor of the past, so important to those who had known it, was probably beyond recapture. The challenge, repeated at suitable intervals, was to prove a spur throughout the research and composition of the history. Color leaped to the eye out of the middle of blurred typescript. But it was inevitable that, considering the far-ranging research of the Bureau, some compromises had to be made.

The record of the scientific and technologic research at the National Bureau of Standards is contained in its more than 10,000 papers published since 1901. No attempt has been made to mention more than a fraction of them or of the investigators who wrote them. Only the outlines of that research and some of its highlights have been presented, for their reflection of the changing nature of Bureau research, and to set it in the framework of the scientific, social, and political history of the past half century as events have impinged upon the Bureau.

Some wonderful controversies have engulfed the Bureau from time to time. They were perhaps unavoidable, in view of the nature of the Bureau mission. I have been permitted a remarkable degree of freedom in setting down my judgment of these and other Bureau affairs as found in the historical records.

I have been immeasurably helped by the strong academic tradition that has been characteristic of the Bureau since its founding, and the sense of so many of its members, renewed from decade to decade, that the Bureau was in the stream of the history of science and creating a history of its own. How else explain the extensive collection of memorabilia found in every section and division, handwritten and typed, and labeled "Save"?

The concern of the administration for historical documents of the Bureau was manifested formally in the spring of 1956 when all divisions were asked to locate historical materials in their possession and forward them to a central file. Many formal documents that were nowhere else available, as well as much that was informal, were thus brought together, and with other historical documents secured in the course of research, made part of the NBS Historical File that was set up as the project began.

I have also been fortunate in being able to interview or correspond with several score members or former members of the staff, the employment and memories of many of them spanning the administration of all five Bureau directors. Their names and those of others outside the Bureau who have furnished knowledge of the Bureau's past appear in the footnotes to the history.

The research and writing of the history was facilitated by the fullest possible cooperation of all members of the present staff, who have made their time, their files, and their information freely available, who have provided leads to material and clues to the meaning of some of that material, and who have patiently read and reread the sections of the history within their province or recollection.

Among the many present or former members who have kindly read the sections on research in their province and made contributions to its historical background or that of the Bureau, to whom I wish to express my particular thanks, are Franz L. Alt, William D. Appel, Howard S. Bean, Louis Barbrow, William Blum, Wallace R. Brode, Fay C. Brown, Edward W. Cannon, Raymond Davis, Hugh L. Dryden, William I. Ellenberger, Paul D. Foote, Irvin H. Fullmer, Roman Geller, Kasson S. Gibson, Raleigh Gilchrist, Clarence H. Hahner, Wilbur S. Hinman, Jr., John Hoffman, Dagfin S. Hoynes, Horace S. Isbell, Victor J. Johnson (Boulder), Deane B. Judd, Lewis V. Judson, Carl C. Kiess, Gordon M. Kline, William B. Kouwenhoven, Percival D. Lowell, A. G. McNish, William F. Meggers, Fred L. Mohler, Douglas E. Parsons, Vincent B. Phelan, Earle K. Plyer, Jacob Rabinow, Mrs. Ida Rhodes, Raymond L. Sanford, Frederick J. Schlink, Ralph W. Smith, Wilbert F. Snyder (Boulder), Wilmer Souder, Harold F. Stimson, Lauriston S. Taylor, J. B. Tallerico, George N. Thompson, Elmer R. Weaver, Samuel C. Weissburg, and Lawrence A. Wood.

I wish to express my gratitude to all on the Bureau staff who have been levied on for fact and clarification, singling out Miss Sarah Ann Jones, librarian at the Bureau since 1920, W. Reeves Tilley, chief of technical information and publications, and Dr. Archibald T. McPherson, former NBS Associate Director, for their unfailing enthusiasm and help with the work in progress.

I am deeply indebted to the retired chief of the electrical division, Dr. Francis B. Silsbee; the former Director of the Bureau, Dr. Edward U. Condon; and the present Director, Dr. Allen V. Astin, for their close reading of the complete text for errors of fact, emphasis, and omission.

A special word of thanks is owed to my two most able research assistants, Mrs. Margaret M. Iwamoto, who read through the vast collection of NBS correspondence files in the National Archives, and Mrs. Elisabeth Bregenzer, who searched the congressional documents in the Library of Congress, in addition to countless other distracting tasks allotted to them.

Despite the wealth of assistance that has been rendered it, the history inevitably reflects the final decision of the historian himself. Mine alone therefore is the responsibility for the ordering and weighing of the available facts and for the excesses of simplification of highly complex scientific research—an amiable contention from first to last with the specialists at the Bureau.

REXMOND C. COCHRANE

Baltimore, Md.
January 1966

CONTENTS

Chapter I. AT THE TURN OF THE CENTURY—Continued

Chapter II. FOUNDING THE NATIONAL BUREAU OF STANDARDS (1901–10)

Chapter II. FOUNDING THE NATIONAL BUREAU OF STANDARDS—Continued

Chapter III. ELECTRICITY, RAILROADS, AND RADIO (1911–16)

Chapter III. ELECTRICITY, RAILROADS, AND RADIO—Continued

Chapter IV. THE WAR YEARS

(1917–19)

Chapter IV. THE WAR YEARS—
Continued

Chapter IV. THE WAR YEARS—
Continued

Chapter V. THE TIDE OF COMMERCE AND INDUSTRY (1920–30)

Chapter V. THE TIDE OF COMMERCE AND INDUSTRY—Continued

Chapter V. THE TIDE OF COMMERCE AND INDUSTRY—Continued

Chapter VI. THE TIME OF THE GREAT DEPRESSION (1931–40)

Chapter VI. THE TIME OF THE GREAT DEPRESSION—Continued

Chapter VII. WORLD WAR II RESEARCH (1941–45)

Chapter VII. WORLD WAR II RESEARCH—Continued

Chapter VII. WORLD WAR II RESEARCH—Continued

Chapter VIII. THE NEW WORLD OF SCIENCE (1946–51)

Chapter VIII. THE NEW WORLD OF SCIENCE—Continued

APPENDICES—Continued

AT THE TURN OF THE CENTURY

CHAPTER I

MAIN STREET, 1900

On May 3, 1900, the House Committee on Coinage, Weights and Measures met to consider a letter recently submitted by the Secretary of the Treasury. The Secretary requested the establishment of a national standardizing bureau.

Knowing little, perhaps, of the science of measurement, but learning that it was "a matter in which a great many people seem to be interested, one which is thought to be very necessary for this country," the committee heard out the group of eminent men called from science and industry to testify at the hearing. It was a brief hearing, lasting less than 2 hours and reported in 15 pages, yet so persuaded was the committee that its members reported to their colleagues in the House:

> It is therefore the unanimous opinion of your committee that no more essential aid could be given to manufacturing, commerce, the makers of scientific apparatus, the scientific work of the Government, of schools, colleges, and universities than by the establishment of the institution proposed in this bill.[1]

There were some in Congress by no means certain such an agency was needed, but 10 months later the bill founding the National Bureau of Standards passed both houses of Congress.

The idea of a national bureau of standards was presented at an auspicious hour. America in the year 1900 thought well of itself. The hard times of 1893–95 were all but forgotten in the aura of prosperity and sense of achievement that energized the Nation. Industry and invention boomed and business flourished as never before. The prophets at the turn of the century unanimously agreed on the good years to come.

The Nation was now an industrial power to be reckoned with. In the 3 years preceding 1900 the value of American manufactured goods sold abroad almost trebled, and total foreign commerce passed the 1 billion mark as exports exceeded imports for the first time. The great commercial invasion of Europe had begun.

---

[1] H.R. 1452, "National Standardizing Bureau," 56th Cong., 1st sess., May 14, 1900 (U.S. House Reports, serial 4026, vol. 6, 1899–1900). This is the inscription over the new Bureau laboratories at Gaithersburg, Md.

In a reverse invasion that had been going on for a century, immigration had swollen the population to 76 million, more than two-thirds of the increase occurring since 1850. Although concentrated in the East, fully a quarter of the population had spread across the Midwest, clustered in Texas, and settled along the Pacific coast. Gold miners, oil prospectors, homesteaders, ranchers, and builders of railroads and cities had followed the course of empire westward, urged on by the growing financial power of the bankers and industrialists in the East. And with the splendid prizes of the recent Spanish-American War, the United States had at last become a world power, complete with an oversea empire.

The little war with Spain from May to August 1898 freed Cuba, Puerto Rico, and the Philippines. Cuba, returned by our troops to the revolutionists who had called for help against Spanish oppression, became a protectorate in all but name; Puerto Rico was made an outright protectorate, as was Guam, ceded to us at the peace table. But the Philippines, destined for self-government, but then coveted by Germany and Japan and eyed with concern by England, France, and Russia, we decided to annex. Soon our burgeoning industry would be glad of those 7 million customers, and beyond them the teeming millions of China. Our share in that great market in the Orient was assured through Secretary of State John Hay's announcement of the Open-Door policy, in a note sent in 1899 to the major European powers. That same year the Hawaiian Islands came under our wing, gaining territorial status the next year, and in 1900 Samoa was thrust upon us by her island king, made uneasy by the European warships roaming the Pacific.

The new sense of power was flaunted at the Pan-American Exposition that opened in Buffalo in May 1901 to proclaim the coming of age of the Western Hemisphere. The great fireworks display that closed each day of the fair ended with an emblematic pageant entitled "Our Empire," dramatizing in patriotic pyrotechnics our winning of Cuba, Puerto Rico, and the Philippines.

Looking back as the new year came in, all America acclaimed the century of science and invention to which it was heir. In the past 30 years alone the steam engine had changed the Nation from an agricultural to an industrial economy, turning the wheels of factories, farm machinery, locomotives, and electric dynamos. The original 13½ miles of railroad track built in 1830 between Baltimore and Ellicott's Mills, Md., now sprawled across almost 200,000 miles of the Nation, and a new high-speed train was making the trip between New York and Chicago in an incredible 20 hours.

The character of the Nation's waterfront was also changing under the force of steam. Two-thirds of the ships built in 1900 were still sailing vessels or auxiliaries—barks, schooners, sloops, canal boats, and barges—but that year also saw 19 side-wheelers, 117 stern-wheelers, and 216 propeller-driven ships built for the lake, river, and coastal traffic.

The marvel of the age, however, was not steam, whose power could only be used in place, but electricity—power made portable over wires. And the turn of the century saw the greatest threat to further development of electric power removed. The reciprocating steam engine had about reached the extreme limit of practical size for the production of electricity when it was replaced by the high-speed steam turbine. Originally designed for the propulsion of battleships and ocean liners, the new turbine proved a peerless electric generator.

The commercial application of electricity, beginning with the telegraph, was half a century old, but checked by hit-or-miss methods of development, costly power sources, and the natural conservatism of the public, its promise had been redeemed only in the last decade. In urban transportation electric trolleys were rapidly replacing the old horse cars. Electrification of the elevated railroads in Boston and New York would soon end the noise, smoke, and ash of the overhead steam trains. It had made practicable the 5 miles of subway recently completed in Boston, and New York and Chicago planned similar systems under their streets. New York's rapid transit line, begun in 1900 and completed 3 years later, ran 9 miles under Manhattan, from City Hall to the Harlem River. As ground was broken there was talk of extending the line by a tunnel under the East River, connecting Manhattan and Brooklyn.

Beginning with a single strand on poles set up between Baltimore and Washington in 1845, electric telegraph wires now festooned city streets everywhere and followed the railroads from coast to coast. A new development was a printing telegraph, in which the Postal Telegraph Co. and the Associated Press were interested. More amazing were the reports of Guglielmo Marconi's experiments in transmitting electric signals without wires. His signal had already spanned the English Channel. In December 1901 he would astound the world with his demonstration of transatlantic wireless telegraph.

If the telegraph was everywhere, the telephone, even with more than half a million subscribers, was still found only in the largest cities and towns, in business houses, shops and factories, and the homes of the well to do. Even Edison's electric lamp, invented in 1879 and first sold commercially 3 years later, was still a novelty. His Pearl Street power station opened in September 1882 with six generators of 125 horsepower each, sending current along 13 miles of wire and lighting a few streets and shops with arc and incandescent lamps.[2] But in 1900 most of the streets in New York, as elsewhere, were still lighted by gas lamps, and except in the city homes of the

[2] Only one generator was used that night in September, to light 400 lamps for 85 customers. By 1904 a single generator supplied enough current to light 100,000 lamps; by 1914 it lighted 1,700,000 lamps.

Carriages and buggies and horse-drawn wagons continued to predominate on Pennsylvania Avenue in 1908, but the electric trolley had replaced the horse car.

By 1904 the elevated railroads in New York had been electrified. None of the new electric trucks is visible here in Herald Square. The elegant car in the foreground is probably a 1904 Locomobile, a gasoline car that was made by the Stanley Steamer Co. for several years. Almost half of the 54,590 cars then registered in the United States were new that year.

prosperous more than a decade would pass before electric wire and bulbs began to replace the oil lamps and gas mantles in common use.

The promise of things to come dominated the Pan-American Exposition of 1901. As gaudy and significant as its patriotic fireworks display was the symbol of the fair, the 410-foot Electric Tower. Lighted by the three 5,000-horsepower generators built at Niagara Falls 6 years before, 40,000 lamps made a torch of the tower for 50 miles around.[3]

For all the islands of light in city and town, the application of electricity most in evidence at the turn of the century was in transportation, propelling the trolleys that went out to the suburbs and the vans and drays in the commercial center of the big cities. Electric delivery wagons capable of speeds up to 15 miles an hour trundled along with the throngs of wagon teams in downtown New York, while up on Fifth Avenue electric taxis sped past the horse-drawn stages and weaving crowds of bicycles. As late as 1913 the National Bureau of Standards in Washington did not own a single gas-driven car or truck, depending on electric vans for ordinary express and teams of horses to bring heavy equipment up the hill to the laboratories.[4] The electric truck, more reliable and efficient in city traffic than the gasoline-driven car, had but one drawback. Its huge storage battery had to be recharged after every 20 or 30 miles of service.

Yet the gasoline auto had ceased to be a rarity by 1900. Henry Ford had built his first buggy, run by a two-cylinder, 4-horsepower engine, in 1892 while working at the Edison Illuminating Co., in Detroit. By 1900 at least 80 firms, owned by or hiring the services of the Duryea brothers, Ford, Elwood Haynes, F. E. Stanley, A. Winton, Elmer A. Sperry, Ranson E. Olds, and the Studebaker brothers, were making gasoline, electric, and steam automobiles. About 700 of their cars were on the road as the century began, and almost 4,000 more were rolling before the year was out.[5]

---

[3] Communication from Mr. Gardner H. Dales, Niagara Mohawk Power Corp., Jan. 26, 1962 (in NBS Historical File). The symbol recurs: the Tower of Light planned for the 1964–65 New York World's Fair was to be a 24-million-candlepower beacon, visible by night from Boston to Washington. As actually erected, its brilliance was of the magnitude of 24-billion-candlepower, but it was not visible for any great distance because it was a stationary light and because of the great quantity of ambient lighting on the fairgrounds.

[4] Letter, Stratton to Assistant Secretary of the Treasury, July 13, 1913 (National Archives, Record Group 167, NBS Box 11, file IG). NBS records in the National Archives will hereafter be identified only by NBS box number and file letters.

[5] Gardner D. Hiscox, Horseless Vehicles, Automobiles and Motor Cycles (New York: Norman W. Henley, 1901), p. 14, said 700 "was probably an exaggeration." An appendix in Hiscox listed 272 manufacturers of automobiles and parts across the country. Bulletin 66, U.S. Bureau of Census, April 1907, reported 1,681 steam, 1,575 electric, and 936 gas automobiles manufactured in 1900.

The Bureau's electric van, with "Bureau of Standards, Department of Commerce and Labor," somewhat blurred, inscribed on its panel, at the express office on Pennsylvania Avenue, picking up a shipment of instruments or equipment. The van has been identified as a Pope-Waverly, probably the 1903 or 1904 model.

The great wonders of the age, everyone agreed, were electricity and the electric light, the automobile, the telephone, the railroad, and telegraph lines threading the Nation, and the growing number of farm machines operated by steam engines.[6] Tributes to new engineering skills included such stone structures as the Cabin John Bridge above Washington, the great steel Brooklyn Bridge, and the combination of these materials in the new skyscrapers in Chicago and in the 21-story Flatiron Building, New York's first skyscraper, then under construction.

[6] Of the telephone Thomas C. Mendenhall, president of Rose Polytechnic Institute, said: "But the wonder of it all is [that it works]. Nothing like it in simplicity of construction, combined with complexity of operation, is to be found in any other human contrivance." A Century of Electricity (Boston and New York: Houghton & Mifflin, 1887), p. 208.

Equally amazing were the phonograph and gramophone with their sound tracks on cylinders and disks, the Pianola, and the kinetescope parlors exhibiting Mr. Edison's 1-minute amusements on film. Everybody seemed to be inventing something and looking for ways and means to make their notions commercial. A crude washing machine had recently been patented and would soon be on the market, but the zipper, invented back in 1893, was still being tinkered with and as yet had no use.

Business firms by the thousands had spawned across the country to provide raw materials or to make new products, as well as to supply the increasing everyday needs of the soaring population. Small, inefficient, and often brutally competitive, they were destined to be swallowed up by combines and corporations organized to exploit their growing success. The last decade of the 19th century became an age of trusts as industrialists, bankers, and speculators bought out or merged the multitudes of individual enterprises into great monopolies. The first had been Standard Oil, founded in 1882 when it began consolidating the oil industry by taking in 80 companies that year. By 1900, sugar, whisky, tobacco, glass, lead, cordage, copper, rubber, timber, waterpower, coal, steel and iron, wire nails, tinplate, sheet steel, urban railroads, farm machinery, gas, electric, and telephone utilities, stoves, watches, carpets, beef, flour, matches, candles, kerosene, and even coffins, school slates, and castor oil had passed into the hands of trusts.[7] With no other power to appease but its conscience, monopoly in these commodities more often than not resulted in higher rather than lower prices and frequently in an inferior product. On the other hand, it was a manifest stage in industrialization, the consolidation of scores and sometimes hundreds of small businesses engaged in a single commodity leading to a degree of standardization of product and introducing economy and quantity production and centralized management.

Under a traditionally laissez-faire government, public and private complaints against the abuses of big business fell on deaf ears, and the Sherman Anti-Trust Act of 1890 remained unexercised lest it endanger continued prosperity. Even Theodore Roosevelt, that maverick wielder of the big stick, was to clinch his place on the McKinley ticket in 1900 by declaring: "We are for expansion and anything else that will benefit the American laborer and manufacturer." All monopolies profited from the assumption that such so-called natural monopolies as the railroads, the telephone and telegraph, gas and electric companies, and the traction systems in the cities were public necessities, and theoretically at least, subject to some degree of regulation in the public interest.

---

[7] Ernst von Halle, Trusts or Industrial Combinations and Coalitions (New York and London: Macmillan, 1895), pp. 328–337, lists over 473 commodities controlled by trade combinations.

In the half-century between 1850 and 1900, as a result of the development and marketing of inventions, the enormous growth of business, industry, commerce, and banking, and the ascendency of the empire builders, the national wealth increased from $4½ to $88 billion.[8] Much of this was concentrated wealth through the consolidation of industry and few of its rewards reached the marketplace. Prices had actually gone up slightly in the past decade. Yet the standard of living of the man on Main Street in 1900 was said to compare favorably with that anywhere else in the world.

For much of the Nation, the comparison of American living standards with those of other nations did not stand up very well in daylight. At least two-thirds of the workers, immigrant and native born, in the mills, mines, factories, farms, and offices of the country, who put in a 12- to 14-hour day, 6 days a week, made less than $600 a year (roughly equivalent to $2,400 today), or well below what economists then considered a living wage. The relatively small middle-income group, the professions, technicians, businessmen, and minor executives, however, with incomes between $1,000 and $5,000, lived comfortably and by present-day standards sometimes well.[9]

A house in the best residential section (Dolphin Street in Baltimore, for example) cost a middle-income executive less than $5,000. A two-story house with bay windows and a furnace, in a slightly less desirable section or out in the suburbs, could be had for as little as $750; a three-story house for $1,200. Or the young executive could rent a 7- to 10-room house in the city for between $10 and $25 per month. Other expenses were commensurate. His good business suit might cost as much as $10.65, his wife's wool Kersey and covert cloth outfit, $5.98 ("Buy now and pay later," the 1901 handbill said). A felt hat was $0.89, children's shoes sold for $0.19, those for men and women from $0.98 to $2. Food prices in the city were not considered excessive when an 8-pound leg of mutton came to $1.20, prime rib roast was $0.15 a pound, corned beef $0.08 a pound, butter $0.28 a pound, eggs $0.22 a dozen, and milk $0.08 a quart.

---

[8] U.S. Bureau of the Census, Historical Statistics of the United States, Colonial Times to 1957 (Washington, D.C., 1960), p. 151. Hereafter cited as Historical Statistics.

[9] John A. Ryan, A Living Wage (New York: Macmillan, 1906, reprinted 1908, 1910, 1912), pp. 136, 150, 161–162. His "reasonable and irreducible minimum" for a family of seven came to $601.03 (p. 145). In a city like Baltimore it was $750, in Chicago $900, and in New York $950. See 18th Annual Report of the Commissioner of Labor: Cost of Living and Retail Prices of Food, 1903 (Washington, D.C., 1904), p. 648, and Historical Statistics, pp. 179–180.

Prices in 1900 were not appreciably greater than those itemized in Catherine Owen's Ten Dollars Enough: Keeping House Well on Ten Dollars a Week (Boston and New York: Houghton, Mifflin, 1887), in which, on $100 a month a young couple spent $20 for rent, $12 for a full-time servant, $45 for housekeeping, $15 for clothes and general expenses and $8 for commutation into the city.

Among the small pleasures of life was a trolley ride to the suburbs for 3 cents (soon to advance, amid bitter outcries, to 5 cents), and on special occasions one might hire a coach with rubber tires, electric lights, and carbon heater for a day in the country for $3. And there were no city sales taxes, no State, county, or Federal income taxes.

Freedom from taxes made it possible for Andrew Carnegie to keep every penny of his personal income in the year 1900, well over $23 million, and for Henry Clay Frick to spend $17 million for a marble and limestone palace covering a square block on Fifth Avenue. Charles Schwab's house built on Riverside Drive in 1905 had 75 rooms and 40 baths, but was no match for Edward Stotesbury's 130-room hall in Philadelphia, or John D. Rockefeller's $30 million estate near Tarrytown, N.Y.

Under a benevolent and business-minded Government, more than 20 percent of the total wealth of the Nation was in the hands of fewer than 4,000 men, the bankers, speculators, and industrialists who through headlong exploitation of the world about them created immense fortunes for themselves and controlled the fortunes of the Nation. "Malefactors of great wealth," Teddy Roosevelt in the White House might call them, but as yet only they had the resources and power to turn the discoveries of science, invention, and exploration into the shape of things to come.

THE SHAPE OF THINGS TO COME

The builders of America's industrial complex had little interest in standards as such, but the scientists, engineers, and experimenters working for industry or independently found themselves increasingly hampered without them. The need for a Federal bureau of standards was talked about for almost 20 years before legislation for its establishment was introduced in 1900. By then the necessity had become imperative as science and industry, ready to take giant steps in the new century, looked for better measurements and more uniformity, precision, and control in the laboratory, factory, and plant.

The climate that produced the National Bureau of Standards is thus to be found in the world of science and technology as it appeared at the turn of the century. Some of this has been described in the previous section. More is furnished by contemporary historians who catalogued in book after book the century's birthright of invention. The promise was great, and prophets abounded with predictions of the future of science, industry, and society.

Without exception, the calendars of invention and histories of progress published in the early years of the new century gave first place to the electrical marvels of the previous decade and the "electrical magicians,"

Still the largest stone arch in America, the Cabin John Bridge was completed in 1859, a 220-foot span carrying a water conduit and carriage way over Cabin John Creek. For 44 years it was the largest masonry arch in the world, until larger ones were built in Saxony and France. Since then masonry has been replaced by concrete in great bridges, as more economical.

Thomas Edison and Nikola Tesla. Succeeding chapters in the histories recounted the latest developments in electric, gasoline, and steam vehicles and the new roadways being built for them, the growth of the iron and steel industry, of railroads and steamships, and the development of the machine tool industry, of petroleum products, textiles, clay products, rubber goods, glass making, and leather goods.

Among the new instruments of science described were the spectroscope and improved telescopes, opening new prospects in astronomy; the X-ray machine and fluoroscope; and according to one contemporary historian, Edison's phonograph and kinetoscope, which "belong naturally under this chapter," though they also had their "commercial and amusement purposes."[10] (Yet it is doubtful whether he foresaw the use science would

[10] Charles H. Cochrane, Modern Industrial Progress (Philadelphia & London: J. B. Lippencott, 1904), pp. 406, 409. See also Edward W. Byron, The Progress of Invention in the Nineteenth Century (New York: Munn & Co., 1900); William H. Doolittle, Inventions in the Century (The Nineteenth Century Series, London & Philadelphia: Linscott, 1902); Trumbull White, Our Wonderful Progress (Chicago, 1902); Calendar of Invention and Discovery, compiled by John C. Wait (New York: McGraw, 1903); and anticipating these, Robert Routledge's Discoveries and Inven-

make of recording devices and of slow-motion photography.) Engineering feats included new triumphs in bridge-building, the first great dikes and dams along the Mississippi, and canals and tunnels, while among "odd and curious developments" were listed the comptometer, the trackless trolley, the new towering smoke stacks of industry, the extension fire ladder, and the escalator and elevator, the latter developed to serve those "modern tall steel skeleton fire-proof buildings, commonly called skyscrapers."

The marvels achieved presumed greater ones to come, and more than one prophet looking into the new century envisioned a utopian age of science and industry within a matter of years, made possible, as John Bates Clark said in the Atlantic, by "omnipresent and nearly gratuitous electrical energy!" In addition to coal and water power, Clark optimistically predicted that it would not be long before the waves and tides and even the electric currents generated within the earth itself would be harnessed for the production of cheap and virtually unlimited electric power. Industry, commerce, and the home would be filled with automatic machines (". . . we touch a button and they do the rest," said Clark), putting in the hands of every man a hundred silent servants, raising wages, dispelling poverty, and stilling the unrest of the laboring classes.[11]

H. G. Wells, with frequent glances at the American promise, agreed in his "Experiment in Prophecy" in 1901 on the equalizing force of the electrical century to come, saw homes and factories heated, ventilated, and operated by electricity. But with this revolution, he predicted, would come a world so closely linked and controlled by electrical conveniences and communications as to reduce all to a gray mass, to a virtually classless world of respectable mechanics.

Even greater social and political changes than those resulting from electricity, Wells thought, would come from the inevitable mass production of commodities and the future development of the internal combustion engine. Certain to come was a smooth-riding, powerful, and stenchless gasoline automobile and great networks of paved roads for it, making journeys of 300 miles in a day possible. Then motor trucks would replace the railroads, and motor coaches supplant the horse cars and electric trolleys that ran out to suburbia, where, as Wells said, the conforming gray mass of the future lived.[12]

---

tions of the Nineteenth Century (London: Geo. Routledge, 1876) and the survey of the century's wonders in Sci. Am. 75, 50–96 (1896).

[11] John Bates Clark, "Recollections of the Twentieth Century," Atlantic, 89, 4 (1902). Clark was professor of political economy at Columbia University from 1895 to 1923, specializing in trusts and monopolies. See also George Sutherland, Twentieth Century Inventions: A Forecast (New York & London: Longman's Green, 1901).

[12] H. G. Wells, "Anticipation: an experiment in prophecy," North American Review, vols. 172–173 (June–November 1901).

The visible achievements of technology and invention, though many were still crude and far from generally available, made prophecy a game any number could play, and with some knowledge of human nature, foreseeing the social changes they would bring only meant projecting the changes already begun. Predicting the future of pure science, however, was something else, and the few who ventured any guesses did so cautiously and in the vaguest of terms.

One who ventured was John Trowbridge, director of the Jefferson Physical Laboratory at Harvard. The work of Maxwell, Hertz, Roentgen, and Thomson between 1873 and 1897, in demonstrating the electromagnetic nature of light and formulating the concept of the electron, in mass much less than one-thousandth part of the chemist's lightest known atom, had almost certainly, said Trowbridge, made the study of the infinitely small the new direction physical science would take.

The word "electronics" had not been invented, and Professor Trowbridge saw no "use" in the study of the electron yet, except as it might possibly lead to an answer to an unexpected problem recently encountered. This was in the electrolytic effects observed in Boston, where the iron mains carrying water under Boylston Street had been found badly corroded by the electric current of the trolley system. The investigation of this phenomenon, declared Trowbridge, "has laid the foundation of a new branch of science, that of physical chemistry, which promises to be one of the most important sciences in the world." Electrochemistry, the branch of physical chemistry concerned with electrolysis, seemed to Trowbridge certain to provide the key to exploration of the nature of the smallest particles of matter yet found.[13]

But the world of electronics and the physicist's exploration of the atom was still far off. For the most part, the world of science in 1900 had little conception of the truly revolutionary ideas to come. Robert A. Millikan was to say that of the basic principles of universal order taught at the end of the 19th century, not one but its universal validity was to be questioned by serious and competent physicists, while most were definitely proved to be subject to exceptions. In 1895, the very year some physicists were declaring that "the great discoveries in physics have all been made," that the field of physics was "dead," Roentgen announced his discovery of X rays. A year later came Becquerel's discovery of the radioactivity of uranium, marking the birth of nuclear physics, and in 1897, J. J. Thomson in England established beyond question the existence of electrons as fundamental con-

---

[13] John Trowbridge, "The study of the infinitely small," Atlantic, 89, 612 (1902). Professor Trowbridge, a physicist and specialist in electricity, was director of the Jefferson Physical Laboratory from 1888 to 1910.

stituents of all atoms in the universe.[14] Seventeen years would pass before the latter discovery, stirring Professor Trowbridge to prophecy, would be applied to the electronic amplifier tube, making possible the first wireless telephone and the long distance telephone.

The breakthrough in the world of physics continued in the first quarter of the 20th century with Planck's quantum theory (1901), Einstein's concept of the relativistic transformation of mass into radiant energy, expressed in his equation $E=mc^2$ (1905), and his elaboration of the principle of relativity (1905–25). That same period witnessed the isolation and measurement of the electron (1910–17), the discovery of the wave nature of X rays (1912), and the quantitative working out of their properties (1910–25). These revelations were followed by Bohr's model of the atom (1912–22), the investigation of crystal structures with the aid of X-ray spectroscopy (from 1913 on), the discovery of isotopes through the chemistry of radioactive elements (1913), and the discovery of cosmic rays (1926).[15]

Thus, active as pure science was at the turn of the century, in this country its efforts were largely unknown. For one thing, most of the work was done abroad. We were not to develop any significant number of pure scientists, let alone theoretical physicists, until the 1930's. The early career of the Bureau of Standards, so much of it given to basic research in standards and to technological research, is witness. (When Louis W. Austin came to the Bureau in 1905 by way of Cambridge, after 2 years' study at the Reichsanstalt, the national physical laboratory of Germany, he brought with him Rutherford's book on radioactivity, just published by the Cambridge University Press. Reviewed at a weekly staff meeting at the Bureau, it caused some stir among the assembled physicists, but more perplexity. The subject was as yet beyond the province of the Bureau.)[16]

Besides being developed abroad, the theories and hypotheses of the new physicists remained incapable of proof or practical application as they awaited better instruments and precision measurements. Hence the general public, when it chanced on notice of them, hadn't the slightest understanding of the new discoveries, and even among men of science their implications for the future of science were not widely understood or appreciated. To the average man, science appeared to be in the hands of the experimentalists, inventors, and mechanics and in the application of their work to new in-

---

[14] Robert A. Millikan, "The last fifteen years in physics," Proc. Am. Phil. Soc. 65, 68 (1926); Millikan, "The evolution of twentieth-century physics," Annual Report, Smithsonian Institution, 1927, pp. 191–199; The Autobiography of Robert A. Millikan (New York: Prentice Hall, 1950), pp. 106, 271.

For repeated statements of the stasis reached in physics, especially in electricity, see T. C. Mendenhall, The Age of Electricity, passim.

[15] Millikan, "The last fifteen years in physics," pp. 70–78.

[16] Interview with Dr. Llewelyn G. Hoxton, Nov. 27–28, 1961 (NBS Historical File).

dustry and enterprise. What the average man did not realize was the extent to which science, pure and applied, was becoming involved in experiment and invention. The genius of Thomas A. Edison is a case in point.

Despite the fact that much of his best work was done before 1900, Edison was in many respects the symbol of the age as he was its hero, widely accepted as the typical self-trained, empirical genius of American science. Though his knowledge of physics and chemistry was ill-grounded and his disdain for mathematics profound, the world owed to Edison through his hundreds of patents the electric light bulb and phonograph, the kinetoscope, the first effective storage battery, and the first practical electric power system. These were the products of his invention factory. Set up in New York with 50 men in 1870 and moved across the river to Menlo Park in 1876, it was unquestionably the greatest of his inventions and the prototype of today's industrial research laboratories. Without detracting in the least from his undeniable genius, the wizard had help. Few were aware of the mathematicians, chemists, and physicists, many of them trained abroad, who worked at Menlo Park to make the necessary calculations for Edison's inventions.

Behind the histories of progress and invention at the turn of the century, wherein Edison was accorded first place, was a new phenomenon, the accelerated pace at which science was contributing to the inventions and processes that apply it to daily life. Commerce and industry could no longer wait while scientists projected theories without demonstrations, while isolated inventors tinkered unassisted with crude working models. By bringing scientists and inventors together, along with talented engineers to translate their theories and models into commercial products, industry sought to telescope time and effort.

By the turn of the century small research laboratories had been set up in the Pennsylvania Railroad yards at Altoona, Pa., at B. F. Goodrich, and Bethlehem Steel & Iron, staffed with inventors, engineers, and chemists. The first systematic effort to incorporate science and technology in industry was, as might be expected, in the electrical field, when the General Electric Research Laboratory, a direct offshoot of Edison's Menlo Park, was organized at Schenectady in 1900. The decade before the First World War saw similar laboratories organized at DuPont, Bell Telephone, Westinghouse, Eastman Kodak, Standard Oil (Indiana), at U.S. Rubber, and Corning Glass. In the 1920's, under the dynamics of mass production, new research factories for the mass production of technological ideas proliferated at the rate of over a hundred a year.

Even before the founding of Edison's laboratory, scientists, whether directly engaged by industry or working independently in university laboratories or in their own workshops, were becoming increasingly active in the commercial life of the Nation. And under pressure to produce or to satisfy their own demands for quantitative results, it was the scientists who sought better standards of measurement, better tools, precision instruments, and materials. It was they who realized that the arbitrary standards they worked with or of necessity had to create for themselves were all but meaningless and represented a needless loss of time, effort, and money. Science, better than industry, was aware that only Federal legislation could establish the necessary criteria, criteria that would possess national as well as international validity.

Other nations, more advanced in commerce and industry, had long since recognized the need for such legislation and had established national standards laboratories. America, growing in commerce and industry, in national power and prestige, had nothing comparable to them. The meeting of these forces at the end of the 19th century—the growing needs of science and technology, coinciding with a new sense of national pride—was the impulse that created the National Bureau of Standards.

When the Bureau was founded, the first power-motored flight by Orville Wright was just 2 years away. That first decade would see the development of audion tubes by Fleming and DeForest, long-distance telephony, the diesel engine, high-speed tool steel, the mercury vapor arc, and the first real plastic (bakelite). In the ever-widening fields of electricity, automotive engineering, aviation, plastics, textiles, and construction materials, the Bureau was to do basic and in some cases pioneer research. And in doing so it was to lay the groundwork for its later investigations in fields as yet undreamed of, in the application of the new physics to metrology, in free radical research, cryogenic engineering, atomic and radiation physics, space physics, plasma physics, and radio propagation engineering.

Beginning with the formulation of improved standards of electrical measurement, the Bureau was to develop better standards of length and mass, develop new standards of temperature, light, and time. It would establish standards of safety in commerce and industry, of performance in public utilities, and prepare and maintain hundreds of standard samples of materials for industry. The advance of science would demand increasingly precise instrumentation, greater and greater ranges of measurement, and wholly new standards such as those of sound, frequency, and radiation. The Bureau would eventually become the custodian of and final arbiter over more than 700 different standards.

Such an agency, providing vital services to the Nation outside the province of any possible private, institutional, or industrial organization, might have had its birth simultaneously with that of the confederation of the colonies. Why it was over a hundred years coming into being is an integral part of its history.

GOVERNMENT, SCIENCE, AND THE GENERAL WELFARE

The Nation had been born in an age of scientific exploration and experiment, its very founding a consequence in part of the industrial revolution in England. Among the framers of the Constitution, men of science like Franklin, Madison, Pinckney, and Jefferson looked to the early establishment in the new Nation of a national university and Federal societies of the arts and sciences, for the promotion of agriculture, commerce, trades, and manufactures. But because the new States feared centralization of power of any kind in the Federal Government, these institutions were not spelled out.

The powers granted Congress by the Constitution "to promote the progress of science and useful arts" by issuing patents to authors and inventors, by conducting a periodic census, and supervising coinage, weights, and measures, were exercised in spirit if not to the letter. In any case, their scientific implications were ignored. Small autonomous laboratories appeared before long in a number of the executive departments of the Government, providing certain functional services involving research, but encouragement and support of fundamental science were left to such privately organized agencies as the American Philosophical Society (Philadelphia, 1743), the American Academy of Arts and Sciences (Boston, 1780), and in Washington, the Smithsonian Institution (1846), and the American Association for the Advancement of Science (1848). In no way an adjunct of the Government but merely an advisory body in scientific matters was the National Academy of Sciences, incorporated by an act of Congress on March 3, 1863. Without authority or independent funds, it was only required, "whenever called upon by any department of the Government * * * to investigate, examine, experiment, and report upon any subject of science or art" submitted to it, the investigations to be paid from regular congressional appropriations made for that purpose.

Congress repeatedly demonstrated great reluctance to provide even small sums of money for the support of any private scientific or inventive enterprise, however beneficial to the Nation. Robert Fulton's pleas for Federal aid in the 1830's went unanswered. Governments abroad were more helpful with his submarine, and on his return private funds made his steamboat "folly" possible. Only after 6 years of petitions was Congress persuaded to grant Samuel F. B. Morse the sum of $30,000 to set up his experimental telegraph line between Baltimore and Washington in 1843.

The scant concern of the Federal Government with science is evident in the delayed organization of some of its most essential scientific agencies. Military and civil exploration were provinces of the Army Corps of Engineers until the Geological Survey was established in the Department of the Interior in 1879. The Treasury's Coast and Geodetic Survey, founded in 1807 to chart the coasts for American shipping, provided the only scientific mensuration supported by Federal funds until the miniscule Office of Weights and Measures was set up within the Survey itself in 1836. That same year the Patent Office was established in the State Department, over strong opposition from many in Congress who declared its inclusion in an executive branch an unconstitutional usurpation of authority.

Government concern with medicine and public health was left to the Army Medical Department (1818), and except in the short-lived National Board of Health (1879–83), medical research remained a function of the Army until the establishment in 1902 of the Public Health Service. In the Navy Department was the National Observatory and its Hydrographic Office, organized in 1842, which, with the telegraph facilities operated by the Army Signal Service, provided meteorological and weather services to the Nation until 1890 when these functions were transferred to the Department of Agriculture. That Department itself was not established until 1862, under wartime pressure for greater food production.

In a nation predominantly agricultural until the last decade of the 19th century, these Government services seemed sufficient.[17] Such research as they conducted was restricted by law and lack of funds to that immediately necessary to carry out their functions. Yet inevitably these agencies acquired specialized personnel for their problems, were aided and encouraged by the independent scientific organizations of the Nation, and in some instances achieved on meager appropriations remarkable results. The work of the Naval Observatory in astronomy and of the Army Medical Corps in bacteriology produced contributions to fundamental science well beyond the pragmatic strictures of Congress.[18]

Federal reluctance to enter scientific fields and congressional agreement to keep in bounds those it perforce established grew out of the nature of the Constitution, which reserved to the individual and to the States the greatest possible freedom and the maximum opportunity for private enterprise consistent with the public good. The industrialization of America in the late 19th century coincided with a kind of glorification of this political theory of laissez-faire and its concomitant gospel of work and wealth. It was little wonder that a proposal made in 1884 for the establishment of a Department of Science in the Federal Government foundered even as it was launched.

---

[17] In 1890 agricultural, mining, forest, and fishery products accounted for 82 percent of our exports; domestic manufactures 18 percent. By 1900 agricultural products were 68 percent of exports and manufactures had risen to 32 percent. Statistical Abstracts of the United States, 1900 (Bureau of Statistics, Treasury Department, Washington, D.C., 1901), p. 187.

[18] A. Hunter Dupree, Science in the Federal Government (Harvard University Press, 1957), pp. 184–186, 263 ff.

Yet the time was ripe. By the 1880's science and invention had become as fervid subjects of public concern as welfare would be in the 1930's, With the dramatic rise of the electrical industry there was no longer any question about the necessity of Government support, only about the degree and immediacy of it. Indeed, in 1884 Congress went so far as to appropriate $7,500 for a national conference of electricians at Philadelphia. But it took no action on the recommendation of the conference for a Federal agency "charged with the duty of examining and verifying instruments for electrical and other physical measurements."

Some felt that more than measurement was wanted in the young and directionless industry. Writing in 1887 about the development of the storage battery, Thomas C. Mendenhall, physicist and president of Rose Polytechnic Institute in Indiana, said: "A good deal of valuable information concerning [its] behavior * * * has been accumulated; at an expense far greater, however, than would have been necessary, had the whole subject received in the beginning an exhaustive examination at the hands of a competent commission under Government authority and at Government expense. The vast importance of the questions involved would seem to justify such a course."[19] Such an authority had recently been proposed and, with little debate, dismissed.

The proposal for a Department of Science arose out of an investigation of intramural bickering over functions in the survey agencies of the Government. A joint congressional commission, headed by Senator William B. Allison of Iowa, was directed to consider the possible reorganization for greater efficiency of the agencies involved, that is, the Army Signal Service, the Department of Interior's Geological Survey, the Treasury's Coast and Geodetic Survey, and the Navy's Hydrographic Office. The Allison Commission turned to the National Academy of Sciences and asked it to appoint a committee to make a study of similar European institutions and recommend methods of coordinating the work of these scientific agencies in the Government.

In September 1884 the committee made its report. "The time is near," said the National Academy, "when the country will demand the institution of a branch of the executive Government devoted especially to the direction and control of all the purely scientific work of the Government." It therefore recommended the establishment of such a branch, to be called the Department of Science, with the purely scientific functions of the survey agencies in contention reorganized in this Department. It was to comprise four bureaus: the Coast Survey, the Geological Survey, a meteorological bureau combining the weather services of the Army and Navy offices, and a new physical laboratory. The latter was to take over the little weights and

---

[19] T. C. Mendenhall, A Century of Electricity, pp. 213–14.

measures office in the Coast Survey and extend the present investigations of that office to include electrical standards. It would also undertake "to observe the laws of solar and terrestrial radiation and their application to meteorology, with such other investigations in exact science as the Government might assign to it." [20]

The proponents of the new department agreed that it should undertake no work that "can be equally well done by the enterprise of individual investigators"; that its bureaus would cooperate, not compete, with university research laboratories; that they would investigate only in those fields, still unoccupied, "where private enterprise cannot work"; and confine themselves "to the increase and systematization of knowledge tending 'to promote the general welfare' "—in particular, to research vitally affecting the establishment or expansion of new industry in the Nation.

The committee pointed to photography, which since the daguerreotype in 1839 had grown into a $30 million a year industry, and to the new, promising electric telegraph, telephone, light, and electric railway industries, as proof that "the pursuit of science is now directly connected with the promotion of the general welfare" and therefore a Federal responsibility.

But the old arguments prevailed. The Government could not fail to compete with the university laboratories or the enterprise of individual scientists. With its "capacity * * * for indefinite expansion," a Federal agency of science would encroach more and more upon individual effort and on industry, and by proliferation and publication soon come to create, control, and diffuse the scientific knowledge of the Nation.[21] The Allison Commission shelved the proposal for a department of science. The prospect of anything like a centralized research agency in the Government was bad enough, but that it might ultimately lead to some kind of intervention in industry or regulation of business was too much for the times.

In those last decades of the century, as Frederick Lewis Allen has said, "business was supposed to be no affair of the government's." The farm States in 1887 had forced creation of an Interstate Commerce Commission to regulate the railroads, but its powers were small, uncertain, and unexercised. There was no Department of Commerce, no Department of Labor, no Federal Trade Commission, no Federal Reserve System, and when in need of credit, Washington without the aid of John Pierpont Morgan was helpless.[22] The Federal Government was without the power or inclination either to inter-

---

[20] Report of M. C. Meigs, Chairman of NAS Committee, to O. C. Marsh, President, NAS, Sept. 21, 1884 (Allison Commission, Testimony, Mar. 16, 1886, 49th Cong., 1st sess., S. Misc. Doc. 82, serial 2345), p. 8.* Hereafter cited as Allison Commission, Testimony.

[21] Ibid., pp. 7*–8*, 66–69, 177–179, 999–1001; Dupree, Science in the Federal Government, pp. 215–226, 231.

[22] Frederick Lewis Allen, The Big Change: America Transforms Itself, 1900–1950 (New York: Harper, 1952; Bantam Books, 1961), p. 72.

fere with business or to aid it, and its concept of the public welfare remained nebulous to the end of the century.

The golden years of unregulated private enterprise were abruptly interrupted almost singlehandedly by Teddy Roosevelt, who became President following the assassination of McKinley at the Pan-American Exposition on September 6, 1901. After a century of unfettered enterprise, a quarter century of trusts and monopolies, Roosevelt's mediation in the anthracite coal strike of 1902, the indictment of the meat-packing trust in 1905, the passage of the Pure Food and Drug Act in 1906, and his victory over Morgan's steel trust in 1907 came as unprecedented and incredible intrusions by the Government.

The fight against monopoly in business and industry, buttressed as they were by their special franchises, tax privileges, tariffs, and patents, would continue in the new century. But while the maverick President established the Government's right to regulate, and to mediate between big business and the public, he did not deny the very real benefits of the corporations in the industrialization of the Nation. With curbs, they were destined to be tolerated and even aided by the Government that had subdued them.

LOOKING BACK

Except for the recognition by the committee of the National Academy of Sciences that areas of investigation existed in the realm of "exact science" that were Federal responsibilities, little in the Office of Weights and Measures in the year 1884 recommended it as the nucleus of a physical laboratory in the proposed Department of Science.

In charge of weights and measures and of gravimetric studies in the Coast Survey at that time was Charles S. Peirce (1839–1914), a brilliant scientist, philosopher, and logician, lecturer at Harvard, and a member of the National Academy of Sciences, who spent 20 years of his life with the Coast Survey. Long before the necessary precision instruments were available he made the first attempt to use the wavelength of a light ray as a standard unit of measure. He is deservedly the subject of one of the longest and most interesting memoirs in the Dictionary of American Biography.[23]

Testifying before the Allison Commission—the question of a department of science had already been disposed of—Peirce was asked about the work of his office. "The office of weights and measures at present is a very slight affair, I am sorry to say," he had to admit, "* * * a nonentity, having hardly any legal existence." It consisted of himself and two assistants, and

[23] See also Victor F. Lenzen, "The contributions of Charles S. Peirce to metrology," Proc. Am. Phil. Soc. 109, 29 (1965).

was maintained only "to keep up the supply of standards and balances" to the States, territories, and the country's agricultural schools, as required by law, and to "take occasion to verify any standard that is referred to us." The latter service was of questionable value since in most instances "we want the means of executing the verifications asked of us." [24]

The full title of Peirce's agency in appropriation acts at that time was the Office of Construction of Standard Weights and Measures, indicating its limited scope in the eyes of Congress.[25] Its history reflects the century-long hestitation of the Federal Government to exercise even that most elementary degree of control in the affairs of the individual citizen—the imposition of a discipline of weights and measures—and the failure of the States to exercise it in the absence of Federal regulation.

The provision in article 9 of the Articles of Confederation (1777–78) granting Congress "the sole and exclusive right and power of * * * fixing the standard of weights and measures throughout the United States" was repeated in article I, section 8, clause 5 of the Constitution (1789), its principal purpose to make "all Duties, Imposts and Excises * * * uniform" throughout the colonies. Without direct taxation, funds to maintain the Government depended largely on these imposts. Yet excises on flour, sugar, and other imported commodities, as well as the tonnage tax on vessels, the Government's other principal source of income, depended upon guesswork of a low order so long as barrel sizes and their contents and the weight of a ton met no uniform definition or standard. For over a hundred years it was to prove as difficult to legislate standards as it was to determine them.

President Washington in his annual messages in 1790 and 1791, Secretary of State Thomas Jefferson in an elaborate report to Congress in 1790, President James Madison in his eighth annual message in 1816, and Secretary of State John Quincy Adams in a report in 1821 that has been called "a classic in weights and measures literature," all urged the establishment by law of uniform and reliable standards in weights and measures.[26] To allay public fears and lessen the inconveniences attending the introduction of uniform standards, when determined, Jefferson recommended that they be introduced first in the customhouses, to familiarize merchants with them, then among merchants and traders in foreign commodities, and finally offered to the

---

[24] Allison Commission, Testimony, p. 370.

[25] The Appropriation Act of Aug. 5, 1882 (22 Stat. 230) first designated the agency as the Office of Construction of Standard Weights and Measures. The name continued in appropriation acts until 1901, although after 1891 the agency was otherwise officially designated the Office of Standard Weights and Measures.

[26] Source references for these documents appear in Ralph W. Smith's "The Federal basis for weights and measures," NBS C593 (1958). For a recent study of Jefferson's report see The Papers of Thomas Jefferson, ed. Julian P. Boyd (Princeton University Press, 1961), XVI, 602–675.

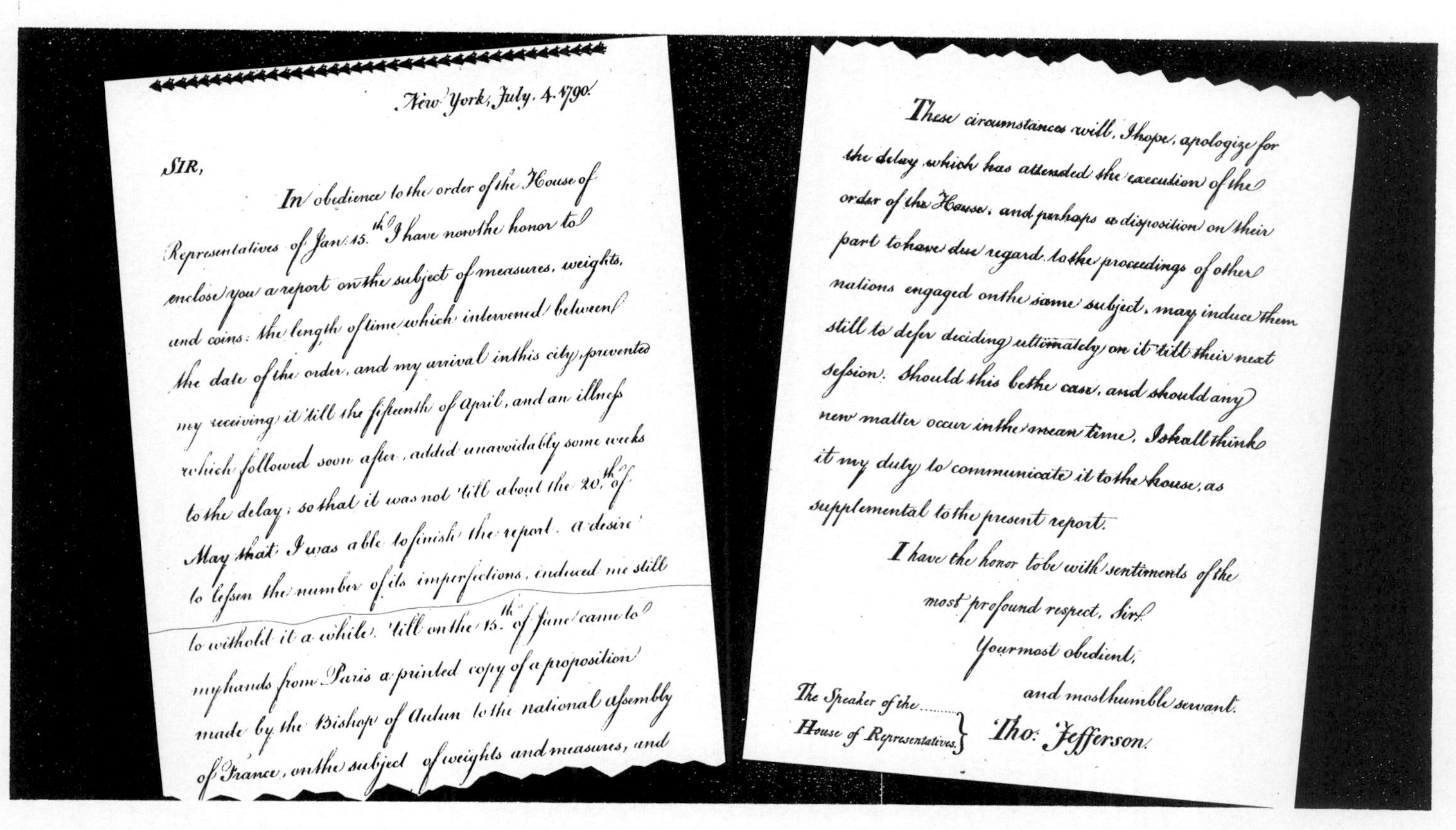

New York, July. 4. 1790.

SIR,

In obedience to the order of the House of Representatives of Jan. 15.th I have now the honor to enclose you a report on the subject of measures, weights, and coins: the length of time which intervened between the date of the order, and my arrival in this city, prevented my receiving it till the fifteenth of April, and an illness which followed soon after, added unavoidably some weeks to the delay; so that it was not till about the 20.th of May that I was able to finish the report. A desire to lessen the number of its imperfections, induced me still to withold it a while, 'till on the 15.th of June came to my hands from Paris a printed copy of a proposition made by the Bishop of Autun to the national assembly of France, on the subject of weights and measures, and

These circumstances will, I hope, apologize for the delay which has attended the execution of the order of the House, and perhaps a disposition on their part to have due regard to the proceedings of other nations engaged on the same subject, may induce them still to defer deciding ultimately on it till their next session. Should this be the case, and should any new matter occur in the mean time, I shall think it my duty to communicate it to the House, as supplemental to the present report.

I have the honor to be with sentiments of the most profound respect, Sir,

Your most obedient,

and most humble servant.

The Speaker of the House of Representatives.

Tho: Jefferson.

A fragment of Jefferson's letter of transmittal accompanying his report to Congress on measures, weights, and coins in 1790, shortly before he became Secretary of State. The original of the copperplate transcription of Jefferson's message is in the National Archives, Record Group 59.

general public. Adams suggested that public officials such as custom officers, public land surveyors, and postmasters be the first required to adopt the new standards, when devised, with general enforcement of them left to the individual States.[27]

Scientists, statesmen, and business men throughout the first quarter century of the Republic repeatedly called for such legislation, and House and Senate committees were appointed in 1791, 1795, 1798, 1804, 1808, 1816, 1819, 1821, and 1826 to fix on a uniform plan of standards for adoption by Congress. None denied their necessity, but a majority invariably bridled at the thought of general enforcement. A standard of coinage was another matter, and on April 2, 1792, Congress established without a demur the decimal system for the money of the United States. Weights of coins, on the other hand, fared little better than commodity weights until in 1828 Congress adopted the British troy pound of 1758 as the standard for American coinage.

Troy weight had been more or less "standard" since colonial days, and continued to be even after Great Britain reformed her system of weights and measures in 1824, at which time she adopted new imperial standards, including a new avoirdupois pound. Nevertheless, in 1827 Albert Gallatin, Secretary of the Treasury from 1801 to 1814 and at that time American Minister to Great Britain, secured a brass copy of the old troy pound. It was deposited with the Director of the Mint at Philadelphia and the next year additional copies were made and supplied to all U.S. mints as the basis for the weight of a pound of gold.

But as Charles Peirce pointed out to the Allison Commission more than 50 years later, the troy pound at the mint was not suitable for precision weights of any kind. For one thing, it had never been weighed in a vacuum to determine its true weight, and in point of fact, the Government had no balance that could do that. Moreover, since the destruction of its prototype when the Houses of Parliament burned in 1834, there was no way of telling how much that brass pound at Philadelphia really weighed, except in terms of the British avoirdupois pound. In other words, said Peirce, the weight of the American pound "is not known." [28] Nevertheless, this pound remained the standard for coinage until 1911 when it was replaced by weights certified by the National Bureau of Standards in terms of the platinum-iridium kilogram.[29]

But coinage was not alone in dealing with unknown quantities. The history of weights and measures in this country had more than its share.

---

[27] Gustavus A. Weber, The Bureau of Standards: Its History, Activities, and Organization (Institute for Government Research, Service Monograph No. 35, Baltimore: The Johns Hopkins Press, 1925), pp. 2, 3, 9.

[28] Allison Commission, Testimony, pp. 372–374.

[29] NBS Annual Report 1910, p. 7; Annual Report 1911, p. 11.

The troy pound of the U.S. Mint at Philadelphia, with the nested packing cases in which it was shipped to the United States in 1827. An exact copy of the imperial troy pound, this standard for coinage virtually became the fundamental standard of the United States. from which the avoirdupois pound in common use was derived.

The first real effort to provide accurate, if nonlegal, standards of weights and measures was made by Ferdinand Rudolph Hassler (1770–1843), a Swiss engineer and metrologist who emigrated to this country at the age of 35. Upon the establishment of the Coast Survey in the Treasury Department, Hassler became its first superintendent, holding that office from 1807 to 1818. When in 1830, acting on complaints of unsatisfactory customs collections at the ports, a Senate resolution directed the Secretary of the Treasury to make an examination of the standards used in the customhouses, Hassler, then 60, was called back to Washington to undertake the investigation. Two years later he was reappointed superintendent of the Coast Survey.[30]

He collected the standards then in use in the various Government departments, the weights and measures used at the customhouses, and as

[30] See app. A for a biographical sketch of Hassler.

many more as he could obtain from other domestic and foreign sources, and presented his findings in two reports on January 27 and June 29, 1832. As had Secretary of State Adams in 1820, Hassler found no two customhouses in the country where the pound or bushel were the same, the great discrepancies producing "inequalities in the duties levied at the different ports." In fact, "hardly any custom houses have actual standards. All equally refer, for weights and measures of any kind, to the city sealers of the place or those

Ferdinand Rudolph Hassler, first Superintendent of Weights and Measures, from a painting made probably sometime between 1830 and 1840, by Capt. William G. Williams of the Topographical Corps, U.S. Army.

According to a long inscription pasted on the back of the canvas, the recollection of Mary Hassler Newcomb, granddaughter of Hassler and wife of Prof. Simon Newcomb, the portrait hung for many years after its completion on a bare brick wall in the Lee home in Arlington, Va. In April 1864 it came into the hands of Prof. Louis Agassiz, who gave it to the National Academy of Sciences, to keep "as a forerunner of portraits of our noted scientists."

It was hung for several years in the west end of the Smithsonian, then disappeared until 1874, when Professor Newcomb, going "to the tower of the Smithsonian to see after the working of the artificial transit of Venus," found it there covered with dust and somewhat damaged. Hassler's granddaughter claimed it and plans were made to send it to the Coast Survey. In concert with Prof. Joseph Henry, Prof. Julius E. Hilgard, and Prof. Charles S. Peirce, Mrs. Newcomb had the painting restored at Mr. Hein's studio for $20.

Either the Coast Survey refused the portrait or Mrs. Newcomb decided to keep it, for it has remained in the Hassler family since. In 1965 its present owner, Dr. Hassler Whitney of Princeton, N.J., had the painting restored once more and presented it to the Coast and Geodetic Survey, to be hung in its new quarters at Rockville, Md.

appointed by the respective States." And most customhouses, like the city sealers, used "coarse iron, or other weights * * * which * * * on account of their great mass, could not be adjusted but upon common balances." [31]

While Congress debated, the Secretary of the Treasury directed Hassler to secure apparatus and a shop and prepare copies of the standards he recommended in his reports. The Treasury Department at least, with its coinage and customhouse functions, had to adopt something like uniform standards. Thus in 1832, "with the President's approbation," Secretary Louis McLane preempted a corner in the United States Arsenal in Washington, and "with all the exactness that the present advanced state of science and the arts will afford," Hassler set to work on his standards.[32]

He adopted brass for their construction, as did most European countries, because it was "the cheapest metal, not subject to prompt very evident oxidation," and its ordinary expansion was "too minute to have any effect upon the practical application to standards within the limits of magnitude they generally have." Platinum, despite its less destructible nature, was not well enough known, he said, and might have unsuspected differences greater than brass.[33]

The units as defined by Hassler were not new but were those most widely used in the United States. By defining them, he gave them an authority they had not had previously. The standards which he constructed were the best then obtainable, and to them Hassler gave precise and reproducible values so that careful copies derived from them would at least assure uniformity in the offices of the Treasury throughout the nation.

His standard of length was an 82-inch brass bar, made for the Coast Survey in 1813 by Edward Troughton, the best of the London instrument-makers, and brought to this country by Hassler himself 2 years later. The yard measure on this bar was between the 27th and 63d inch marks and was supposed to be identical with the English standard at 62° F, although it had never been directly compared with that standard. The standard of weight remained the troy pound, that made by the English metrologist, Captain Kater, for the United States Mint in 1827, and from it Hassler derived the avoirdupois pound in common use, the ratio of the avoirdupois to the troy pound precisely defined as 7,000 grains to 5,760 grains.

The gallon, based on the English wine gallon of 1703, was a vessel with a volume of 231 cubic inches (holding 8.3389 pounds avoirdupois of distilled water, or 58,372.2 standard grains) when weighed in air at 30 inches

---

[31] [Hassler,] "Weights and Measures", Report from the Secretary of the Treasury, July 2, 1832 (22d Cong., 1st sess., H. Doc. 299), pp. 1, 95.

NOTE.—By common balances Hassler meant ordinary commercial scales, since precision balances were not yet made or available in this country.

[32] Ibid., pp. 1–2.

[33] Ibid., p. 16.

barometric pressure and 62° F. The bushel, based on the old English Winchester bushel, established in the reign of Henry VII, was a measure with a volume of 2,150.42 inches (holding 77.6274 pounds avoirdupois of distilled water or 543,391.89 grains), weighed at the same barometric pressure and temperature as the gallon.[34]

Two years after the Treasury's adoption of Hassler's weights and measures, the 1758 originals of the Troughton yard and Kater pound were irreparably damaged by fire. Despite the fact that their prototypes were lost, Congress recognized the merit and enormous convenience of the new standards. If it could not bring itself to legalize them, it could at least approve them, and in 1836—the generally accepted date of the establishment of an Office of Weights and Measures in the Treasury—a joint resolution of Congress directed the Secretary of the Treasury to make copies of Hassler's standards,

> to be delivered to the governor of each State in the Union, or such person as he may appoint, for the use of the States, respectively, to the end that a uniform standard of weights and measures may be established throughout the United States.[35]

Arbitrary and without any authority but Hassler's (except that Congress had been fully informed of Hassler's choice of units), these were in most instances promptly adopted by the States as their sole legal standards, thus becoming the first nationwide standards in this country.

Two years later another congressional resolution directed that a standard balance be made "under the superintendence of Hassler" for each State. Resolutions, however, are not statutory laws, but further than that Congress would not go.

Constructing these weights and measures with all their multiples and submultiples was slow and difficult work, and not until 1838 were sets of the weights delivered to the States. The customhouses received them a year later. When Hassler died in November 1843 at the age of 73, only half the capacity measures and a third of the measures of length had been completed, and work on the balances had just begun.

---

[34] [Hassler,] "Weights and Measures", p. 12; Louis A. Fischer, "History of the standard weights and measures of the United States," NBS M64 (1925), pp. 7–10. NOTE.—M64 refers to the numbered series of Miscellaneous Papers of the NBS, as C designates its series of Circulars.
The British abolished the wine gallon of 1703 and the Winchester bushel in 1824 when imperial measures were adopted. The imperial gallon was considered as 277.274 cubic inches of distilled water (10 pounds of water), the imperial bushel 2218.19 cubic inches (8 gallons of water), both at 62° F and 30 inches barometric pressure. Thus as Peirce testified in 1885, the English and American gallons and bushels differed by about 17 percent and 3 percent, respectively, as they do today. Apothecaries' weights in the two countries differ by almost 10 percent.

[35] Quoted in NBS M64, pp. 10–12.

In 1856, 13 years later, a report by Alexander D. Bache, Hassler's successor as superintendent of the Coast Survey and in charge of the Office of Weights and Measures, said that full sets of weights, measures, and balances for the States had at last been completed and nearly all delivered. Most of the hundred or more customhouses were now equipped with weights, but only 91 standard gallons, 24 sets of their subdivisions, 22 standard yards, and 11 standard bushel measures had been completed and sent to them.[36] A decade later, as the last of Hassler's measures was dispatched, the metric system arrived in America.

Established in 1791, the French metric system had been adopted during the past century by most civilized countries, with the notable exception of Great Britain and the United States.[37] Then in 1864 Great Britain, compromising with science and commerce, authorized the use of the metric system concurrently with its imperial system. Two years later, on July 28, 1866, Congress in a singular gesture legalized the use of the metric system in this country—something our common system of weights and measures has not achieved to this day. However, use of the metric system was neither then nor later made compulsory, but by legalizing the relationship between the yard and meter (construing the meter as 39.37 inches), Congress sanctioned continued use of the common system based on Hassler's adaptation of the British imperial yard and pound.

Implementing the new law, a joint resolution of Congress that same year authorized the Secretary of the Treasury to furnish each State with a set of metric weights and measures. Until replaced at the end of the century by new international metric standards, a brass meter brought by Hassler to this country in 1805 and a brass copy of a platinum kilogram obtained by Gallatin in 1821 were the basis for the sets made by the Office of Weights and Measures. By 1880 practically all the States had sets of metric standards.[38] What became of these, as well as Hassler's standards distributed earlier, was, as we shall see, disclosed during an investigation begun shortly after the founding of the present National Bureau of Standards.

---

[36] [Bache,] Report of the Secretary of the Treasury on the Construction and Distribution of Weights and Measures (34th Cong., 3d sess., S. Ex. Doc. 27), Washington: A. O. P. Nicholson, 1857, pp. 2–8.

Long current has been the legend that in July 1864 when Jubal Early's army crossed at Harper's Ferry and approached Washington, the Troughton yard, Bronze yard No. 11, Troy pound of 1827, Imperial pound of 1855, Arago kilogram and other standards collected by Hassler and his successor were sent into the Vermont countryside for safekeeping (letter, F. S. Holbrook, May 23, 1936, and attached correspondence, NBS Box 400, IW).

[37] See app. B for a brief history of the metric system.

[38] NBS M64, pp. 16–19. See also metric legislation in app. C.

Prototypes of the weights and measures distributed to the States at the direction of Congress in 1836 and 1866. The newly established Office of the Construction of Weights and Measures fashioned these sets modeled after British standards (1836) and the metric measures of France (1866). From top to bottom are complete sets of standards of capacity, mass, and length, and their handling equipment. The standard of flatness, a quartz disk, did not become a standard provided to the States until many years later.

Meanwhile, the simple and logical metric system had been found wanting. In 1867 serious differences in metric measurements came to light in France while carrying out a series of geodetic surveys. The metric system was based on a natural concept which assumed the meter to be one ten-millionth part of a meridional quadrant of the earth. Investigation disclosed that realization of the concept in the adopted meter was erroneous, and further, that the original standards, kept in the Archives of France, had simply not been constructed with the degree of precision possible three-quarters of a century later.

With the United States participating, the series of international conferences that were held in 1872–73 to construct new metric standards led to the selection of a graduated line standard as a new basis for the metric system. Rejection of a natural basis for the meter made international agreement necessary in order to maintain the validity of this artificial meter. The conferees therefore agreed to the establishment of a permanent International Bureau of Weights and Measures, to be located at Sèvres, near Paris, which would not only keep custody of the new prototype meter and kilogram when constructed, but make comparisons between them and the fundamental standards of nonmetrical weights and measures in other countries. The convention was signed on May 20, 1875, by representatives of 17 countries, including the United States, and ratified by President Rutherford B. Hayes, on the advice of the Senate, on September 27, 1878.[39]

In 1889, after more than 10 years of labor, the instrumentmakers at Sèvres completed the new metric standards. From among 30 carefully constructed meters and 40 kilograms, all of platinum-iridium, a committee selected an International Meter and International Kilogram as prototypes. The remaining standards were then distributed to the contributing countries, the United States receiving meter Nos. 21 and 27 and kilogram Nos. 4 and 20.[40] The Coast Survey's Office of Weights and Measures accepted custody of them the next year. Subsequently two other meter bars designated Nos. 4 and 12, made of an earlier platinum composition, the alloy of 1874, as it was called, were secured.

On April 5, 1893, Thomas C. Mendenhall, then superintendent of the Coast Survey and its Office of Weights and Measures, adopted with the approval of the Secretary of the Treasury the new meter and kilogram as the fundamental standards of length and mass in the United States, deriving from them the common yard as $\frac{3600}{3937}$ meter and the avoirdupois pound as 0.453 592 427 7 kilogram.[41] In doing so Mendenhall assumed, as did Hassler, considerably more authority than he had, since he changed the value slightly for the kilogram from that given in the law of 1866, on the basis of more recent comparisons made between the kilogram and the English pound.

From the beginning, use of the metric system in Government agencies as elsewhere was a matter of choice, except for laws passed in 1866 and 1872 requiring balances marked in metric grams for all post offices, and an order of 1894 enjoining use of the metric system in requisitioning medical supplies for the War Department. Though extensively used in scientific and technological research, the metric system made very meager inroads into ordinary government or commercial transactions in this country.

---

[39] A contemporary account of the organization of the International Bureau appears in Statement of Professor J. E. Hilgard before the Committee on Coinage, Weights and Measures, May 8 and June 3, 1878 (45th Cong., 2d sess., H. Misc. Doc. 61). Julius E. Hilgard (1825–91), a Bavarian geodesist hired by Bache, was with the Coast Survey from 1834 to 1885, succeeding Bache as superintendent in 1881.

[40] Letter, B. A. Gould to Secretary of State James G. Blaine, Nov. 4, 1889. In Correspondence of the Office of U.S. Standard Weights and Measures, vol. V, pp. 436–449 (National Archives, Record Group 167).

[41] "Fundamental standards of length and mass," Coast and Geodetic Survey Bull. 26 (1893) ; NBS C593 (1958), pp. 15–16.

Without the force of law the two sets of weights and measures deposited in the National and State capitals, one based on British standards, the other on French, tended to gather dust. Special legislation or departmental orders were necessary to enforce their use in Federal agencies, and for want of direction and centralized authority Federal and State statute books became crowded with acts setting up still other standards. Many of these were freely conceived, merely expedient, and as often as not limited in application to a single agency.

Among the plethora of Federal standards alone were those enacted between 1825 and 1875 for the Treasury Department and Commissioner of Internal Revenue specifying the kinds of hydrometers to be used to determine the proof of distilled spirits, defining the term "proof gallon," the number of pounds of grain in bushel measures used in distilleries, and the number of gallons to a barrel. In 1868 a standard gage for bolts, nuts, and screw threads, adopted by the Secretary of the Navy, became mandatory in all Navy Yards but nowhere else.

Other acts between 1789 and 1880 established the measurement of vessel tonnage, prescribed rules and measures for surveying public lands, and fixed procedures for examining and testing steam engines used by the Government. Periodically, revised acts specified the number of pounds in a bushel of grain, peas, and similar commodities for estimating import duties, defined the weight and measure of a ton of coal or a cord of wood when bought for Federal agencies, and authorized Treasury standards for the quality of imported sugar. Still another act provided funds for investigating the physical properties of wool and other animal fibers, and one even imposed the use of proper weights and measures (without defining them) for determining the provisions served to American seamen.

This year to year legislation in measurement, operating nowhere below the Government level, became increasingly unsatisfactory and was of no use to science or industry. By 1884 the telephone and electric light had become commercial realities, the first commercial electric trolley car was a year away, the first commercial electric power plant 2 years away. These and other electrical developments would continue to advance by wasteful trial and error methods, for lack of definitions and measurements that neither scientific institutions nor industry were qualified to provide. That Congress recognized its responsibility seems evident from the appropriation it made underwriting the conference of electrical workers and scientists that met at the Franklin Institute in Philadelphia in the autumn of 1884.[42]

In complete agreement on the necessity for Federal intervention, the conference appointed a committee headed by Prof. Monroe B. Snyder to make a strong recommendation to Congress for "the establishment of a

---

[42] See above, p. 18.

Bureau of Standards * * * charged with the duty of examining and verifying instruments for electrical and other physical measurements [and] * * * to determine and reproduce all the physical standards with relation to each other." [43] That was the year the National Academy of Sciences proposed a Department of Science in the Federal Government.

By 1893 some sort of agreement on electrical measurements had become imperative, and an international electrical congress held at the Columbian Exposition in Chicago that summer adopted values for the basic units of electricity. In December, Mendenhall, in one of his last acts as superintendent of the Coast Survey, issued a bulletin announcing their formal adoption by the Office of Weights and Measures. On July 12, 1894, Congress enacted the definitions and values of these units into law. The founders of electrical science were honored by using their names for the units, and by international agreement the *ohm* was designated the unit of resistance, the *ampere* the unit of current, the *volt* the unit of electromotive force, the *coulomb* the unit of quantity, the farad or *faraday* the unit of capacity (now, capacitance), the *joule* the unit of work, the *watt* the unit of power, and the *henry* the unit of induction (inductance).

Congress also charged the National Academy of Sciences with prescribing and publishing such specifications as might be "necessary for the practical application of the definitions of the ampere and volt," from which all the other electrical units could be derived. The next year Dr. Frank A. Wolff, Jr., in the Office of Weights and Measures, was directed to begin preliminary experiments and tests on certain specifications adopted by the Academy.

But as Peirce pointed out a decade earlier, the metrological work of that office had little standing and less legal status; nor was it, for lack of funds, to be notably enhanced upon assumption of this new responsibility. From 1832 until 1870 the expenses of the Office were met out of general appropriations made to the Treasury Department and later to the Coast Survey. Then in 1870 Congress for some reason made all its appropriations for the Coast Survey specific that year, leaving no funds whatever for weights and measures.

The Office languished until the Appropriation Act of March 3, 1873, for the first time included an explicit appropriation in Coast Survey funds "for construction and verification of standard weights and measures for the customhouses and for the several States, and of metric standards for the States, $12,000." The first recognition of the Office by name and as a separate agency, in any legislative act, occurred in the Appropriation Act of August 5, 1882. But except for the addition of the clause in 1890, "and for such

[43] Report of the Electrical Conference at Philadelphia, September 1884 (reprinted in 49th Cong., 1st sess., S. Ex. Doc. 45, 1886), pp. 45–48.

necessary repairs and adjustment * * * to the standards furnished to the several States and Territories * * * [and] Customhouses," the functions of the Office, as quoted, remained unchanged until 1901.[44]

Little wonder that Peirce declared that "an office of weights and measures in the sense in which it exists in every other country * * * which should be prepared to make exact verification of all sorts of standards and certify officially to them, does not exist in the United States." Asked what his office should be equipped to do to fulfill reasonably public and Federal requirements, Peirce, in keeping with the mood of Congress, replied modestly that besides acquiring units of electrical measurement it should be ready to verify the legal units of length and weight, "say the yard, the meter, the pound, and the kilogram," and be prepared to verify speedily and certify officially for the public the multiples and submultiples of these units of mass and length. More importantly, in order to carry out these responsibilities, it should be given legal recognition and support. This would permit the Office to act with authority at home and to work for international agreement on the imperial measures shared by the United States, Russia, and Great Britain.[45]

Such a program, said Peirce, could be carried out with an increase of nine members in the Office, making a total of twelve, who would confine themselves to supplying and verifying standards within the scope he had outlined. Ignoring the fine work in astronomy then being done by Simon Newcomb at the Naval Observatory, Peirce rejected the idea of basic research in his Office, or in any government agency, for that matter. "A bureau of the government cannot very properly be expected to do original scientific work," said Peirce. "Its natural functions are to do routine work. * * * It is hardly to be expected that scientific investigation undertaken incidentally by a Bureau of the Government should, in the long run, be of the very highest character." No one contradicted him.

A further natural limit to the scope of work of the Office, declared Peirce, was that "it need not enter upon the business of inspecting commercial standards, because that is done already by the States in a satisfactory way."[46] One must remember that the year was 1884.

LAISSEZ-FAIRE STANDARDS

The States were no better equipped to control commercial standards than the Office of Standard Weights and Measures was to provide national standards. In 1892, William Mason, a member of the Rensselaer Poly-

[44] Weber, The Bureau of Standards, pp. 35–36.

[45] Allison Commission, Testimony, pp. 370, 371–372, 375.

[46] Ibid., pp. 372, 378.

technic Institute faculty, complained in the pages of Science magazine that he had to contend with eight different "authoritative" values for the U.S. gallon, including two accepted by the U.S. Pharmacopoeia, three found in current standard chemical textbooks, one in Oldberg's Weights and Measures (1885), and two in Treasury Department reports—that given by Bache in his 1857 report describing Hassler's 8.3389-pound gallon and a currently adjusted standard, an 8.3312-pound gallon. In this confusion, Professor Mason declared he had elected to work with a ninth value, one he had determined for himself.

Although dignified by the term "standard," said Professor Mason, the truth was, "the U.S. gallon has no statutory existence whatever," nor had any of our common weights and measures with the single exception of the troy pound. "It seems * * * highly desirable that this whole question of standards and relation of weight to measure, be finally settled by law, and preliminary to this, by a new scientific investigation." [47]

Thomas C. Mendenhall, author of A Century of Electricity (1887) and in charge of weights and measures as superintendent of the Coast Survey from 1889 to 1894, fully agreed: "The system of weights and measures in customary use is so confusing, so unscientific, and, in some instances, apparently so contradictory that it is difficult to write of it, even briefly, without falling into error." [48] Permissive use of standards, poor construction of commercial weights and measures, and the progress of science had long since combined to vitiate the merits of Hassler's good work.

Some degree of the confusion in precision measurement at least may be traced to Hassler's standard of length—and the basis for all the other standards. As Mendenhall said: "The Troughton 82-inch scale was formerly accepted as a standard of length, but for many years it has not been actually so regarded. By reason of its faulty construction it is entirely unsuitable for a standard, and for a long time it has been of historic interest only." [49]

The hazard in Hassler's yard measure, based on the Troughton scale, seems to have been first pointed out by John Henry Alexander, Maryland metrologist and later professor of natural philosophy at the University of Maryland. For lack of the necessary equipment, Alexander carried out many of the metrological tests for the construction of his yard measures for

---

[47] William P. Mason, "Confusion in weights and measures," Science, 20, 358 (1892).
[48] Mendenhall, Science, 21, 79–80 (1893).
[49] Upon completion of construction of its new imperial standards in 1855, Great Britain presented copies of the yard and avoirdupois pound to the United States. The new bronze yard No. 11, when compared with the Troughton yard, revealed that the accepted 36 inches of the Troughton scale was 0.00087 inch longer than the British imperial yard. Since the new yard was far superior as a standard of length, the Office of Standard Weights and Measure adopted it as the U.S. standard. NBS M64 (1925), pp. 12–14.

the State of Maryland in Hassler's Washington laboratory and continued to work there after Bache took over.[50] The brass in Hassler's yard scale, made with "ingenious and novel methods" and containing a zinc of more than usual purity, said Alexander, presented—

> in several physical characters a marked difference from the ordinary brass of commerce; it is softer, freer, more uniform in texture, of a more agreeable color, and oxidates even with a pleasanter aspect. This last particular was a point upon which the late Superintendent, whose remarkable versatility of genius found nothing too great or too small for attention, in a manner piqued himself; and the bright eye of the aged philosopher gleamed brighter as it watched the deepening of what he called his "oerugo nobilis." * * * All these peculiarities would have made the employment of such metal, had it been possible, of great interest and advantage: but it was only to be procured by a repetition of the original process—a step manifestly disproportionate to the end now in view. Under these circumstances, resort was had to the article as more usually obtained.[51]

Alexander's use of ordinary brass made comparison with the original standard all but impossible because there was no "means of knowing positively the expansion of Mr. Hassler's brass." The 30 different yard-measures that Alexander constructed for the State of Maryland between 1842 and 1845, each with a "correction for excess of U.S. Standard," agreed with one another within two parts in a ten-thousandth of an inch. Even though this was "a quantity fully observable," Alexander nevertheless considered his bars entirely satisfactory for "measuring the yards in common use that may be applied to them." [52]

Alexander appears to have been a careful craftsman, and he had access to the best equipment available in this country, that in Hassler's laboratory. It is doubtful whether many other State metrologists enjoyed either advantage. Yet a comment he made on Hassler's mission at the beginning of his report provides, unwittingly, a clue to the attitude of the age toward weights and measures and to the outcome of Hassler's efforts:

> The Establishment of a system of Weights and Measures belongs not merely to the domain of mechanical science, but enters also into the regions of metaphysics and the higher generalizations of history.

---

[50] J. H. Alexander, Report on the Standards of Weights and Measures for the State of Maryland and on the Construction of the Yard-Measures (Baltimore: John D. Toy, 1845), pp. 167, 183.

[51] Ibid., pp. 178–179.

[52] Ibid., pp. 208–210.

When in addition reproducibility of the basic standard was doubtful and comparison with the original impossible, metrology indeed became metaphysical. And so it proved.

Fifty years later Mendenhall was to report that, supplied with replicas of Hassler's standards, "nearly all of the States made these copies their standards, and thus practical uniformity was secured. Theoretically or rigorously, however, there are about as many systems of weights and measures in use to-day as there are States in the Union." [53]

In its effort to maintain the highest accuracy of the yard and pound, Mendenhall's Office had itself contributed to the confusion. While interested States continued to construct their standards as best they could on Hassler's models, the Office of Weights and Measures, rejecting Troughton's scale, defined the U.S. yard as identical with the imperial yard of Great Britain, the standard of mass with the imperial or avoirdupois pound. In 1893, 27 years after legalization of the metric system by Congress, the Office turned to that "infinitely more perfect order" and redefined its yard and pound in terms of the meter and kilogram.[54]

Without an authoritative national standard or an adequate testing and comparison agency, regulation of Hassler's standards had been left to the States, and they had few funds for proper construction, maintenance, or control. With almost no precision instrument makers in this country, industry and science turned to Europe, while the construction of commercial weights and measures was left to business supply houses. Some measure of the general ensuing chaos may be seen in the report in John Perry's The Story of Standards, that in Brooklyn, N.Y., in 1902, "city surveyors recognized as legal four different 'feet': the United States foot, the Bushwick foot, the Williamsburg foot, and the foot of the 26th Ward. All legal, all different. Some strips of Brooklyn real estate were untaxable, because, after two surveys, made with different units, these strips, legally, didn't exist!" [55]

The widening gap between so-called Federal and State standards, and the inability of the Office of Weights and Measures to supply the growing variety of standards needed in the Nation, inevitably led to the creation of a whole galaxy of entirely arbitrary standards affecting almost every measurable quantity required by farm, factory, or laboratory. Standards were further debased as the classic laissez-faire control supposedly exercised by a free market broke down completely at the end of the century, a market that ceased to exist when not only the necessities of life but virtually every article of commerce came under the control of trusts and monopolies.

---

[53] Mendenhall, Science, 1893.

[54] Ibid. See above, p. 30.

[55] The Story of Standards (New York: Funk & Wagnalls, 1955), pp. 5, 13. Perry's book, with the National Bureau of Standards as its frame of reference, is a brief, highly readable history of the idea of standards from ancient times to the present.

Some of the consequences were revealed in an article in Scientific American in 1896 describing the increasing unreliability of household products, industrial goods, and construction materials. In the construction of buildings, between 15 and 20 percent more material than needed had to be ordered to allow for the uneven quality found in every lot. The tensile strength of cement varied with the shipment, a certain quantity of steel tubing and forgings could be counted on to prove defective, and in one recent test sampling only two of six makes of white lead submitted deserved the name. Among household items, a conspicuous example of outright fraud was lard oil containing a high percentage of paraffin oil.

A number of independent testing agencies had sprung up to assist industry, the article continued, but their subjective standards were in no way comparable to those established in the bureaus under government supervision in Europe. As a result, "at present it is very difficult to get a paint which is worth anything, or a good lubricating oil at a reasonable price, and many of the soaps sold throughout the country are so injurious to clothes as to be worse than useless. Is this not, after all, a matter for governmental control?" [56]

Henry Ives Cobb, designer of the Chicago Opera House and Newberry Library and consulting architect to the Federal Government, concurred on the state of construction materials, and in testimony before a congressional committee some 4 years later, he and other highly qualified witnesses left no doubt of the consequences in this country of laissez-faire standards. Although the Office of Weights and Measures had adopted the English standard of light, said Carl Hering, president of the American Institute of Electrical Engineers, it was so indefinite and inadequate that scientific laboratories referred instead to the German standard as more precise and reproducible. The electric light industry, finding neither the British nor German standards useful, had adopted standards of its own in the manufacture and sale of lighting equipment. By agreement among the electric light companies, Prof. Henry A. Rowland of the Johns Hopkins University testified, a lamp requiring 10 amperes of current at a pressure of 45 volts was called 2,000 candlepower, when in reality—that is, by British or German standards—it amounted only to 400 to 500 candlepower.[57]

Dr. Henry S. Pritchett, then superintendent of the Coast and Geodetic Survey, acknowledged that the Nation was without a definite, accurate photometric standard or even the means to arrive at one. But then neither had we accurate means to test thermometers, barometers, pressure gages, electrical standards and measuring apparatus, polariscopes, instruments of

---

[56] L. S. Randolph, "Systematic inspection of material," Sci. Am. 75, 347 (1896).

[57] Hearings before the Subcommittee of the Committee on Commerce, Dec. 28, 1900 (56th Cong., 2d sess., S. Doc. 70, serial 4033), pp. 12, 15.

navigation, steam engine indicators, or almost any other instrument of precision. Even though many of these were being made in this country, "nearly all such instruments have to be sent to Europe * * * for standardization." As for those used in high-precision work in university laboratories, in scientific institutions, and Government laboratories, they could only be procured from abroad. The same was true of all our chemical apparatus. It came from abroad.[58]

The electrical industry by 1900 represented a $200 million investment in this country, Prof. Arthur E. Kennelly of Harvard testified, yet for lack of recognized standards the industry was involved in frequent and costly litigation, putting a brake on its continued growth.[59] As the crowning insult resulting from our failure to establish national standards, the Physikalisch-Technische Reichsanstalt, Germany's national standards laboratory, used the Weston voltameter-ammeter, an American-invented and American-made instrument, for its precision measurement of electrical currents and electrical pressures, but refused to accept the calibration of its manufacturer. The Reichsanstalt had also adopted the Weston cell in preference to its own standard, for the determination of electromotive force. These and other electrical instruments made in this country for domestic sale and export were regularly sent first to Germany for recalibration, because the manufacturers' standards were either not known or not accepted.[60]

National laboratories abroad were already at work answering the demands of science and industry for instruments of greater reliability, accuracy, and range. In this country we were still incapable of supplying either a certified instrument to a scientific laboratory or an authoritative common measure to the marketplace. Besides impeding the scientific and commercial development of the Nation, witness after witness told Congress, the necessity of sending abroad for certification was consuming of time, expensive, and damaging to our national prestige. Establishment of a national standardizing laboratory could be deferred no longer.

"A NATIONAL NEED . . . A NATIONAL HUMILIATION"

A Federal standards laboratory had been under discussion for almost 20 years before the burst of nationalism at the turn of the century and the surging growth of American industry together conspired to assure its serious consideration. The coincidence made for compelling arguments. As a result of the Spanish-American War we had in a few short months become a

[58] Hearings before the Committee on Coinage, Weights and Measures, May 3, 1900 (56th Cong., 1 sess., H. Rept., no document or serial number), p. 2.
[59] Ibid., p. 13.
[60] Hearings * * * Dec. 28, 1900, p. 17.

world power, intensely proud of the new respect with which the nations of the world now dealt with us. Our foreign and domestic commerce flourished as never before; in the decade before 1900 the export of American manufactures almost doubled. Only Germany's oversea trade had exceeded this rate of increase in the same period, largely because, as our manufacturing and trade associations pointed out, she was able to guarantee the uniformity and quality of her exported goods.

Since the 1870's, Austria, Russia, Germany, and England had established national standardizing laboratories or reorganized existing agencies, all with the avowed purpose of applying science and scientific methods to their nation's commerce and industry.[61] Most successful had been Germany, working with industry through the great Physikalisch-Technische Reichsanstalt, organized in 1887. In a single decade she had achieved world monopoly in the manufacture of aniline dyes and dye products, and her porcelain industry, artificial indigo industry, Jena optical glass, and scientific and precision instrument industries had no peers. Employing 13,600 people in 760 firms, the instrument and optical glass industries alone had trebled the export of their products in the past decade, making no secret of their debt to the Reichsanstalt for their growth.[62]

Great Britain, in an admittedly desperate effort "to retain her supremacy in trade and in manufacture," established her National Physical Laboratory in 1899.[63] The United States remained the only great commercial nation without a comparable standards laboratory. Our further development of the remarkable discoveries made in pure and applied science of the past century might well be forfeited, Scientific American warned, without sound and accepted commercial and industrial standards. A national laboratory had become "a national need." [64]

The initiative came from Lyman J. Gage, Secretary of the Treasury since 1897 and executive head of the Office of Weights and Measures. Gage, a solid, conservative Chicago banker, who had been brought to Washington by McKinley and possessed a talent for charming Congressmen with his diplo-

---

[61] Among the great powers, only France (and the United States) had lagged. The great service of France in fostering international standards of length and mass was widely recognized, "but her national bureau for this purpose [was] considered to be too limited in scope to solve * * * new problems * * *." H. S. Carhart, "The Imperial Physico-Technical Institution in Charlottenburg," Science, 12, 702–703 (1900).

[62] Henry S. Carhart, "The Imperial Physico-Technical Institute in Charlottenburg," Annual Report, Smithsonian Institution, 1900, pp. 403–415. In an earlier (1892) account of the PTR, Prof. A. G. Webster had urged it as a model for an American standards laboratory. See Science, 56, 170 (1922).

[63] Richard Glazebrook, "The aims of the National Physical Laboratory of Great Britain," Annual Report, Smithsonian Institution, 1901, pp. 341–357.

[64] Editorial, Sci. Am., 82, 307 (1900); Science, 10, 342 (1899).

Lyman J. Gage, Secretary of the Treasury under President McKinley, who initiated and led the campaign for a national standardizing laboratory in the Federal Government.

macy and wit, was to prove a wise and able mentor in the establishment of the Bureau.

In the late summer of 1899 he asked his Assistant Secretary, Frank A. Vanderlip, subsequently president of the National City Bank of New York, who had come to Washington as Gage's private secretary, to suggest someone to prepare a report proposing legislation for a national standards laboratory. Vanderlip wrote to Samuel W. Stratton, a classmate when they were undergraduates at the University of Illinois and at that time a 38-year-old professor of physics at the University of Chicago.

Stratton was invited to Washington. On October 28, 1899, the incumbent officer in immediate charge of weights and measures, "an expert leveler but without a glimmer of knowledge of physical principles," [65] was transferred and Gage appointed Stratton to the nominal position of Inspector of Standards. Before long Stratton was at work drafting the bill to be included in the Secretary's letter report to Congress and organizing the arguments for the congressional hearings to come.

Securing endorsements for the proposed standards laboratory proved no difficulty. It had the overwhelming support of the National Academy of

[65] Speech, Dr. Frank A. Wolff, 25th anniversary of the NBS, Dec. 4, 1926 (NBS Blue Folder Box 3, APW–301c).

Sciences, the American Philosophical Society, the American Association for the Advancement of Science, the American Physical Society, the American Chemical Society, the American Institute of Electrical Engineers, and other scientific institutions and associations. In personal testimony, letters, resolutions, and editorials, the leading scientists of the country, virtually every scientific agency in the Federal Government and in the States, leading manufacturers and commercial concerns, the railroad and iron and steel industries, manufacturers of electrical apparatus and appliances, and all scientific and technical journals and periodicals endorsed the proposed bill without reservation.[66] As James H. Southard, Representative from Ohio and champion of the bill in the House, said: "Never has a bill come with such a number of endorsements."

The arguments in the avalanche of endorsements were summed up in "the conditions which necessitate the establishment of a national standardizing bureau," set down in Secretary Gage's letter to Congress on April 18, 1900, and here slightly abbreviated:

> The establishment of uniform standards, their maintenance, and the solution of problems connected with them, has until recent years been confined to standards of length, mass, capacity, and temperature; "but the increased order of accuracy demanded in scientific and commercial measurements and the exceedingly rapid progress of pure and applied science have increased the scope of such work until it includes many important branches of physical and chemical research, requiring * * * a complete laboratory, fitted for undertaking the most refined measurements known to modern science."
>
> An examination of the functions and sums of money devoted to the maintenance of the German, English, Austrian, Russian, and French institutions "is the most convincing evidence of the importance of problems pertaining to standards and standard-measuring apparatus."
>
> Institutions of learning, laboratories, observatories, technical institutions, and scientific societies in this country are proliferating and growing "at a rate never equaled in the history of any nation," their work "requiring accurate reliable standards, which in nearly every case must be procured from abroad, or cannot be procured at all."
>
> "The extension of scientific research into the realm of the extremes of length, mass, time, temperature, pressure, and other physical

[66] These endorsements will be found in the congressional documents dated Apr. 18, May 3, and Dec. 28, 1900, cited in footnotes below.

> quantities necessitates standards of far greater range than can be obtained at present."
>
> "The introduction of accurate scientific methods into manufacturing and commercial processes involves the use of a great variety of standards of greater accuracy than formerly required."
>
> More and more, "commercial transactions are * * * based upon the reading of electrical measuring apparatus, inaccuracies of which involve great injustice and financial losses." It should be possible "to calibrate or test electrical standards of all kinds for commercial, as well as the most refined scientific work."
>
> "The scientific work carried on by the different departments of the Government involves the use of many standards and instruments of precision, which are too frequently procured from abroad" and regularly returned there for testing.
>
> The manufacture of scientific apparatus and instruments of precision recently begun in this country is growing, and "to secure the requisite degree of uniformity and accuracy" in their products, "American manufacturers of such apparatus must have access to a standardizing bureau equivalent to that provided for the manufacturers of other countries, notably Germany and England."

Not least,

> "The recent acquisition of territory by the United States increases the scope and importance of the proposed institution, since the establishment of a government in these possessions involves the system of weights and measures to be employed," and in the near future "large public inmprovements * * * [such as] schools, factories, and other institutions will be established, all of which require the use of standards and standard-measuring apparatus." [67]

These were, for the most part, immediate and pressing considerations. They indicated clearly the degree of dependence of American science, industry, and commerce upon European agencies, and made glaring the contrast between the work possible in the little Office of Weights and Measures and in the German Reichsanstalt.

Interestingly enough, except for the general reference to the scientific work of Government agencies, no mention was made in the "conditions" of better standards required in the collection of customs and internal revenue, in the purchase of supplies for the Government, or in establishing specifica-

---

[67] Letter, Secretary of the Treasury, Apr. 18, 1900, sub: National Standardizing Bureau (56th Cong., 1st sess., H. Doc. 625, serial 3997), p. 3. See also Annual Report, Secretary of the Treasury, 1900, p. lxvii.

tions for Government purchases, which were to occupy so much of the time of the Bureau in its early years. Nor did the conditions include better standards for the general public, whose every purchase and transaction is based on standards. Yet from the beginning the Bureau was to become involved in Government specifications, crusade for the consumer, and act to put better weights and measures in the hands of State and municipal authorities.

The proposed bill contained in Gage's letter of April 18 recommended that the Office of Standard Weights and Measures be reorganized as a separate agency to be designated the National Standardizing Bureau, and that it remain under the Secretary of the Treasury. As stated in the letter,

> *The functions of the bureau shall consist in the custody of the standards;*
>
> *the comparison of the standards used in scientific investigations, engineering, manufacturing, commerce, and educational institutions with the standards adopted or recognized by the Government;*
>
> *the construction when necessary of standards, their multiples and subdivisions;*
>
> *the testing and calibration of standard-measuring apparatus;*
>
> *the solution of problems which arise in connection with standards;*
>
> *the determining of physical constants, and the properties of materials when such data are of great importance to scientific or manufacturing interests and are not to be obtained of sufficient accuracy elsewhere.*[68]

These six functions, subsequently enacted into law without change, made the Bureau the source of national standards and their custodian. The Bureau was to have no regulating or policing powers; enforcement of standards was left to the discretion of the States. On the other hand, the responsibility of the Bureau for the establishment of standards, standard instruments, tests, and analytic procedures, and for the determination of physical constants and the properties of materials, made its scope of research in the physical sciences virtually unlimited. And the delegation of responsibility to it for the investigation of any problem in connection with standards was to enable the Bureau to span the gap between standards of measurement and standards of performance in the coming age of mass production, and to leap thence to the age of atomic research and space physics.

---

[68] Letter, Apr. 18, 1900, p. 1. The bill as enacted into law appears in app. C.

The proposed bill made the services of the Bureau freely available to the Federal Government and to State and municipal governments, and, for a fee, to any scientific society, educational institution, firm, corporation, or individual within the United States engaged in manufacturng or other pursuits requiring the use of standards or standard-measuring instruments.

All Bureau personnel, scientific, technical, clerical, and custodial, were to be under Civil Service appointment, and to insure that the Bureau served the best interests of science and commerce, a visiting committee of five members appointed by the Secretary of the Treasury from among the leading scientists and industrialists in the Nation was to visit the Bureau at least once a year and report to the Secretary upon the efficiency of its work and the condition of its facilities and equipment.

The staff of the new agency recommended in Gage's proposed bill consisted of a director at $6,000 per year, a physicist at $3,500, a chemist at $3,500, two assistant physicists or chemists at $2,200 each, two laboratory assistants at $1,400 each, two others at $1,200, a secretary at $2,000, two clerks at $1,200 and $1,000 respectively, a messenger at $720, an engineer at $1,500, a fireman at $720, three mechanicians at $1,400, $1,000, and $840 respectively, a watchman at $720, and two laborers at $600 each, making a total of 21.

The bill asked for appropriations of $34,900 for staff salaries, $10,000 for general expenses, $25,000 for the purchase of a laboratory site, $250,000 for a suitable laboratory, and $25,000 to equip the laboratory. These sums, Gage pointed out, were in no way excessive by comparison with those allowed the national laboratories abroad. The Normal Eichungskommission, established in 1868 in Berlin to regulate and inspect weights and measures, had been granted an appropriation equivalent to $250,000 in 1899 for new buildings and equipment, and its annual appropriation was $36,000. The Reichsanstalt at Charlottenburg had cost $1 million and had an annual appropriation of $80,000. Together the German bureaus were spending $116,000 a year.

In England the testing bureau at the Kew Observatory (1871), the Standards Department (1879), the Electrical Standardizing Laboratory (1890), and the new National Physical Laboratory (1899) had total appropriations equivalent to $62,100. Austria's Normal Eichungskommission, established in 1871 in Vienna, currently spent $46,000 a year, and the Russian Central Chamber of Weights and Measures, established in 1878 at St. Petersburg, with laboratories costing $175,000 and added structures built in 1895, spent $17,500 annually. By contrast, the appropriation for the U.S. Office of Weights and Measures for 1897–98 had been $10,000.[69]

---

[69] Ibid., pp. 9–11.

Secretary Gage's letter was referred to the House Committee on Coinage, Weights, and Measures on April 23, 1900. At the first hearing, on May 3, several members of the committee wondered aloud at the willingness of the superintendent of the Coast Survey to lose an office of his agency, demurred at creating another bureau in the Federal Government, and, coming to the heart of the matter, expressed the opinion that both the salaries and construction costs for the new bureau seemed much too high.

Dr. Henry S. Pritchett, superintendent of the Coast Survey but soon to become president of MIT, had been consulted by Stratton on the matter of salaries. Pritchett told the committee that he himself received $5,000, although by law the position called for $6,000, the same salary proposed for the director of the new bureau. There was apt to be considerable difference between a $5,000 and a $6,000 a year man, he said, and if the right man was found he should have the higher figure. As for the salaries of the other scientists, they were "about what they would get in college life"; a good, even a first class, chemist or physicist such as the bureau must have could probably be found for $3,500.[70]

When someone questioned whether the head of the proposed bureau should receive a salary within $2,000 of that of the Secretary of the Treasury himself, Lyman Gage briskly replied: "Almost anybody will do for the Secretary of the Treasury * * * [but] it takes a very high-grade man to be chief of a bureau like this. There are plenty of patriotic citizens who are willing to be Secretary * * * at almost any salary they might get, but this * * * [man] must have and hold the esteem and confidence of all * * * scientific men everywhere, and unless he is as good or a better man than is found in private institutions and concerns he will not have the respect and confidence of the community." [71]

To objections that the amount asked for the laboratory seemed too large, the committee was told that the structure would have to be erected outside the city proper, in an isolated place free from vibration, traffic disturbances, and interference from electric streetcar lines. It would have to be solidly built with at least twice as much material as in an ordinary building of the same size, with twice as complex heating, piping, and plumbing arrangements, and with four or five times more wiring. In addition, it must have a heating plant, engines, dynamos, motors, pumps, and other heavy machinery, as well as instrument shops, in a separate structure apart from the main laboratory.[72] It was an impressive structure Stratton described, and he won his point.

---

[70] Hearing before the Committee on Coinage, Weights, and Measures, May 3, 1900 (56th Cong., 1st sess., H. Rept, no document or serial number), p. 14.

[71] Ibid.

[72] Congressional Record, 56th Cong., 2d sess., Mar. 2, 1901, p. 3475.

On May 5, 1900, after defeat of a motion to reduce the director's salary to $5,000, James H. Southard, Chairman of the Committee on Coinage, Weights, and Measures, introduced the bill (H.R. 11350), essentially identical with that proposed in Gage's letter, in the House. His final argument, insuring the unanimous endorsement of his committee, was that under proper administration the expenses of the new agency would be "largely repaid by fees resulting from its work." [73] On May 14, Jonathan Rose of Vermont introduced the bill in the Senate (S. 4680). Further hearings were delayed until after the summer recess of Congress.

The hearing before the Senate Subcommittee of the Committee on Commerce opened on December 28, 1900. Once again the proposed salaries of the scientists came under fire. Secretary Gage admitted that they were "relatively high as compared with * * * the salaries the Government pays in a good many other directions," but in the new bureau the United States had to have "the best in the world." Stratton added that they were no higher than those for corresponding positions in the leading universities, and further, that an academic career was apt to be preferred as less likely subject to political weather changes. Moreover, bureau personnel would not have the 3 or 4 months of annual vacation available to academic faculty for study or travel. As for the salary proposed for the director, said Stratton, scientific directors in some of the large industrial corporations were able to command as much as $10,000 a year.[74]

The Senate subcommittee nevertheless cut back the salary schedule from $34,900 to $27,140 by reducing the director's salary to $5,000 and eliminating 8 of the 21 positions, including 2 laboratory assistants, the secretary, a clerk, the fireman, 2 mechanicians, and a laborer. Other modifications in the Senate bill saw the sum for equipping the main laboratory reduced from $25,000 to $10,000 and "the general expenses of said bureau, including books and periodicals, furniture, office expenses, stationery and printing, heating and lighting, expenses of the visiting committee, and contingencies of all kinds" reduced from $10,000 to $5,000.

Returned to the House for full debate on March 2, 1901, the bill met with predictable mixed reactions. Upon its reading, Mr. John W.

---

[73] Although by the 1960's fees from calibrations, testing, and other services exceeded $6 million annually, the Bureau was never to be, as Congress seemed to think it should be, self-supporting. See Hearings before the Subcommittee of the House Committee on Appropriations * * * for 1906 (Dec. 2, 1904), p. 230 (L/C:HJ10.B33 and HF105.C55). House appropriations hearings will hereafter be cited as Hearings * * *.

[74] Hearings before the Subcommittee of the Committee on Commerce, Dec. 28, 1900 (56th Cong., 2d sess., S. Doc. 70, serial No. 4033), pp. 4–7. $10,000 was the salary of Albert Ladd Colby, chief metallurgical engineer of the Bethlehem Iron & Steel Co. and member of the first Visiting Committee, whose physical and chemical laboratory employed 36 people. See also Congressional Record, March 2, 1901, p. 3476.

Maddox of Georgia rose to say: "I do not know anything about the bill. If I understood it, or if it was possible for me to understand it * * * I might be in favor of it. I want to know what it will cost." Southard explained. Mr. Joseph G. Cannon of Illinois, who as "Uncle Joe Cannon" was to be the long-time autocratic Speaker of the House (1903–11) but was then Chairman of the House Appropriations Committee, proved characteristically forthright: "I don't think there ought to be any [such] bureau organized." [75] But Mr. John F. Shafroth of Colorado, who had objected earlier to the idea of another bureau in the Government, spoke up again, saying he had changed his mind. Perhaps moved by the reading in the House of a telegram from Carl Hering of the American Institute of Electrical Engineers ("National humiliation not to have own standards"), he declared: "There is a new creation * * * of measure and of standards in the world * * *. [The bill] is a measure which this Government should have passed long ago." [76] He was for it, and he was in the majority.

"To meet all possible objections in the amended bill," the House accepted the Senate salary and expense changes and on March 3, 1901, the bill was enacted into law (31 Stat. 1449), to take effect on July 1. The functions and responsibilities of the bureau as originally described in Secretary Gage's letter remained unchanged, but instead of "National Standardizing Bureau," the name by law became the "National Bureau of Standards." [77]

In 1903 when the Bureau was transferred from the Treasury to the new Department of Commerce and Labor, the word "National" was eliminated from the name at the direction of the new department chief. No reason was given but it was said the change was made because the word "National" was inconsistent with the titles of such similar bureaus as the Coast and Geodetic Survey and the Geological Survey. Thirty years later, in 1934, as the proliferation of "bureaus of standards" in State governments, chambers of commerce, and even department stores threatened total loss of identity of the Federal agency, the original name was restored.[78]

---

[75] As Dr. Frank A. Wolff remembered it, "Speaker Cannon, the then watchdog of the Treasury, though [later] a friend of the Bureau, HAD to oppose it. In his speech he ridiculed the idea of a $250,000 building to house 14 men." Speech, 25th anniversary of the NBS, Dec. 4, 1926.

[76] Congressional Record, Mar. 2, 1901, pp. 3476–3477.

[77] Ibid., pp. 3472–3473.

[78] Memo, Secretary of Commerce for Director, NBS, Apr. 27, 1934 (NBS Box 370, AG); Science, 78, 453 (1934); interview with Dr. Lyman J. Briggs, Nov. 1, 1961.

A 16th century measuring rod, for measuring pastures, fields, vineyards, meadows, and fruit gardens. "To find the length of a measuring rod the right way and as it is common in the craft . . . Take sixteen men, short men and tall ones as they leave church and let each of them put one shoe after the other and the length thus obtained shall be a just and common measuring rod to survey the land with." Jacob Köbel, Geometrei, von Künstlichen Messen und absehen . . . (1536), Dii–Diii.

FOUNDING THE NATIONAL BUREAU OF STANDARDS (1901–10)

CHAPTER II

SAMUEL WESLEY STRATTON

For much of its first decade and a half, until shortly before America's entry into World War I, the Bureau's energies were almost wholly engaged in developing its staff and organization, establishing new and much needed standards for science and industry, and proving itself as a valuable adjunct of Government and industry. It assumed responsibilities as readily as it accepted those thrust upon it, and found them proliferating at a rate faster than the Bureau could grow. In 1914, making its first pause to take stock, the Bureau discovered that it had virtually to rewrite the functions of the organic act that had created it. This is the story told in the next two chapters.

From the day he arrived in Washington, Samuel Wesley Stratton (1861–1931) was the driving force behind the shaping of the National Bureau of Standards. Louis A. Fischer and Dr. Frank A. Wolff, Jr., who had been with the Office of Weights and Measures since 1880 and 1897, respectively, and had friends and acquaintances who knew many members of Congress, did much of the work of bringing the proposed bill to the favorable attention of members in both Houses. But it was Stratton, enlisting the aid of other scientists and officials in the Government, who drafted the text of Secretary Gage's letter, prepared the arguments that were to persuade Congress, and secured the imposing and unprecedented array of endorsements for the proposed laboratory.[1]

At his very first meeting on Capitol Hill, Stratton "mesmerized the House Committee," Wolff recalled, "and splendid hearings were held which were printed for distribution without stint."[2] He was to be the director of the Bureau for the next 21 years.

As a youth, Stratton's interest in machines and mechanical processes led him to major in mechanical engineering when he entered the University of Illinois in 1880. With his bachelor of science degree and a summer of intensive reading in Ganot's Physics—the training text of so many 19th-century American physicists—he was appointed instructor of mathematics and physics in the fall of 1884. In 1889 he was promoted to assistant pro-

[1] Stratton's correspondence on behalf of the bill may be found in Box 1 of the Stratton Papers in the Archives Library of the Massachusetts Institute of Technology.

[2] Speech, Dr. Frank A. Wolff, 25th anniversary of the NBS, Dec. 4, 1926.

Dr. Stratton at his desk in South building, 1905. The Bureau was still in its infancy, but already, according to Rosa, second only to the great German Reichsanstalt among government standards laboratories. The portrait of Michael Faraday on the wall, symbolizing the age of electricty, did not come down until 1950.

fessor of physics and electrical engineering, another subject he acquired on his own.

In 1892 the University of Chicago opened its doors, startling the academic world by paying its head professors "the princely salaries, for those days, of $7,000 each." [3] At the invitation of the renowned experimental physicist, Albert A. Michelson, then organizing his department at Chicago, Stratton came as assistant professor of physics, his salary of $2,000 as great a persuasion as the opportunity to work with Michelson.

Although Stratton, in addition to his teaching, worked on numerous experiments with Michelson or at his direction, and was promoted to associate professor in 1895 and to full professor in 1900, the association was not a happy one. According to Robert A. Millikan, who came to the university in 1896 as a $900 instructor in physics, Michelson was an intense individualist and did not like cooperative ventures in the laboratory. His absorption in his scientific work made him wholly indifferent to people in general and almost impossible to work with. As he once told Millikan, he wanted only a hired assistant who would do just as he was told, not expect any credit for himself, or make any demands other than to ask for his pay check. For Stratton who was outgoing, accessible, and without a trace of affectation, it must have been difficult, and as director of the National Bureau of Standards he was never to forget the Chicago lesson.[4]

How much of Stratton's work at Chicago came out in the stream of papers Michelson published is impossible to say, but at least two bore both their names, one on a new form of harmonic analyzer, a device for high-precision measurement of electrical frequencies, the other a note on the sources of X rays.[5] Millikan, a supreme egoist himself, was to say that he—

> never collaborated with Professor Michelson in any of his researches as both of my predecessors, Professors Wadsworth and Stratton, had done with somewhat unfortunate results in both cases. He never used me as an assistant, as he did some of the younger members of the staff. When Professor Stratton left about 1900 to assume directorship of the Bureau of Standards he warned me that my "turn would come next," meaning, of course, that friction would develop.[6]

---

[3] The Autobiography of Robert A. Millikan, p. 224.

[4] Ibid., pp. 87–88; s.v., S. C. Prescott, "Stratton," DAB.

[5] Michelson and Stratton, "Harmonic analyzer," Am. J. Sci., 5, 1–12 (1898); "Source of X-rays," Science, 3, 694–696 (1896).

Stratton's principal research efforts in Michelson's laboratory were in interferometry, he said later, "the field of measurement in which I am personally interested and in which I was engaged when called to take charge of the bureau" (Hearings * * * 1923, Nov. 16, 1922, p. 191).

[6] Millikan, Autobiography, p. 86.

Commissioned in the Illinois naval militia unit that Michelson organized in 1895, Stratton first left the University of Chicago in the spring of 1898 to serve as a Navy lieutenant in the Spanish-American War. He returned to the University that fall. Soon after, Arthur E. Kennelly, the Harvard dean of electrical engineering, said in his memoir of Stratton, he was asked to go to Washington to invite Admiral Dewey and Secretary Gage of the Treasury to give addresses at Chicago, and on that occasion fell into a discussion with Gage about weights and measures and the scientific work being done on them in the national laboratories abroad.[7] Lyman Gage therefore knew Stratton when the Assistant Secretary, Frank Vanderlip, in the summer of 1899 brought up his name as the man to take charge of the faltering Office of Weights and Measures, and invited him to Washington. As Stratton recalled it:

> While on a visit to Washington in 1899, the Secretary of the Treasury asked me to accept a position as head of the Office of Weights and Measures in the Coast and Geodetic Survey, which was declined. However, I pointed out to the Secretary, the Assistant Secretary, and the Superintendent of the Coast Survey the necessity for a government bureau having to do with standards and methods of measurement in the broad sense, and at the request of the Secretary of the Treasury drew up a plan for the establishment of such an institution. I agreed to devote a year's vacation [sabbatical], upon which I was just entering, to the preliminary steps for the establishment of the institution, the first of which was the securing of the necessary legislation.[8]

In later years both Dr. Henry S. Pritchett, superintendent of the Coast Survey, and Frank A. Vanderlip, Assistant Secretary of the Treasury, claimed credit for bringing Stratton to Washington. Pritchett said that shortly after coming to the Coast Survey in 1897 he had—

> asked Congress to appropriate a salary sufficiently large to induce a physicist of high standing to take charge of the office, under direction of the superintendent. An appropriation of $3,000 was made. With this sum some difficulty was found in inducing any physicist of standing and reputation to accept the place, and only after many interviews and considerable correspondence I succeeded in persuad-

---

[7] Natl. Acad. Sci., Biographical Memoirs, XVII, 254 (1935). See also personal letter, L. J. Briggs to Prof. E. Merritt, Cornell University, Oct. 31, 1933 (NBS Box 359, IG.).

[8] Letter, S. W. Stratton (hereafter SWS) to R. S. Woodward, president, NAS, Feb. 10, 1914 (Stratton Papers at MIT, Box 12; copy in NBS Historical File).

> ing Professor S. W. Stratton * * * to become a candidate. The appointment to the position was made after competitive examination.[9]

With this account Stratton agreed, in part at least:

> When I first came to Washington and met the Superintendent of the Survey, he asked me to join his force temporarily and make a report as to what could be done to place the weights and measures work upon the basis necessary in the present day of precision measurement of all kinds.

Although he at first declined the offer, Stratton said that on the train back to Chicago he made notes for a plan to revitalize the weights and measures work at the Coast Survey. Persuaded by his note-making, he gave up his planned trip to Europe and agreed to work in Washington during his sabbatical year.

In October 1899 he was formally appointed Inspector of Standard Weights and Measures and began preparation, says Stratton, of—

> two reports, one based upon the enlargement of that work [in the Survey office] to the extent possible in its present quarters, and dealing solely with weights and measures * * *. The other suggested the establishment of an institution having weights and measures functions in the broadest sense, covering measurements in the various lines of physics, the properties of materials and physical constants, etc. * * *.
>
> It was the Superintendent of the Coast and Geodetic Survey, Doctor Pritchett, who saw that the second plan was the preferable one. He recommended it to the Treasury Department, and the Secretary of the Treasury directed that a bill be drawn looking toward the establishment of such an institution.[10]

---

[9] Pritchett, "The story of the establishment of the NBS," Science, 15, 281 (1902). This account also appears in letter, Pritchett to Dr. Wolff, Nov. 16, 1926 (NBS Blue Folder Box 4, APW–301c), and Abraham Flexner, Henry S. Pritchett: A Biography (New York: Columbia University Press, 1943).

[10] Stratton, "The Bureau of Standards and its relation to the U.S. C. & G.S." Centennial Celebration of the U.S. C. & G.S., April 5–6 1916 (Washington, D.C., 1916), p. 34. Stratton's reports, both dated Dec. 15, 1899, are in NBS Box 22, PRA. See also Science, 10, 941 (1899).

Stratton's civil service appointment as "Inspector of Standards" is dated Dec. 12, 1899 (Stratton Papers, Box 12). Another who took the examination for Inspector of Standards (in July 1899) was Charles S. Peirce, member of the Coast Survey from 1871–91, who had been in charge of weights and measures in 1884–85 and was then in his 60th year. Although strongly endorsed by Henry Cabot Lodge and others, Peirce was not considered, and later protested to Pritchett at the outcome of the inspectorship (communications from Dr. Max H. Fisch, University of Illinois, Sept. 13, 1962 and Mar. 23, 1965, at work on a biography of Peirce).

In his autobiography, written more than 30 years later, Frank Vanderlip recalled the event:

> In the Coast and Geodetic Survey there was a little sprout of an organization called the Bureau of Standards [sic]. Previously its function had been chiefly to serve as the depository of the nation's standards of weights and measures; although some other things were done there, the bureau was a puny affair. We wanted a new head for it and I found myself thinking of one who had been a close friend of mine at the University of Illinois, a boy named Sam Stratton. He had become a physicist, and at the University of Chicago Professor Stratton had come to rank next to Michelson, the measurer of light. On my recommendation the place was offered to Sam with the idea that he could develop the bureau into larger purposes. He was a thorough scientist with a great deal of imagination and not narrow in any part of him. It is satisfying even so many years afterward to realize that I had a hand in bringing such a valuable servant into the employ of the government. That Bureau of Standards grew to its present vast importance nourished chiefly in its growth by the intelligence of my old college friend.[11]

Vanderlip may have called him "Sam," but no one at the Bureau was ever to approach that degree of familiarity. As a full professor, even without his doctorate, he had the courtesy title of "Doctor," as was customary then. Later he was awarded six honorary doctorates, the doctor of engineering from Illinois and doctor of science from Pittsburgh in 1903, two more doctorates of science from Cambridge in 1908 and Yale in 1918; Harvard in 1923 gave him an LL.D., and Rensselaer in 1924 the Ph. D. At the Bureau he was "Dr. Stratton" to his friends and colleagues, or the "Old Man," among the frivolous youngsters on the staff, behind his back.

In appearance, Dr. Stratton at 40 was of medium height, mature, his sturdy frame and resonant voice commanding authority. He was a storehouse of specialized knowledge of industrial materials and mechanical devices of every sort and of the latest technical advances in physics and engineering. He delighted in constructing instruments and apparatus, and until his administrative duties became all consuming, maintained a private shop and laboratory near his office. Dr. Stratton never married, and he had as strong opinions about women in authority at the Bureau as in his home.[12]

---

[11] Frank A. Vanderlip, with Boyden Sparkes, From Farm Boy to Financier (New York: D. Appleton-Century, 1935), p. 77.

[12] He would not even accept women as clerks and secretaries at the Bureau until forced by the manpower shortage of World War I.

For over 20 years Samuel Stratton dominated the National Bureau of Standards, shaping it to serve the Nation and to hold its own or even surpass the national standards laboratories abroad. Like all good administrators, he recognized potential ability in young scientists he met or who applied to him. And as Kennelly says, he knew how "to organize them into cooperative effort for the purposes of applied science, without any consideration of his own personal advantage. His mind was dominated by the ideals of improving all engineering enterprise through scientific study and research." While it is true, as Kennelly implies, that his interest in technology was strong, Stratton knew that the Bureau must establish a solid basic research program and keep it at a high level if the Bureau was to fulfill its promise. Fundamental research was often difficult to justify to a cost-conscious Congress, but as he told a House committee in 1902, "If we are to advance we have to create original things." [13] More often than not he got his funds for basic research.

Stratton's office was to have its share of bureaucratic troubles, within the organization itself, with other government agencies, with members of the public, and with politicians. When differences arose, Dr. Stratton could be stern with the members of his staff—his flaming temper was famous—but he would defend them with all his might against the slightest interference or criticism that he believed unjustified. By its very nature, as impartial ruler and arbiter of standards, the Bureau could not escape controversy, but Stratton spoke with facts and a firm voice that kept controversy within bounds.

He never allowed anyone to forget that the Bureau's mission was to serve science and industry in the Nation, and he himself became filled with concern when a commercial chemist wrote of his difficulties with a product, an engineer with his materials, or an enquiring citizen sought technical help or information. He would scrawl in the margin of their letters: "Can't we do something about this?" "Why can't we do this?" "This deserves answering." But he was impatient with armchair inventors who thought the Bureau ought to construct working models for them from vague descriptions of vague ideas. Incoming mail at the Bureau, particularly in 1918, was freighted with suggested weapons and materials for winning the war, many of them, as Stratton said of a flux of letters proposing new alloys, "products which, although found excellent enough, are not in any way unusual, except in the secrecy about the composition which is observed by the inventor." [14] And he could be withering when a colleague was vilified for trying to let a crank down gently: "It is perfectly evident that you are more

---

[13] Hearings * * * 1904 (Dec. 4, 1902), p. 70.

[14] Letter, SWS to Dir, Bureau of Foreign and Domestic Commerce, Jan. 21, 1918 (NBS Box 11, IM).

The Coast and Geodetic Survey building, home of the Office of Weights and Measures, in the 200 block of New Jersey Avenue, S.E., as Dr. Stratton saw it in 1900. The Butler building, into which the new Bureau of Standards expanded, is probably the structure next door. "Bushey House," at 235 New Jersey Avenue, is out of the picture, down the street.

interested in giving information about a subject which, judging from your correspondence, you know little or nothing about, than you are in securing such information." [15]

But that was years later. When in the summer of 1899 Stratton arrived at the Office of Standard Weights and Measures, in the Coast and Geodetic Survey building at New Jersey Avenue and B Street, S.E., where the present House Office Building stands, its staff consisted of Andrew Braid, officially Assistant-in-Charge; Louis A. Fischer, adjuster of weights and measures; Dr. Frank A. Wolff, Jr., verifier of weights and measures (but then spending most of his time on problems of electrical measurement), and four others, a mechanician, an adjuster's helper, a messenger, and a watchman. On October 28, 1899, Stratton replaced Braid, with the temporary title of Inspector of Standards, at $3,000 per year.

Less than an hour was sufficient to tour the Office, see all its equipment, and comprehend its work. In Mr. Fischer's section "most of the apparatus * * * on hand [had been] designed many years ago." There was no "suitable instrument for the comparison of standards of length of

[15] Letter, SWS, Dec. 27, 1920 (NBS Box 14, IPR).

Mr. Louis A. Fischer, verifier of weights and measures, who came to the office in the Coast and Geodetic Survey in 1880 at the age of 16, when there were still men there who had worked with Hassler. This picture may have been taken shortly after the Bureau was founded, but no later than 1910, the year Mr. Fischer began his weights and measures crusade across the Nation.

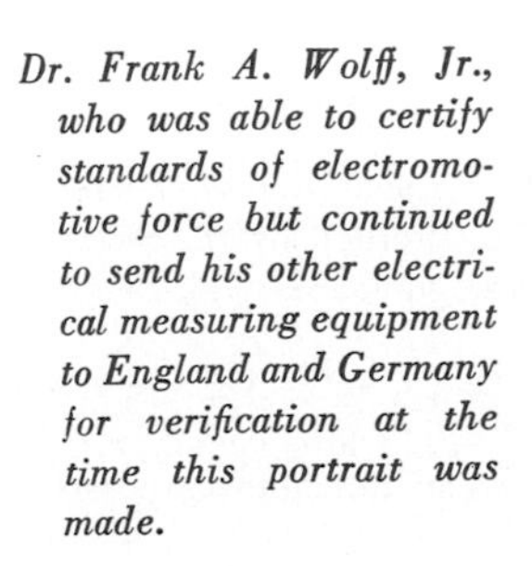

Dr. Frank A. Wolff, Jr., who was able to certify standards of electromotive force but continued to send his other electrical measuring equipment to England and Germany for verification at the time this portrait was made.

1 metre or less," nor was the Office "prepared to make comparison of thermometers at temperatures lower than zero or higher than 50 degrees Centigrade." [16] Nevertheless, Fischer that year was to verify a number of thermometers, flasks, weights, and polariscopic apparatus used by the customs service in levying duties on imported sugar, adjust and verify the set of standards used in the State of Maine, and work on three sets of standards for States not yet supplied. He also prepared a set of metric standards for Puerto Rico, and graduated and verified 100-foot and 30-meter bench standards for the city surveyor of Boston, to be used in reverifying tapes and chains submitted to him.[17]

In the intervals free from pressing routine work, Dr. Wolff had set up a number of Clark standard cells for measuring standards of electromotive force and verifying direct-current voltmeters and millivoltmeters, had acquired equipment for testing resistance standards, and was at work on alternating-current testing apparatus, preparatory to answering some of the problems recently raised by long-distance transmission of power. But as Dr. Wolff said, "No claim to originality is made for what has been accomplished." The Office was still "obliged, as heretofore, to send to the national standardizing laboratories of Germany and England for verification [of] the large class of alternating current measuring instruments, condensers, and photometric standards." [18]

On June 30, 1900, the Office reported that in the past year it had compared 65 thermometers and 69 surveyors' tapes, had graduated and verified 772 sugar flasks, replied to 75 requests for information, and with routine weights, measures, and balance tests, had answered a total of 1,037 "calls" on it. Its appropriations amounted to $9,410.00, of which $8,237.44 was for salaries and $944.18 for contingent expenses.[19]

The law establishing the National Bureau of Standards, passed in March 1901, did not become effective until July 1, but within a week of its passage Stratton received his appointment as Director of the new Bureau from President McKinley.[20] During the interim 4 months he was to find a site for the new laboratory, plan its equipment, find the additional personnel

[16] Annual Report, Coast and Geodetic Survey, 1899, p. 49.

[17] Annual Report, Secretary of the Treasury, 1900, p. lxviii.

[18] Annual Report, Coast and Geodetic Survey, 1900, p. 68; Annual Report, Secretary of the Treasury, 1900, p. lxviii. Also, Wolff, "The facilities afforded by the Office of Standard Weights and Measures for verification of electrical standards and electrical measuring apparatus," Sci. Am. Suppl. 49, 20304 (1900).

[19] Annual Report, Coast and Geodetic Survey, 1900, pp. 58–59, 69. Appropriations for 1899 had been $5,690 for salaries and $2,475 for expenses.

[20] The Presidents and executive secretaries under whom Bureau directors have served appear in app. D.

THE EVENING STAR, MONDAY, MARCH 11, 1901

CORRECT MEASURES

Function of the New Bureau of Standards.

LABORATORY TO BE ERECTED

Prof. Stratton, the Director, Details Need of Establishment.

A HANDICAP REMOVED

A new bureau of the government, authorized by the last Congress, will be established in this city in the near future and will give employment to a number of persons. It is to be known as the national bureau of standards and is to be under the control of the Treasury Department. A separate building for a laboratory, to cost not to exceed $250,000, is to be erected on a site to be purchased at a cost of $25,000.

Mr. Samuel W. Stratton of Chicago has been appointed by the President to be chief of the bureau at an annual salary of $5,000. Prof. Stratton is to have the following as-

Director Stratton.

sistants, to be appointed by the Secretary of the Treasury: One physicist, at an annual salary of $3,500; one chemist, at $3,500; two assistant physicists or chemists, each at an annual salary of $2,200; one laboratory assistant, at $1,400; one laboratory assistant, at $1,200; one secretary, at $2,000; one clerk, at $1,200; one messenger, at $720; one en-

One of the first newspaper notices of the new Bureau in the Federal Establishment appeared in the Washington Evening Star. A half page feature in the Sunday Washington Times of August 23, 1903, included a picture of Secretary Cortelyou of the Department of Commerce and Labor laying the cornerstone of the main (South) building the day before, and described the ceremony as "a memorable event in the history of the country."

the Bureau would need, visit the more important laboratories here and abroad to see their construction, equipment, and the work they were doing, and set in motion, in the present Office, some of the more important lines of investigation to be pursued by the new Bureau.

It is not known in what order these tasks were taken up, but it seems probable that Stratton first secured additional laboratory space, in the Butler building, adjacent to the Coast Survey, hired a typist, which the Office had formerly lacked, and set the staff to work planning an expanded program. This included setting up an investigation of photometric measurements; developing means for testing high and low temperature instruments, clinical thermometers, and chemical glass measuring apparatus; developing electrical apparatus for measuring alternating currents, and equipment for testing pressure gauges and meteorological instruments.[21]

With his staff busy, Stratton may have begun visiting some of the larger Government laboratories in and near Washington, to see their work and learn what the Bureau might do for them. In April he sailed for Europe, to place orders for apparatus and equipment in Paris and Berlin, and to visit the International Bureau of Weights and Measures at Sèvres, the Reichsanstalt at Charlottenburg, the new National Physical Laboratory being organized at Teddington, and the Cavendish Laboratory at Cambridge.[22]

If the recent establishment of Britain's physical laboratory at Teddington helped prompt the creation of the National Bureau of Standards, the Reichsanstalt as the finest laboratory of its kind in the world was unquestionably to serve as the model for Stratton's organization of the Bureau. It seems probable that from the beginning Secretary Gage intended the Bureau to be a second Reichsanstalt. Early in 1899 he had corresponded with Henry S. Carhart, professor of physics at the University of Michigan, concerning American representation at the electrical congress to be held at the Paris Exposition in 1900. Further correspondence is missing, but it is possible that Gage was instrumental in sending Carhart to Berlin in the fall of 1899, where he secured permission to work at the Reichsanstalt as a scientific guest for several months. While there he "learned rather intimately the methods employed and the results accomplished in this famous institution for the conduct of physical research, the supply of standards, and the verification of instruments of precision for scientific and technical purposes." [23]

Carhart's detailed report on the organization and operation of the German institute, complete with architectural plans of the grounds and floor plans of the laboratories, was probably seen by Gage and Stratton before Carhart presented it as a paper to the American Institute of Electrical Engineers on September 26, 1900. It was published later that year in the Transactions of the Institute and also in Science magazine, and the next year

[21] Annual Report, Secretary of the Treasury, 1901, p. 59.

[22] Notice in Science, 13, 515 (1901). In September 1902, Stratton was again in Germany "studying the Reichsanstalt with a view to the buildings to be erected in Washington" (Science, 16, 437, 1902).

[23] Carhart, "The Imperial Physico-Technical Institution in Charlottenburg," Report of the Committee on Commerce, to accompany S. 4680 (1901), p. 6 (L/C:QC100.U58–1901b).

The first description, in English, of this institution appeared in Arthur G. Webster's article, "A national physical laboratory," The Pedagogical Seminary (Worcester, Mass.), II, 90–101 (1892). The article, Webster later recalled (Science, 56, 170, 1922), had been refused by a number of scientific periodicals, their editors rejecting his plea for a similar laboratory in this country as an improper function of the Federal Government.

appeared as an appendix to a congressional report of the Committee on Commerce, in the Annual Report of the Smithsonian Institution for 1901, in the Western Electrician, and, for a seventh time, in the London Electrical Review. There seems little doubt that the report was regarded as a blueprint.

With modifications, the Bureau was to organize its work, like the Reichsanstalt, in two spheres, scientific and technical, including "a division for pure scientific research, mechanical measurements of precision, electrical measurements and instruments, the measurement of large direct and alternating currents and electromotive forces, an optical department, a department of thermometry, a department of pyrometry, and a department of chemistry. To these as auxiliaries should be added the power plant and the workshop." [24] Their re-creation in Washington was only a matter of time.

On his return from abroad, Stratton met with Lyman Gage to recommend members for the Secretary's Visiting Committee, a liaison group composed of prominent men of science and industry who were to keep Gage informed of such national interests as were within the Bureau's domain, and report annually to the Secretary on the work of the Bureau. Thoughtfully, Stratton suggested his former superior at Chicago, Professor Michelson, for membership on the Committee. Although Michelson was greatly interested in standards, had worked at the Bureau International des Poids et Mésures in 1892–93, and served on the International Committee of Weights and Measures since 1897, he declined the invitation.[25] Letters were then sent by Gage to Albert Ladd Colby, chief metallurgical engineer at Bethlehem Steel and secretary of the Association of American Steel Manufacturers, as representative of manufacturing interests in the country; to Dr. Elihu Thomson, chief electrical engineer at General Electric, who held almost 500 patents for electrical inventions and improvements, and would represent electrical interests; to Dr. Ira Remsen, professor of chemistry and president of the Johns Hopkins University, representing chemical interests; to Dr. Henry S. Pritchett, now president of the Massachusetts Institute of Technology, representing technical education institutions; and to Dr. Edward L. Nichols, professor of physics at Cornell University, as representative of physical interests.[26]

---

[24] Ibid., p. 7.

[25] While at the International Bureau, Michelson with a new interferometer he had designed carried out a pioneer study in standards measurement, relating the cadmium red line to the meter, the first significant beginning of a wavelength definition of the meter.

[26] Letter, Gage to Michelson, June 6, 1901, and letters, June 18, 1901 (Correspondence of the Secretary of the Treasury, 1900–1901, V series, vol. 6, NARG 56). A complete list of members of the Visiting Committee to the NBS from 1901 to 1960 appears in app. E.

Little is known of the Visiting Committee's assistance to Dr. Stratton in the early months of the Bureau except that it met for the first time in the summer of 1901 "to pass on proposed sites for the laboratory." [27] Stratton had already toured the Washington area looking at possible sites and had tentatively settled on a location out on Connecticut Avenue, almost 3½ miles from the White House and within 2 miles of Chevy Chase, Md. Just inside the site of the line of forts built to the North to protect the city during the Civil War, the heavily wooded height comprising nearly 8 acres rose more than 75 feet, the highest ground in the vicinity, overlooking Connecticut Avenue. A laboratory up there would be well away from the street noise and interference from the electric cars running out Connecticut Avenue to Chevy Chase.

The site, "one of the most beautiful in the District of Columbia," Stratton thought, was for sale, and its owner, the Chevy Chase Land Co., was persuaded to let it go for $25,000, the sum available.[28]

By July 1, 1901, when with minor ceremonies the old Office of Standard Weights and Measures became the new National Bureau of Standards, two contracts had been let. One was for a mechanical laboratory, to house the power and service plant and shops of the main laboratory, scheduled to be completed by July 1902. The second, for the physical laboratory itself, was to be completed by January 1903. That same day, July 1st, Dr. Edward B. Rosa arrived at the Bureau.

EDWARD B. ROSA

Dr. Stratton's most pressing need upon his appointment as Director of the Bureau was to find an outstanding man to plan and direct the electrical research that had dominated the arguments for the creation of the Bureau. Demands for routine electrical testing now took all of Dr. Wolff's time, and original research or even planning such research was out of the question.

Stratton's attention was drawn to a professor of physics at Wesleyan University who in the past decade had published a dozen papers on electricity. With Prof. Wilbur O. Atwater, he had recently devised an ingenious respiration calorimeter that was to prove highly useful in subsequent pioneer investigations of food values and problems of nutrition in this country.[29] His

[27] Notice in Science, 14, 340 (1901); Visiting Committee correspondence, 1902, in "General Correspondence Files of the Director, 1945–55," Box 6 (in process in NBS Records Management Office for NARG 167) (see Bibliographic Note).

[28] NBS Annual Report 1905, p. 4; Remarks of SWS at the laying of the cornerstone of the Chemical Laboratory, March 23, 1916 (NBS Historical File); Remarks of SWS on the 30th Anniversary of the NBS, March 7, 1931 (Stratton Papers, Box 12).

[29] See Atwater and Rosa, "A new respirator calorimeter * * *," Phys. Rev. 9, 129, 214 (1899), and the special notice of it in William North Rice's article, "Scientific thought in the nineteenth century," Annual Report, Smithsonian Institution, 1899, p. 399.

Dr. Edward B. Rosa, who set the pace for the high level of research at the Bureau in its first two decades. Rosa probably sat for this portrait about 1915, but according to Dr. Silsbee, who knew him, it could have been made at almost any time, for Dr. Rosa did not change much in all his years at the Bureau.

name was Rosa (pronounced Ro-zay), and meeting him, Stratton knew he was the man he sought.

Edward Bennett Rosa (1861–1921), of Dutch ancestry, had taught physics and chemistry after getting his B.S. degree at Wesleyan University in Connecticut and then entered the Johns Hopkins University as a graduate student in physics under Henry A. Rowland. Receiving his doctorate in 1891, he returned to Wesleyan as associate professor of physics, becoming full professor the next year. He came to the Bureau as a physicist at $3,500 and a decade later, his electrical group firmly established as the premier division of the Bureau, he was made chief physicist.

Like Stratton, Rosa was of distinguished appearance. He was not as outgoing in temperament as the Director, yet he made a strong impression on scientific and administrative visitors to the Bureau and before long became its stellar ambassador at home and abroad. If Stratton was the autocratic paterfamilias of the Bureau, interested in every laboratory and its occupants and the source of intense staff loyalties, it was Rosa, the autocrat of research, who set the pace for the high level of achievement in the early years of the Bureau. The names of Stratton and Rosa are inseparable in any consideration of the period.

It is a tribute to Rosa's character, as those with long memories recall, that his own forceful personality rarely clashed with that of Stratton. The Director fully agreed with Rosa's concept of the importance of the electrical work of the Bureau and saw that he had the best of equipment and the best of assistance to conduct his program. Where the Bureau was concerned, they acted as one, and during Stratton's frequent absences on official business, Rosa's decisions were final.

A diligent investigator—he published over 75 papers while at the Bureau—Rosa demanded the same industry from his staff. But while their minds were kept firmly on electrical matters, his increasing administrative responsibilities, as well as his peripheral interests and zest for public affairs, drew him repeatedly out of the laboratory. Unlike Stratton, he enjoyed talking to groups of people and gave many lectures, later published, on the work of the Bureau, the progress of electrical research, and the range of scientific work being done in the Government. His most ambitious effort late in his career was an exhaustive study of Government research and its relation to the Federal budget, which was to lead indirectly to the establishment of the present Bureau of the Budget.

It was said of Dr. Stratton that he was "continually on the lookout for worthy research and testing work, and so the staff always seemed overburdened."[30] It was equally true of Rosa, who followed closely each new development in the field of electricity, saw research projects everywhere, and brought in a stream of bright young men to investigate them.

In its early years the Bureau regularly hired young men who were potential specialists in their fields, only to win them to the ever-increasing range of interests spanned by the Bureau. Before midcentury the advance of science would demand many at the Bureau working at the extremity of specialization. But Dr. Rosa, with wide interests himself, was wary of the possible narrowing influence of high specialization—that should be left to the universities, he said—and warned his division of its inevitable consequences, that "we grow taller and thinner."[31] The justification for the Bureau's ranging research was the clause in its enabling act making it responsible for the "solution of problems which arise in connection with standards." Since almost every aspect of science, technology, industry, and commerce is rooted in standards of some kind, all knowledge in these fields was by definition within the Bureau's province. So Stratton, who had written the clause, interpreted it, and under the guidance of Stratton and Rosa, the Bureau acted upon it.[32]

[30] Fay C. Brown, "Samuel Wesley Stratton," Science, 74, 428 (1931).

[31] W. W. Coblentz, "Edward Bennett Rosa," Natl. Acad. Sci., Biographical Memoirs, xvi, 356 (1934).

[32] Years later Stratton was to say that he thought an enumeration of the organic functions of the Bureau covered "about 99 percent of the field of research." Only food, drugs, and materia medica were exempt. SWS address on the 25th anniversary of the NBS, 1926 (Stratton Papers).

Free exercise of the clause, as we shall see, enabled the Bureau to conduct an abundance of original research, some of it only vaguely connected with standards. At the same time, it subjected the Bureau to a plethora of investigations for Federal agencies and the public that at times tended more to dissipate its energies than to increase its knowledge. The legacy of accommodation left by Stratton and Rosa created occasional difficulties in later years. Periodically, as its investigations became too far ranging, the Bureau found it necessary to stop, reassess its scope and functions, and shift course. But it never lost sight of its primary responsibility, and the whole focus of its early research, the pursuit of standards.

During the 3½ years in its temporary quarters in downtown Washington, the Bureau was completely taken up with planning new work on standards, searching for personnel, acquiring or designing new equipment, and overseeing the construction of its new laboratories. In September 1901 Henry D. Hubbard, who had been private secretary to President Harper at the University of Chicago, came as secretary to the Bureau, his desk in Dr. Stratton's office in the Butler building. He was to serve the Bureau for almost four decades.[33] That same month Dr. Charles W. Waidner, a young physics instructor trained at Johns Hopkins, who had taught there and at Williams College, arrived to organize the Bureau program in heat and thermometry. In the laboratories over in the Coast Survey building, Rosa, Wolff, and their assistants continued to acquire equipment and carried out electrical tests, while Fischer, with his new assistant, Roy Y. Ferner, looked after the weights and measures work.

Orienting a growing staff and organizing its work permitted little forward motion. One new member was later to say that while he did some testing of instruments, the major part of his time in his first year at the Bureau "was spent in library work. * * * Only the functions of the old Office of Standard Weights and Measures were operating normally." [34] In December 1901 Dr. Stratton announced in Science, apparently in answer to inquiries, that the range of Bureau services was as yet limited. More exact determination of values for certain of the fundamental electrical constants, better photometric measurements, and calibration services such as those requested for clinical thermometers, pressure gages, and many other instruments, while urgently needed, were simply not yet possible. For the time being the work of the Bureau was confined to the comparison of a few standards and measuring instruments, that is, to length, weight, and capacity

---

[33] A contribution to scientific literature, Hubbard's modernization of Mendeleev's periodic table of the elements, first printed in 1924, is currently published by the Welch Scientific Co. of Skokie, Ill.

[34] MS, N. Ernest Dorsey, "Some memories of the early days of the NBS," Oct. 28. 1943 (NBS Historical File).

Henry D. Hubbard, secretary to Dr. Stratton and the Bureau, made a contribution to instruction in physics that is still in use today, his modernization of Mendeleev's periodic chart of the atoms. First constructed in the 1920's, it has been frequently revised and reprinted. It now includes the isotopes of the elements, unknown to the twenties.

Dr. Charles W. Waidner, a decade after he came to the Bureau, who with Dr. Burgess in the heat and thermometry division attempted to construct an absolute standard of light, not to be experimentally realized until 1931, 20 years later.

measurements, testing of ordinary commercial thermometers, polariscopic apparatus, hydrometers, resistance instruments, standards of electromotive force, and direct current apparatus.[35]

By July 1902 the original staff of 12 had increased to 22, and the 15 offices and laboratories of the Bureau were crammed with crated and uncrated apparatus and machinery. To get elbow room, Stratton rented a four-story house at 235 New Jersey Avenue, not far from the Coast Survey building, converting its space into an instrument shop, dynamo, and storage battery rooms, and additional laboratories. Approximately equivalent only in their antiquity, the high, narrow residence at 235 was promptly christened "Bushey House," after the stately mansion in England that had recently become the home of the National Physical Laboratory. Much of the new apparatus was moved there to be set up and tested, while on the upper floors preliminary studies began in alternating current measurement and in pyrometry.[36]

During the summer of 1902 Wolff and Waidner went abroad to visit the principal government laboratories and instrument makers in Europe, taking with them a number of electrical and pyrometric standards to verify while in Berlin. The next summer Fischer visited Paris with his copies of

---

[35] Stratton, "Circular of information on the NBS, No. 1," Science, 14, 1019 (1901).
[36] MS, Dorsey, "Some memories of the early days"; NBS Annual Report 1902, pp. 4–5.

the international meter and kilogram, but like Wolff and Waidner he spent most of his time in Germany, securing new instruments and apparatus and ordering equipment for the laboratories under construction at home. In Washington a change of departmental administration was in the making that was to have important consequences for the development of the Bureau.

THE NEW BUREAU LABORATORIES

Dr. Stratton and his staff were still in downtown Washington when the Bureau was transferred from its original home in the Treasury Department to the newly created Department of Commerce and Labor. For more than a hundred years the head of the Treasury had been in fact "secretary of commerce and finance," but with increasing fiscal responsibilities and the growth of agencies required by the commercial expansion of the Nation, his Department had become unwieldy. In December 1901 a bill was introduced in the Senate to transfer some of his functions to a separate Department of Commerce.

The Commissioner of Labor (first appointed in 1888) was seeking cabinet rank at the time, but loath to expand the President's Cabinet by two, Congress compromised by merging a number of bureaus in the Departments of the Treasury and Interior with those in the Office of the Commissioner of Labor. On February 14, 1903, the new Department of Commerce and Labor came into being, its Secretary, George B. Cortelyou.[37]

With 13 subdivisions, the new Department was at once one of the largest and most complicated branches in the Federal Government. Curiously enough, the transfer of the Bureau of Standards to Commerce and Labor was an 11th-hour decision. Like the Coast and Geodetic Survey, whose transfer had occasioned some discussion before it was included in the new Department, the Bureau was apparently considered by Congress to be a purely scientific agency, with only a remote relation to commerce.

A member of the House Committee on Interstate and Foreign Commerce, aware late in the proceedings that the Bureau was likely to be left out, rose to urge its transfer: "The newly created National Bureau of Standards is a bureau which necessarily goes into a department primarily devoted to manufacturing and commercial interests. This Bureau is destined to

---

[37] Organization and Law of the Department of Commerce and Labor, Doc. No. 13 (Washington, D.C., 1904), pp. 7, 12, 450.

A genius of managerial efficiency, Cortelyou had been stenographer to Cleveland, assistant secretary to McKinley, and secretary to Roosevelt before his appointment to the new Department. Two years later he was appointed Postmaster General, and in 1907 became Secretary of the Treasury. In 1909 he left Government service to head the Consolidated Gas Co. in New York.

exercise great influence upon the development of business and commerce of our country." Commerce and Labor was already outsize, but the Bureau was voted in.[38]

Had it remained in the Treasury, the Bureau might well have become a giant in precision measurement alone, its research almost certainly more narrowly confined to the functions of its enabling act. But under a succession of strong Secretaries of Commerce, vigorously promoting business and industry, the Bureau was to be used unsparingly to introduce scientific methods more rapidly in industry, to urge the standardization of parts and products, and the use of new and improved materials, and even do the spadework to encourage the manufacture of products previously imported. The wonder is that the Bureau accomplished as much basic research as it did in the years that followed.

Except for the change of name to "Bureau of Standards," omitting the word "National," the transfer to the new Department was without incident. Relations between the new Secretary and "Prof. S. W. Stratton," as Cortelyou addressed him in correspondence, were cordial, and Cortelyou willingly approved a Bureau request for an increase in its staff from 28, authorized by a previous appropriation act, to 58, authorized on February 25, 1903.[39]

Finding room for the growing staff in the downtown quarters of the Bureau was another thing. Construction of both buildings out on Connecticut Avenue was behind schedule. The smaller mechanical laboratory, well under way, was now promised for September of 1903, but work on the main building, the physical laboratory, had just begun that March. It would not be ready for occupancy before October 1904, almost 2 years later than originally planned.

Some of the delay was understandable, for the site was distant and transportation of materials was slow. The teams of horses under their heavy loads had to rest frequently on the long grade uptown and more often still as they struggled up the steep of Pierce Mill Road, the dirt track through the woods to the top of the hill. Four- and eight-horse teams were frequently needed to haul building materials up the height, and it is possible that some of the big equipment for the mechanical building may even have required a 16-horse hitch.

The Bureau site was, for that time, truly remote. In the 2½ mile stretch of Connecticut Avenue between Cleveland Park, then a sparse residential section to the north of the business center of Washington, and Chevy

---

[38] James R. Mann (Ill.), Chairman of the Committee, Jan. 30, 1902, quoted in Organization and Law of the Department of Commerce and Labor, pp. 529, 539.

[39] Ibid., pp. 415–417, 417n. Graphs and charts of congressional appropriations and other working funds of the Bureau, of special appropriations, of the rise in the Bureau staff, and its output of publications appear in apps. F, G, H, and I.

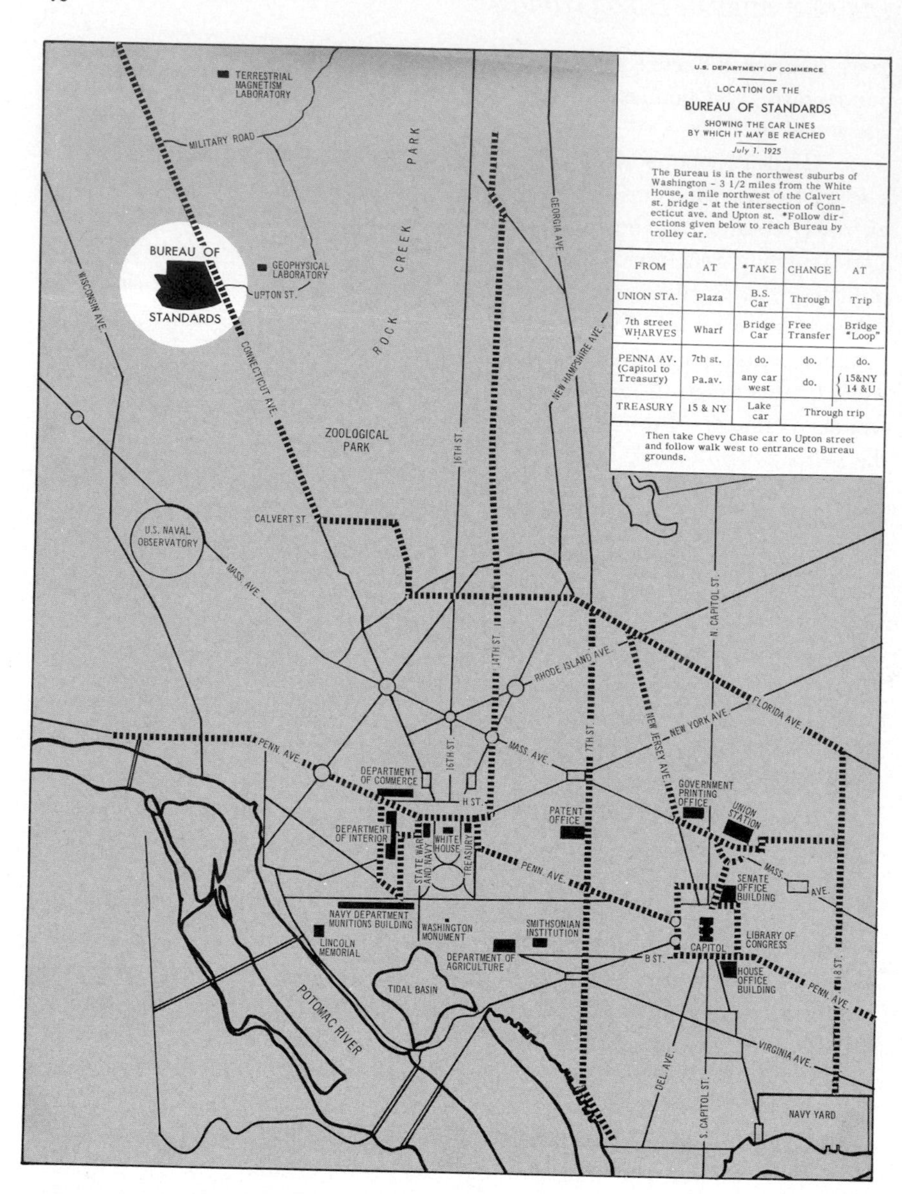

The remoteness of the Bureau made it necessary to send vest-pocket transit maps to early visitors to show them the way out. When they arrived they were to look for the boardwalk that led up the hill to the Bureau grounds, since the first buildings were invisible from Connecticut Avenue.

Chase, the small Maryland community on the border of the District of Columbia, there were but two buildings, occupied by a preparatory school. The Bureau up on the hill was invisible from the avenue, and these lone school buildings, just north of what is now Upton Street, served to show staffers and strangers alike on the way to the laboratories where to leave the electric cars.[40]

The mechanical building was above ground but excavation for the physical laboratory had not begun when Dr. Rosa, with the architect's plans before him, described for Science magazine the Bureau plant as it would appear when completed. Both buildings were to be constructed of dark red brick with Indiana limestone trim, the smaller mechanical laboratory two stories tall but with its basement at ground level on the north slope of the hill. The physical laboratory, four stories tall, would be supported solidly on concrete piers in a largely unexcavated basement.

Since the principal experimental work of the Bureau was to be carried on in the physical laboratory, later called South building, it had to be free from mechanical and magnetic disturbances and therefore housed scarcely any machinery. All heavy equipment was located in the mechanical laboratory or North building, its basement and partial sub-basement containing the boiler room, engine and dynamo room, storage battery room, and a refrigeration plant with a capacity equivalent to melting 30 tons of ice a day, phenomenal for that time. Through a spacious tunnel 170 feet long leading out of North building's sub-basement, a maze of air ducts, steam, gas, and water pipes, and electrical circuits supplied the major facilities of the laboratories in South building.

On the first floor of North building were the heavy current and alternating-current instrument testing laboratories, the instrument shop, and stock and shipping rooms. High potential laboratories and magnetic and photometric laboratories occupied the second floor, with a proposed hydraulic laboratory on that floor extending through the ceiling into the attic. Another photometric laboratory and storage rooms occupied the other half of the attic. With its heating and ventilating plants, machinery, and special facilities, North building was to cost $125,000. Additional laboratory space was created in 1931 when the roof was raised and a third story added to the building.[41]

In the huge physical building, facing south overlooking the city of Washington, all the laboratories were to be provided with gas, compressed air, vacuum, hot and cold water, ice water, and distilled water. All windows

---

[40] MS, Dorsey, "Some memories of the early days."

[41] Ostensibly added to make North building conform architecturally with the other buildings in the quadrangle. NBS Annual Report 1928, p. 42.

in the first and second floor laboratories were double-paned and sealed tight, and each room could be darkened completely. Filtered air, artificially cooled in summer, circulated in the building, and each laboratory was equipped with controls to regulate room temperature and humidity precisely. Special facilities available in certain of the laboratories included cold brine, carbon dioxide, and liquid air for low temperature work; gas and electric furnaces for high temperature studies; direct electric currents at potentials up to 20,000 volts and currents up to 20,000 amperes.

Weights and measures, optical research, high and low temperature laboratories, and electrical standards laboratories occupied the ground floor. On the second floor were additional weights, measures, and optical laboratories, the inductance and capacity laboratories, and electrical measurements rooms. The director's office, a reception room, the library, a publication and mailing room, and Dr. Stratton's private laboratory occupied the third floor, and on the fourth were to be the thermometer laboratories. A large lecture room (subsequently diverted to storage) and apparatus space utilized the attic. With its connecting tunnel, but exclusive of equipment, South building cost $200,000.

In this initial complex, based on Bureau specifications and designed by the Supervising Architect of the Treasury Department, said Rosa, the Bureau intended "an intimate association between research and testing in the domain of physics, extending into the field of chemistry on the one hand, of engineering on the other." [42]

The program of work then planned by no means utilized all the laboratories provided in the two buildings. But Congress had said that the building appropriations must cover the first 5 years of the Bureau, and it took little imagination to see that as its resources and range of skills were recognized, the demands on the Bureau would increase. Even then Stratton and Rosa foresaw the necessity of East and West buildings, to complete the quadrangle, although their purpose, except to provide additional laboratory space, was not yet plain.

Startlingly plain, once spotted, however, was something entirely omitted in the original architectural plans of the two buildings. There was no place to eat. The "thermometer and photometric standards laboratories" on the fourth floor of South building had to give way to a council lunch room (later the senior lunch room) and a junior lunch room, with a kitchen between. By the time the staff moved in, these were equipped with tables

[42] Rosa, "Plans for the new buildings for the NBS," Science, 17, 129 (1903). For later modifications in the interior planning and details of facilities and equipment, all more or less minor, see Stratton and Rosa, "The National Bureau of Standards," Proc. AIEE, 24, 1039 (1905).

made in the Bureau workshop and furnished with chairs, dishes, and kitchen equipment carted out from the city. Discussions about providing a more expensive lunch for the seniors and a less expensive one for the juniors foundered on the single kitchen they shared, and the staff was not yet large enough to afford a cafeteria. It became the great insoluble problem of the first decade.[43]

But that problem was not in sight when, during the winter of 1903–4, the instrument shop downtown was moved out to the North building and its great dynamos, motor generators, refrigeration plant, storage batteries, gas-making machine, air compressor and other apparatus were installed. In the spring, Dr. Rosa and his group, bringing their lunches with them each day, moved into North building as the remainder of the staff spread out in the vacated rooms downtown.

ACQUIRING NATIONAL STANDARDS

No one knew better than Dr. Stratton that the Bureau had started trom scratch and that for a long time it would have nothing spectacular or even noteworthy to show for its efforts. The Bureau would have to live on borrowed time, borrowed standards, and borrowed instruments while it acquired the materials and methodology for research. Members of the Bureau visiting abroad had found the standards laboratories of France, Germany, and England openhanded, the instrument-makers of those countries helpful in the extreme, and they came home laden with the best equipment and knowledge of standards then available.

At the end of its third year the Bureau had achieved a sense of unity and purpose, and sufficient personnel to do something more than make comparison of a limited number of standards. It was ready, as Rosa said, to "do in its field what the Coast Survey and the Geological Survey and the Department of Agriculture are doing in theirs."[44] It had acquired almost $225,000 worth of apparatus and equipment, much of it abroad, some bought from instrument-makers and manufacturers in this country, and not a little constructed in its own shops. Two of the three divisions were well advanced in their organization (see below), although with the limited staff Dr. Stratton not only directed the Bureau but was in personal charge of a division and of one of its sections, while Dr. Rosa in his division also supervised two of its sections. For the first time it was possible to see just what had been ac-

[43] MS, Dorsey, "Some memories of the early days."

[44] Rosa, "The organization and work of the Bureau of Standards," Science, 19, 937 (1904). Much of the material of this chapter is based on this article.

complished, what the Bureau was prepared to do, and what were the immediate tasks before it.

The Staff of the Bureau of Standards, June 24, 1904[1]

Director—Dr. Samuel W. Stratton (University of Illinois, University of Chicago)

Division I—Dr. Samuel W. Stratton

1. Weights and measures:
   - Louis A. Fischer (Columbia University)
   - Llewelyn G. Hoxton (University of Virginia)
   - Roy Y. Ferner (University of Wisconsin)
   - Nathan S. Osborne (Michigan School of Mines)
   - Lloyd L. Smith
2. Heat and thermometry:
   - Dr. Charles W. Waidner (Johns Hopkins University)
   - Dr. George K. Burgess (MIT, University of Paris)
   - Dr. Hobart C. Dickinson (Williams College, Clark University)
3. Light and optical instruments:
   - Dr. Samuel W. Stratton
   - Dr. Perley G. Nutting (University of California, Cornell University)
   - Dr. Frederick J. Bates (University of Nebraska)
4. Engineering instruments: Albert S. Merrill (MIT)
5. Office: Henry D. Hubbard
6. Instrument shop: Oscar G. Lange

Division II (*Electricity*)—Dr. Edward B. Rosa (Wesleyan University)

1. Resistance and Emf:
   - Dr. Frank A. Wolff, Jr. (Johns Hopkins University)
   - Francis E. Cady (MIT)
   - Dr. George W. Middlekauf (Johns Hopkins University)
2. Magnetism and absolute measurement of current: Dr. Karl E. Guthe, (University of Marburg, University of Michigan)
3. Inductance and capacity:
   - Dr. Edward B. Rosa
   - Dr. N. Ernest Dorsey (Johns Hopkins University)
   - Frederick W. Grover (MIT, Wesleyan University)
4. Electrical measuring instruments:
   - Dr. Edward B. Rosa
   - Dr. Morton G. Lloyd (University of Pennsylvania)
   - Herbert B. Brooks (Ohio State University)
   - C. E. Reid (Purdue University)
   - Franklin S. Durston (Wesleyan University)
5. Photometry: Edward P. Hyde (Johns Hopkins University)
6. Engineering plant: Charles E. Sponsler (Pennsylvania State College)

---

[1] Source: Science, 19, 937 (1904). Details of the education and experience of the original Bureau staff and a résumé of current activities appear in Report of the Dir, NBS, to the Visiting Committee, June 12, 1903 ("Gen Corresp Files of the Director, 1945–1955," Box 6).

Charts of the organization of the Bureau and its supervising personnel, at 5-year intervals from 1901 to 1960, appear in app. J.

Division III (Chemistry)—Dr. William A. Noyes (Johns Hopkins University)
Dr. Henry N. Stokes (Johns Hopkins University)

[Additional personnel included 1 librarian, 1 computer, 1 draftsman, 4 clerks, 2 messengers, 1 storekeeper, 4 mechanicians, 2 woodworkers, 3 apprentices, 2 laborers, 1 assistant engineer, 1 electrician, 2 firemen, 2 watchmen, 1 janitor, 1 charwoman—a total of 58 at the Bureau.]

But first a word about the hierarchy of standards with which the Bureau was, as it still is, concerned.[45] At the apex are the *prototype standards,* those of length, now defined in terms of the red radiation from krypton 86, and mass, the platinum-iridium kilogram cylinder maintained by the International Bureau of Weights and Measures at Sèvres; and of time and temperature, based on the revolution of the earth around the sun and the freezing and boiling points of water (now, the triple point of water).[46] These are the standards which, with certain defining relationships, fix the size of all units in a measuring system and are absolute in the sense that they do not depend on any other standards.

National standards are those which fix the prototype or international value on a national basis, as in the instance of the copies of the prototype meter and kilogram maintained at the Bureau; or are derived standards, such as the standards of frequency, volume, or electricity, depending by definition upon natural or material standards of the prototype category.[47] Thus until the establishment of the absolute ohm in 1948, the ohm was defined by an act of Congress of 1894 as "the resistance offered to an unvarying electric current by a column of mercury at the temperature of melting ice, 14.4521 grams in mass, of a constant cross-sectional area, and of the length of 106.3 cm." [48]

---

[45] The nomenclature for standards of measurement has itself never been entirely standardized. What are called prototype standards are also known as international standards. Primary (now, reference) standards were those either maintained at the PTR or constructed as such by the Bureau and intercompared with the standards abroad. Secondary and working (now, derived and calibration) standards were lower orders of primary standards.

The hierarchy of standards described here is largely based on A. G. McNish, "Classification and nomenclature for standards of measurement," IRE Trans. Instru. 1–7, 371 (1958), and "Measurement standards report," ISA J., February 1961, pp. 1–40.

[46] As the standard of length, long based, as Stratton knew it, on the international meter bar at Sèvres, gave way to the wavelength of krypton 86 light, with superior standards possible in mercury 198 and later sources, so the standard of time, long based on the ephemeris second, is now provisionally based on the resonance frequency of the cesium atoms in the atomic clock. See ch. VIII, pp. 462–463, 477.

[47] See flow chart in NBS C531 (1952), p. 2, for the Bureau's experimental establishment of the eletrical units by absolute measurement.

[48] For the absolute ohm, see ch. VI, p. 337.

Since national standards, whether definitions or materials made of precious metal or of delicate construction and necessarily preserved under special conditions, may be impractical, or frequent use may impair their accuracy, the Bureau maintains *national reference standards,* often of its own construction, the values of which are derived directly from the national standards, but of suitable material or form for more frequent service.

Next are the *working* or *calibration standards,* those which are ordinarily used in calibration and which are themselves calibrated in terms of the corresponding reference standards. They are compared as frequently as necessary with the reference standards and sometimes even with the national standards.

In most instances it is the Bureau's reference or calibration standards that are the immediate source of industrial and commercial standards and of the precision measurements of science. Against these are calibrated the *laboratory reference standards* of science and industry. Whether a precision thermometer, a kilowatt hour meter, or a standard of length, weight, or mass, it is brought to the Bureau periodically and carefully calibrated against the Bureau's reference standard. Returned to the factory or plant, the laboratory reference standard then becomes the basis for calibration and adjustment of the *laboratory working standards,* by which shop instruments and measuring apparatus in daily use by technicians and inspectors are calibrated.[49]

This sequence of standards is of course meaningless without special comparison equipment—longitudinal and geodetic comparators for length standards, the balances used in comparing masses or weights, the potentiometers, bridges, and consoles used in electrical measurements—by means of which all standards of a given type are intercompared in order to determine the order of agreement among them. Differences naturally exist between the nominal value of any standard (except a prototype) and the value it is found to have when compared with a known standard, by reason of differences in their composition or construction, circumstances of measurement, or other irreducible factors, but the discrepancy as an observable quantity, can be adjusted or compensated for, or even within certain limits may be accepted as a permissible tolerance.

In the relatively uncomplicated world of 1904, scientifically speaking, American industry had need for stability and accuracy of measurement rather than high precision. Industry had little requirement as yet for working measurements closer than a thousandth of an inch, but to achieve that with a milling machine, for example, the accuracy of the company master standard had to be on the order of a ten-thousandth of an inch, the Bureau's

[49] For the operation of laboratory standards, see NBS C578, "Suggested practices for electrical standardizing laboratories" (1956), p. 1.

reference standard a hundred-thousandth of an inch, and its primary standard a millionth of an inch.[50] A time would come when industry would have need for that millionth of an inch, and science for the ten-millionth. Continual research looking toward more precise standards, instruments, and techniques was to narrow the gap everywhere in the hierarchy of standards.

Apart from length and mass and certain electrical units, few standards were inherited by the Bureau from the old Office of Weights and Measures. The major part of the Bureau's activities in its early years was thus spent in establishing the discipline of standards for this country, such as other nations already possessed, and obtaining or making the measuring apparatus and instruments to carry out the calibrations required by science and industry. Besides new measurements of length and mass, there was need for new standards of electrical quantities, standards of heat and temperature, of light and radiant energy, density and pressure, and even new values for the factor of gravity. Only the most immediate of these had been accomplished by 1904. Not all of them were wholly satisfactory as yet but an impressive beginning had been made.

In the *weights and measures* section (see above), soon to become an independent division, as were the heat, optical, and engineering groups, the Bureau had the two platinum-iridium copies of the international meter bar, to which all length measurements, both customary and metric, were reduced. Fischer had taken one of the platinum-iridium bars to Paris the previous year and with new apparatus acquired there recompared it with that at the International Bureau of Weights and Measures at Sèvres and found it satisfactory.

The Bureau was now prepared to determine any standard of length from 1 decimeter to 50 meters, to calibrate the subdivisions of such standards, and to determine their coefficients of expansion, that is, the slight changes in dimensions when in use at ordinary ranges of temperature. Working standards derived from the Bureau's two platinum-iridium copies of the international kilogram made it possible to verify masses from 0.1 milligram to 20 kilograms. For their comparison, a number of precision balances were under construction to give the Bureau a complete series of the very best balances possessed anywhere.

For determining the density of solids and liquids, the section had secured two sets of Jena glass hydrometers and verified them at the Normal Eichungskommission in Berlin. The section was working on means for standardizing capacity measures from 1 milliliter to 40 liters and also on

---

[50] "* * * where ordinary reading of micrometers to thousandths of an inch is pretty generally understood, reading to 10-thousandths is not." Joseph V. Woodworth, American Tool Making and Interchangeable Manufacturing (New York: Norman W. Henley. 1911), p. 270.

methods for testing a variety of chemical measuring apparatus in large quantities, for which there had been insistent demands. Apparatus designed at the Reichsanstalt for testing aneroid barometers had been secured, and in the planning stage was a new program, the testing of watches and other time-measuring apparatus.

As primary standards, the *heat and thermometry* section had acquired a number of specially constructed mercury thermometers in Paris, verified at the International Bureau of Weights and Measures in the range −30 to 550 °C. Gas-filled thermometers and copper-constantan thermocouples, also verified at Sèvres, were available for low temperature work down to −200 °C. In addition, Dr. Waidner had himself constructed as further primary standards several platinum resistance thermometers in the interval between 100 and 600 °C, as well as the necessary apparatus for their comparison. As working standards in this same interval were special mercury thermometers of both French and German make, and these were intercompared from time to time with the platinum resistance thermometers.

The Bureau was therefore prepared to certify almost any precision thermometer used in scientific work, most low-temperature engineering and industrial thermometers, and all ordinary commercial thermometers. In addition, special apparatus had recently been designed and constructed for testing clinical thermometers on a large scale, permitting 600 of them to be read at any given temperature in half an hour.

For high-temperature measurements between 600 and 1,600 °C, the Bureau had as primary standards a number of thermocouples acquired in Berlin, their scale that used at the Reichsanstalt. (Here it might be mentioned that America's dependence upon German science and technology before World War I was never more clearly demonstrated than in the circumstances of the Bureau's acquisition of its initial basic instrumentation.) With its German instruments, the Bureau was ready to test and calibrate extreme range thermocouples, platinum resistance thermometers, and expansion and optical pyrometers; determine the melting points of metals and alloys, as well as their specific heats and coefficients of expansion at high temperatures; and to determine the calorific value of any fuel in common use.

Establishment of these standard scales and the development of the necessary testing apparatus had taken most of the effort of this section since 1901. Now with much of the basic work completed, Waidner and Burgess were beginning exploratory research in some of the problems raised by these scales.

Work in the *light and optical instruments* section had thus far been chiefly confined to preliminary investigations in spectroscopic methods of analysis and the determination of standard wavelengths and their use in optical methods of measurement. While waiting on facilities to be provided in the new physical laboratory, Nutting was in the midst of an investigation of electrical discharges in gases in connection with spectrum analysis, and Bates was at work on new methods and apparatus looking toward improved polariscopic standards. At the request of the Treasury, Noyes and Bates had already begun supervision of the polariscopic analysis of sugar at the customhouses.

The *engineering instruments* section was currently occupied with planning tests of gas meters, water meters, pressure gages, and other instruments used in large numbers by public utilities for production control and for determining consumer rates. By far the largest piece of equipment destined for this section was a 100,000-pound machine for testing the strength of building materials. It seems possible this was acquired not long after the Bureau learned that the Reichsanstalt had under construction a new laboratory structure, the Material Prufungs Amt, for testing engineering and building materials.[51] The Bureau similarly planned studies in the behavior of structural and building materials when this crushing machine and other equipment on order were properly set up in North building.

In the *resistance and electromotive force* section of the electrical division, Dr. Wolff and his assistants had been kept busy making tests for Government agencies and for the electrical industry, verifying resistance standards for current measurements, testing standard cells, and determining the temperature coefficients and thermoelectric properties of resistance materials. Every calibration of an electrical instrument, all ratings of electric light bulbs, and practically every meter by which electricity was sold to home or factory started with a measurement of the device against a 1-ohm standard of resistance and a standard cell, by which the electrical pressure (electromotive force), and the current were determined. The Bureau had a number of 1-ohm manganin standards acquired at the Reichsanstalt and reverified there from time to time, using the primary mercury standards maintained in that laboratory. Wolff intended soon to construct a number of his own primary mercury standards in the Bureau shops.

No such effort at independence was necessary in the case of the Clark standard cell, the legal standard of electromotive force. At the electrical congress held during the Columbian Exposition in 1893, its value had been established as 1.434 international volts at 15 °C. Since then the Reichsanstalt, using the same cell as its standard, had determined a new value, 1.4328, nearly 0.1 percent smaller, and the Bureau hoped to settle this discrepancy at the next international electrical congress.

Work had just begun in the *magnetism and absolute measurement of current* section, where Guthe and Rosa were in the midst of two important

[51] See Hearings * * * 1906 (December 2, 1904), p. 233.

researches. One was a study of the silver voltameter, used in measuring current; the other comprised two closely related studies, a redetermination of the electrochemical equivalent of silver and of the absolute value of the Clark standard cell and its rival, the Weston cell.[52]

Dr. Rosa's account of the *inductance and capacity* section suggests that he thought it probably one of the best and most completely equipped at the Bureau. As section chief, with Dorsey and Grover running the research, he had high hopes for the work it had begun. Hundreds of mica and paper condensers had been purchased from German, English, French, and American firms and studies made to find the best performance among them as standards of capacity. Two large air condensers had been constructed as loss-free working standards against which commercial condensers sent to the Bureau were compared. In conjunction with new apparatus under construction, these air condensers were to make possible absolute measurement of currents and electrical pressures up to 1,000 volts.

With a carefully constructed absolute standard of inductance (an electrical quantity analogous to mechanical inertia), the section planned, "by a method never before used," a new determination of the ohm, preliminary to an extended investigation in the absolute measurement of the fundamental electrical units, the ohm, volt, and ampere.[53] Establishment of the Bureau's standard of inductance would also make possible a thorough study of common sources of error in inductance measurements, of considerable concern to new developments in the communications industry.

The *electrical measuring instruments* section, also under Rosa's fervent eye, possessed a wonderful array of precision instruments for measuring electric current, voltage, and power, both direct and alternating, acquired from the best instrumentmakers at home and abroad or designed and built in the Bureau shops. The section was prepared to test and calibrate any laboratory or commercial instrument then in use. Its heavy equipment included powerful direct-current as well as alternating-current generators and allied equipment, and in testing direct-current instruments the section was prepared to handle capacities up to 1,000 amperes and 1,000 volts. The first high-voltage studies would begin with the installation of a giant storage battery with a potential of several thousand volts, then under construction for the Bureau.

---

[52] The Clark cell, invented in England, had been in use since 1872. The American Weston cell, using cadmium instead of zinc, appeared in 1893, and at the turn of the century, because of the availability of better chemical components, was being made in Berlin. The superiority of the Weston cell had led to its adoption as a working standard by the PTR. In 1908, by international agreement, it displaced the Clark cell as the standard of electromotive force.

[53] Stratton and Rosa, "The National Bureau of Standards," Proc. AIEE, 24, 1075 (1905).

The work begun by Dr. Wolff in *photometry* had been turned over to Mr. Edward Hyde, who was studying a number of photometric standards acquired from the Reichsanstalt. Among his problems was the ratio of the candle to the Hefner amylacetate lamp which he had determined as 1 to 0.88. In preliminary tests the Hefner lamp, generally accepted abroad as a primary photometric standard, proved to have so many defects as to be unfit for measurements of the accuracy he hoped to attain. The Bureau had therefore established a temporary standard by arbitrarily assigning a mean value for a number of ordinary 16-candle commercial carbon filament lamps. By means of potentiometers, current and voltage to the lamps could be kept constant to within one-hundredth of 1 percent while making comparisons. Thus very accurate comparisons and very exact copies of standards were possible.

The Bureau had recently requested a number of lamp manufacturers in this country to submit carefully rated samples of their 16-candlepower lamps for comparison with the Bureau standards. They were found to vary from 15.4 to 17.6 candlepower, averaging 16.48 candlepower or about 3 percent high. This fairly close agreement resulted, the Bureau learned, from the manufacturers' use, as standards, of incandescent lamps rated at the Reichsanstalt.

But these were "model" lamps that had been sent to the Bureau. Subsequent testing of the commercial product was to reveal wide variations in their performance. Meanwhile, until the Bureau had devised methods for testing commercial lamps on a large scale, it could only verify those used as industrial standards or make special investigation of any particular lamps submitted to it. Better lamp and light standards and many other aspects of photometry remained to be explored, and this work would be pressed when the section moved into its new quarters.

The *chemistry* division, not yet organized, was to be headed by Dr. William A. Noyes, who had come to the Bureau from Rose Polytechnic Institute, where his starting salary had been the highest ever offered to a professor there. Through the courtesy of Professor Remsen, he was now at the Johns Hopkins University making a study of chemical standards needed in research laboratories, his quest interrupted by occasional trips away to supervise sugar analyses at the customhouses. His associate, Dr. Stokes, appointed from the Geological Survey, was at Dr. Wiley's Bureau of Chemistry in the Department of Agriculture, investigating equipment and measurement problems of its chemists with which the National Bureau of Standards might assist. As soon as Noyes and Stokes moved into their new laboratories and acquired assistants, they would begin much needed work on the standardization of some of the more important chemical reagents. They would be busy, too, assisting the other sections of the Bureau in the chemical analysis of materials going into the construction of standards.[54]

In addition to all the work on standards, instrumentation, and planning of research in that period, the number of tests made for universities, industry, and Government agencies had increased eight times over that possible in the former Office and would more than double again within the year. Surveying this program, Dr. Stratton had cause to be proud of the bureau he had constructed. In a little more than 3 years he had put together the men and materials for an organization that, "judged by the magnitude and importance of the output of testing and investigation," said Rosa, "ranked second only to the great German Reichsanstalt among the government laboratories of the world doing this kind of work." [55]

A sound beginning had been made in the formulation of standards and the main lines of their further investigation were laid out. The Bureau was humming. Fresh from a tour of the highly complex laboratories nearing completion on Connecticut Avenue, Stratton reported to a subcommittee of Congress: "You will not find the same combination of apparatus nor as complicated machinery except in . . . a battleship." [56] It was a neat thrust, considering that the entire cost of the Bureau to date came to less than a sixth of the price of just one of the great fleet of battleships President Roosevelt was currently building.

AN AUTUMN FIRE AND A CONSUMERS' CRUSADE

As the Bureau announced itself ready to expand its testing program in the late spring of 1904, the electrical division, with the help or advice of practically everyone else at the Bureau, was building a special electrical testing laboratory to take out to the Louisiana Purchase Exposition. The fair, celebrating the hundredth anniversary of the purchase of the territory, and the first of countless occasions for exhibiting Bureau activities, opened in St. Louis that summer.[57]

---

[54] For additional notes on the early chemistry division, see letter, Campbell E. Waters to John F. Waldron, Jr., Aug. 15, 1940 (NBS Box 442, IC).

[55] Rosa, "The National Bureau of Standards and its relation to scientific and technical laboratories," Science, 21, 162 (1905). Based on an address given at Wesleyan University, Dec. 7, 1904.

[56] Hearings * * * 1906 (Dec. 2, 1904), p. 230.

[57] Details of this and other NBS exhibitions from 1904 to 1922 will be found in NBS Box 21, PE.

Once there, several members from Dr. Stratton's division presided over an historical exhibit of weights, measures, and instruments located in the Government building, while 10 from Rosa's division, at the request of the Exposition authorities, were kept busy in the great Palace of Electricity verifying the measuring instruments used by the jury of awards in testing electrical machinery, instruments, and apparatus submitted by exhibitors in competition. The German exhibits, as might be expected, won hands down. But for its design as a working exhibit and for its service to the many electrical interests at the fair, the Exposition authorities awarded the Bureau's laboratory one of the grand prizes.[58]

When free from Exposition commitments, the electrical staff carried out considerable routine testing and even some research in its Palace laboratory. More a novelty resulting from Nutting's gas spectra work than a piece of serious research, however, were the luminous script signs in glass tubing exhibited by the staff at the fair. When excited by electric discharges, the noble (inert) gas in the tubes—it was neon—lit up with a reddish glow.[59] Its commercial application came 26 years later.

The Bureau's self-contained electrical exhibit, cooled all that hot humid summer by a 10-ton refrigerating machine, "was a favorite retreat for the electrical jury," and its wizard equipment remained a special attraction until the end of October. Elsewhere on the fair grounds was another kind of "cooler," the first liquid hydrogen plant seen in this country, designed by James Dewar of the Royal Institution in London and exhibited at the fair by the British Oxygen Co. As an instrument of research, particularly in low-temperature thermometry, it was a prize, and Rosa at once began negotiations to acquire it. In Washington, Dr. Stratton approached Congress and obtained not only the asking price for the plant, £500 ($2,400), but an additional $12,000 for the construction of a low-temperature laboratory to house

---

[58] MS, Dorsey, "Some memories of the early days"; Stratton and Rosa, Proc. AIEE, 24, 1084–1090 (1905).

[59] Dr. Nutting's neon signs—two special glass tubes blown by Mr. Sperling in the Bureau shops, one reading "HELIUM," the other "NBS"—resulted from a modification he made in the laboratory instrument known as the Plücker tube and reported in NBS Scientific Paper No. 6, "Some new rectifying effects in conducting gases" (1904). The Plücker tube, like the earlier Geissler tube, was used in the study of spectra of gases and metals. By substituting rod or disk aluminum electrodes for the thin platinum wire in the tube, Nutting obtained a much steadier and brighter light. Although never made public, the neon phenomenon has long been considered the Bureau's first notable laboratory accomplishment, and the forerunner of modern neon signs and fluorescent lamps. Interview with Dr. William F. Meggers, Aug. 4, 1964.

A series of charts of significant scientific and technologic achievements of the Bureau, for each of the decades covered by the chapters of this history, will be found in app. K.

it, adjacent and connected by tunnel to the North building.[60] The first cryogenic (low-temperature) investigations at the Bureau were begun by Franklin Durston that same year. The new building was not completed until the spring of 1906.

Although the Bureau up to this time had been principally concerned with establishing fundamental standards and planning basic research programs, an incident late in the autumn of 1904 sharply reminded the staff of its responsibilities in the field of commercial standards. One evening a fire started in the dead leaves near the railed boardwalk that had been built from the top of the hill down through the woods to the avenue. Franklin Durston, who as a very junior member of the electrical division was also acting night watchman, got out all the hose in the North and South buildings to get a line to reach the fire. He found that because of differences in the threads the hoses could not be coupled. With some difficulty and damage to his shoes, the fire was finally stamped out. The next day "there was quite a discussion as to how it happened that hose from two buildings of the National Bureau of Standards was not sufficiently standardized to admit of mutual coupling." [61]

The same lack of uniform threads had been largely responsible for the raging destruction of the great Baltimore fire back in February of that year. Engine companies arriving by special train from Washington within 3 hours after the fire began found themselves helpless when their hoses would not fit Baltimore hydrants. As one by one "completely fire-proofed" buildings burned like torches all that day and the next, and the fire raced through block after block of the business district, additional fire units from the nearby counties, from New York, Philadelphia, Annapolis, Wilmington, Chester, York, Altoona, and Harrisburg, arrived in the city only to discover that few of their hoses matched any other or fitted the local hydrants.

"If there had been nozzles enough, we could have flooded the burning district," the Baltimore Fire Chief said afterward, for at no time was there any shortage of water. Instead, 1,526 buildings and all electric light, telegraph, telephone, and power facilities in an area of more than 70 city blocks

---

[60] Stratton and Rosa, Proc. AIEE, 24, 1056 (1905). Stratton foresaw need of still another building, attached by tunnel to the opposite or east end of North building, to house laboratories for the testing of engineering instruments and structural materials, and two additional buildings, each about the size of South building, at the east and west ends of that structure, one exclusively for electrical work, the other for chemical and metallurgical studies (ibid., pp. 1041–1042). These four new structures, as detached wings of North and South buildings, were to be enclosed by the east and west buildings proposed earlier. Why the Bureau plant did not expand in this fashion has not been learned.

[61] MS, Dorsey, "Some memories of the early days."

The Baltimore fire of 1904. The turn of the century was still an age of kerosene lamps and wooden cities, except in the business districts which were largely of "fire-proof" brick and stone. But there were wooden stables and sheds behind the buildings, and the structures themselves were filled with highly combustible partitions and furnishings, and there was actually little that was fireproof in their construction.

Despite progress, as late as 1964 firefighters in at least one county adjacent to Baltimore were confronted with two types of hydrants in use, one with the national standard thread and the other with the Baltimore steamer thread. Although they had adaptors, the firemen were asking that fireplugs be coated with colored fluorescent paint, to distinguish the two threads at night and reduce delay in hooking up. The Baltimore Evening Sun, Oct. 1, 1964, p. D2.

in the business district were razed before the fire burned out, 30 hours after it began.[62]

For over a quarter of a century the National Board of Fire Underwriters and the National Fire Protection Association had been advocating standard couplings for all fire departments but had received little support. Shortly after the disaster, a Baltimore steamship line called on the Secretary of Commerce for help with shipboard hose and couplings and the Bureau of Standards was asked to investigate. Thus several months before its own humiliating experience, Stratton had already set Albert Merrill of the engineering instruments section to work on the problem of fire-hose couplings.[63] Before the investigation ended, over 600 sizes and variations in fire-hose couplings were collected across the country.

In 1905, a year after Merrill began his study, the National Fire Protection Association, with the active concurrence of the Bureau, adopted as the national standard what it considered the most serviceable hose coupling then in use, together with an interchangeable device for nonstandard couplings. But the expense of converting or replacing fire hose, as well as normal civic inertia, made agreement in the cities of the Nation a slow process. By 1914, 9 years later, the American Society of Mechanical Engineers reported that only 287 of 8,000 cities and towns had fire-hose couplings and hydrant outlets conforming to the standard. Up to 1917, 897 cities had agreed to adopt them, but only 390 had put them in service. By 1924 the number of cities with standard fire-hose couplings had risen to 700. Conversion was to continue at this slow pace. In many cases, municipalities would make the change only when they had experienced their own version of the Baltimore fire.[64]

Efforts at standardization in another direction offered somewhat better, and certainly more spectacular, results. They began in the spring of 1901 when Louis A. Fischer visited some of the larger cities in New York State to inquire about their inspection of commercial weights and measures. The answers were discouraging. On his return he made a compilation of the laws of all the States relating to weights and measures, revealing a hopeless tangle of regulations, as remarkable for their variety as for their inadequacy. Fischer's section subsequently drew up designs for simple, accurate,

---

[62] Harold A. Williams, Baltimore Afire (Baltimore: Schneidereith, 1954), pp. 11, 20, 43.
[63] Stratton and Rosa, Proc. AIEE, 24, 1070 (1905).
[64] NBS C50, "National standard hose couplings and fittings for public fire service" (1914, 2d ed., 1917). Press release, American Engineering Standards Committee (AESC), June 25, 1924, "Screw threads for fire hose couplings approved as American standard" (NBS Box 77, IDA).

NOTE.—C designates Circular of the NBS, as M, when cited hereafter will designate an NBS Miscellaneous Publication.

inexpensive working standards for the use of State, county, and city sealers and put them in the hands of several manufacturers. Thus sealers for the first time could buy sets of standard weights, measures, and scales specifically designed for their use and send them to the Bureau to be verified and certified.[65] But it was not enough. The old standards had been around a long time and there was no rush to acquire the new sets. The States had to be stirred up.

Dr. Stratton's first proposal to the Governors of the States in 1903 for a meeting of State sealers fell through, it was said, for lack of State travel funds. In November 1904, shortly after moving out of downtown Washington and into the new buildings on Connecticut Avenue, Stratton renewed the invitation. Although there were few acceptances, he was determined to hold the meeting anyway.

The first conference, meeting in January 1905, with representatives from seven States and the District of Columbia, disclosed that in most of these States the laws relating to weights and measures were "exceedingly lax * * * with nothing obligatory" or were "practically a dead letter," that the State sealer's office was usually unsalaried, and the duties of county sealers were often imposed on the county treasurer or even the superintendent of schools. In more than one State, the county and city sealers were not compelled to procure standards, and several of the State representatives knew nothing about their State standards or even where they were to be found. In one State Hassler's standards had been destroyed by fire some years earlier and the $550 necessary to replace them had never been appropriated. In another instance the standards were said to be "hoary with age from long confinement in the dingy and dark recesses of the basement of the capitol."

The consequence of this almost studied disinterest, it was admitted, had long made fraud and trickery in weights and measures commonplace in most of the States represented at the conference. And as Dr. Stratton commented: "Remarkable as have been the statements made today we have not heard the worst, as there are States in which absolutely nothing is done and which are not represented here today." The Bureau agreed to host further meetings in order to discuss means for securing uniform laws and inspection of commercial weights and measures.[66]

At the second conference, in April 1906, it was decided to set up a permanent organization of State officials, make the conference an annual event to discuss the testing and sealing of commercial weights and measures,

[65] Letter report, Fischer to O. H. Tittmann, Supt., U.S. C. & G.S., June 15, 1901 (Stratton Papers, Box 12); NBS Annual Report 1904, pp. 6–7.

[66] "Conference on the weights and measures of the United States * * * January 16 and 17, 1905," NBS M4 (1905), pp. 26, 27, 31, 40, 42. See the voluminous correspondence with State officials in NBS Box 18, IW, 1901–11.

and work toward adoption of uniform laws. Seventeen States were represented at the third conference in 1907, and as at the previous meetings the discussion soon centered around "the question of honest weights and measures in all business transactions," the almost infinite variety of laws affecting weight and measures, and the meager funds provided by the States for their inspection. The conference began work on a model weights and measures law, to be offered for adoption by all the States, and recommended unanimously that additional powers be given the Bureau of Standards to make the State laws effective.[67] Such enforcement, of course, the Bureau could not undertake, but it offered its cooperation to State governments in establishing effective inspection systems while it sought other means to "police" weights and measures. The means was exposure.

Since 1901, as Stratton said, "a great reform [had been] going on throughout the country," its principal target the commercial oligarchy that ruled the Nation.[68] It had been touched off by journalists such as Ida M. Tarbell, Lincoln Steffens, and Ray Stannard Baker through their exposure in the periodical press of the knavery in big business, the roguery of politics and politicians, of labor leaders and employers alike. Aroused by the literature of exposure, a passion for change, for honesty, and for justice swept the Nation. Among the consequences of the reform wave were Roosevelt's indictment of the meat-packing trust in 1905 and passage of the Pure Food and Drug Act in 1906.

Before the wave receded, the whole Nation became aware of the presence of the Bureau of Standards in the Federal Government. Beyond anything its proponents could have contemplated, the coincidence of the founding of the Bureau with the age of reform shaped its history for the next 30 years. Weights and measures was to be the trigger.

The annual conferences of State sealers at the Bureau made it clear that through ignorance and neglect of State responsibilities the American public was being robbed of enormous sums daily in the marketplace. Since the State governments showed little interest in weights and measures reforms, said Stratton, the Bureau "must reach the public through State and city officials by testing their standards." In December 1908 he asked Congress for a special grant of $10,000 "to investigate what the States are doing with their standards, and to encourage them to take up and supervise the local work as they should." [69] It was the Bureau's first request for special funds, and Congress approved it without question. What Stratton intended was an investigation to reveal the extent of false and fraudulent weights and measures in use throughout the Nation.

---

[67] NBS Annual Report 1907, p. 6.

[68] Hearings * * * 1908 (Nov. 30, 1906), p. 351.

[69] Hearings * * * 1910 (Dec. 4, 1908), pp. 185–186.

Between 1909 and 1911, inspectors from the Bureau visited every State of the Union, testing over 30,000 scales, weights, and dry and liquid measures in 3,220 different shops and stores. They were not surprised to find that almost half the scales tested were badly inaccurate, that 20 percent of the weights, half the dry measures, and a quarter of the liquid measures were in error, or that with remarkable consistency these scales and measures favored the storekeeper. The Bureau estimated that in the case of print butter alone the annual loss to the consumer, through rigged or faulty weighing devices, amounted to more than $8,250,000.[70]

From the start, journalists and reporters followed the track of the Bureau inspectors, and with the first disclosures of what the journalists termed "the knavish distortion of weights and measures," the crusade began. New York State's superintendent of weights and measures, Dr. Fritz Reichmann, and Mayor Gaynor of New York City soon launched investigations of their own and other States followed. Over the next 2 years almost a hundred articles in the periodical press reported the weights and measures campaign across the country.[71]

As a result of the widespread demand for better laws and better inspection of trade weights and measures in the wake of the survey, first New Jersey and then other States enacted the model law proposed by the Bureau, and State after State exhumed and submitted for verification to the Bureau the standards that had been furnished them some 50 years earlier or purchased new equipment for their State sealers.[72] Answering urgent appeals, the Bureau drafted a model weights and measures ordinance for municipalities, and detailed its experts to first one and then another of the States which requested aid in setting up their inspection departments.

A Bureau proposal to require that the net weight, measure, or numerical count of contents be printed on sealed packages was accomplished by an amendment to the Pure Food and Drug Act in 1913, and in 1915 Congress passed a standard barrel law; but efforts of the Bureau to promote national legislation to define the weights and measures used in everyday trade, to

---

[70] Louis A. Fischer, "Recent developments in weights and measures in the United States," Pop. Sci. Mo. 84, 345 (1914), reported the Bureau's findings, State by State. See also NBS Box 18.

[71] For example, F. T. Cordage, "Serious leakage: short weights and measures," Good Housekeeping, 48, 744 (1909); F. Reichmann, "The necessity of the supervision of weights and measures," Am. Stat. Assoc. 12, 146 (1910); Sloan Gordon, "Is the housewife guilty?" Cosmopolitan, 50, 73 (1910); Francis J. Dyer, "The Government to the rescue," Good Housekeeping, 52, 334 (1911). In Reichmann's "Savings through proper supervision of weights, measures and standards," Ann. Am. Acad. Pol. Soc. Sci. 50, 94 (1913), he estimated that as a result of reforms in New York State, annual savings to consumers in the past several years had amounted to $15 million.

[72] NBS Annual Report 1909, pp. 11–12.

fix the sizes of other common shipping units besides the barrel (such as the bale, box, and basket), and to require certification by the Bureau of all weights and measures apparatus manufactured and sold in the United States, got nowhere.[73]

The crusade ended, but not before the Bureau had made the Nation conscious of the meaning of measure at the market—temporarily, at least. Ninety-eight officials representing 25 States and 34 cities attended the Bureau conference held in February 1912, and except during wartime years, these conferences have been held annually ever since.[74] Through the conferences, the continuing research at the Bureau, the training of sealers, and the furnishing of informaton and assistance to State and local officials, the pioneer work of Louis A. Fischer lives in the weights and measures control we know today.

THE BEGINNING OF GOVERNMENT TESTING

The era of exposure not only served to acquaint the general public with the name of the Bureau of Standards but it brought to the notice of other agencies of the Government a new and versatile auxiliary in the Federal family. Even before the weights and measures crusade began, the Federal Government, alerted by the hue and cry of the reformers calling citizens and consumers to arms, discovered that as a consumer it was itself being victimized.

Incandescent lamps, bought by the Government at the rate of a million a year, were burning out at a fearful rate in Federal offices. When a purchasing agency sent one of its recent shipments to the Bureau for tests, the Bureau promptly threw out three-quarters of the bulbs. They were neither uniform in accordance with the manufacturer's own standards, nor did they even come up to the simple specifications suggested by the Government. The Bureau was soon to find similar shortcomings in the clinical thermometers, electric meters, chemical glassware, inks, mucilages, and indeed the whole catalog of supplies purchased for Government use.[75]

---

[73] NBS Annual Report 1911, pp. 13–15. NBS C61, "Specifications and tolerances for weights and measures and weighing and measuring devices" (1916, 2d ed., 1920), was adopted at the weights and measures conference of 1916 for use in ordinary commercial transactions and had wide acceptance.

[74] By 1929 the Bureau reported there were almost 300 officials on the State level dealing with weights and measures work and 1,400 on the local level (NBS letter report, May 2, 1929, NBS Box 285, IW). For later reports, see NBS M172, "Index to reports of the National Conference on Weights and Measures, 1905–41" (McCormac and Smith, 1942).

[75] Hearings * * * 1906 (Dec. 2, 1904), pp. 231–232; Hearings * * * 1909 (Jan. 30, 1908), pp. 496–497.

The light bulb incident occurred in 1904. By 1906, Stratton reported, there was "a wave of reform going on all through the Government service as to proper specifications and proper tests to determine whether goods purchased complied with specification." [76] And Bureau testing for the Government began to double annually as increasing varieties and quantities of Government supplies and materials were sent to the Bureau before acceptance. The Bureau was called on to test the tensile strength of a new cable for the elevator in the Washington Monument, the cement used in the construction of the new House Office Building, paper and inks for the Government Printing Office, paints, oils, and varnishes for the Lighthouse Board, and virtually every instrument and piece of apparatus destined for a Federal laboratory.

Congress, concerned over the repeated increases in personnel and funds that Dr. Stratton found it necessary to ask for, complained that it was "shocked a little bit by the way [the Bureau] is developing." In answer to the question, "Do you not think that you are broadening the scope of the work of your Bureau?" Stratton described the growth of the Government testing program.[77] This testing had not been specified in the organic act, nor even contemplated when the Bureau was founded. But the Bureau laboratories were uniquely well fitted to make such tests, and great economies accrued to the Government as a result. It was, Stratton told Congress, almost entirely "commercial testing" and offered little opportunity for original investigation or research; still, it necessitated hiring specialists in many fields and large numbers of aids, apprentices, and assistants.

By 1908 two-thirds of all testing at the Bureau was for Federal agencies alone. During that year it carried out tests for 37 bureaus and divisions of the Government, analyzing rag and wood papers for the Post Office Department and the Government Printing Office, investigating naphthas and celluloids as cargo hazards for the Steamship Inspection Service, assisting in Pure Food and Drug Law analyses, and carrying out a long series of cement and concrete examinations for the Panama Canal Commission. As an illustration of the usefulness of its tests, said Stratton, the Bureau had recently rejected outright 4 of 6 samples of varnish and 14 of 24 samples of paint submitted for analysis by the Lighthouse Board.[78]

So extensive had this testing program become by 1909 that the Bureau had to restrict its own research and was experiencing difficulty in handling

---

[76] Hearings * * * 1908 (Nov. 30, 1906), p. 351.

[77] Hearings * * * 1904 (Dec. 2, 1904), p. 229; Hearings * * * 1907 (Feb. 23, 1906,) p. 657.

[78] Hearings * * * 1909 (January 30, 1908), pp. 495–496; Hearings * * * 1910 (Dec. 4, 1908), p. 171.

requests for investigations from university and industrial laboratories. Stratton feared for the Bureau: "Nothing could cause the institution to deteriorate more quickly than to flood it with routine testing. It must do a certain amount of original investigation to develop standards and methods of measuring or it will soon become a second-rate institution." [79]

Yet in addition to greater economy in Federal housekeeping, much good was coming from the Government testing, as Stratton was well aware. It was supplying a much needed incentive to industry. The high rate of rejection by the Bureau and the impartiality and justice of the tests thoroughly alarmed hundreds of firms supplying goods and materials to the Government. Supplying the Government was good business, and even though the Bureau did not publish its findings by brand name, word got around. A manufacturer or supplier who lost a Government contract found he lost other contracts. Manufacturers began beating a path to the laboratories on the hill for advice and help with their materials, measuring, and testing apparatus, and methods of quality control.[80]

"Scarcely a day passes," Dr. Stratton reported, "that some manufacturer does not visit the Bureau to learn how to measure or to secure standards." In many instances the Bureau did not have the answers industry sought, since no criteria existed for the products or materials in question. But with the manufacturer's assistance, the Bureau would agree to undertake the necessary research and establish the required standard. In this manner industry, and Government agencies as well, were to provide the kind of research the Bureau wanted to do.

The Bureau was quick to see the importance to the public as well as to industry of expanding its random commercial testing for the Government into a large-scale research program that would cover as widely as possible the range of materials and products of commerce. As early as 1905 the Bureau reported that "numerous cases of dispute regarding the quality of construction materials, such as iron, steel, brick, stone, cement, concrete, etc., have been referred to the Bureau for a determination of the physical properties in question." [81] Virtually no data existed, for example, on the tensile and compressive strength, specific gravity, and time of set of cement and cement mortars, or on the thermal conductivity and effects of temperature upon the compression, expansion, and durability of concrete aggre-

---

[79] Hearings * * * 1910 (Dec. 4, 1908), p. 177.

[80] As Henry S. Carhart pointed out in Pop. Sci. Mo. 79, 209 (1911), the Government purchased only about 1 percent of the incandescent lamps made, the other 99 percent being sold to the general public, but Bureau testing elevated the quality for all.

[81] NBS Annual Report 1906, p. 15.

gates, poured concrete, or concrete building blocks. And so with other construction materials.

Search of the literature on materials submitted for Government purchase disclosed that no standard methods or apparatus existed for the testing of wood, paper, twine, textile fabrics, inks, mucilages, and related materials, or for the testing of lubricating oils, resins, varnishes, protective coatings, and glues, all of whose qualities were as important to the buying public as to the Government. In order to provide proper specifications to industry for the manufacture of these materials, the physical, chemical, and other properties of their composition had to be investigated. The program of structural, engineering, and miscellaneous materials research thus begun was to consume much of the Bureau's energies for many years to come. By 1911 the program, originally scattered throughout the laboratories, had attained divisional status. It had a special appropriation of its own, and was well on the way to becoming the largest single activity at the Bureau.

Allied to this research in commercial and industrial products, but actually derived from the function calling for "the determination of physical constants and the properties of materials," was the Bureau's standard samples program. This began in 1905 when the American Foundrymen's Association turned over to the Bureau its work of preparing and distributing samples of standardized irons to its member industries. To prepare these samples, a quantity of iron was reduced to fine borings and then carefully analyzed, divided into samples of known composition as certified by the Bureau, and sold to manufacturers as a check on their own laboratory analyses.

Preparation of like samples of a number of alloys, iron ores, and copper slags prompted Albert Ladd Colby, representing engineering interests on the Visiting Committee to the Bureau and a leading authority on metallurgy, to suggest that the Bureau produce samples of steels as well. The work began the next year when the Association of American Steel Manufacturers requested preparation of a series of 17 standard steel samples. The Bureau's samples won high praise and requests for similar certification of other basic materials. When the American Chemical Society assigned its standard sample work to the Bureau, Dr. Stratton announced the Bureau's intention of preparing an entire spectrum of sample materials, covering hundreds of products, for American industry.[82]

The chemistry division, increasingly involved in its investigation of properties of materials for the Government testing program, found itself

[82] NBS Annual Report 1906, p. 16; Annual Report 1907, p. 13. The methods of analyses and range of samples were described in NBS C14 (1909), NBS C25 (1910), NBS C26 (1910) and their successive editions.

pressed for time and staff as the work on standard samples grew. Nevertheless it borrowed time from these efforts to launch a much needed investigation of impurities in analytical chemicals. Other groups at the Bureau, now grown to divisions, were also pushing out exploratory parties into new lines of inquiries. The weights and measures staff had begun its investigation of State standards, the pyrometry and heat divison sought new methods and instruments for high-temperature measurement in industry, the optics division attacked theoretical problems in polarimetry, spectroscopy, and radiometry, and the electrical division became involved in absolute measurement, electrical instrumentation, and photometry. But making constant inroads into the research efforts of all divisions was the acceleration of routine testing and calibration for science, industry, and above all for the Government. Between 1905 and 1910 the number of such tests increased from 16,500 to almost 50,000, the Government's share rising from 26 to 70 percent of all calibration and testing. And complicating the testing was the demand for new research in technology, in order to establish a methodology and instrumentation that would put testing on an increasingly scientific basis.

The volume of testing, doubling in 1909 over the previous year under the impact of Government work, soared again the next year when, to consolidate effort and responsibility, the staff and equipment of the structural materials laboratories of the Geological Survey were transferred to the Bureau of Standards.[83] The transfer on July 1, 1910, involved 53 engineers, chemists, and assistants. It included a small group in Washington under Dr. Samuel S. Voorhees, who with his chief assistant Phaon H. Bates was engaged in chemical research in mineral pigments, paints, and other building materials, mainly for the Supervising Architect's Office; a Pittsburgh laboratory under Dr. Albert V. Bleininger, where cements for navy yard and dry dock construction, as well as clays, ceramics, lime, steel, and other structural materials were tested; a Northampton, Pa., laboratory under R. L. Humphrey, testing cement at the plants supplying the Isthmian Canal Commission; and still another laboratory at Atlantic City under Rudolph J. Wig, where the effect of sea water upon concretes and protective coatings was being investi-

---

[83] The Geological Survey, ordinarily concerned with assaying and mapping the earth resources of the Nation, began its structural materials program in 1904 when it was persuaded to make tests of cement-making materials, building stones, and clays for an exhibit of the American Portland Cement Manufacturers at the St. Louis fair. By 1910 the Survey, since restricted by law to research for the Government, was testing a wide range of structural materials, principally for the Panama Canal (under construction from 1904 to 1914) and for some 400 public buildings planned or under construction in the United States. See Annual Report, Department of the Interior, 1910, pp. 202, 206; Weber, The Bureau of Standards, pp. 48–49.

The Bureau about 1910, just prior to the construction of the electrical laboratories (East building). From left to right: the corner of West building, South building, the Low Temperature Laboratory, and North building.

gated. Soon after, the Bureau itself established a fifth field laboratory, at Allentown, Pa., to sample and test cement produced in plants there for the Navy and War Departments.[84]

Well before this augmentation of the Bureau, its test program had already crowded into the last of the laboratories available in North and South buildings. Planning expansion of both the Bureau's work in structural materials and that of the former Geological Survey group, Dr. Stratton asked Congress for new mammoth testing machines and a special building to house them. The funds were approved and a 1-million-pound crushing machine for compression tests of brick, stone, cement, and concretes, another of 230,000-pound capacity, a 100,000-pound universal (compression and tension) machine, and a specially designed 2,300,000-pound Emery universal testing machine, for breakdown and exhaustion tests of girders and other large structural members, all built to Bureau specifications, were ordered.[85] Well before they arrived, West building, a four-story laboratory situated between North and South buildings, was completed in December 1909 at a cost of $175,000.

Surpassing West building's giant Emery machine in capacity if not design was the Olsen machine acquired with the Pittsburgh laboratory. It was the most powerful testing machine in the country at that time, capable of exerting a force of 10 million pounds slowly and irresistibly in destruction tests of massive masonry columns. Structural materials testing at the Bureau and its field stations, nowhere contemplated in the organic act, began to expand.

In 1911, with almost no further increase in staff over the previous year, the number of tests and calibrations leaped from 50,000 to more than 80,000, almost 77 percent of them for the Government. The Bureau was to maintain this level until we entered the war in 1917.

Largely as a consequence of the Government testing program, authorized personnel for the Bureau, including the group transferred from the Geological Survey, rose from 87 to 269 between 1906 and 1911. Acquiring that number of trained scientists and craftsmen—and keeping them—had for some time become a serious problem. The Bureau could not compete in salaries either with the larger universities or with industry, and the increasing interest of manufacturers in the application of science to industry made them particularly eager to entice specialists away from the Bureau. Industry was willing to pay twice the Government salary for men it wanted and even

---

[84] Annual Report, Department of the Interior, 1910 p. 297; ibid. 1911, p. 377; NBS Annual Report 1911, pp. 26–28.

[85] Detailed descriptions and correspondence concerning the acquisition of these machines will be found in NBS Box 5, EI.

The 2,300,000-pound Emery testing machine in Washington, for making exhaustion tests of beams, girders, and other large metal structural components. A similar compression-to-exhaustion giant, the Olsen machine, was at the Pittsburgh laboratories, for destruction tests of piers and other masonry columns.

the universities offered lures hard to resist, as Dr. Stratton demonstrated graphically at a congressional hearing in 1906: [86]

Harvard University		*Bureau of Standards*	
Instructor	$1,200–$1,500	Laboratory assistant	$ 900–$1,200
Assistant professor	2,500– 3,000	Assistant physicist	1,400– 1,800
Associate professor	3,500– 4,500	Associate physicist	2,000– 2,200
Professor	4,000– 5,500	Physicist	3,500– 4,000

The Bureau, said Dr. Stratton, had lost a number of its staff that year, and some of its most valuable members were strongly tempted to leave. One was Dr. Noyes, the Bureau's chief chemist, who between 1904 and 1907 had won international fame for his development of standard methods of analysis and standard specifications for chemicals while at the Bureau. He had had university offers as high as $4,750, although the Bureau could not pay him more than $3,500. Two years later Dr. Noyes went to the University of Illinois as head of its chemistry department. Dr. Rosa refused an invitation to go to MIT, but Dr. Edward Hyde, in charge of Bureau research in photometry, left his $2,000 position for similar research in the Edison lamp laboratories at $5,000 a year.

Congress was not inclined to be sympathetic about such losses. "Is not that thing likely to occur with any reasonable salary that the Government can pay?" asked Washington Gardner, Republican representative from Michigan and member of the House Subcommittee on Appropriations. It was, Dr. Stratton replied, but the nature of the work at the Bureau made its staff particularly vulnerable to good offers outside, especially since "nearly every great manufactuing concern in this country is establishing a research laboratory" and looking for trained men. "I think it [is] a good thing for the country to have them go out into the world," answered Mr. Gardner, and suggested that the Bureau continue to hire men at its lower grades and promote them as vacancies occurred.[87]

Despite the low salaries, employment with the Bureau of Standards had many compensations, not least the prestige of working for a new, important, and rapidly growing scientific agency of the Federal Government. Status and tenure were apt to be more certain than in a university or in industry since all positions, then as now, were filled through competitive civil service examinations, thus guarding against personal whim or favoritism, with permanency and promotion determined by civil service law.

Except for division chiefs, whom he selected on the basis of demonstrated productivity and promise, Stratton, hampered by the competition in salaries, adopted the policy of bringing in talented graduates of first-class scientific or technical colleges, appointing them to the lower grades of

[86] Hearings * * * 1907 (Feb. 23, 1906), p. 602.
[87] Hearings * * * 1911 (Jan. 27, 1910), pp. 332–336.

assistantships, and advancing them as their proficiency increased and vacancies occurred. To provide minor assistants for routine testing and experimental work, he set up a system of apprentices and aids, taking on graduates of manual training and technical high schools as apprentices, advancing them to aids after 2 years, and thence to the lowest grades of laboratory assistant when they had acquired the requisite mathematics and training in theoretical science through evening courses given at George Washington University in downtown Washington.[88]

Many who were later to be luminaries of the scientific world came to the Bureau as laboratory assistants, among them Dr. William F. Meggers, dean of American spectroscopists; Dr. George K. Burgess, who succeeded Stratton as Director of the Bureau; Dr. Frederick J. Bates, one of the country's outstanding sugar physicists; Dr. William W. Coblentz, founder of modern radiometry; and Dr. Paul D. Foote, pioneer in high temperature measurements.[89]

The Bureau grounds, remote from the city, tree-shaded, and populated predominantly by young college graduates, possessed from the beginning an unmistakable campus atmosphere. The group loyalties and mild intramural competition that naturally resulted were diligently fostered by Dr. Stratton, as a means of keeping his staff from straying. He did more. Many of the young holders of B.S. and M.S. degrees who came to the Bureau, some with wives and all with ambition, wanted their doctoral degrees. Stratton proposed a plan for giving graduate courses at the Bureau in mathematics, physics, and chemistry equal to those in the best universities, and

---

[88] Stratton and Rosa, Proc. AIEE, 24, 1043–1044 (1905).

[89] One measure of the caliber of the physicists that Stratton brought to the Bureau is represented in the star system of American Men of Science. From its first (1906) to it seventh (1944) editions, American Men of Science, by an intricate ballot system, periodically starred the thousand outstanding scientists in the Nation. Among the 150 top physicists (headed by A. A. Michelson) that were selected in 1906 (actually chosen in 1903), Bureau members included Austin, Dorsey, Guthe, Nutting, Rosa, Stratton, Waidner, and Wolff. (This 1906 list appeared in American Men of Science, fifth edition, 1933, pp. 1269 ff.)

By the fourth edition (1927), the Bureau had increased its number of leading scientists from 8 to 23 members, its group of physicists alone representing the strongest collection of any institution in the country, ranking above Harvard, General Electric, University of Chicago, Bell Telephone Laboratories, Johns Hopkins University, Columbia, California Institute of Technology, Cornell, and Yale. And at that time the number of entries in American Men of Science had risen from 4,000 (1906) to 13,500 (1927). Starred members of the Bureau in the 1927 edition included Acree, Austin, Bleininger, Blum, Briggs, Brown, Buckingham, Burgess, Coblentz, Crittenden, Curtis, Dellinger, Dickinson, Dorsey, Foote, Heyl, Meggers, Mohler, Skinner, Priest, Washburn, Wenner and Wolff (American Men of Science, fourth edition, 1927, p. 1128 ff. See also J. McKeen Cattell, "The scientific men of the world," Sci. Mo. 23, 468, 1926, and Science, 66, 516, 1927.)

permitting staff members to offer parts of their Bureau research results as graduate theses, provided their universities would accept this course work and research.

Precedent for the latter had been established even before formal adoption of the plan. Original research at the Bureau had been accepted toward the doctorate when the Johns Hopkins University admitted an investigation in photometry by Edward P. Hyde for his degree in 1906, when the University of Michigan accepted work on magnetic testing by Charles W. Burrows in 1907, and also that year when George Washington University accepted an investigation of capacity and power factors of condensers by Frederick W. Grover.[90]

The experience of Harvey L. Curtis, one of the first to secure his doctorate through Bureau courses and research, and long-time member of the electrical division, was typical of many who followed him. In the spring of 1907, with a master's degree in physics from the University of Michigan, a wife and two children, and 4 years' experience as instructor at $700 at Michigan Agricultural College, Curtis, then 31, chanced upon a notice of an examination for assistant physicist at the Bureau. He had just been promoted to assistant professor when he received word he had passed the examination. He was offered the Bureau appointment at $1,200. When he declined because the college assistant professorship paid better, Rosa sent him a telegram asking him to come to Washington anyway for an interview. He was offered $1,400, and was persuaded to accept when Dr. Stratton told him of the graduate course plan being inaugurated.

Soon after Curtis began work in the electrical laboratories, he wrote at Dr. Stratton's suggestion to Prof. Henry S. Carhart at the University of Michigan about the course plan. Carhart replied that the faculty had voted to give Curtis a hearing when he presented the completion of his work. Other youngsters at the Bureau, Roy Y. Ferner, Paul G. Agnew, E. C. McKelvy, J. Howard Dellinger, and Hobart C. Dickinson, also wrote to their universities. A few of the replies were discouraging, some were tentative, but Prof. Joseph S. Ames, head of the physics department at the Johns Hopkins, wrote enthusiastically to one of his former pupils:

> There is not a college or university in the United States that can give a student as much apparatus for experimental work and as

[90] H. L. Curtis, "Establishment of graduate study courses at the NBS," J. Wash. Acad. Sci. 29, 351 (1949). See also MS speech, G. K. Burgess, "The Bureau of Standards as an educational institution," June 28, 1924 (NBS Box 77, IDP). Memo, L. B. Tuckerman for L. J. Briggs, Oct. 12, 1927 (NBS Box 489, AP), reported that 11 of the 72 doctorates in physics granted by Johns Hopkins between 1906 and 1926 went to Bureau members, 2 others had received degrees for Bureau research in chemistry and 2 in electrical engineering. Dr. Briggs received his Hopkins degree in 1901 for work done at the Department of Agriculture.

much help in the theoretical field of the physical sciences as he can obtain at the Bureau of Standards.[91]

Stratton proposed a 3-year cycle of evening courses in physics, mathematics, and chemistry, each course to be given 2 hours a week for 30 weeks, at $25 per course. The first subjects offered in the fall of 1908 were in differential equations, given by Dr. John A. Anderson, who came out weekly from the Hopkins physics department; theoretical mechanics, taught by Dr. Albert F. Zahm of Catholic University; and thermodynamics, by Dr. Edgar Buckingham of the Bureau.

Dr. Rosa was to have given a weekly 4-hour course in experimental methods in electrical measurement that same autumn when a call for consultations on electrical standards at the British and German physical laboratories took him abroad. The course was given instead by three of the students who had signed up for it, Dellinger, then working in the resistance and electromotive force section, Curtis in the inductance and capacity section, and Agnew in the electrical instruments section. Upon his return in January 1909, Rosa completed the course with a series of lectures on advanced electrical measurements.

In the spring of 1909 a Bureau committee composed of Stratton, Rosa, Hillebrand, Wolff, Waidner, Burgess, Dorsey, Nutting, Waters, and Fischer was set up to direct the graduate program. To the classes already in progress, Dorsey began teaching a new course in electricity and magnetism and Dr. Kanolt began another in physical chemistry.

Including advanced work taken earlier at the University of Michigan, Harvey Curtis completed the course work at the Bureau in the spring of 1910. With his thesis on "Mica condensers as standards of capacity," based on a recently completed investigation published that same year in the Bulletin of the Bureau, he went to Ann Arbor, passed his orals, and returned with his degree.[92]

The cyclic system of graduate course work established by Dr. Stratton continued for the next 50 years, and what was begun as an expedient to keep promising personnel, came to attract them as well. In 1960, 1,322 members of Bureau laboratories and affiliates were taking a total of 72 undergraduate and graduate courses offered in the physical sciences, mathematics, and engi-

---

[91] Quoted in H. L. Curtis, Recollections of a Scientist: An Autobiography (privately printed at Bonn, Germany: L. Leopold Press, 1958), p. 27.

[92] Ibid., pp. 22, 26–30. Three years later, in 1913, Dr. Curtis became an associate physicist at the Bureau, in 1918 physicist, in 1924 senior physicist, and in 1928 principal physicist. He published a book on electrical measurements and almost 50 papers prior to his retirement from the Bureau in January 1947. The retirement was purely statutory. Like many other long-time employees of the Bureau, Curtis continued to experiment as a guest worker in his old laboratory, coming in daily until shortly before his death at the age of 80.

neering for advanced degrees or promotion. Since Dr. Stratton established the graduate program in 1908, more than 15,500 registrations have been recorded, resulting in the award of 270 graduate degrees by 40 different universities, for research carried out in part at least at the Bureau.[93]

After the 1920's all the physical sciences were levied on for degrees, but in the age of electricity, as historians of modern technology have called the period prior to World War I, much of the doctoral research was done in the laboratories presided over by Dr. Rosa, where a hundred years of basic and empirical electrical research awaited standards and new measurements and the scientists to determine them. Well before the end of the first decade Rosa's had become the premier division of the Bureau.

[93] Annual Report, Research Highlights of the NBS, 1960, pp. 159–160. See also eight-page account of the program attached to letter, L. J. Briggs to U.S. Office of Education, Federal Security Agency, July 12, 1940 (NBS Box 443, ID-Misc).

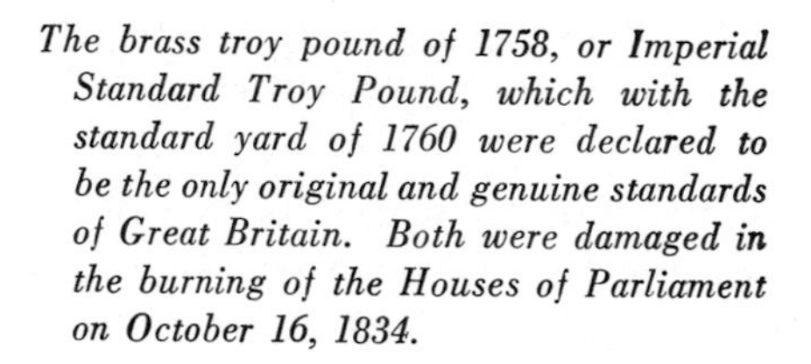

The brass troy pound of 1758, or Imperial Standard Troy Pound, which with the standard yard of 1760 were declared to be the only original and genuine standards of Great Britain. Both were damaged in the burning of the Houses of Parliament on October 16, 1834.

ELECTRICITY, RAILROADS, AND RADIO (1911–16)

CHAPTER III

STANDARDS FOR THE AGE OF ELECTRICITY

The first two decades of the 20th century witnessed a new industrial revolution, the electrification of American industry. In 1899 less than 5 percent of all power used in industry had been electric. By 1909, with the development of more efficient generators, better electric motors, and transmission lines of greater carrying capacity, it had risen to 25.4 percent, and by 1919 to 55 percent.[1] An age of electricity had arrived, its challenge to the long dominance of heavy industry, by promising lighter and more specialized products, as revolutionary in its impact on the lives of ordinary men as the present age of computers and automation.

Dr. Rosa was speaking of the electrical industry when he said: "It is largely to meet their needs [the electrical instrument-makers and manufacturers] that the bureau was organized, and if by serving them the standard of excellence of American-made instruments and machinery is raised, the bureau will have served the public also." [2] Or as Dr. Stratton wrote to Secretary of Commerce and Labor Cortelyou, in a letter of 1904 describing the spheres of interest of the Visiting Committee: "The work of the bureau is perhaps more closely related to electrical interests than any other." [3]

Electric light and power companies, appliance manufacturers, communication and traction companies developed at a phenomenal rate throughout the period. So numerous were the demands of the electrical industry and of electrical research laboratories for basic measurements, instrumentation, tests and calibrations that almost half the new people coming into the Bureau went into Rosa's division. By 1910 the testing of materials for Government agencies, by its sheer volume, was in the ascendant, but Stratton reported that electrical research and testing was still, "next to structural

---

[1] Samuel H. Schurr and Bruce C. Netschert, Energy in the American Economy, 1850–1935 (Baltimore: Johns Hopkins Press, 1960), p. 187.

[2] Rosa, "The organization and work of the Bureau of Standards," Science, 19, 949 (1904).

[3] Letter, SWS to Cortelyou, Dec. 10, 1904 (NBS Box 296, APV-Remsen).

materials * * * the largest division of the bureau's work." [4] As the world of electricity grew Rosa's division grew with it, extending its research in measurement into electrolysis and electrochemistry, into radio research and engineering, and radiology.

To satisfy the industry's need for better electrical standards and better measuring instruments, much of the early work of the Bureau was concentrated in fundamental electrical measurements. N. Ernest Dorsey of the electrical division reported some of the results:

> The progress that was made in the seven years 1903 to 1910 in the accuracy of [these] measurements was great. In 1903 it was generally believed that it was not possible to make absolute electrical measurements to a higher accuracy than one in one thousand; by 1910, such measurements had been made with an accuracy of a few parts in 100,000.
>
> In 1903, manganin resistances were subject to large unexplained irregular variations; before 1910, these variations had been shown by [the] Bureau to be caused by the effect of varying humidity upon the insulation, and sealed coils largely eliminating that effect had been constructed.
>
> In 1903, the results obtained with the silver coulometer [i.e., voltameter] were distressingly variable; by 1910, the major cause of the variations had been discovered, and several types of coulometers yielding high reproducibility had been designed.
>
> [Finally,] much improvement had been made in the constancy and reproducibility of the standard cell.
>
> By the summer of 1910, the modern era of high accuracy in electrical measurements had begun.[5]

Most of the electrical values that were available to science and industry in 1903 were far from precise and tentative at best. The first application of electricity, to the telegraph, required few quantitative results other than resistance measurements. But by the 1880's, as electric energy was applied to light and power, the necessity for accurate measurements of other electrical quantities, of capacitance, inductance, electromotive force, and current, became acute. The Electrial Congress held in Paris in 1881, the first of many such international conferences, recommended that electric and magnetic quantities be measured in terms of absolute units, that is, the same units used to measure mechanical energy—the centimeter, gram, and second

---

[4] Hearings * * * 1912 (Dec. 2, 1910), p. 267.

[5] MS, N. Ernest Dorsey, "Some memories of the early days."

(CGS). But precise values for electrical units in relation to fundamental mechanical effects are difficult to establish, and electrical science and industry needed units that could be readily reproduced in their laboratories.

By 1903 general agreement on reproducible primary electrical standards had been reached. The international ohm was arbitrarily defined as the resistance of a specified column of mercury, the international ampere by its rate of deposition of silver, and the international volt as a specified fraction of the electromotive force of the Weston standard cell. Commerce and industry, assuming that the units defined by reproducible standards were indistinguishable from absolute units, were satisfied. But for the most precise work, science looked to the Bureau for an accurate statement of the small but very real difference between these reproducible units and fundamental (absolute) units.

Defining an electrical unit was one thing, determining its value relative to absolute units was quite another, and the standards set up in accordance with these definitions by the national laboratories here and abroad did not show the agreement that had been hoped for. Yet as Dorsey pointed out, between 1903 and 1910 the silver voltameter, standard resistors, standard cells, and instruments for comparing the standards were much improved.

The work at the Bureau on the silver voltameter and standard cell, in terms of which current and voltage were measured, was to be of special importance in establishing more precise values for the volt. This was true of J. G. Coffin's construction and calculations of absolute standards of inductance, completed in 1906, a consequence of Rosa and Grover's extensive theoretical examination of inductance formulas. The work not only proved valuable for absolute measurement but of considerable service to the electrical industry in determining the inductance of circuit configurations.[6]

Earlier experience in the absolute measurement of current, the results of which were expressed in electromagnetic units, led to Rosa and Dorsey's painstaking experiment in 1907 which demonstrated that the measurement of a current in electromagnetic CGS units was related to its measurement in electrostatic CGS units by exactly the numerical value of the speed of light, accurate to within 0.03 percent.[7] An important confirmation of Maxwell's theory of light, the investigation otherwise had little immediate practical application, except as an immensely prestigious piece of work that paid dividends in recruiting young physicists for the Bureau.

---

[6] S9 and S10 (Rosa and Grover, 1903–5); S29 (Coffin, 1906).

NOTE.—S designates the Scientific Papers of the NBS, issued from 1904–28, as hereafter RP will represent a Research Paper in the Journal of Research of the NBS, 1928 to date, T designates the Technologic Papers of the NBS, 1910–28, and H the NBS series of Handbooks. For further information on these and other Bureau publications, see notes to app. I.

[7] S66 (Rosa and Dorsey, 1907).

Members and assistants of the International Technical Committee of 1910 gather on the lawn at the Bureau upon completion of the work to establish new values for the international ampere, ohm, and volt. From left to right: F. Laporte (France), Sir Frank Smith (England), Dr. Frank A. Wolff, Jr., Dr. W. Jaeger (Germany), M. P. Shoemaker, Dr. Stratton, Dr. Frank Wenner, Dr. A. S. McDaniel, G. E. Post, Dr. Frederick W. Grover, Dr. Rosa, and Dr. George W. Vinal.

Most of the early research in Rosa's division, however, was specifically concerned with electrical standards, and before long the work of the Bureau and that of the national laboratories abroad had sufficiently increased the possible accuracy of the values established for the primary electrical standards to call for a new international agreement. At the International Conference on Electrical Units and Standards held in London in 1908 a resolution was drawn up to adopt a new international ampere, ohm, and volt.

Two years later a technical committee representing the British, French, German, and American national laboratories, with Dr. Rosa as chairman, met at the Bureau in Washington to carry out the resolution of the Conference. In May 1910 the committee completed its work, reaching agreement on new values to be assigned to the ampere and ohm and from these deriving a new value for the international volt. Adoption of these values promised for the first time international uniformity to a high degree of precision in the electrical units. With high satisfaction, Rosa wrote: "There is reason to believe that the values adopted now will be satisfactory for a generation at least without change." [8]

The progress made by the committee had been reported in the Washington newspapers, and Congress was ready for Dr. Stratton when he appeared on Capitol Hill just prior to the announcement of worldwide adoption of the committee's work. In the Bureau budget before the Subcommittee on Appropriations was a request for a new electrical laboratory building, needed to regroup Rosa's division, now scattered all through North, South, and West buildings. Members of the subcommittee immediately challenged the need for the building. To Congress it seemed that the most pressing task of the electrical division of the Bureau was finished.

Dr. Stratton had to reassure Congress that the recent work of the international committee did not mean that electrical measurements were "all done." "The work in connection with these standards," said Stratton, "is going on all the time. Some of them must be continually produced. For instance, the standard of electromotive force must be produced from year to year. The work in connection with the standard [of] current is not nearly completed * * * . We must maintain continuously the standards of resistance, of current, of electromotive force, of inductance and capacity, and the magnetic standards. Every electrical problem goes back to these standards." [9]

Stratton's argument may only have heightened the mystery of electricity to the layman, but Congress was convinced. The electrical laboratory was

---

[8] Rosa in Science, 31, 601 (1910), and Engr. Mag. 39, 263 (1910); NBS C29, "Announcement of a change in the value of the international volt" (1911); correspondence of 1911 in NBS Box 8, IE; Annual Report, National Physical Laboratory, 1912, p. 7.

[9] Hearings * * * 1912 (Dec. 2, 1910), p. 267.

The silver voltameter used to determine a new value for the international ampere. The experiments at Washington in 1910 made it possible to assign mutually consistent values to the standard cells and standard resistors used in the respective national standardizing laboratories, in terms of the resistivity of mercury and the electrochemical equivalent of silver. The units thus established formed the basis for all electrical measurements throughout the world for the next 37 years.

approved and the sum of $175,000 appropriated for its construction. As East building, it completed the quadrangle on the hilltop, and Rosa and his division moved in during the spring of 1913.[10]

Useful and even necessary as the new international values were to electrical science and industry, they were, as Stratton had said, far from permanent. Continued research in instrumentation and procedures resulted in greater refinements of the values and the standard resistances and standard cells slowly began to drift. By 1925, serious discrepancies were evident among the standards maintained in the national laboratories here and abroad. Where measurements had been made with once satisfactory accuracies within a few parts in 100,000, certain of them could now be kept constant within a few parts in a million. There was need for agreement on the new values possible.

---

[10] The building was accepted in June 1913 but not actually completed until several months later, after members of the electrical division themselves installed the wiring. See correspondence in NBS Blue Folder Box 77. That wiring was still functioning satisfactorily when it was replaced with modern fireproof conduits in the 1950's (interview with Dr. F. B. Silsbee, Jan. 29, 1963).

In 1929 the International Committee of Weights and Measures at Sèvres, to which the establishment and conservation of electrical standards had been assigned in 1923, approved a resolution to replace the international system of electrical units by the absolute or CGS system originally proposed for them. The need for conveniently reproducible standards had diminished with the expansion of testing services in the national laboratories. Electrical methods of measurement, of increasing importance to science and engineering, demanded higher and higher degrees of precision that apparently only an absolute system of measurement could satisfy. Also the discovery of isotopes in 1913, with their hitherto unsuspected variation among different samples of silver and mercury reduced the certainty of international units defined by properties of these elements and favored absolute units independent of isotopic variations.

The conference of 1929 agreed that the pursuit of "ideal" measurements must be resumed within the framework of the absolute system, and from the 1930's on this became the direction of fundamental electrical research. The same decade saw a marked acceleration in the work of extending the range of measurement of electrical quantities. Here, earlier pioneer work such as Dr. Herbert B. Brooks' development of the deflection potentiometer for measuring current and voltage in lamp testing came to full fruition. It was the first of many highly specialized potentiometers he subsequently designed.[11]

These lines of research continue to the present day at the Bureau and in the electrical standards laboratories abroad. Bureau research alone in the field of modern electrical measurement has been reported in almost 300 separate publications. The early work of Rosa, Wolff, Grover, Agnew, Wenner, Vinal, and Lloyd was continued in the 1920's and 1930's by Curtis, Brooks, and Silsbee, by Sanford, Snow, Thomas, and Moon, and from 1940 on by Curtis, Snow and others.[12]

In the early years of electrical research at the Bureau, something more than international agreement on standards of measurement, and provision of quantitative standards and instruments for the industry, was at stake. Out of its research, the Bureau also recommended to the industry equally important, if not equally welcome, standards of a quite different nature, those of service and safety.

---

[11] S33 (Brooks, 1906).

[12] Lyman J. Briggs, "Early work of the NBS," Sci. Mo. 73, 167 (1951); F. B. Silsbee, "Establishment and maintenance of the electrical units," NBS C475 (1949); F. B. Silsbee, "Extension and dissemination of the electrical and magnetic units by the NBS," NBS C531 (1952).

STANDARDS FOR PUBLIC UTILITIES

Still developing along the empirical lines evolved in the previous century, the electrical industry in the early century was as much in need of standards of quality, of performance, of safety, and of service as it was of standards of quantity. A contemporary historian's indictment of the gas industry, that owing to its monopoly in many cities it used fraudulent meters, supplied inferior gas, and collected excessive rates from helpless consumers, applied equally well, he said, to the electric lighting industry, street railways, and the telegraph and telephone companies.[13]

The Bureau was more charitable. Talking with utility company representatives, manufacturers, and industrial scientists, Stratton and Rosa found that many of the shortcomings of the industry were "not entirely [the fault] * * * of the manufacturer, but [resulted from] the lack of uniform standards and specifications." [14] So Stratton reported when in 1904 the Bureau threw out three-quarters of a shipment of electric light bulbs submitted for testing by a Government purchasing office. Not long after, the Bureau of Corporations, the new watchdog agency set over trusts in the Department of Commerce (and predecessor of the Federal Trade Commission, organized in 1915), asked the Bureau to investigate the relative illuminating power of a number of kerosene oils on the market. Their quality proved no less dubious than that of some of the gas and electric lamps already determined by the Bureau. Standards of illumination and uniform specifications for the lighting industry were manifestly needed. And because the Bureau's investigation began with the incandescent lamp, photometry or the scientific measurement of light became a function of Rosa's electrical division and remained so for 40 years before it was transferred to the optics division of the Bureau.

Before long the Bureau became involved with much more than gas, oil, and electric lamps. In the wake of Roosevelt's crackdown on the trusts, the public service monopolies came under fire. Many States and cities, goaded by the press, the muckraking periodicals, and reforming citizenry, instituted reforms of their own, first attempting to regulate the utilities by legislation and lawsuit and then setting up public service commissions and other local regulatory agencies. Beginning in 1907, city and interurban street railways, gas and water companies, electric light and power companies, the telegraph and telephone, and even the all-powerful railroads found their rates and services increasingly subject to a measure of regulation.

---

[13] Harry T. Peck, Twenty Years of the Republic: 1885–1905 (New York: Dodd Mead, 1906), p. 315.

[14] Hearings * * * 1906 (Dec. 2, 1904), p. 232.

Very much aware of the weights and measures investigation of the Bureau and its assistance in setting up inspection systems in cities and States, the new public service commissions turned to the Bureau for help. The ensuing research that began with the measurement of lamp light was eventually extended to almost every aspect of public utility service.

One difficulty in establishing a uniform standard of light hinged on the use of the term "candlepower," based by tradition on a natural light source, the light value of an open flame measured by comparison with a sperm oil candle. By reason of the varying sizes and designs of the sperm candles used, the values originally derived from them differed considerably. Thus the "candles" of the electric lamp and illuminating gas industries bore little relation to one another, and even within the same industry the Bureau found the "candle" had little constancy.[15]

As working standards, some gas and electric companies referred to the English parliamentary candle. Most electric lamp manufacturers, however, had turned to the standard of light maintained by the Reichsanstalt, the Hefner amylacetate lamp, for their "candle" value. The flaws that Rosa's group found in the Hefner standard shortly after the establishment of the Bureau led him to propose as a new standard for the electric lamp industry the mean value of a number of 16-candlepower commercial lamps, and to make this applicable to gas light as well as to electric light.[16]

When the value of this new standard "candle" proved to be only slightly greater than the unit maintained by the national laboratories of England and France, the Bureau proposed an adjustment of its own value looking to an international candle. The proposal was accepted, and in 1909 the new value, based on a simple relationship between the British Hefner unit, the French bougie décimale, and the carbon-filament unit maintained in Washington, became the standard for all photometric measurements in this country.[17]

Interestingly enough, a year earlier, in 1908, Waidner and Burgess in the heat division of the Bureau attempted to construct an absolute standard

---

[15] NBS Annual Report 1909, p. 7.

[16] See letter, SWS to Edison Lamp Works of General Electric, Harrison, N.J., Apr. 30, 1904, and attached correspondence (NSB Box 8, IEL).

In July 1904 an instructor at Cornell, Eugene C. Crittenden, was brought to the Bureau to investigate flame standards in photometry. He remained for more than 50 years. Under his guidance the problems of a light standard were finally resolved by the international acceptance of a "new candle" in 1948, based on two accomplishments of the Bureau, the platinum black body standard of Wensel, Roeser, Barbrow, and Caldwell, and the determination of spectral luminosity factors by Gibson and Tyndall. See ch. V, p. 245, and ch. VI, p. 337.

[17] NBS C15, "The international unit of light" (1909; 3d ed., 1911). The Reichsanstalt's Hefner unit was assigned the value of 0.90 international candle.

of light, for use in pyrometrical measurement. For lack of suitable materials at that time, 20 years passed before the work was resumed and an absolute prototype standard was at last experimentally realized. With it the incandescent lamp standard, always difficult to maintain, was reduced to a working standard.

A uniform standard of light was not enough to assure acceptance of the lamps made by the electric industry, and 2 years before adoption of the international candle representatives of the lamp manufacturers in this country met with Government engineers at the Bureau to adopt standard specifications for electric lamps. Although the General Electric Co. had introduced its G.E. metalized (GEM) carbon-filament lamp in 1905, and in 1907 put its first tungsten-filament (Mazda) lamp on the market, the first specifications were based on the Edison carbon-filament lamp, then owned and manufactured by General Electric and its subsidiaries and the most widely used of electric lamps available.

It was agreed that the carbon-filament lamps sold to the Government must initially consume no more than 3.76 watts per mean spherical candle (the Bureau standard) and their "life," before decreasing to 80 percent of their original light value or burning out, must be 300 to 450 hours. Failure of 10 percent of the test lamps in any lot would automatically result in rejection of the entire lot. The details of these specifications were published in NBS Circular 13 (1907) and revised editions of the circular appeared with the adoption of the international candle and as each of the new types of electric lamps came into general use.[18]

Although Bureau testing of incandescent lamps was the entering wedge, it was not by electric light but by old-fashioned gas light that the Bureau prepared its first proposals for the regulation of a public utility. For years the illuminating gas and oil industry had referred to Hefner and pentane lamps for its photometric standards. How unreliable these standards were the Bureau learned in 1906 when some 40 kerosene oils were submitted to it for tests of their composition and illuminating power.[19]

Preliminary studies revealed the necessity of a thorough investigation of gas and oil illuminants, and in 1908 the Bureau requested and received from Congress a special 2-year appropriation to work on this problem, in cooperation with the American Gas Institute. Russell S. McBride, a bright young graduate in chemistry from the University of Wisconsin, was brought into Rosa's electrical division, sent to school for courses in gas engineering, and put in charge of the investigation.[20]

---

[18] The last edition of C13, "Standard specifications for incandescent electric lamps," was the 10th, in 1923, after which the Federal Specifications Board, recently established in the Bureau of the Budget, took over the function of promulgating lamp specifications.

[19] Hearings * * * 1907 (Feb. 23, 1906), p. 653.

[20] See Hearings * * * 1915 (Feb. 26, 1914), p. 910.

Laboratory setup for testing the candlepower of incandescent lamps about 1910. This was the brightness test, using a horizontal bar photometer.

Dr. Brook's deflection potentiometer permitted the measurement of direct current and voltage more precisely than with any former laboratory indicating instrument. The potentiometer has come into wide use in the manufacture and rapid checking of precise indicating instruments with direct reference to a standard cell.

The work that McBride and his group did between 1909 and 1911 resulted in new methods for calibrating pentane lamps in terms of the Bureau candle and laid the basis for establishing standards of gas service, both illuminating and heating. The results were furnished to State and municipal authorities that had requested Bureau assistance in drafting gas service regulations.

The Bureau urged that the quality of gas be determined by its heating value rather than its candlepower, as was then the practice in most cities, and that it be sold on the basis of the British thermal unit (Btu), not by the cubic foot. Gas company engineers argued that the consumer was not concerned with heating value, certainly not in gas lamps; but statistical studies by the Bureau showed that the usefulness of gas to the consumer was almost exactly proportional to its heating value, whether used in heating appliances or in gas-mantle lamps, and successfully refuted the claims of some of the companies that the amount of gas used by consumers was not increased when the heating value was reduced. So long as gas was sold by the cubic foot, the gas companies had little incentive to purify their product, and it permitted them to sell excessive and useless quantities of nitrogen and sulfur compounds in their gas, introduced during the manufacturing process.[21]

The Bureau circular putting standards of gas service into the hands of public service commissions recognized the hostility of the utilities to the regulations it recommended. It reassured the industry that the Bureau "in no way concerned itself with the financial regulation of gas companies * * * [or with their] works management." It carefully stressed that "the attitude of the Bureau is entirely advisory, and its intention is only to place in the hands of the technical and general public an impartial and, as nearly as may be, accurate summary of the facts which must be considered in connection with the inspection and testing of the quality and distribution of * * * gas." The circular also pointed out that the utilities stood in need of public confidence and would therefore gain much from the passage of local laws and ordinances regulating their services.[22] But a decade passed before the in-

---

[21] Elmer R. Weaver, MS, "History of the gas chemistry section, NBS, 1910–1957" (October 1964), pp. 2, 6 (NBS Historical File).

[22] NBS C32 (1912), pp. 5–6. "Drastic" was the word Henry L. Doherty used to describe some of the Bureau's proposed regulations. A self-made gas utilities magnate, whose Cities Service holding company was to take over 53 independent operating companies in 1913 alone, Doherty spoke for the industry when he wrote to the Bureau: "I certainly do not want to see any burdens placed on the gas companies that will be hard for them to meet." Confidential letters, Doherty to NBS, Mar. 9 and Apr. 2, 1912 (NBS Box 7, IGC).

The original and somewhat intimidating title of C32, "State and municipal regulations for the quality, distribution and testing of illuminating gas," was changed to "Standard dustry accepted the findings of the Bureau and agreed to sell gas on the basis of its heating value.

One of the early investigations of the Bureau's gas engineering group led to modifications in the street gas lamps in the District of Columbia that increased street illumination by 50 percent, with no rise in the cost of service.[23] The gas industry was further aided, against its will, by later Bureau investigations of gas appliances, gas stoves, and gas furnaces. The results led to notable increases in gas efficiency and safety, as well as in sales.[24]

Dr. Rosa's division continued its research in gas photometry and gas engineering until the early 1920's when the work was transferred to a section in the chemistry division under Elmer R. Weaver, and gas instruments research became the province of the weights and measures division. By then the electric light had begun to replace gaslight almost everywhere and gas appliances were rapidly making wood and coal stoves obsolete. For lack of a satisfactory Btu meter, gas continued to be measured in cubic feet, as it is to this day, but in more and more States it was gas monitored by State laboratories equipped with chemical and calorimetric test equipment.

Four years passed before the Bureau undertook to establish standards of service for the electrical utilities as it had for gas. Meanwhile, the electrical industry continued to seek Bureau help with its measuring instruments, in particular the ammeters, voltmeters, wattmeters, and watthour meters by which its power production and consumer rates were measured. For almost 40 years, beginning with his arrival at the Bureau in 1903, Dr. Herbert B. Brooks dominated this section of the electrical division, devising a long series of ingenious new instruments for more accurate and rapid measurement of current and voltage. And the Bureau aided in other ways. As electric power consumption rose, not only Federal agencies, but business firms, and the public reacted to what they considered excessively high electric bills and called on the Bureau for meter tests. The meters were not at fault. The tests proved them to be much more reliable than generally supposed, and if neglected they actually tended to favor the consumer.[25] The Bureau was swamped as company meters poured in for calibration.

As long-distance power transmission developed out on the Pacific coast, Dr. Paul G. Agnew began his pioneer studies in the analysis and testing of current transformers for high-voltage power stations. Out of the work came the insulating materials (dielectrics) program of the Bureau, begun

---

regulations for manufactured gas and gas service" in the second edition, 1913, and to "Standards for gas service" in the third edition, 1915. A fourth edition came out in 1920, and in 1934 was superseded by C405.

[23] NBS Annual Report 1911, pp. 8–9.

[24] See ch. V pp. 263–265.

[25] Letter, Rosa to Secretary of Commerce and Labor, Dec. 2, 1910 (NBS Box 9, IEP).

about 1912, and 2 years later the first high-voltage studies.[26] Other investigations in Rosa's enterprising electrical division in that decade included preparation over several years of a complete set of copper wire tables, for the American Institute of Electrical Engineers; preliminary studies in color photometry, a development of the gas flame standards work, later transferred to the optics division; and photometric measurement of locomotive headlights, carried out at the request of several States preparing new regulations for the railroads.[27]

Another kind of railroad problem came to the Bureau when the Interstate Commerce Commission, aroused by mounting complaints, requested that a study be made of railroad, elevator, grain-hopper, and other large-capacity scales used in determining freight charges in interstate shipments. Few States inspected scales, the Bureau found, and many railroads maintained such scanty supervision over their freight scales that some were little more than "guessing machines." As a result, railroad freight scales, upon which more than $2 billion annually in revenues were determined, had long been a source of bitter complaint and litigation. So high had feeling run against the railroads, Dr. Stratton reported, that they were more than willing to cooperate with the Bureau in order to "get right" with the public again.[28]

In 1913, with an appropriation from Congress of $25,000 for the investigation, the Bureau had a special railway scale test car built, hitched it to a series of slow freights headed north, and began testing railroad scales in the States of New Jersey, New York, Connecticut, and Vermont. The results matched the earlier experience with market weights and measures. Allowing a fair tolerance for such scales, between 75 and 80 percent of the track scales tested were candidates for outright rejection, some weighing short by as much as 1,349 pounds with a load of 35,000 pounds and 2,459 pounds with loads of 70,000 pounds. Acquiring another test car, the Bureau extended its investigation of scales into the Midwest and the South.[29]

---

[26] The first high-voltage work began in a room in North building in 1911, when the Bureau acquired 3 voltage transformers, none with a maximum voltage exceeding 2,300 volts. The Bureau's high-tension laboratory, adjoining East building and housing two 100,000-volt transformers, was completed in July 1914. Present-day surge generators at the Bureau deliver 2 million volts. (See correspondence in NBS Blue Folder Box 80, and interviews with Dr. Silsbee.)

[27] NBS Annual Report 1909, pp. 5, 7; Annual Report 1911, p. 8. For the extensive correspondence on the copper wire tables program, 1910–14, see NBS Box 9, IER. Rosa's range of interests is displayed in his article, "The work of the electrical division of the Bureau of Standards," Science, 35, 8 (1912).

[28] Hearings * * * 1914 (Nov. 26, 1912), pp. 305–306.

[29] NBS Annual Report 1912, p. 14, et seq.; Science, 37, 937 (1913); NBS C83, "Specifications for * * * railroad track scales" (1920; revised as C333, 1927). For correspondence on the investigation, 1912–20, see NBS Box 20, IWS.

The first NBS railway scale test car for the standardization of railroad track and master scales.

Its equipment consisted of eight 10,000-pound weights, four 2,500-pound weights, 10,000 pounds of 50-pound weights, and the truck itself, a 5,000-pound weight which carried the test load on the rails.

Together with small auxiliary weights, the total testing equipment made it possible to determine weights between one-ten thousandth pound and 105,000 pounds or over 50 tons.

The crane for handling the weights was powered by an electrical generator driven by a gasoline engine. The equipment, mounted in a standard boxcar, was constructed for the Bureau by the A. H. Emery Co. of Connecticut, which built many of the Bureau's heavy test machines.

As the railroads, as well as manufacturing concerns and State agencies, set up inspection procedures under Bureau direction and large-capacity scales began to register more nearly true (i.e., with a tolerable error of 200 pounds in 100,000 pounds gross weight), the Bureau test cars with their master scales still continued their rounds, adjusting track scales and calibrating the scale cars that were acquired by the railroads. At a standstill during the war, the Bureau cars resumed their travels across the Nation into the 1930's, when the depression curtailed all but a fraction of this work.[30]

Yet another railroad investigation was prompted by a series of alarming statistics that appeared in the Interstate Commerce Commission annual report for 1912. Legislation enacted 2 years previously had for the first time required monthly reports of railroad accidents, and the returns, disclosing deaths and injuries resulting from collisions and derailments alone at the rate of almost 13,000 a year, shocked the Commission into further study. Going back into records for the years 1902 to 1912, the ICC came up with a total of 41,578 derailments caused by broken rails, broken wheels, flanges, and axles. Faulty maintenance, inferior iron and steel, severe service, and excessive wheel loads were suspected. The Secretary of Commerce urged the Bureau to make a thorough study of the cause of railroad accidents and related problems.[31]

Specimens of failed parts, sent to the Bureau by the ICC and the railroads, were subjected to chemical, microscopic, and mechanical tests. In every instance of rail failure, hidden defects or splits, identified as transverse fissures, were found in the interior of the rails. In track inspections made by the Bureau in the field, as many as four or five of these fissures or points of internal stress were found in a single mile of track.[32]

With the cooperation of the big steel companies, the recently organized metallurgical division at the Bureau and the engineering and chemical divisions began an investigation of the constitutents of railroad iron and steel, of heat stress and heat treatment and related problems in the manufacturing process. Here seemed to be the source of failed rails and wheels. The steel industry, behind Europe in this technology, had insuffi-

---

[30] See track scale testing appropriations, NBS Annual Report 1934, p. 76.

In 1917 Bureau scale testing was extended to the scales used in weighing coal at mines (NBS Annual Report 1918, pp. 28–30), and in 1936 to vehicle or truck scales (NBS Annual Report 1937, pp. 61–62). As the programs began, the relative gross errors in the scales on which miners' wages were based and those on which safe operation on the highway depended matched or even exceeded those found earlier in railroad scales.

[31] ICC Annual Report Dec. 16, 1912, pp. 53, 63; letter, Secretary of Commerce Redfield to SWS, July 1, 1913, and attached correspondence, 1913–15 (NBS Box 11, IM).

[32] "Report on the formation of transverse fissures in steel parts * * *" (ICC Report by James E. Howard, NBS engineer physicist, 1923) L/C: TF258.U6.

cient knowledge of rail and wheel characteristics, the Bureau metallurgists reported, and had not established uniform practices in their manufacture.[33]

The Bureau investigation of railway materials, begun with special funds appropriated by Congress in 1912, continued until 1923 when the program was absorbed in the statutory research work of the metallurgical division. Answers were slow in coming, and during the war years railroad accidents hit an alltime peak. But from 1921 to 1930, as better steel through better technology went into rails and rolling stock, the rate of accidents from these causes fell by more than two-thirds.[34]

When the Bureau began its "high iron" investigation, it was already deeply involved in another rail problem, this one concerning city street cars. Of all its public service investigations, few defied the concerted efforts of Bureau physicists, utility company engineers, and municipalities as did the problem of electrolytic corrosion. The trouble began in the year 1887 when Frank J. Sprague laid out the first commercially successful trolley system in this country, 12 miles of track in the streets of Richmond, Va. In the next decade more than 2,000 miles of trolley track were put down in cities and towns and out into their suburbs. By 1917, over 40,000 miles of street and interurban railways spidered the Nation. New York City alone contained almost 700 miles of trolley track, and it was actually possible to ride from Brooklyn, up the length of Manhattan, out through Westchester to Bridgeport, on to New Haven and Providence, all the way to Boston by street car, paying a total of 48 five-cent fares for the trip.[35]

The majority of the trolleys operated on Sprague's overhead wire system, with the electric current flowing into the rails through the car wheels after passing through the car motor. In theory, the current then flowed back to the generating station by way of the tracks and earth, completing the electrical circuit. In fact, much of the current strayed on its return, following paths of least resistance through underground pipes, cables, and metal structures.

The first signs of trouble turned up in Boston in 1902 when, excavating to repair a break, the water mains under Boylston Street were found badly corroded. The moisture and ordinary salts in the earth

---

[33] Hearings * * * 1913 (Feb. 10, 1912), pp. 761–762; Hearings * * * 1915 (Jan. 27, 1914), p. 677.

[34] From an annual average of 13,000 collisions and derailments in the period 1902–12, they rose to 25,000 in 1918 and 1919, to more than 36,000 in 1920, and then began a steady decline. By 1930 the total had dropped to 12,313. See Annual Table No. 61 in ICC Accident Bulletin Nos. 70 (1918), 74 (1919), 78 (1920), 99 (1930). L/C: HE1780.A2.

[35] Robert A. Futterman, The Future of Our Cities (New York: Doubleday, 1961), pp. 52–53.

made soil a fine conductor of electricity, and current straying from the trolley tracks into nearby water pipes and gas mains ate away the metal by electrolytic action as the current flowed out again.

The same condition was found elsewhere in the lead sheathing around telephone and telegraph wires that had been put underground after the series of city conflagrations around the turn of the century. When electrolytic pitting and corrosion was also discovered on underground light and power cables, at the foot of bridge structures, and in the reinforced concrete supports of piers and buildings, the press, the utilities, and construction people raised cries of alarm. Losses were estimated in the millions of dollars as a result of leakage from gas and water mains, the necessity of repairs and replacement, and devaluation of capital investment, to say nothing of the fire hazard traceable to electrolysis and the losses due to interruption of service.

In 1910 Stratton reported to a Senate committee that the problem had become nationwide, and the Bureau was granted a special 3-year appropriation to investigate earth electrolysis and find ways to mitigate its effects. Dr. Rosa's first move was to bring in Burton McCollum and Kirk H. Logan, two talented young electrical engineers then teaching in the Midwest, to head the investigation.

Working with municipal authorities and engineers in St. Louis, Chicago, Philadelphia, in Elyria, Ohio, and Springfield, Mass., McCollum and Logan identified the nature of the problem, developed procedures to enable utility engineers to make their own electrolysis surveys, and as the congressional appropriations came to an end, had devised an insulated feeder system as one way of mitigating electrolytic corrosion. The street railways, confronted with litigation brought by the utilities and hoping for a more economical solution than insulation, pressed the Bureau to continue its research. Aware that the problem was yet far from solution, the Bureau resumed the investigation under its regular funds.

With the organization in 1919 of the American Committee on Electrolysis, representing the principal national associations of utility companies, a research subcommittee was appointed to work with the Bureau. Of considerable importance was the development by the Bureau of an earth-current meter in 1921. In maintenance testing of pipe systems that the utilities established, it accurately measured the currents directly responsible for electrolytic corrosion and hence the rate of corrosion. Although electrolysis seemed impossible to eliminate entirely, almost 20 methods of mitigating it were devised by Bureau and utility engineers.[36]

[36] NBS Annual Reports 1911, et seq.; NBS C401, "Abstracts * * * of NBS publications on stray-current electrolysis" (Shepard, 1933).

One phase of the electrolysis problem, the study of the corrosive action of soil itself on metals, without the agency of stray currents, continued. Urged by the utilities, particularly the gas companies transporting and distributing natural and manufactured gas via pipelines cross country and in the cities, the Bureau set up its Corrosion Laboratory in 1922. After more than two decades of research in corrosive-resistant materials and protective coatings, a new approach through cathodic protection came to seem most promising. Its principle was well known, going back to early 19th-century experiments made by Sir Humphrey Davy. As applied to soil corrosion, it involved the use of replaceable zinc anodes attached to the underground structure to be protected, making the structure cathodic or resistant almost indefinitely to the adjacent soil.[37]

If electrolysis wrought great damage to property but posed little life hazard, almost every other manifestation of electricity, from its generation to its consumption, threatened both. The mining industry that produced the coal for electricity was among the first to electrify many of its operations. But electric sparks often proved disastrous in the mines, and in 1909 the American Mining Congress called on the Bureau for assistance in setting up standards of electrical practice in mines and mining practices.[38]

The Bureau investigation for mines led to other studies of life and property hazards in the generation of electricity, both in its distribution at high voltages and in its industrial and domestic uses. These in turn prompted studies of lightning hazards, particularly as they affected the power industry.[39] In 1914, assembling the data amassed, the Bureau published a comprehensive set of safety rules for the electrical industry. A year later it prepared the first nationwide electrical safety code.[40]

Like the standards proposed for the gas industry earlier, the electrical safety code met strong resistance for a number of years. The very formulation of a safety code, protested the industry, gave undue publicity to the hazards of electricity. Its recommendations, and above all its origin in a Federal

[37] NBS C450, "Underground corrosion" (Logan, 1945), superseded by NBS C579 (1957); RP1876 (Dension and Romanoff, 1948).

[38] NBS C23, "Standardization of electrical practice in mines" (1910). Although the Bureau of Mines for a time protested the NBS investigation, it later acknowledged that its own interest was in "improving mining practices," not standardizing them. Letter, SWS to Director, Bureau of Mines, Oct. 14, 1914, and attached correspondence (NBS Box 9, IES). With the NBS circular as guide, the Bureau of Mines assumed responsibility for electrical safety in mining operations. Letter, SWS to Congressman William B. McKinley, May 28, 1920 (NBS Box 10, IG).

[39] T56, "Protection of life and property against lightning" (Peters, 1915), superseded by M95 (1929) and H13 (1929); M92, "Code for protection against lightning" (1929), superseded by H12 (1929), H17 (1934), H21 (1937), H40 (1945).

[40] NBS C49, "Safety rules * * * in the operation and maintenance of electrical equipment and lines" (1914); NBS C54, "Proposed national electrical safety code" (1915).

agency, seemed an infringement of management and a threat to the independence of the industry.[41] Not a few city and State commissions, persuaded by the industry that the Bureau was setting intolerable standards, took up the proposed code only to let it languish.

The Bureau, with no authority but the congressional appropriation for the work, found it necessary to issue a special circular explaining the code and its scope, "to give [it] more publicity * * * and gain wider acceptance of it." Driving home its point, the circular included accounts of 100 typical electrical accidents, most of them fatal, taken from the newspapers of 1913, as representative of what was happening daily throughout the United States. Yet up to 1920 less than half the States had adopted the code or any part of it.[42]

But the years of unregulated operation of public utilities were running out. The State of Wisconsin had set up the first public service commission in 1907. Less than a decade later some 30 States and twice as many cities had established similar commissions or enacted regulating ordinances. Confronted with often hastily drawn and confusing rules and regulations by State and city authorities, the utilities in time came to welcome the Bureau's efforts to apply scientific and uniform principles to their services.

In 1913 Dr. Rosa reported that the Bureau, in cooperation with the Interstate Commerce Commission or with State commissions, was engaged in almost a score of investigations involving engineering problems and standards relating to the natural monopolies. All in one way or another looked to the resolution of "the mutual distrust and mutual misunderstand-

---

[41] The utilities misunderstood Bureau recommendations and for years complained that by its appropriations Congress was "extending the field of regulation and control by the Bureau of Standards over the public utilities of the country." Letter, Acting Secretary of Commerce to Congressman Carl Hayden, May 26, 1919, and other correspondence in NBS Box 2, AG.

[42] NBS C72, "Scope and application of the national electrical safety code" (1918). Letter, Rosa to Prof. A. C. Lanier, University of Missouri, Feb. 26, 1918 (NBS Box 9, IES), recounted Bureau efforts to promulgate the code.

NBS C72 (3d ed., 1920), also issued as a handbook, H3, said the code had been approved by the American Engineering Standards Committee and adopted by administrative authorities in nearly half the States. The revised fourth edition in 1926 (issued as H4 in 1928) said this revision "more nearly meets the views of the various interests involved, some of which are to a certain extent conflicting."

For many years the able assistant of Dr. Lloyd in negotiations on the electrical safety code was Dr. J. Franklin Meyer, who represented the Bureau on the AESC electrical committee. Much of the success in establishing a national code was through his efforts, and the series of handbooks on safety rules in the operation of electrical stations and electrical equipment that appeared between 1920 and 1944 were the joint work of Lloyd and Meyer.

ing existing between the leaders of the financial and industrial world, on the one hand, and the great body of the American people, on the other." [43]

Dr. Stratton, however, did not feel that these scattered investigations by the Bureau in a few of the public utilities were enough. Standards of service and safety applied to all the utilities, he told Redfield, the new Secretary of Commerce, and could best be provided by making the Bureau the central "place of reference and * * * clearing house for scientific and technical matters pertaining to the public utilities." [44]

The Secretary agreed, and with his support Stratton proposed to Congress a large-scale study covering the public interest in all utilities, including gas, water, light and power, telephone, and street railways. It would include "the study of public relations questions, the preparation of specifications regarding the quality of service, methods of testing and inspection employed by municipalities and commissions, safety rules for use by the utility companies to safeguard their employees and the public, and the collection and distribution of information by published papers and through correspondence." [45]

With little debate, Congress in 1914 appropriated a special fund of $25,000 for the investigation of public utility standards. (By 1920 the annual appropriation exceeded $100,000 and continued at that level into the 1930's.) To allay the misapprehensions and continuing hostility of the utilities, the Bureau in articles, talks, and through friendly editors assured industry that its work was "not inquisitorial * * * but is thoroughly scientific, being handled by impartial engineers concerned only in the study of economic problems." [46]

With its congressional appropriation and, by inference, the directive to proceed, the Bureau began the preparation of a circular (4 years after that for the gas industry) on uniform standards for electric service. Thirty-three States and the District of Columbia, in many cases with the help of the Bureau, had already enacted laws regulating electrical service to some degree or another; evidence, said the Bureau circular, that "it is now generally recognized that the supply of electrical service is a natural monopoly and should be regulated." The standards proposed, the circular

---

[43] Senator Root, quoted in Rosa's article, "The function of research in the regulation of natural monopolies," Science, 37, 579 (1913).

[44] See letter, SWS to Director, Department of Public Works, Philadelphia, Dec. 9, 1913 (NBS Box 4, AGC).

[45] NBS Annual Report 1915, p. 60; SWS letter of Mar. 10, 1914, inserted in Hearings * * * 1915 (Jan. 27, 1914), pp. 977–980.

[46] Herbert T. Wade, "The NBS and standards for public utilities," Eng. Mag. 49, 240 (1915). Wade was science and technology editor for the New International Encyclopedia and author of many books and articles on weights and measures, the metric system, electricity, and popular science.

explained, were principally to unify existing laws and regulations, to ensure the adequacy and safety of electrical service, and to establish procedures for inspection laboratories set up by the State commissions.[47]

Still educating the public and the utilities, another circular issued in 1917 described the scope of Bureau investigations on behalf of the utilities, its gas and electric work, gas analysis studies, the progress made in gaining acceptance of the national electrical safety code, its work on electrolysis, and its railroad investigations. All these were to continue and be extended as new problems arose, while in the planning stage were a gas safety code and circulars on street lighting and on telephone service and apparatus.[48]

The Bureau was well on the way to becoming the clearinghouse Dr. Stratton intended, its investigations springing from the need of the utilities to avoid long-drawn out or expensive litigation, or unfair and inconsistent regulation by local authority. As a spokesman for the Bureau said, it assembled facts in field and laboratory studies and reduced them to standard practices, "which may be adopted or not as those concerned may elect, and the published record of which will be available to all." [49] Held temporarily in check by the war, by 1920 special appropriations to the Bureau for public utility standards were exceeded only by those for industrial research, the testing of structural materials, and the testing of Government materials.

TESTING GOVERNMENT MATERIALS

While electrical, optical, pyrometrical and other fundamental measurement work at the Bureau grew steadily in the years prior to the war, structural and miscellaneous materials research and testing and calibration soared. In the period 1911–17 the volume of testing work at the Bureau almost tripled, with engineering, structural and miscellaneous materials tests alone rising from 38 percent to 84 percent of the total.[50] The establishment of a General Supply Committee in the Treasury Department in 1910, encouraging purchase by specification and standardization of miscellaneous supplies bought for the

---

[47] NBS C56, "Standards for electric service" (1916, 2d ed., 1923).

[48] NBS C68, "Public utility service standards of quality and safety" (1917). Of the circulars projected, only that on standards of telephone service later appeared in a new publication, as NBS C112 (1921).

[49] Wade, "The NBS and standards for public utilities."

[50] In the fiscal year 1910–11, approximately 62 percent of the 80,100 tests and calibrations carried out in the Bureau laboratories were in weights and measures, temperature, optics, photometry, and chemistry, the remaining 38 percent in engineering, structural, and miscellaneous materials. By 1916, less than 16 percent of the year's total of 217,400 tests and calibrations were in basic measurements; all else comprised physical and mechanical tests of materials. In 1917, as the Bureau shifted to wartime research, the number declined to 155,800, still almost 80 percent in materials. See NBS Annual Reports 1911–17.

Government, sharply increased Bureau testing. The transfer to the Bureau of the Geological Survey materials program occurred less than a month later. The two events coincided with a Government building boom just getting under way, and Dr. Stratton with his enormous interest in the artifacts of commerce saw for the Bureau an opportunity for research in the widest sense, in the instruments, materials, and products of American industry.

The principal structural materials that the Bureau began testing were cement, clays, lime, structural iron and steel, and protective coatings. Miscellaneous materials included Government housekeeping items ranging from rubberbands and rubber belting to paper, ink, paints, textiles, and cordage. Initially limited to the determination of their physical, chemical, and mechanical properties, the tests soon raised problems of their manufacture and performance, requiring full scale investigations. What began as simple testing solely for the information of Government agencies in many instances became programs of product research, necessitating close cooperation with the industries and trade associations involved.

While not entirely representative of the development in each of the materials investigated, a brief account of the Bureau's work on cement is illustrative.

In 1911 the cement laboratories of the Bureau tested over 23,900 samples, representing almost 2½ million barrels of cement purchased for Government construction projects. The sampling required 521,000 physical tests, for fineness, specific gravity, tensile strength, and time of setting. These tests did little more than determine whether the samples met current Government specifications. In many instances the specifications were far from clear or consistent, and nowhere did the Bureau find any two Government agencies purchasing cement upon the same specifications.

Early in 1912 the Bureau called manufacturers and Federal engineers to the first Portland Cement Conference, in order to consider preparation of a single standard specification. As a result, a Presidental Executive order was issued on April 30, 1912, declaring that all portland cement purchased by the Government was to conform to the specification agreed upon. Four years passed before final concurrence was reached and an acceptable specification was adopted by the principals, the American Society for Testing Materials and the American Society of Civil Engineers.[51]

Even the most elementary of physical and chemical tests of cement disclosed the inadequacy or imprecision of many procedures and instruments in common use in the industry, and the test sections and the engineering group at the Bureau set to work developing better test methods and

---

[51] NBS C33, "U.S. Government specifications for portland cement" (1912); letter, Secretary of Commerce to Engineer Commissioner, Washington, D.C., Dec. 26, 1916 (NBS Box 15, IRC).

equipment. Under Stratton, the lines of research at the Bureau were far from rigid, and he worked hard to keep them from becoming so. Afternoons he toured the laboratories inquiring about the work in each, beginning his tour the next day where he had left off the previous afternoon. In this way he carried ideas and problems from one division to another. Thus it was that Dr. Wilmer Souder, in the weights and measures division, hearing of the extreme difficulty with cement sieve measurements, became interested and devised new 100- and 200-line ruled scales for testing and certifying the sieves used by the cement industry.[52]

Improved test procedures and instruments disclosed the need for better understanding of the constitution and characteristics of cement materials, and as testing became routine, the Bureau extended its investigations. A petrographic laboratory set up at Pittsburgh studied the raw materials of cement, and an experimental cement plant with grinding apparatus and rotary kilns made it possible to determine changes in cement properties by various methods of manufacture. Next, Bureau staff members developed a granulometric analyzer and separator, to study fine grinding of cement. Before long the test principles and equipment developed for cement were being applied to other building materials, to sands and silica cements, concretes and concrete aggregates, mortars and plasters, stucco, marls, stones, and paving blocks.

Meanwhile, engineers at the Bureau subjected blocks of concrete and full-scale concrete columns to compression and tensile strength tests. The group at Atlantic City, investigating the action of sea water on cements, mortars, and concretes, established a second exposure station at Charleston, S.C. At Pittsburgh and Washington studies were made of the effect of alkali salts on cement, of temperature on its hardening, of the permeability of cement to water, and its resistance to heat, moisture, and pressure. The steady stream of reports announcing the results of these investigations brought inquiries from architects, engineers, contractors, and builders for still other tests and investigations that they were not equipped to make, and from the general public, for help with cement problems in and around the home.

Much the same pattern of development, from simple testing of Government purchases to devising test procedures, new instrumentation, and finally to the establishment of a full-fledged technological research program in the product, occurred in other materials used in large quantities by Government agencies—in clays and clay products including brick, building tile, porcelain, terra cotta, fire clay, glass, and white-ware china; in lime, lime mortar, and gypsum; protective coatings such as asphalt, felt, paints, oils,

---

[52] NBS C39, "Specifications for and measurement of standard sieves" (1912); correspondence in NBS Box 19, IWL; interview with Dr. Souder, Jan. 16, 1961.

and varnishes; lubricating oils; rubber and rubber materials, papers of all kinds, textiles and fibers, rope and cordage, and leather and leather goods.[53]

Gradually a procedure evolved to bring the Bureau's testing program into closer association with the industries making these materials. At an early stage in each investigation, manufacturers' representatives, laboratory personnel, and industrial engineers were invited to the Bureau to discuss their problems. To assure as wide cooperation as possible, the Bureau held conferences with industrial associations, technical societies, and educational institutions concerned with the materials investigated by the Bureau. And research that started with establishment of a specification before long enabled the Bureau to suggest better materials or methods in the manufacture of the product, improved quality control, new uses for the product, and even utilization of waste materials.

The Government testing program that began with a batch of incandescent lamps in 1904 achieved its main outlines by World War I. Almost three-quarters of the work of the chemical division was in materials testing and research. Dr. Stratton, in addition to heading the optical group, had taken over the new engineering research division, to supervise personally the construction of special test apparatus and to study and test instruments, devices, or machinery of interest to the Bureau but outside the province of its scientific divisions.[54] And out of the testing of structural iron and steel came another new division, for research in metallurgy, under Dr. George K. Burgess.

In charge of high temperature investigations since 1903, Dr. Burgess had done notable work in optical pyrometry, high temperature platinum resistance thermometry, determination of melting points of pure metals, and with Dr. Waidner, chief of the heat division, had proposed a theoretical absolute standard of brightness that was destined to be realized experimentally two decades later. Meanwhile, the testing of engineering instruments, metals, and metal materials—from alloy wire and flexible copper hose to car couplers, boilers, and girders—to see that they met Government specifications, had led the Bureau into the chemistry of metals, into studies of their electrical, magnetic, and mechanical properties, and into the field of stress measurement. Frequently consulted on these tests, Burgess became especially interested in the properties of metals at high temperatures and in the working of metals in foundry processes. Despite the fact that iron and steel was the industrial giant of America and its metallurgical processes were carried out with great technological virtuosity, Burgess found a distressing lack of application of scientific principles.[55]

---

[53] See NBS C45, "The testing of materials" (1913).

[54] NBS Annual Report 1914, p. 15

[55] Burgess, "Metallography and metallurgy at the Bureau of Standards," Met. & Chem. Eng. 10, 1 (1912).

In 1911, at the suggestion of Henry M. Howe, professor of metallurgy at Columbia University and a recently appointed member of the Visiting Committee to the Bureau, Burgess undertook the determination of the critical points on their heating and cooling curves of a number of special steels. As the investigation continued, Burgess won Dr. Stratton to his proposed plan for a long-range investigation of basic physical metallurgy. In 1913, as the investigation of rail and wheel failures for the Nation's railroads began, his metallurgy section in the heat division was raised to divisional status.[56]

An allied field even more empirically operated at that time than metallurgy was that of electrodeposition, the deposition by electrolysis of metallic coatings on a variety of materials. As electrotyping, it was widely used to produce facsimile plates of metal type from a wax impression. Electroforming was employed in the phonograph industry to make master plates and molds to produce recording discs. Electroplating coated metals to improve their appearance and protect them against corrosion.

In 1913 the Government Printing Office asked the Bureau for help with their electrotyping baths. A young man in the chemistry division, Dr. William Blum, who had been preparing standard samples since his arrival at the Bureau in 1909, was sent to see what he could do. The GPO, he found, had no method for controlling the composition of the bath, and there was little or nothing in print on the subject. His calculations for restoring the sulfuric acid content of the solution as it was used up in the plating process solved the difficulty, and Blum's career in electrodeposition began.[57]

Blum's work on the structure of electrodeposits, on current distribution and throwing power in solutions, on pH control of the baths, and on alloy deposition was among the first scientific studies in this country to supplant the hit-or-miss information upon which the industry rested. His introduction in 1921 of electrolytic reproduction of plates used in printing currency at the Bureau of Engraving and Printing replaced the hand method of rolling into case-hardened soft steel, which was capable of approximately 70,000 impressions at best, while electrolytic plates with a chromium surface that could be recoated permitted as many as a million impressions. He directed electrodeposition research at the Bureau for over 30 years.

Not all Bureau work with metals was to be as rewarding as that in Burgess's division or in Blum's section. One such instance was the ingenious instrument developed during the early work on metals, a new type of permeameter, devised in 1909 by Dr. Charles W. Burrows of the magnetic

---

[56] Bureau Announcement No. 28, July 1, 1913 (NBS Box 3, AG).

[57] NBS C52, "Regulation of electrotyping solutions" (1915, 2d ed., 1916); Hearings * * * 1918 (Dec. 1, 1916), p. 483; interview with Dr. Blum, Oct. 15, 1963

section, from an idea supplied by Rosa. For several years Burrows' permeameter became the standard instrument for determining the magetic properties of irons and steels, and was used in the preparation of magnetic standard bars which the Bureau sold as standard samples to manufacturers of electrical equipment.[58]

Elated by early results with the permeameter, Burrows became convinced that a close correlation existed between the magnetic and mechanical properties of materials and went on to develop magnetic test equipment which he was certain had great promise. The iron and steel industry had long sought a simple and effective means for detecting flaws produced in metal during the manufacturing process, as in rifle barrels and prison bars, in steel beams and track rails, to avoid the slow and costly destruction tests otherwise necessary.

During the Bureau investigation of railroad materials involved in derailments and wrecks, Burrows and his group worked to develop a magnetic method for quick determination of such flaws as the mysterious transverse fissures found in steel rails. So promising did the first tests appear that the Bureau reported the method might "possibly become commercially feasible." [59] In 1918, with special apparatus he constructed incorporating his permeameter, Burrows left the Bureau to set up a magnetic analysis firm to do this kind of testing.

Subsequently, other workers at the Bureau found that magnetic and mechanical properties in metals showed little true correlation, and as a result the Bureau abandoned its magnetic standard sample work. For almost a decade the Bureau continued its efforts to develop magnetic tests for proving metals. Except in the case of soft steel and small metal objects the tests in most instances were inconclusive. So, to his disappointment, were Burrows' private efforts, and his firm folded with his death in 1925. Continuing research at the Bureau indicated that with the permeameter it was "not possible to realize any units of magnetic quantity in concrete form," and that it was "only by the greatest care in the selection of test specimens and manipulation of testing apparatus that an accuracy of 1 percent can be attained." [60]

Although this early work on the magnetic properties of metals—a phase of Bureau research in the physical constants—led to largely negative results, some of the most successful work on the determination of physical constants was soon after to be done in the temperature laboratories of the

---

[58] NBS C17, "Magnetic testing" (1909).

[59] NBS Annual Report 1915, p. 50; Annual Report 1917, pp. 52–54; Hearings * * * 1920 (Dec. 12, 1918), p. 955.

[60] NBS C17 (4th ed., 1926), p.. 22, and repeated in its sucessors, C415 (1937), and C456 (1946).

Bureau, particularly that on the temperature scale and on refrigeration constants.

In 1909 the American Society of Refrigerating Engineers, in search of physical data for more efficient refrigeration, asked the Bureau to determine the specific heats of several calcium chloride brines. Upon completion of the work several years passed while the heat division which had made the study went on with investigations in the constants of gases for the use of gas engineers, in heats of combustion, its preparation of standard combustion samples, and its experiments preliminary to establishing new fixed points on the standard temperature scale maintained by the Bureau.

Then in 1913, at the request of the refrigeration industry, Congress appropriated the sum of $15,000 for an investigation of the physical constants involved in the construction and operation of large-scale refrigeration machinery, such as that used in meat-packing and other cold storage plants and in refrigerated cars. Under Dr. Hobart C. Dickinson, D. R. Harper 3d, and N. S. Osborne, studies were made of such fundamental constants as the specific heat of ice, the specific and latent heats of the liquids and vapors used in refrigeration, and their density and pressure-temperature relations. Engineering aspects of the investigation included the study of insulating and other materials used in the construction of large-scale refrigeration structures. It was, Stratton reported to Congress, "a splendid piece of work" and a distinct contribution in the field of physical constants.[61] By 1918, when most of the original staff was diverted to military research, the basic investigation had been completed and the accumulated data were reported to the industry. The chemistry division took over certain portions of the work as a long-term project.

A year after the study of refrigeration constants began, Congress authorized an appropriation for another special investigation, a study of fire-resistant properties of building materials. Fires were claiming thousands of lives annually in this country, with property losses exceeding $250 million—10 times the rate of any country in Europe. Particularly baffling to many, in the series of disastrous fires that struck American cities around the turn of the century, was the fact that skyscrapers and lesser structures purported to be fireproof often burned out as completely as the older buildings. It was an investigation long overdue.

Upon surveying city building regulations, Bureau engineers found them "full of the most absurd data regulating the properties of materials." [62]

---

[61] Hearings * * * 1919 (Jan. 25, 1918), p. 979; letter, SWS to Secretary of Commerce, May 31, 1922 (NBS Box 17, ITH).

[62] [Senate] Hearings * * * 1913 (May 22, 1912), p. 236. Stratton also noted that "The greatest [fire] losses are in the cities having fire laws and regulations" (Hearings * * * 1913, Feb. 10, 1912, p. 759).

In many of the codes it was assumed that brick, mortar, plaster, cement, and metals were uniformly fire resistant. No distinction was made between the various kinds and compositions of bricks, cements, metals, and other materials. Rules for their use had been set up without any real knowledge of their melting points or their behavior at high temperatures, without any real knowledge of the stress and support limits of common building materials under attack by fire.

In a joint undertaking with the National Fire Protection Association and the Underwriters' Laboratories, the Bureau aimed at a thorough study of the behavior and safety of building materials in various types of construction under all possible fire conditions. The study would furnish architects, builders, State and city building bureaus, and insurance interests with fundamental engineering data long needed but nowhere available. In nominal charge of the program was Simon H. Ingberg, born in Norway and trained in structural engineering in this country, who was with a midwestern construction company when the Bureau brought him to Washington to plan the investigation. Less than a year later a fire-resistance section was established in the heat division, with Ingberg in charge.

But so broad became the scope of the investigation that it soon involved almost every one of the scientific and engineering laboratories of the Bureau. It included high-temperature measurements, fire tests, and thermal conductivity studies by the heat division; solution of composition and construction problems by the chemistry and structural materials divisions; electrical wiring and safety code studies by the electrical division; and the behavior of structural materials under heat as a special study in the weights and measures division.[63]

Besides data furnished city and State authorities on the fire-resistant and heat-insulating properties of common building materials and those used in fire-resistive construction, on fire tests of building columns, wood and metal frame partitions and walls, the Bureau evolved a standard time-temperature curve which specified the furnace temperatures to which the elements of a structure became subject in any period of time up to 8 hours. Building materials and construction design were classified by their hours of ultimate fire resistance, making it possible to set up regulations that would insure building into any structure a reasonable degree of fire resistance.[64]

As the program developed, panel-testing furnaces were constructed and partial buildings, steel and concrete columns and numerous other structures were erected and destroyed in endless controlled tests. For years Bureau members in the project made hurried trips out of Washington to probe

---

[63] NBS Annual Report 1914, pp. 29–30.

[64] See BH14, "Recommended minimum requirements for fire resistance in buildings" (J. S. Taylor, 1931), summarizing more than a decade of research.

Fire-severity tests of buildings, deliberately made on abandoned structures in downtown Washington the 1920's. In the picture at left, the walls of a non-fire-resistive building began to bulge after 40 minutes. In the picture at right, a five-story and adjacent two-story structure, near the old Post Office Buildings, that were soon to be razed were loaded with typical office furniture, along with 30 types of office safes. Besides determining the progressive temperatures of the fire, observations were made on the destruction of the buildings and the effects of the fire on the structure and contents of the safes. The fire threatened to get out of control and local fire officials never again permitted such Bureau tests in a congested area.

in the debris of large city fires for additional data for their studies. Research and technological papers, handbooks and circulars recorded the results of the long-term investigation, and were reduced to rules and specifications in new and revised building and fire codes issued by city and State authorities and by fire insurance associations. Fire research continues in the building research division of the Bureau to the present day.

Bureau records suggest that in its second decade, despite more than a score of other research projects going on, three investigations were paramount, certainly in the eyes of the public, and of great interest to their Congressman at budget time. These were the weights and measures, public utility standards, and structural and miscellaneous materials programs. And it was the results of these investigations that were levied on for a remarkable series of circulars that came out just before the war, designed not for Federal or State agencies or for industry, but for the ordinary citizen, the ultimate consumer.

STANDARDS FOR THE CONSUMER

The publication of lamp specifications in Circular 13 in 1907—the first of its kind—raised a problem that long plagued the Bureau. The circular, available to the public for 10 cents, was a technical report, as were later circulars on textiles, inks, soaps, paper, paint, varnish, and other materials. It was filled with complex data and it made no mention of brand names. How then was the ordinary consumer to identify the lamps or other products tested by the Bureau without the laboratory apparatus described in the circular?

In England, the National Physical Laboratory, governed by the Royal Society, was largely supported by private funds, with only meager assistance from the British Government. It was therefore relatively independent, and free if it chose to make open recommendations of products it tested. The National Bureau of Standards, on the other hand, was an agency of the Federal Government. It had come into being at a time when business and industrial interests were synonymous with the national interest. Without power to enforce adoption of standards or specifications, the Bureau could only offer its technical findings to Government purchasing agencies and by making them public suggest that their adoption was in the best interests of industry.

Dr. Stratton insisted from the start that the Bureau must be free to make test results public, but in doing so the Bureau must show no bias. All products and materials tested had therefore to remain anonymous. Yet in hearings before Congress, Stratton made much of the fact that the test and

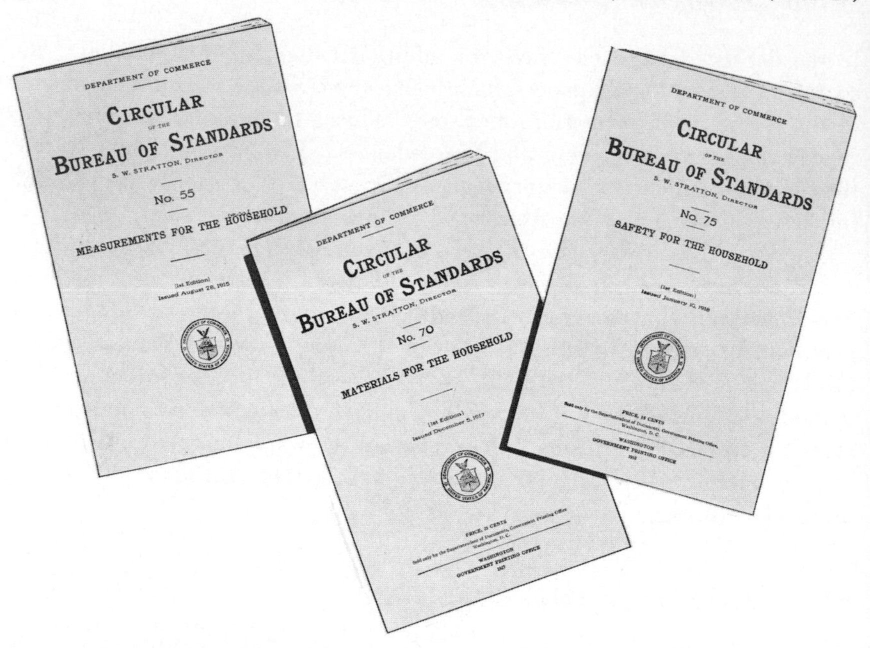

So great was the success of the first of the NBS "household" circulars with the American public that Secretary of Commerce Redfield wrote to Stratton: "I think the time is peculiarly fit now for the immediate publication of the book 'Materials in the Household.' I hope nothing will be allowed to delay it longer and that you may be able to tell me that it will appear within a very short time. It seems to me that it is wanted at this time more than ever before and at least as much as it will be wanted in the future." Letter, Aug. 22, 1917, NARG 40, Box 118, 67009/5.

research work of the Bureau for the Government was of equal service and value to the public. Through publication of the specifications of a Bureau standard, he said, "the public can see what should be allowed * * * and what should not." [65]

That the "public" he referred to was industry rather than the ordinary householder, and in some cases only the industry for whom the specifications were established, was evident from the nature of the Bureau reports. The circular on incandescent lamps, for example, specifically stated that "only those thoroughly instructed in the art of lamp manufacture and in the science of photometry should undertake to determine upon the acceptability of lamps under the terms of the specification." While of considerable use to organizations with laboratories possessing the apparatus and skills for

[65] Hearings * * * 1912 (Dec. 2, 1910), p. 261; Hearings * * * 1917 (Feb. 2, 1916), p. 974; Hearings * * * 1917 (Dec. 1, 1916), p 478.

making the same tests, the data of the circulars were of little use to the general public. [66]

Long concerned with this apparent impasse, the Bureau found a way around through a series of circulars specifically written for the general consumer. The first, Circular 55, on "Measurements for the household," appeared in 1915. The 149-page guide, based on data gathered during the weights and measures investigation, during the electric lamp and gas and electric service and appliance studies of the Bureau, was widely publicized in Edward Bok's Ladies' Home Journal and other publications and became the first best-seller among Bureau publications.[67]

Up to that time 200 to 300 copies of a Bureau publication was customary and few had exceeded 5,000 copies. Within 3 months 10,000 copies of Circular 55, at 45 cents each, were distributed, the Government Printing Office had in press a second, cheap paper edition of 8,000 copies, to sell at 15 cents, and the Bureau requested a third printing of another 10,000. With a further printing of 5,000 copies early in 1917, a total of 33,000 copies of Circular 55 were sold.[68]

It was the first work of its kind issued by a national laboratory, or indeed by any scientific agency, and it caused an immense stir. One British publication called it "a treatise on domestic science," the first to demonstrate "the place of science in practical affairs." [69] In simple language the circular described the operation of common household measuring appliances: scales and balances, gas, water, and electric meters, the thermometer, barometer, hydrometer, hygrometer, cooking measures, and household clocks.[70] The

---

[66] In testing for the Government, Stratton told Congress on another occasion, "we are compelled to establish standards of quality, methods of testing and proper specifications * * * which are given freely to the public and to industries, and that is worth tenfold what we save the Government in the purchase of materials" (Hearings * * * 1913, Feb. 10, 1912, p. 755). The ambiguity in the words "public" and "industries" are resolved if Stratton meant that as industry improved the products it sold to the Government, the public also received a better product.

[67] The most common household weights and measures in C55 were also reprinted on a "kitchen card" and issued as M39 in 1919. Requests for the card reached the half million mark within a year, but Bureau funds restricted the supply to a tenth of that number (NBS Annual Report 1920, p. 51). New editions of the card in 1920 and 1926 included a meter-inch conversion rule and a table of heights and weights of children.

[68] Memo, Director of Publications, Department of Commerce, for Secretary of Commerce, Feb. 16, 1916 (NARG 40, Office of the Secretary of Commere, File 67009/48); Director of Publications, Annual Reports, 1916–17.

[69] Editorial, "The American state and household science," Nature, Feb. 17, 1916. See also Herbert T. Wade, "Efficiency in the household," Sci. Am. 113, 448 (1915).

[70] C55 seems to have assumed that every household had a hydrometer and hygrometer, or ought to have, but it is not likely that even the hydrometer became a kitchen staple until the rise of home brewing during Prohibition.

succeeding chapters explained how to use these in household operations and in planning and buying for the house.

Although no firm names, no trademarks or brand names appeared in the circular, in many instances the Bureau left little doubt of the product involved. A notable example appeared in the section on causes of high bills for electricity wherein the Bureau questioned the quality of some of the electrical lamps then on the market. There was reason to raise the question.

It had come as no surprise to the Bureau when in 1911 General Electric and 33 other companies manufacturing and marketing lamps under GE patents were accused in a Federal antitrust suit of price fixing. The Federal courts ordered General Electric's National Electric Lamp Association (NELA) dissolved, but were less successful in restraining General Electric from "bringing pressure to bear in order to market types of lamps lacking any legitimate demand." This referred particularly to the GE-metalized (GEM) lamp which General Electric, supplying both the lamp and, indirectly, its electric power, continued to manufacture profitably by the millions.[71] The Bureau circular on lamp specifications had drawn attention to the inferiority of this old-fashioned carbon-filament lamp over tungsten, especially after Coolidge's development of ductile tungsten in 1911 and Langmuir's use of a gas-filled bulb in 1913 resulted in lamps with 14 times the efficiency and 13 times the light per watt of the early carbon lamps.

Though the name "GEM" did not appear in "Measurements for the household," what this particular lamp meant to the consumer was clearly spelled out: "The tungsten lamp has been improved in quality and reduced in price to such an extent that no customer can afford to use carbon lamps, even if he were paid a bonus on each lamp for so doing. Many householders cling to the use of carbon lamps because they are usually supplied free." [72] It was true. Anyone could get GEM lamps for nothing, and for a good reason: the GEM lamp used almost three times as much electric current as the tungsten Mazda lamp for equal light values.

As Rosa explained, when tungsten lamps were first introduced, the electric power companies, fearing loss of revenue, began the practice of giving away or exchanging burned out GEM carbon lamps and even tungsten lamps of 100 watts or more in order to maintain high power consumption. The public gladly accepted them. Neither Federal frowns nor Bureau exposure of these lamps won the public away from them or reduced their high rate of manufacture. As late as 1917, Secretary of Commerce Redfield told Dr.

---

[71] John W. Hammond, Men and Volts: The Story of General Electric (New York: Lippincott, 1941), pp. 335–336, 342, 388–389.

[72] NBS C55, p. 84. The warning was repeated in NBS C56, "Standards for electric service" (1916), p. 157.

Stratton that when he moved into his new home he had to replace 74 GEM lamps with Mazdas.[73]

The second Bureau publication designed "to make scientific results available for those with little or no technical training" was Circular 70, a heavy 259-page manual on "Materials for the household," of which 15,000 copies were sold in 1917, the year it came out. It was an excellent summary in simple terms of Bureau testing results in engineering, structural, and miscellaneous materials, with chapters on structural materials in the home, flexible materials (rubber, leather, etc.), stationery, cleansing agents and preservatives, fuels, illuminants, and lubricants, and a final chapter on "Quantity in purchase and use of materials."

In style and contents Circular 70 anticipated by many years the appearance of such publications as Consumer Reports and Consumer Bulletin, and had as in its declared purposes to stimulate intelligent interest in household materials, to explain the nature of their desirable properties, aid in their selection, and promote their effective use and preservation. The circular admitted that few standards of quality existed in the market as yet, and where possible it offered simple home tests of materials, such as the use of a spring balance to test the strength of thread. If home tests were not possible, the Bureau could only recommend that householders "buy of local reliable dealers, as learned from common repute or experience." Sounding very like the voice of Stratton himself, the circular noted that buying well-known brands "may not be an economy, but it is some safeguard as to stability of quality. There is no certainty, however, that the quality will improve with the art." [74]

Neither the circular on "measurements" nor that on "materials" seems to have been revised for a second edition, perhaps because of the size of the printing in the first instance and the transitory nature of the subject matter in the second. More enduring was the third publication, Circular 75, "Safety in the household," which came out in 1918 (10,000 copies), was revised in 1932, and again in 1948.[75] If the inspiration of the first two

[73] Letter, Redfield to SWS, Mar. 16, 1917, and letter, Rosa to Redfield, Mar. 27, 1917 (NBS Box 8, IEL). Edward Bok told Stratton that after reading "Measurements for the household," he found and replaced 140 GEM lamps in his home (letter, SWS to Redfield, Jan. 15, 1916, NBS Box 21, PA).

The lure of the GEM lamp seems comparable to a present-day continuing phenomenon, the futile efforts of the Food and Drug Administration to warn the public against costly and useless food diets, drugs, and nostrums. The warnings in FDA and medical publications apparently reach no greater public than did the NBS circulars.

[74] NBS C70, p. 11.

[75] NBS C75 was superseded by C397 (1932) and C463 (1948). A consolidated edition of the three circulars appeared as "Measurements, materials, and safety for the household" in 1918. For further note of these circulars, see letter, SWS to Secretary of Commerce Hoover, Jan. 25, 1922 (NBS Box 21, PP).

circulars may be traced in some degree to the muckraking and reform movements of the period, the "safety" circular, as the introduction said, was prompted by the increase in hazards "in modern times from the service of gas and electricity and the use of such dangerous articles as matches, volatile oils, poisons, and the like."

Drawing on the mass of safety code data gathered by the electrical, chemistry, engineering, and materials divisions of the Bureau, the 127-page handbook on safety in the home covered electrical hazards, lightning hazards, gas, fire, and chemical hazards, and in a final chapter covered falls, cuts, scalds, burns and other miscellaneous accidents in the home.

Nothing since the Bureau's weights and measures crusade made so great an impression on the public as did the publication of these circulars, and for years the Bureau was identified in the public mind with testing of household materials and appliances and besieged with correspondence requesting personal help with home problems. Reported for the most part in specialized publications and periodicals, the work of the Bureau in electricity, in thermometry, photometry, calorimetry, radiometry, polarimetry, and spectroscopy, in metallurgy and in chemistry, was known only in scientific and technical circles. It came as a shock to Dr. Stratton when late in 1915 the Secretary of Commerce told him that Thomas Edison, unaware of the fundamental research carried on at the Bureau, had suggested that the Government establish such a laboratory.[76]

Four years later, better acquainted with the Bureau, Edison wrote saying that its recent publication, The Principles Underlying Radio Communications, was "the greatest book on this subject that I have ever read * * *. Usually, books on radio communication are fairly bristling with mathematics, and I am at a loss in trying to read them." [77] The early radio work at the Bureau introduced a large public to the scientific research of which it was capable.

RADIO, RADIUM, AND X RAYS

In the autumn of 1904 a young man came to the Bureau with a new book and an assignment in a new field of physics, neither of which aroused more than passing interest at the time. He was Dr. Louis W. Austin, an assistant professor of physics at Wisconsin who had spent the past 2 years as a guest worker at the Reichsanstalt in Berlin. Returning home by way of

[76] Personal letter, Secretary of Commerce to Secretary of the Navy, Oct. 11, 1915 (NBS Box 3, AG).

[77] Letter, Edison to SWS, Apr. 25, 1919 (NBS Box 4, AGC). He referred to Radio Pamphlet 40, prepared by the Bureau and issued by the Signal Corps in March 1919.

Cambridge, he picked up a book just issued by the university press, Ernest Rutherford's Radioactivity.

Rutherford's book was the first summary account of the experimental work of Roentgen, Becquerel, Thompson, Mme. Curie, and Rutherford himself in the decade following the discovery of radium and X rays. A young man in Rosa's division, Llewelyn G. Hoxton, given the book to discuss at one of the weekly meetings of the Bureau staff, recalls that when he sat down, Dr. Rosa came over and said, "Let me see that book!" But little in the book except the chapter on methods of measurement, describing the crude "electrical method" as the best then available for the quantitative determination of radiation and emanation, seems to have interested Rosa, for he returned the book the next morning.[78]

A second edition of Radioactivity, enlarged by the avid research abroad from 382 to 558 pages, appeared a year later, and Rutherford himself, who won the 1908 Nobel prize in chemistry for his work on alpha particles, visited the Bureau to lecture on radium and radioactivity not long after.[79] Such was the Bureau's introduction to the coming age of nuclear physics.

Dr. Austin himself was not particularly interested in radioactivity but in another kind of emanation and a still newer phenomenon, that of radio telegraphy or wireless, as it was called. Radio as we know it today was as yet remote, although in 1901, the same year that Marconi received his wireless signals across the Atlantic, Reginald A. Fessenden, recently appointed head of electrical engineering at the University of Pittsburgh but still then with the U.S. Weather Bureau, heard at a distance of a mile the first faint voice by electromagnetic waves over his wireless apparatus.[80] Six years later Lee de Forest invented his audion detector or three-element tube and applied it to the long-distance telephone. When used in 1912 to amplify a feeble audio-frequency current, modern radio was born.

Although experimentation continued, much of it in secrecy and attended by barbaric litigation, voice radio remained primitive, found no application on the battlefields of World War I, and was not developed commercially until the 1920's. For the first two decades of the century

[78] Interview with Dr. L. G. Hoxton, Charlottesville, Va., Nov. 27–28, 1961 (NBS Historical File). Austin's copy of Radioactivity is in the NBS library.

[79] Dr. Hoxton recalls Rutherford's visit to the Bureau. No record of the visit has been found, but in his biography of Rutherford (Cambridge University Press, 1939, p. 129), A. S. Eve says: "About 1905 the world caught fire and radium was the vogue. * * * A great number of Universities and Societies poured in appeals to Rutherford to come and lecture to them about radium. He did what he could."

[80] Helen M. Fessenden, Fesseden: Builder of Tomorrows (New York: Coward-McCann, 1940), p. 81.

the problems still posed by long distance radiotelegraphy were sufficient to keep scientists and electrical engineers fully engaged looking for useful solutions.

Austin came to the Bureau as a guest worker to investigate the practical application of radiotelegraphy for the Navy, and from 1908 to 1932 headed the U.S. Naval Radiotelegraphic Laboratory at the Bureau (in 1923 renamed the Laboratory for Special Radio Transmission Research). Shortly after Austin's arrival, the U.S. Army Signal Service also requested space in the Bureau's electrical division, where their engineer, E. C. Cramm, investigated military applications of wireless.[81]

Not until 1911 did the Bureau itself enter the wireless field, when an engineer in one of the new commercial "electric signaling" companies sent in a wavemeter (frequency meter) for calibration. To set up a standard for this instrument was a problem in inductance and capacity, and the wavemeter was turned over to J. Howard Dellinger, who had come to the Bureau in 1907 from Western Reserve where he had been a physics instructor. He was then taking courses locally for his doctorate in physics, had become interested in the high frequency phenomena associated with radiotelegraphy and as a result was the acknowledged wireless "expert" at the Bureau. Soon Dellinger headed a new section in the electrical division called radio measurements.

Earlier that year a draft of regulations on the use of wireless as a safety aid in navigation, prepared by Prof. A. G. Webster of Clark University for a forthcoming London Wireless Conference, was submitted to the Bureau for review. Dellinger studied the paper and among other suggestions proposed that the word "wireless" everywhere in the text be changed to "radio," in keeping with its connotation of radiation. And "radio" rather than "wireless" became the accepted name in this country.

Bureau research in radio began in earnest with an investigation by Dellinger of ammeters used to measure the high frequency current in transmitting apparatus. As determined then, ammeter measurements were subject to considerable margin of error, and Dellinger's study resulted in a much needed heavy-current standard for radio frequencies. The work earned him his Princeton doctoral degree in 1913.[82]

No conflict of work existed in the several radio laboratories that had been set up at the Bureau, for Austin and Cramm were working on

---

[81] Letter, Chief Signal Officer to Secretary of War, Oct. 18, 1909, and attached correspondence (NBS Box 10, IEW). Although Cramm's tenure at the Bureau is uncertain, Austin headed the Navy laboratory at the Bureau until his death in 1932, publishing much of his research on radio signal intensities, long-wave transmission phenomena, atmospheric disturbances, and long-wave radio receiving measurements in Bureau publications. See Science, 76, 137 (1932).

[82] S206, "High-frequency ammeters" (Dellinger, 1913).

various means of generating and detecting low frequency (long distance) radio waves, while Dellinger concentrated on higher frequency waves, those used by experimental broadcast stations. Considerably later his investigations moved into still higher frequency wave ranges, where they became the short waves of long-distance transmission, and after that into very high frequencies, where he first confronted the problems whose challenge continues to the present day, those found in communication via outer space.

It was also in 1911 that Frederick A. Kolster was brought to the Bureau by Dr. Rosa to investigate some of the difficulties in radio engineering coming into the electrical division from industry. A former assistant in Lee de Forest's laboratory in New York, Kolster proved to be one of the most inventive mechanical geniuses ever to work at the Bureau. As his first assignment, he went to the Wireless Conference in London as technical adviser to Professor Webster.

On the night of April 14, 1912, 2 months before the Conference, the White Star liner *Titanic,* on its maiden voyage, struck an iceberg 800 miles off the coast of Nova Scotia. The disaster disclosed how much an innovation maritime wireless was at that time. The scarcity of trained telegraphers often put ships' wireless in the hands of inexperienced operators who found signals hard to catch, were hampered by the necessity of having to relay their messages, and to send frequent repeats before their messages—most of them for passengers beguiled by the novelty—made sense on shore.

Four ships were within 60 miles of the *Titanic* when it sent out its first call for help. All at various times that day had warned the *Titanic* of the ice fields in the vicinity. One, the *Californian,* was less than 10 miles away when the CQD went out. But its wireless operator, rebuffed earlier by the operator on the *Titanic* for interfering with private messages going ashore, had shut down for the night. Of the others, only the Cunard liner *Carpathia* 58 miles away, dared to chance the ice field in which the *Titanic* lay sinking. When it arrived a bare handful of lifeboats and rafts drifted in the area where the *Titanic* had foundered more than hour before.[83]

Shocked by the disaster but ignorant of the catalog of human errors that had caused it, the Wireless Conference meeting in London gave its attention to the technical aspects of radio it had met to resolve. Of the two wavelengths then used by international maritime wireless, the Conference agreed that the 600-meter wavelength be restricted to the use of ships at sea. It also agreed that in order to reduce interference from the spark transmitters on ocean liners, the decrement or rate of decay of the waves emitted by the transmitting antenna should not exceed the log 0.2.

---

[83] Walter Lord, A Night to Remember (New York: Henry Holt, 1955), pp. 36–38, 171–172; Logan Marshall, Sinking of the Titanic . . . (New York: John C. Winston, 1912), p. 299.

The Conference ruling on interference became the second radio law enacted by the United States. (The first, in 1910, had called for installation of radio apparatus on all steamers, foreign and domestic, operating out of American ports.)[84] Congress, aroused to the importance of radio, also called for more efficient radiotelegraphic service, restriction on the free use of wavelengths, and the licensing of commercial and amateur radio stations. Commerce's Bureau of Navigation, made responsible for these matters, called on the Bureau of Standards to investigate the bases for establishing the laws asked for by Congress, including better radio equipment, test procedures, and standards.[85]

Congress turned over enforcement of the interference ruling to the Bureau of Navigation, and at its request Kolster was assigned to devise a portable measuring instrument for this purpose, to be used by ship radio inspectors. The decremeter he designed, measuring wavelength as well as decrement, was at once adopted by the Bureau of Navigation and by the War and Navy Departments.[86]

The Bureau of Navigation also called for a radio beacon system to aid ship navigation in fog and rough weather. Between 1913 and 1915 Kolster developed an improved radio direction finder or radio compass—the forerunner of modern aviation instrument landing systems—that enabled a ship to establish its position by determining with high accuracy the direction of sending station signals.[87] But it took more than twice as long to put the new direction finder into operation as to design it. The Bureau of Lighthouses proved reluctant to use scarce funds to install beacon stations along the shore until ships were equipped, and ship captains, traditionally conservative, refused to have all that machinery—and electrical, at that—cluttering up their ships.

---

[84] Commerce's Bureau of Navigation C211 (1910) announced that after July 1, 1911, by the Radio Act of June 24, 1910, it became unlawful for any ocean-going passenger steamers to sail without radio communication apparatus. After the *Titanic*, the Radio Act was amended to require two operators, instead of one, on constant watch; an auxiliary power source; and extended the act to include cargo ships. See correspondence with NBS and copy of the act in NBS Box 10, IEW; also Paul Schubert, The Electric Word: the Rise of Radio (New York: Macmillan, 1928), pp. 63–65.

[85] Earlier, in the summer of 1912, Waidner and Dickinson of the Bureau's heat division, aboard Navy patrol boats, investigated methods of detecting the proximity of icebergs. Most promising seemed temperature variations, but they proved as great far removed from icebergs as near them. NBS Annual Report 1914, p. 28, and S210 (1914). Later a salinity meter was developed for the International Ice Patrol to locate icebergs and reported in RP223 (Wenner, Smith, and Soule, 1930).

[86] NBS Annual Report 1914, p. 35; S235, "A direct-reading instrument for measuring * * * decrement" (Kolster, 1915); correspondence in NBS Box 10, IEW.

[87] NBS Annual Report 1916, p. 56; S428, "The radio direction finder * * *" (Kolster and Dunmore, 1922). The original direction finder was the invention of two Italians, Bellini and Tosi, in 1907. See Schubert, pp. 139, 154.

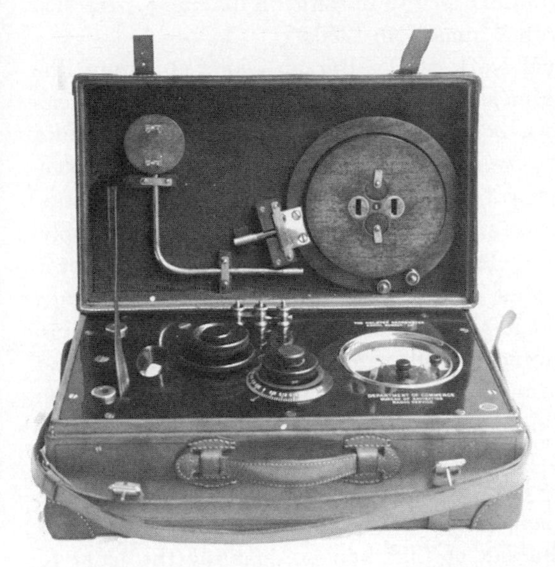

The Kolster decremeter for measuring wavelength and decrement was developed between 1912 and 1914 for the use of the Department of Commerce's Bureau of Navigation and for the armed services.

An early radio receiving set constructed by the Bureau, designed, along with a separate transmitter, for use on ships of the Lighthouse Service, Bureau of Navigation, and the Coast and Geodetic Survey.
It was a closed-circuit type of receiver using a variable condenser of the decremeter type and with a crystal detector connected across the condenser. This particular set served as a wavemeter and decremeter as well as radio receiver.

It was 1919 before the impasse was resolved and the direction finder was successfully demonstrated and officially approved. Soon after, Kolster left the Bureau to set up a company to manufacture his radio compasses. When success eluded him, he turned to the development of radio receiving sets. The radio boom was on, he was hired away by industry, and his inventive genius was exploited, but he got none of the millions made through his work or from the Kolster Radio Corp. set up to trade on his name. He died "a magnificent failure," as he called himself, in 1950.[88]

Until 1917 the electrical work of the Bureau centered around the power industry. There was almost no research in wire telephony or telegraphy, radio research was just beginning, and except for Kolster's radio direction finder, Bureau efforts were concentrated on more precise determinations of the laws and physical quantities involved in radio apparatus, in trying to maintain and improve measurements and standards, and supplying basic information.[89] Nevertheless, some tests and calibrations had been made of available radio apparatus, of circuit components, of various kinds of detectors (electrolytic, Fleming valve, audion), and of the new continuous-wave techniques that were coming in with radiotelephony, putting an end to damped-wave (spark) transmission. For use with Kolster's direction finder, the radio section had devised an automatic device that sent out a characteristic signal once every minute, to guide incoming ships in fog. Unable as yet to obtain specialized equipment from industry, the laboratories also built and installed a number of radiotelegraphic units on Coast Survey steamers and tenders of the Bureau of Lighthouses, enabling the latter to maintain communication between lighthouses and ships at sea.[90]

The Bureau received its first special appropriation for radio research from Congress, the sum of $10,000 "for the investigation and standardization of methods and instruments employed in radio communication," in 1915. A year later Congress appropriated $50,000 for the construction of a radio laboratory building, a two-story structure erected south of the electrical laboratory, with two 150-foot antenna towers adjacent to the laboratory. The ensuing pioneer work in radio at the Bureau was to prove its worth when war came.

Radio and radioactivity, as previously noted, arrived at the Bureau on the same day in 1911, but laboratory interest in radium and radiation, phenomena actually far removed from radio, did not begin until late in 1913. It may well have been the use of electrical methods for the measurement of radioactive quantities that made it seem logical to establish this work in Rosa's division. Or it may have been, as Dr. N. Ernest Dorsey said, that the disintegration hypothesis promulgated by Rutherford, together with his conjectures on the structure of the atom and the phenomena associated with radioactivity, were all "bound up with our ideas of electricity." [91]

---

[88] Letter, Lloyd Espenschied, Bell Telephone Laboratories, to A. V. Astin, Feb. 18, 1954, and attached correspondence on early radio at NBS (NBS Historical File).
[89] George C. Southworth, Forty Years of Radio Research (New York: Gordon and Breach, 1962), p. 32.
[90] NBS Annual Report 1916, pp. 55–56.
[91] Dorsey, Physics of Radioactivity (Baltimore: Williams and Williams, 1921), p. 33.

Kolster's wireless laboratory in East building in 1916, showing models of the decremeter on the left, and in the center, an early radio receiving set. The overhead wiring was the beginning of the intricate webs that were spun with the passing of time in most of the electrical laboratories of East building.

That the two somehow seemed related is evident from Dr. Stratton's frequent use of the portmanteau phrase "radio telegraphy and radio activity." [92]

In Europe, where radium and radiation research had been carried on at fever pitch since the discoveries of Roentgen and Becquerel, a Congress of Radiology and Electricity met at Brussels in 1910 to survey recent progress and discuss the question of standards for radium research. A year later Mme. Curie prepared a carefully measured quantity of radium chloride sealed in a glass tube, based on the proportion of radium to the weight of the radium salts in the tube as measured by its gamma rays. This was accepted by the International Committee on Radium Standards, appointed by the Congress at Brussels, as the international standard and deposited in the International Bureau of Weights and Measures at Sèvres. Research in radium began at the Bureau of Standards in December 1913 when a phial containing 20.28 milligrams of pure radium arrived from abroad. A covering communication certified its equivalence to the International Radium Standard at Sèvres and described its comparison with another quantity of radium salts prepared at Vienna and accepted as a second standard.[93]

Dorsey, who came to the Bureau from Johns Hopkins in 1903 and for almost a decade worked under Rosa on electrical measurements, had followed with excitement the published accounts of radiation research. He became interested particularly in the applications of X rays and radium to medical diagnosis and treatment, then a craze sweeping the country and involving almost as many fakers as reputable physicians.

As early as 1896 Scientific American magazine described the construction of a fairly effective X-ray tube by connecting the carbon filaments of an incandescent lamp to an improvised high-voltage apparatus. These X-ray tubes, as well as fluoroscopic screens, soon became commercially available and doctors and technicians by the hundreds opened offices across the country to practice the new wonder on marveling patients. Pusey and Caldwell's The Practical Application of the Roentgen Rays in Therapeutics and Diagnosis (1903, reprinted in 1904) warned of certain radiation hazards to doctors and patients alike but the dangers were not yet clearly understood. As a result, efforts at protection from the rays tended to lapse after the first meager precautions.[94] X-ray and radium protection standards were not to come within the province of the Bureau until the late 1920's.

Learning of the international standard of radium in Washington, hospitals and physicians sent their radium salts to the Bureau for analysis, and

---

[92] E.g., at Hearings * * * 1918 (Dec. 1, 1916), p. 465.

[93] Dorsey, Physics of Radioactivity, pp. 162–163.

[94] For the early history of medical radiology, see Percy Brown, American Martyrs to Science Through the Roentgen Rays (Springfield, Ill., and Baltimore, Md.: C. C. Thomas, 1936), pp. 144–145.

Dorsey became the radium specialist as he began making intercomparisons of sealed radium standards and started an investigation of the gamma-ray method of radium measurement. Soon Dorsey and his assistants were studying the properties of radioactive substances, the alpha-ray activity of powdered radium salts, of uranium mixtures, radium ores and radium emanations. In a few short months he, like all who were handling radium at that time, had burned the thumbs and the index and middle fingers on both his hands. By 1919, as a result of the amount of radium and luminescent materials containing radium handled during the war, he had developed typical "X-ray hands," characterized by ulcerative tissue, whitlows below the nails, pronounced lack of sensitivity of touch in the fingers, and extreme sensitivity to cold.[95]

Dr. Dorsey left the Bureau in 1920 and, away from radium, his hands though permanently scarred improved rapidly. His book, Physics of Radioactivity, based in part on a Bureau circular he began in 1915 and never completed, was prepared as a text for the medical profession and came out in 1921.[96] For almost a decade he practiced privately as a consultant physicist in radium. He returned to the Bureau in 1928 with independent status and until his retirement in 1943 carried out a number of research projects in physics and acted as advisory consultant to the radium and X-ray section of the optics division.[97]

"REVISING" THE ORGANIC ACT

The year 1913 was a milestone in the history of the Bureau, a time of reappraisal and redirection. Much of the testing of standards, measuring instruments, and materials was now "organized on an accurate routine basis and * * * handled with dispatch, through increased efficiency of appliances and methods of testing." [98] Fundamental research in the scientific divisions continued at a high level, but the principal energies of the Bureau were directed to investigations for the Federal and State governments, for in-

---

[95] Dorsey, Physics of Radioactivity, pp. 175–177.

[96] Announcements of the circular appeared in NBS Annual Reports 1915 and 1916.

[97] Dr. Dorsey, whose research for his book on "water substance" was conducted in that period, was the second of three workers given independent status at the Bureau, free from all administrative duties. The others were Dr. Edgar Buckingham, in 1923, to continue his work in theoretical thermodynamics, and Dr. Louis B. Tuckerman, in 1937, to carry out research in aeronautical mechanics. Memo, Hugh L. Dryden to Division N section chiefs, Dec. 20, 1937 (NBS Box 403, ID-Misc).

[98] NBS Annual Report 1913, p. 36.

dustry and the public utilities.[99] The Bureau had grown far beyond the confines of its organic act and in directions unforeseen.

Seemingly taking all knowledge for its province, the Bureau was currently engaged in over 200 different projects, its Baconian scope of research demanding an extraordinary spirit of cooperation. In his annual report that year Stratton said of this spirit that it alone "minimized the somewhat narrowing effects of a rigid division system. Each problem when studied in a broad scientific spirit leads into every specialty * * *." Cooperation had been "particularly notable in the development of standards for gas, in the researches upon metals, and the methods of testing the properties of materials, in the study of electrolysis experimentally in the field, in the structural materials investigation, and in many other cases where success depends upon many specialties." It had been most striking "in the gradual development of the public-service commission work of the Bureau. This is an outgrowth of the weights and measures activity of the Bureau, of the cooperation with the Interstate Commerce Commission, and with other regulative and inspection services, notably the wireless service, the regulation of navigation, municipal gas regulation, standardization of specifications for materials, and central-station power service * * * simply [applying] measurements and standards to new fields * * *. Such work is an extension of the general purpose of the Bureau as a whole, cooperation in all movements which have for their object increase in efficiency in all fields through measurements and standards." [100]

It was this "extension of the general purpose of the Bureau" that had resulted in its extraordinary growth. In a little more than a decade appropriations for the Bureau had risen from $32,000 to almost half a million dollars a year, with that much again appropriated in 1913 for a new electrical laboratory, additional land, and special test equipment. In addition to the field laboratory at Pittsburgh, three new divisions—engineering research, metallurgy, and structural and miscellaneous materials—had been added to the original five in Washington, and Bureau personnel had risen from 13 to more than 280, of whom at least 50 were high-grade physicists.

Congress sometimes worried about those physicists. Other agencies in the Government didn't seem to need them. "What is a physicist?" Mr. Leonidas F. Livingston of the House Appropriations Subcommittee asked. "I was asked on the floor of the House what in the name of common sense a physicist is, and I could not answer." [101] At a Senate hearing, Mr. Lee S.

---

[99] "The bureau is, to a certain extent, a clearing house for technical information * * * cooperating with all movements tending to improve conditions in which standards of quality or standards of measurement are involved." M18, "The National Bureau of Standards" (1911), p. 7.

[100] NBS Annual Report 1913, p. 3.

[101] Hearings * * * 1912 (Dec. 2, 1910), p. 263.

Overman of North Carolina wondered too: "You have here * * * [a request for] a physicist qualified in optics. I want to know what you do with that fellow. What is his business?"[102] Patiently, Dr. Stratton explained, and the physicists were his.

So well did Stratton get along with Congress that one of his admiring colleagues, sitting with him at the annual hearings, referred to him as "a scientific politician." Congressman Joseph T. Johnson of South Carolina marveled at Stratton's way with a committee, even when the subject was as minor as funds for grading the Bureau grounds. "Now, you have made a specially strong plea—in fact, you always make a strong plea and hypnotize this committee."[103]

Behind the pleas were results, and the kind that a business-minded Congress appreciated. Stratton poured out facts on the dollar-and-cents value of Government testing and the public benefits "from a financial standpoint" of Bureau research in public utility service. He had only to show that "we have never been able to keep up with 25 percent of the demands made on the Bureau," to say that never before had "the Bureau had so many demands for its cooperation in regard to industrial standards, in devising standard methods of measurement and test, and in researches involving precise measurement," for Congress to reach for its purse and add something more.[104]

The annual increases in Bureau staff, equipment, and funds were the envy of other research agencies in the Government. "As you know," Congressman Frank H. Gillett of the Appropriations Subcommittee once said to Stratton, "our liberality to this bureau is one of the things that is criticized somewhat, and [so] we should be glad to get * * * results."[105] And Stratton cited the weights and measures investigation and the testing of Government materials, now being done for almost 60 different bureaus representing every department of the Government, the success of which had led to the organization of the General Supply Committee and almost doubled the test work of the Bureau.

The proliferation of Bureau research interests under Stratton and Rosa had largely changed the mission of the Bureau envisioned in its organic act. Established to provide this country with a scientific basis for accurate measurements and a source of information regarding basic properties of materials determined by such measurements, the Bureau became involved almost at

[102] [Senate] Hearings * * * 1913 (May 22, 1912), p. 232.
[103] Hearings * * * 1916 (Nov. 28, 1914), p. 142.
[104] Hearings * * * 1912 (Dec. 2, 1910), p. 270; NBS Annual Report 1912, p. 3.
[105] Hearings * * * 1912, p. 262. On a later occasion, when asked by Congress how appropriated special funds were being spent, Stratton said that in most investigations from 75 to 80 percent went for staff, the remaining for materials and equipment (Hearings * * * 1921, Jan. 2, 1920, p. 1566).

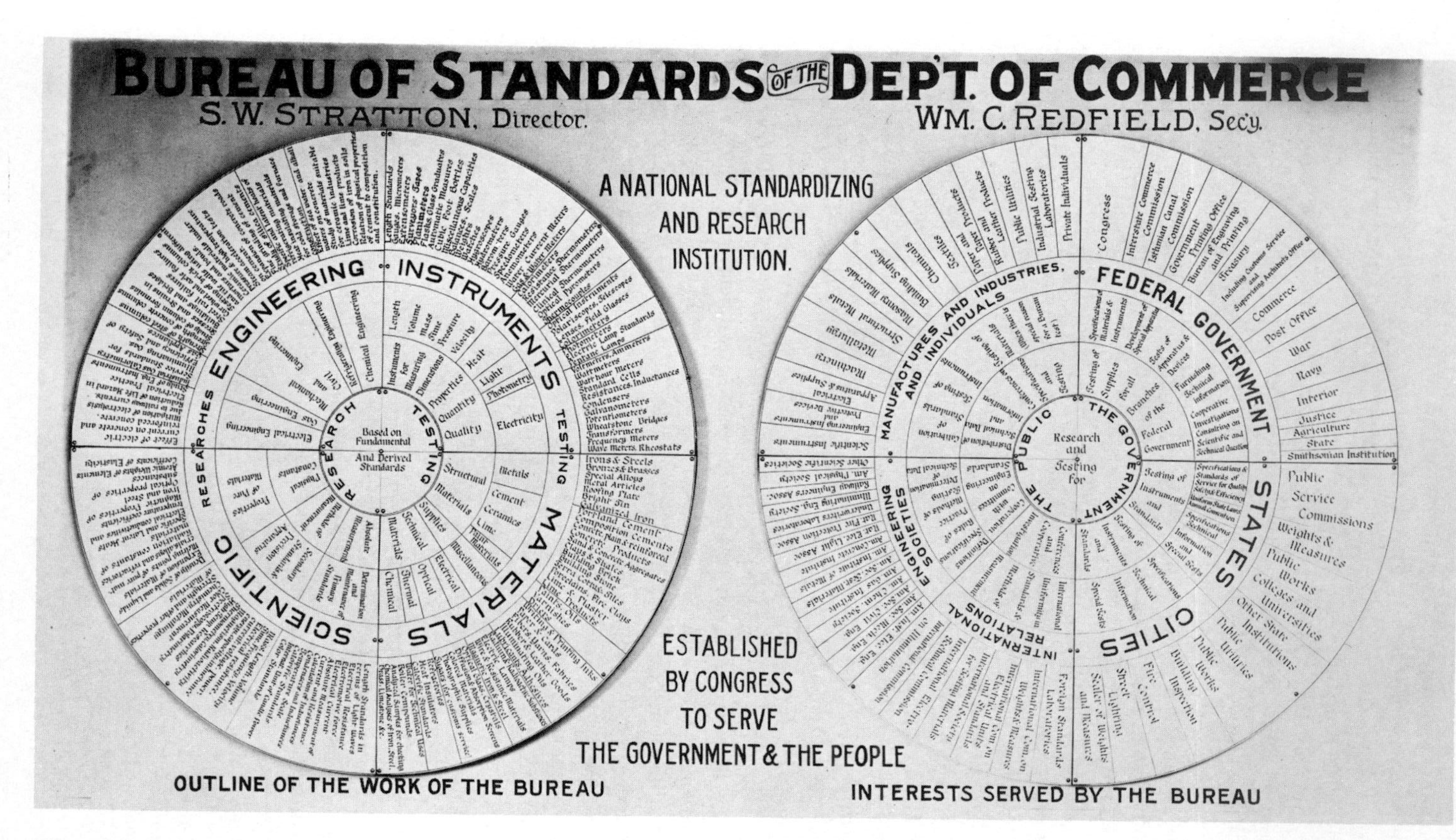

The proliferation of Bureau interests, abetted by special congressional appropriations for investigations not covered in the Organic Act, inspired the wheeled chart of NBS activities. It was probably prepared for an appropriations hearing before Congress about 1915.

once in practical applications of these services to meet the needs of Government and industry. The resulting activities, nowhere referred to in the organic act, fell within the province of the Bureau only through broad interpretation of the clauses calling for "the solution of problems which arise in connection with standards" and "the determination of * * * properties of materials" (ignoring the qualifying clause in the latter case, "when such data are of great importance to scientific or manufacturing interests * * *").

The standards intended in the organic act were physical standards of measurement, but in the technological and engineering fields entered through Government testing, in the preparation of standard samples, and in structural and miscellaneous materials testing, "standards" had come to mean specifications of materials and codes of practice. Other research agencies in the Government began to question the broad interpretation of the Bureau act and its extended use of the term "standards," but not Congress, which found Bureau investigations highly productive of visible and tangible results.

The Bureau was further encouraged by the method adopted by Congress to expand Bureau activities—that is, by the appropriation of specific funds for special investigations.[106] This began in 1910 with the appropriations for the weights and measures crusade and the investigation of gas-light standards and continued thereafter, with special appropriations for one or more new projects almost annually, until 1936. By the thirties, grown to double the amount of direct appropriations by Congress, they had become administratively unwieldly. In 1936 all Bureau operations and activities funded by Congress were consolidated in four general categories: administration, testing, research and development, and standards for commerce.

With the first of the special appropriations the Bureau set up two categories of personnel, those engaged in fundamental research and routine work and paid from statutory funds, and those brought in for its special investigations and paid from specific appropriations. Although most of the special investigations went on for a decade or more, in some instances, as funds were withdrawn, those portions of the investigation that the Bureau thought ought to be permanent were transferred, with their staff, to the regular work of the Bureau. Thus the Bureau grew, but not without some friction.

It seems possible that it was criticism of certain of the Bureau research in this period that first alerted Stratton to a hazard in the latitude of research permitted in the wording of the organic act. In 1908 the Bureau of Chemistry in the Department of Agriculture had complained that the Bureau of Standards was duplicating work specifically delegated to Chemistry, including determination of the quality of volumetric apparatus, testing sugar

---

[106] The chart showing these special appropriations from 1910 to 1935 appears as app. G.

imports at the ports of entry, and chemical analysis of supplies furnished to Agriculture and other departments, in particular of paper and paper materials bought for the Government. Although Dr. Stratton pointed out that the Bureau's physical and chemical tests were to determine specifications of quality and design, improve the standards used in polariscopic work on sugar, and develop paper testing instruments and methods, while Chemistry's investigations were confined to the agricultural side of these problems, the Bureau of Chemistry continued to insist that "no part of the organic act establishing the National Bureau of Standards * * * warrants transfer of this kind of work * * * to the Bureau of Standards." [107]

As Bureau investigations expanded, so did the murmurs of Agriculture, that work "conducted by or projected by the Bureau" was duplicating that being done not only in its Bureau of Chemistry but in its Forestry Service, Bureau of Plant Industry, and Bureau of Animal Industry.[108] And when, at the request of the American Mining Congress, the Bureau made a study of standards for electrical machines and electrical practice in mines, Interior's Bureau of Mines saw it as an invasion of its domain, as it had the investigation of building stones and marls earlier. The Bureau acknowledged that "in spite of [its efforts] to avoid infringing upon the functions of other Bureaus * * * there has been a feeling in some quarters that the Bureau has enlarged its activities unduly." [109]

This problem of function was very much on Stratton's mind when late in 1912 the President's Commission on Economy and Efficiency sent out a questionnaire to all departments in the executive branch asking whether any changes in law pertaining to the organization and form of appropriations for their agencies were necessary for more efficient operation. Dr. Stratton expressed his entire satisfaction with the method of appropriations for the Bureau; his principal concern was over the continuing criticism:

> In view of the fact that the organic act establishing the Bureau has been somewhat misunderstood (generally by those bureaus claiming authority for the same class of work), I have sometimes

[107] Letter, SWS to Secretary of Commerce and Labor, Feb. 15, 1908, and attached correspondence (NBS Box 4, AGA).

[108] Letter, Secretary of Agriculture to Secretary of Commerce, Apr. 28, 1913 (NARG 16, Records of Office of Secretary of Agriculture, sub: Duplication of work, 1913).

[109] Letter, Rosa to Secretary of Commerce, Oct. 2, 1913 (ibid.). The feeling possibly had some warrant, as is indicated later in a memo from P. H. Bates to Stratton, May 1, 1918 (NBS Box 2, AG): "With such active competition as we are now getting in the ceramic work from the Bureau of Mines, it is very essential that we be able to take up and actively push to completion all problems given to us."

thought that the organic act might be made more specific. On the other hand, this would be gained at the expense of flexibility.[110]

Unwilling to tamper with the basic act, Stratton suggested another way around the problem. Because of their national eminence and their connections, the Visiting Committee to the Bureau, then composed of Dr. Elihu Thomson, Dr. Robert S. Woodward, Prof. Henry M. Howe, Prof. Arthur G. Webster, and Prof. John F. Hayford, exerted considerable influence on behalf of the Bureau in high places, as well as on its operations. Stratton proposed to Secretary of Commerce and Labor Nagel that the Committee, presently made up largely of scientific men, be increased from 5 to 8 or 10, to include more representation for the new research interests of the Bureau: "It is highly desirable that the technological and industrial interests be also represented." [111]

Neither an increase in the Committee nor a change in the organic act proved necessary. What amounted to an amendment to the organic act was sufficient. On March 4, 1913 Congress passed an act (37 Stat. 945) that made the testing of industrial and commercial materials for the Government a specific function of the Bureau:

> Materials for fireproof buildings, other structural materials, and all materials, other than materials for paving and for fuel, purchased for and to be used by the government of the District of Columbia, when necessary in the judgment of the commissioners to be tested, shall be tested by the Bureau of Standards under the same condition as similar testing is required to be done for the United States Government.

In Dr. Stratton's view, this act for the benefit of the District of Columbia formally justified the materials testing and public service testing involving materials that the Bureau had been doing since 1904 for the Federal Government, its establishments in this country, in Panama, and in its oversea possessions.

That same month of 1913 the Wilson administration took office, the Department of Commerce and Labor was split in two, and William C. Redfield, soon to become a close friend of Dr. Stratton and one of the most ardent supporters the Bureau has ever had, was appointed the new Secretary of Commerce. Redfield at 55 had been in business and manufacturing most of his life, was vice president of an engineering firm, author of a recent book, The New Industrial Day (1912), and had been a Congressman for the past 2 years when he became Secretary. An intense man, with strong con-

---

[110] Letter, SWS to Secretary of Commerce and Labor, Nov. 14, 1912, and attached correspondence (NBS Box 3, AG).
[111] Ibid.

Secretary of Commerce William C. Redfield, a prince of industry and a splendid presence, who bought his first automobile in 1916 because the trip to the Bureau was too far by horse and carriage.

victions about what his Department should be, he left it in 1919 feeling he had failed it. His books and articles describing his years as Secretary were filled with passionate criticisms of Congress and Congressmen as venal, incompetent, and do-nothing. But of this sense of frustration there was little evidence at the time. He was a better Secretary than he knew.

He found good men everywhere in the "working" areas of the Government, as he called the executive branch, and nowhere so many as in the Bureau of Standards, which he particularly admired for what it was doing for industry, often against industry's will. As he said:

> Long industrial experience taught me what our work at the Bureau of Standards constantly justified, that on the whole American manufacturers failed to apply science to industry * * *.[112]

Dr. Stratton he came to admire for a talent he felt he lacked, the ability to get along with Congress, but he took no credit for his own efforts before Congress on behalf of the Bureau.

> One service, the Bureau of Standards, which deservedly had the confidence of Congress, was not only well housed but well equipped so far as the requirements of that time were concerned. Its need was for steady expansion to meet the growing demands of the Government itself and the increasing call for aid from industry.[113]

Soon after taking charge of his Department, Redfield visited the Bureau and before long began coming up in his horse and carriage every week,

---

[112] Redfield, "Glimpses of our government," Saturday Evening Post, May 17, 1924, p. 44.
[113] Redfield, ibid., May 3, 1924, p. 81.

and sometimes twice a week.[114] Stratton would take him to the laboratories he himself had been recently touring and where investigations that would interest Redfield were in progress.

It was almost certainly as a result of Redfield's visits that in an effort to increase Bureau usefulness as well as to settle an old area of interdepartmental bickering, Redfield sought by agreement with the Secretary of Agriculture to transfer the miscellaneous testing laboratory in the Bureau of Chemistry to the Bureau of Standards. On July 1, 1914 that laboratory, with funds of $26,000 for the testing of textiles, paper, leather, rubber, oils, and paints, was officially transferred and within a week the new group, headed by Dr. Percy H. Walker and F. W. Smither, with eight assistant chemists and a clerk, was organized on the second floor of North building.[115]

Redfield seems to have been diligent in his search for ways to enhance the prestige of his Department, and to have made the Bureau a prime beneficiary of these efforts. By tradition, the executive departments of the Government hid their lights and good works, a fact he resented since it made "informing Congress of one's needs * * * very difficult." Soon after taking office he began making it a point to attend congressional committee hearings with his bureau chiefs and personally brought key people with him to explain their needs.[116] He took an active part in the proceedings, demonstrating a fine talent in the use of the first person plural. His intense personal identification with the Bureau was exhibited on one occasion when Stratton was seeking a new special appropriation by his remark, "I can only say that anything that Dr. Stratton wants I back up." [117]

It was almost certainly Redfield who authorized a major change in format of the annual reports of his bureaus the year he came in. The Bureau report for 1913, 38 pages in length, almost tripled in size to 99 pages in 1914 and continued to swell by nearly 50 percent each year thereafter.[118] Its

---

[114] At Hearings * * * 1919 (Jan. 18, 1918), p. 893, Redfield said he finally bought an automobile in 1916, because the trip to the Bureau was too far by carriage.

[115] Letter, SWS to Redfield, June 5, 1914, and attached correspondence (NARG 16, Office of the Secretary of Agriculture, sub: Duplication of Work, Department of Commerce, 1914).

[116] Redfield, Saturday Evening Post, May 3, 1924, p. 78; ibid., May 10, 1924, p. 19. Results of these trips to the Hill were mixed. Stratton and his staff, Redfield found, explained their scientific problems in terms which laymen could understand. On the other hand, some like Dr. O. H. Tittmann, chief of the Coast Survey, unfortunately "resented the sharp questions that were often asked," an attitude that was reflected in meager appropriations (Redfield, ibid., May 3, 1924, p. 81).

[117] See Hearings * * * 1915 (Jan. 27, 1914), p. 664 et passim; [Senate] Hearings * * * on H.R. 15279 (Apr. 29, 1914), p. 61.

[118] The report of the Bureau of Corporations in Commerce expanded from 8 to 48 pages and all but three of the reports of the other nine bureaus of the Department showed considerable increases in size. No such sudden expansion occurred in other Department reports examined, i.e., Interior and Agriculture.

new table of contents drew attention to the fact that the 8 divisions of the Bureau were engaged in more than 225 separate investigations. Following notes on administration and statistical data on the year's work, the report for the first time appended a list of current Bureau needs, including a new building to house the structural materials work, a radio laboratory, additional ground, and more scientific assistance. And where 300 copies of the Bureau report had been printed the year before, a thousand copies of the 1914 report were distributed.

Most striking of all in the amplified annual report of 1914 was the restatement of the functions, aims, and purposes of the Bureau that appeared in the preface. Still concerned with the "extension of the general purposes of the Bureau," Dr. Stratton sought to clarify the new scope of work for which the Bureau had become responsible. The organic act was unchanged, he said, but a more "convenient" classification of functions as now authorized and exercised made the Bureau responsible for standards of measurement, standard values of constants, standards of quality, and standards of mechanical performance. In the report the next year Stratton amended this list to include a fifth function, standards of practice.[119]

Standards of measurement, he wrote in the annual report, included their custody, construction, and comparison, with methods of comparison presently available ranging from those "capable of measuring the thousandth part of a milligram to the large testing machines capable of measuring a load of thousands of tons." *Standard values of constants,* requiring accurate and authenticated determinations of the many fixed relations between physical quantities, ranged from the relation between heat and mechanical energy, required in designing steam engines and boilers, to the amount of heat required to turn liquid ammonia into vapor or to melt a pound of ice, as in the refrigeration industry.

Standards of quality, "confined almost exclusively to Government purchases," involved the physical and chemical investigation of materials to prepare methods of measurement and uniform specifications for their composition or manufacture. *Standards of performance,* whether of an engine, boiler, or pump, an electric generator or motor, a weighing device, or a telescope, involved the use of standards of measurement, standard values of constants, and standards of quality, and sought to arrive at specifications based on correct scientific and mechanical principles. A function only

---

[119] This classification may have evolved from Dr. Stratton's remarks at a congressional hearing several months before. In a discussion of the investigations in public utility services, the Bureau was, he said, concerned with standards of engineering, comprising standards of practice, standards of construction and operation, standards of service, and standard methods of testing, all of which involved standards of measurement and quality. Hearings * * * 1915 (Feb. 26, 1914), p. 980.

recently assumed by the Bureau, it too would relate almost entirely to Government purchases. *Standards of practice* looked principally to the enactment of laws in technical and scientific matters, to ordinances relating to the regulation of public utilities, and to the establishment of building and safety codes.[120]

The almost wholly pragmatic cast of these functions could not be missed, nor their overwhelming reference to Government testing and Government investigations. The source of the new look of the annual report was explained in a section entitled "The relation of the Bureau's work to the public." Yet not there but elsewhere in the report Dr. Stratton said: "Government purchases are not greatly different from those of the public," and all information and data obtained in this work by the Bureau "is given to the public in the form of suitable publications * * *. In other words, the needs of the public and the Government service are precisely the same as far as standards and specifications are concerned, whether it be standards of measurement, quality, or performance." And "the Government can do no greater service to the country than to place its own purchases on a basis which may be taken as a standard by the public at large." [121]

Two years later an elaborate chart of these "new" functions appeared in the annual report. Asked about it at a congressional hearing, Stratton replied: "There is not a single thing that the bureau does that I can think of * * * which does not fall within five classes of standards * * *. I think it [the chart] will clear up a great deal of uncertainty as to the scope of the work of the bureau." [122]

The new classification of functions and the elaborate reporting of Bureau research projects continued through the annual report of 1923, a tome running to an imposing 330 pages. Then a wave of conservation hit the Nation and the Bureau. The report of 1924, in the third year of Secretary of Commerce Hoover's tenure, totaled a scant 38 pages. The chart of functions and classes of standards that had appeared since 1916 was omitted and the splendid chart of the Bureau organization and map of the Bureau grounds that appeared in the 1923 report were gone. While standards were still pursued under five classes, they were not so listed, and in their place was the statement: "As a matter of convenience the organization of the Bureau is based not on classes of standards, but upon the nature of the work."

In a way, an era as well as a decade had ended.

---

[120] NBS Annual Report 1914, pp. 9–12; Annual Report 1915, p. 14.
[121] NBS Annual Report 1914, p. 12.
[122] Hearings * * * 1918 (Dec. 1, 1916), p. 482.

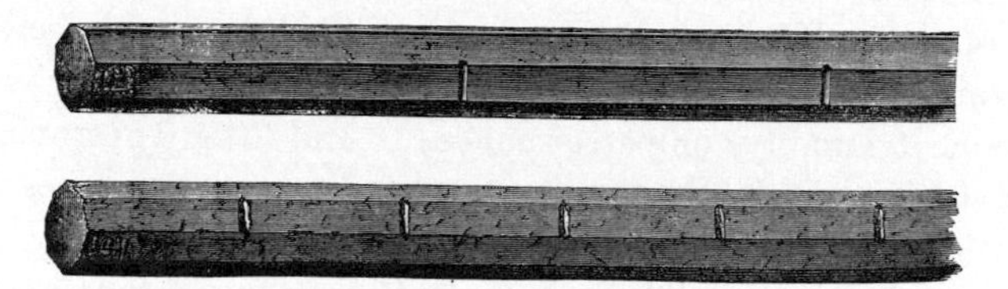

The standard yard of Henry VII, showing sixteenths of yard and, below, the subdivisions of inches.

THE WAR YEARS (1917–19)

CHAPTER IV

THE BUREAU TURNS TO WAR RESEARCH

The war began in faraway Europe on August 4, 1914 and for several months the stock market and the American public were profoundly depressed. Then the long battle line across northern France stabilized, rifle pits became trenches, and as winter approached it appeared that the war had come to stay. Its early threat to American security was countered by President Wilson's declaration of neutrality; its threat to our economic stability dissipated as America became the arsenal of the Allies, supplying them with money, credits, munitions, oil, chemicals, explosives, and foodstuffs.[1]

Pursuing neutrality, no Government agency made the slightest attempt to interfere in the booming production of war materials until a congressional act of August 1916, looking to a "future war of defense inferentially far distant," set up the Council of National Defense. Composed of the Secretaries of War, Navy, Interior, Agriculture, Commerce, and Labor, it was to make recommendations to the President "for the co-ordination of industries and resources for the national security and welfare."[2] Under no pressure and without a directive, the Council marked time until after war was declared, when its principal function was effectively assumed by the all-powerful War Industries Board, under Bernard Baruch.

The first actual war-research agency of World War I was the National Advisory Committee for Aeronautics (NACA), established by Congress in March 1915 to initiate and direct scientific studies in problems of flight. The Bureau of Standards, represented on the Committee by Dr. Stratton, was asked to begin investigations at once of the physical factors in aeronautic

[1] Exclusive of neutral countries, exports to the Allies rose from $927 million in 1914 to $3,013 million in 1916. Arthur C. Bining, The Rise of American Economic Life (New York: Charles Scribner's, 1943), p. 564; William E. Leuchtenburg, The Perils of Prosperity, 1914–1932 (University of Chicago Press, 1958), p. 16.

[2] First Annual Report, Council of National Defense, 1917–18, p. 6; Second Annual Report, 1918–19, p. 5.

design.[3] Many of the aviation problems subsequently assigned by NACA to the Navy and War Departments were, since they lacked research facilities, turned over to the Bureau as it "became the scientific laboratory for the two military services." [4]

The initial attempt to mobilize the scientific and technical resources of the Nation began in the Naval Consulting Board, appointed by Secretary of the Navy Daniels in mid-1915. Headed by Thomas Edison, then in his 68th year, with Willis R. Whitney, Frank J. Sprague, L. H. Baekeland, and Elmer A. Sperry on his staff, the Board, for lack of firm direction, made little headway and found its wartime activity limited to screening the tens of thousands of inventions submitted to the Government by a war-stimulated public. A year later, in July 1916, the National Academy of Sciences, with President Wilson's concurrence, formed a National Research Council (NRC) as its operating subsidiary under George E. Hale, director of the Mount Wilson Observatory, to establish cooperation between existing Government, educational, and industrial research organizations. Important posts went to Dr. Stratton of the Bureau and Dr. Charles D. Walcott, Secretary of the Smithsonian Institution and director of NACA, as Government representatives on NRC. Industrial representatives included Gano Dunn of the J. C. White Engineering Corp. and John J. Carty, president of American Telephone & Telegraph; and Michael Pupin of Columbia University represented educational institutions.[5]

In February 1917 the Council of National Defense requested the NRC to act as its agency for the organization of scientific information and personnel, the Naval Consulting Board to act as its committee on inventions. While neutrality tottered, the emergency councils and committees met and waited for a directive. No estimate, not even a guess, could be made of our possible troop commitment. The Nation was perilously close to war, yet few in this country even realized the nature of the conflict in Europe, that apart

---

[3] Letter, Secretary of NACA to Secretary of Commerce, Dec. 18, 1915 (NBS Box 3, AG). For further details on the establishment of NACA and its relation to the Bureau, see NBS Box 7, IDS.

NACA, established with an appropriation of $5,000, or "such part thereof as may be needed," was the predecessor of the National Aeronautics and Space Administration (NASA) whose budget in fiscal year 1964 was approximately one million times the initial appropriation to NACA.

[4] Hearings * * * 1919 (Jan. 25, 1918), p. 960. Bureau records for December 1917, said Redfield, indicated that demands for scientific work from the military services came in at the rate of one every 20 minutes during that month (With Congress and Cabinet, New York: Doubleday, Page, 1924, p. 100). By then, Stratton reported (Hearings * * * 1919, p. 960), military research constituted 95 percent of Bureau work.

[5] Letter, Hale to Secretary of Commerce, May 15, 1916 (NBS Box 296, APY-Hale). For the wartime organization of science, see Robert M. Yerkes, ed., The New World of Science: Its Development During the War (New York: Century, 1920), pp. 33 ff.

from a titanic struggle of armies it was a war of technology, of materiel, of massive and mechanized production. But of this the military services showed little cognition. Except for an answer to the growing U-boat menace, neither the Army nor Navy appeared to know what would be required of them or what science and technology could do for them.

Even when war was declared on April 6, 1917, the Nation was slow to awake to the fact that it was unprepared. Few believed that American troops in any number would be involved.[6] Two months later, in a show of the flag, Pershing took token elements of the First Division to France, and a month later cabled home the first unvarnished reports on the desperate plight of the Allied armies. Three years of carnage on a battlefront that had not changed by 10 kilometers in either direction had bled the British white. French morale was at its nadir and the armies close to mutiny. Pershing reported he would need 1 million men by the spring of 1918 and 3,200,000 in France by early 1919.[7]

To send that initial force overseas and produce and supply the mountains of material it must have, the scientific, economic, and social life of the Nation became mobilized as never before in its history.[8] There was no time for long drawn out research. For most of its war machine, the Nation had to rely on the research of the Allies. Artillery, ammunition, communication equipment, aircraft, and armored plate, all of Allied design, had to be adapted to American raw materials and American methods and machines. The scientific resources of the country were to be utilized principally in developing new sources and substitutes for war-scarce materials, devising new instruments and equipment for the Armed Forces, and accelerating standardization and mass production techniques in industry.[9] The demand for weapons, armor, engines, rails, trucks, and other heavy duty equipment was to make it a metallurgists' war; the need for substitute materials, for nitrates, for the agents and materials of gas warfare made it a chemists' war. Confronted at last with the nature of its task, the Council of National Defense began by mobilizing the laboratories of the universities, of industry,

---

[6] Frederic L. Paxson, American Democracy and the World War, 3 vols. (Boston: Houghton, Mifflin, 1936–48), II, 9.

[7] John J. Pershing, My Experiences in the War (New York: F. A. Stokes, 1931), I, 94–99; II, 122–123. See also Prof. J. S. Ames' report from Europe in May 1917, quoted in The Autobiography of Robert A. Millikan, pp. 157–158.

[8] Neither the Civil War nor the Spanish-American War "presented the necessity to convert to military use the maximum power of the Nation, nor to create for their use elaborate machines and weapons unknown to peace." Where earlier war manufacture was peace manufacture expanded, "in 1917–18 it was new manufacture upon an unknown scale." Paxson, II, 35.

[9] The first important moving assembly line in this country, at the Ford plant just outside Detroit, went into operation in May 1913, cutting the production time of a car from 12 to less than 6 hours.

and Government, and in particular the two Government bureaus "oriented to industrial problems—Standards and Mines." [10]

Until 1917 the war in Europe had little impact on the Bureau of Standards. Personnel increases remained normal, the volume of Government testing rose briefly in 1916 and then subsided, and industrial testing actually declined between 1914 and 1917. Uncertain of their requirements, the military services made few demands. In 1915 the Signal Corps requested some tests of airplane frames, wing fabrics, and engines. The NACA asked for a study of the characteristics of airplane propellers. In 1916 the Navy Department sought tests of steels going into its new warships. That same year Army Ordnance, soon to be swamped in problems, asked only for a study of several failures it had encountered in elevating gun screws.

Although heavy industry began producing munitions for the Allies in 1914, no call was made on the Bureau for certification of the gages used in their manufacture.[11] But with something like prescience, Louis A. Fischer urged Dr. Stratton to seek out a gage expert and organize a special laboratory. Harold L. Van Keuren was brought in and set to work planning the laboratory. It was one of the few areas in which this country was prepared when we entered the war.[12] Stratton also became concerned as German sources of chemical laboratory ware and high-grade optical glass were cut off, and early in 1916 he sought funds for additional furnaces and kilns at the Pittsburgh laboratory of the Bureau to undertake their experimental production.

The gage laboratory and glass plant were not the first such resources acquired by the Bureau. Well aware that in the testing of materials, analysis could not be separated from synthesis, Stratton had acquired five of these small-scale "factories" before the war. Learning that the machinery firm of Pusey and Jones in Wilmington was constructing several small paper mills for paper research companies, Stratton had managed to obtain one of

---

[10] Dupree, Science in the Federal Government, p. 304.

[11] Export of American explosives, principally to England, increased from $6 million in 1914 to $467 million in 1916. Bureau correspondence with the Secretaries of War and Navy in 1915–16 reported that munitions drawings were going to manufacturers with no mention of the necessary gages or with insufficient gages, and warned of the "grave danger that [these war supplies] would not fit when delivered to the field" (NARG 40, file 67009/43). Not surprising, many of the shells on arrival overseas proved to be "of a low standard," and in June 1916 the British War Mission established its own gage testing laboratory in New York. It came too late. In the Battle of the Somme that opened in July 1916, "the faultiness of the [American-made] ammunition in the preliminary artillery barrage was particularly severe * * * [resulting in] numerous premature bursts, falling short of shells, and unexploded shells." Brian Gardner, The Big Push (London: Cassell, 1961), pp. 63, 86.

[12] NBS Annual Report, 1917, pp. 20–21; SWS Address, 15th Annual Conference on Weights and Measures, May 23, 1922 (NBS Historical File).

Above, the NBS small-scale experimental paper mill in which all the operations of paper-making could be studied under controlled conditions. Below, the rotary cement kiln at the Pittsburgh laboratory, brought to Washington in 1918, for determining the effects of various processes in the manufacture of cements.

Above, the experimental rolling mill in the metallurgical division, a 16-inch mill equipped for rolling plates, rods, or bars, both hot and cold. Below, the NBS experimental cotton mill, acquired after the war, showing the knitting machine on the left and the creel (sets of bars with skewers for holding paying-off bobbins) on the right.

them for the Bureau at a fraction of its cost.[13] Components and processes in the manufacture of rubber products were determined on a small rubber mill similarly acquired, in which rubber compounds could be mixed and tubing and other small rubber articles made. The Pittsburgh laboratories had several small-scale kilns for firing clays and clay products, in which the effect of various compositions were determined, and a cement kiln with a capacity of a barrel at a burn. The metallurgical division had both an experimental foundry and a small rolling mill, for the preparation and heat treatment of alloys, where over 3,000 foundry castings were turned out during the war.[14]

With the acquisition of the gage shop and optical glass plant, the Bureau thus had seven of these small plants engaged in special production and process problems all through 1917–18. It was negotiating for two others, a small woolen mill and a cotton mill, as the war ended.

The wartime expansion of the Bureau might be said to date from 1913 when, to the original 8 acres of hilltop, an additional 9 acres were added on three sides of North building. In 1918 another 10 acres to the north gave the Bureau its first frontage on Connecticut Avenue, and small parcels totaling almost 8 acres purchased over the next 2 years brought the site close to its present form, except for the great slope down to the avenue, not acquired until 1925.[15]

New field laboratories of the Bureau included two structural materials (cement testing) stations at Denver and San Francisco, transferred from the Department of Interior's Reclamation Service in July 1917. The next year another cement laboratory, for Army, Navy, and Shipping Board construction projects, was set up at San Diego, and branch laboratories for gage testing were opened in New York, Cleveland, and Bridgeport, Conn.[16] In Washington, the fourth major structure, East building, housing the electrical laboratories, was completed in the spring of 1914. Later that year a large storage and workshop structure called the Far West building went up; a handsome new Chemistry building, begun in 1915, was occupied in

---

[13] Conversation with Dr. Robert Hobbs, Feb. 19, 1963.

[14] For descriptions of these plants, see Stratton, "The work of the National Bureau of Standards," an address before the Engineers' Club, Dayton, Ohio, May 4, 1915, pp. 43–45 (in Stratton Papers, MIT), and interview with SWS by H. E. Lobdel, editor, Technology Review (MIT), 24, 7–10 (1922). For the foundry work, see NBS Annual Report 1918, p. 188; Annual Report 1919, p. 263.

[15] See app. L for the sequence of NBS land acquisitions.

[16] NBS Annual Report 1918, p. 139; letter, SWS to Bureau of Public Roads, Department of Agriculture, Jan. 24, 1919 (NBS Box 15, IRC).

Mule teams leveling the ground for the new Chemistry building in the early fall of 1915. The rear of North building and the edge of the Low Temperature laboratory are in the background.

the spring of 1917; and in 1918 the Radio Laboratory and its towers, adjacent to East building, was completed.[17]

Of the hundred-million-dollar National Security and Defense Fund voted by Congress to President Wilson in 1917, a little over $2 million was allotted to the Bureau in 1918–19 for the construction and equipping of two large "war-emergency" laboratories and two lesser structures. Northwest building, centralizing metallurgical research, the gage work, and military equipment and military instrument research, was completed in March 1918, and an imposing Industrial building, almost three times larger than any previous Bureau structure, was finally completed early in 1920.[18]

The first occupants of the Industrial building, moving in late in 1918, were the structural materials laboratories, crowded out of West building, and Dr. Stratton's paper and rubber mills. Into a new Kiln building, back of Industrial, went an enlarged optical glass plant, as well as the cement and ceramic kilns brought from the Pittsburgh laboratory where the Army had commandeered much of the Bureau space for its own use. The fourth structure was an Altitude Laboratory (later called the Dynamometer Laboratory), in which high-altitude conditions could be simulated for testing airplane engine performance under flight conditions.[19]

While the President's emergency fund provided much needed buildings for the Bureau, special wartime funds for military research, amounting to $487,000 in 1917–18 and $622,000 in 1918–19, made it possible for the Bureau to acquire scientists it could never otherwise have afforded.[20] The scientific, technical, and administrative staff rose from 517 in 1917 to 1,117 a year later, some of the newcomers advancing to key positions and

---

[17] For construction details of these buildings, see NBS Blue Folder Boxes 77–79, 81. Among minor structures built following the influx of warworkers were the Standard Store and gas station, erected at the entrance to the Bureau grounds and operated by staff members in their off hours. Since the nearest stores were almost a mile away in either direction, the Bureau shop was a convenience, offering fruit, vegetables, canned goods and other groceries, tobacco and sundries, as well as gas and oil, at cost. By 1925 commercial enterprises began to close in, and that spring the store and gas station were closed. Letter, GKB to H. W. Bearce, Dec. 1, 1925 (NBS Box 108, AG).

[18] NBS Blue Folder Boxes 82–84.

[19] For the altitude laboratory, see letter, Secretary of Commerce to President Wilson, Aug. 6, 1918 (NBS Box 5, FPG).

[20] Approximately half the funds were special military appropriations by Congress to the Bureau, the other half transferred funds from Army and Navy appropriations. See app. F.

The Standard Store and gas station down on Connecticut Avenue, at the corner of Van Ness Street (formerly Pierce Mill Road). The recently completed Industrial building is in the background. The Ford passenger-freight van back of the store is being serviced, as a trolley approaches to pick up the waiting soldier and scientist. The year, 1918.

destined to remain at the Bureau through the intervening years between wars.[21]

The universities and, to a lesser extent, industry were to furnish numbers of young scientists needed at the Bureau, but not before the services, indiscriminately accepting or drafting every male of military age, had made serious inroads on the staff. Those with Navy appointments were the first to go, and the cavalry units at nearby Fort Myer carried off a large group, including most of the textile section, before a halt was called.

Dr. Stratton's long reluctance to hire women to work at the Bureau—he is reported to have said once that the sight of his scientists in shirtsleeves might offend them—broke down as the services not only called up many on the clerical and administrative staff but great numbers of the laboratory aids, apprentices, and assistants. While Stratton felt it was not "in the interests of the service to open such positions as assistant or associate

---

[21] Statutory employees in December 1918 numbered 341, those paid from special appropriations 424, those from the President's allotment and military funds 295, the remaining 57 on loan from universities and other Government agencies. Hearings * * * 1920 (Dec. 12, 1918), p. 934.

From the universities in 1917 came Dr. Edward Wichers to work in the chemistry of platinum metals; Dr. Fred L. Mohler, a spectroscopist assigned to optical pyrometry in airplane engine research; Dr. Lewis V. Judson, to work on the calibration of military scales; Dr. Henry T. Wensel, on optical lenses and glasses; Laurens E. Whittemore, in radio; and Dr. Englehardt A. Eckhardt, to investigate sound-ranging problems. From industry came Arthur F. Beal (military timepieces), Howard S. Bean (gage testing), Carl S. Cragoe (methane analysis), and Francis W. Dunmore (radio). "Drafted" from other Government agencies as Stratton combed the lists for physicists and chemists were Dr. Lyman J. Briggs, later Director of the Bureau, to work in aviation physics, and Dr. Gustave E. F. Lundell, to do alloy research and head the standard samples section.

In 1918 recent university graduates arriving at the Bureau included Archibald T. McPherson, assigned to gas chemistry studies of combustion engines; Raleigh Gilchrist, analytical chemist in platinum metals; and James I. Hoffman, iron and steel chemist. From industry that year same Ralph E. Gould (timepieces), Enoch Karrer (searchlights), Roman F. Geller (optical glass refractories), and Alexander I. Krynitsky (experimental foundry).

Uniforms appeared on the Bureau grounds as the Army and Navy assigned specialists to work on military assignments, among them Cpl. Frederick A. Curtis, in paper research, and Herbert N. Eaton, in aeronautical instrument research.

Among university personnel on temporary assignment to the Bureau were Dr. Frederick W. Grover, who had been there from 1903 to 1912 and returned to work on radio measurements; Dr. Llewelyn G. Hoxton, who came back to make physical studies on combustion engines; Prof. Albert A. Michelson, in a lieutenant commander's uniform, to work on optical problems for the Navy Department; and Dr. William B. Kouwenhoven, electrical engineer from Johns Hopkins, to make studies in the magnetic testing of rifle barrels.

physicist" to women, and few at that time could qualify, he had no choice in replacing his laboratory assistants.[22]

Almost a hundred girls and women came to the Bureau during the war, among them Miss Johanna Busse, a researcher in thermometry, who in 1929 became chief of that section and held the position until her retirement 20 years later. The first woman with a doctoral degree in physics to work at the Bureau arrived in 1918, to assist in the preparation of a radio handbook for the Signal Corps. A second joined the colorimetry section a year later. From then on the doors were open and the question of ability to qualify was never raised again.[23]

More serious than the exodus prompting the distaff influx, the military services and new war agencies also levied on key Bureau personnel, among them Louis A. Fischer, commissioned a major by Army Ordnance; Roy Ferner, called to the Emergency Fleet; and Rudolph Wig and Joseph Pearson, drafted by the Shipping Board. As requests continued to come in, Stratton did what he could to stop the raids on his staff.[24]

The war ended Dr. Stratton's hours in his private workshop. To attend to new and pressing responsibilities and allow him more time to look after the scientific work going on in the laboratories, he was obliged to seek help with the routine operations of his office. In the fall of 1917 he brought in as his technical assistant, Frederick J. Schlink, an associate physicist in the weights and measures division.[25] As an executive of Consumers' Research in the 1930's, Schlink was to become a gadfly of the Bureau, making use of his experience and knowledge gained there in handling the disposition of incoming technical and scientific mail and administering the Government testing work in his divison.

Acquiring personnel was in some respects the Bureau's most difficult wartime problem. Shifting from peacetime to military research was almost the least. So much of its work before the war was keyed directly or indirectly to industry that at congressional hearings on appropriations for 1917, Stratton had no difficulty in pointing out the wartime potential of every investigation at the Bureau. Asking for increases in funds for these investigations and proposing four new ones, in color standards, clay products, the physical

---

[22] Letter, SWS to Secretary of Commerce, May 25, 1918, and attached correspondence (NBS Box 4, AP 1917).

[23] Dr. Louise McDowell, Cornell, 1909, on leave from the physics department at Wellesley College, remained through 1918–19. Dr. Mabel K. Frehafer in colorimetry remained from 1919 to 1923. Interview with Dr. Silsbee, May 23, 1963.

[24] See letter, Secretary of Commerce to President Wilson, June 6, 1918 (NBS Box 4, AP).

[25] Hearings * * * 1918 (Dec. 1, 1916), p. 470.

constants of metals and alloys, and standardization of machines, mechanical appliances, and tools, he declared:

> There never was a time in the history of the country when we should be looking at such matters as critically as at present. The items submitted—I think I can say all of them—are as fundamentally concerned with both industrial and military preparedness as any that will come before you.[26]

When war came, Stratton later said, it was not necessary to "change the bureau's organization one bit." [27] The metallurgy division turned from its rail and wheel investigations to armament steel research, the electrochemistry section took up battery research, the electrolysis section turned to sound-ranging problems, and the weights and measures division undertook the preparation of military scales and gage testing. Photometry turned to searchlight and other military illumination projects, pyrometry to optical glass and aeronautical engine research, radiometry studied invisible signaling devices, spectroscopy worked on military photography, and colorimetry took up problems of camouflage. As still other inquiries and requests for research poured in from the military services, from the NACA and the National Research Council, and from the civilian war agencies—the Shipping Board, the War Industries Board, the War Trade Board, the Railroad Administration, the Fuel Administration—the Bureau shifted its electrical, optical, and chemical investigations and its structural and industrial materials programs to their military applications with scarcely a hitch.[28]

NEW SOURCES, RESOURCES, AND SUBSTITUTES

The 299-page report, "The War Work of the Bureau of Standards," suggests that except in medicine and foodstuffs, there was scarcely an investigation of the National Research Council or War Industries Board or a problem of the military services in which the Bureau was not concerned in one way or another. From aircraft construction to camouflage, from coke-oven investigations to concrete ships, from precision gages to illuminating shells, from optical glass to rubber, from submarine detection to X-ray and radium research, the Bureau participated in almost the whole range of America's wartime effort. As standards laboratory and as research institute

---

[26] Hearings * * * 1917 (Feb. 2, 1916), pp. 991–992.

[27] Hearings * * * 1919 (Jan. 25, 1918), p. 975.

[28] For a roster of the scientific staff and the wartime projects of the Bureau as of September 1918, see app. J.

it was called on to (1) furnish scientific and technical information and recommendations, (2) undertake specific research, (3) develop and standardize tests and test procedures, (4) standardize materials and equipment, and (5) make new as well as routine precision measurements.

The first direct contact of the Bureau with the war in Europe occurred in the spring and summer of 1917 when members of the Bureau went abroad with a scientific mission "to obtain information concerning applications of science to warfare and the part to be played by scientific men in the war." [29] That same spring British and French scientific missions arrived in this country and visited the Bureau, bringing with them new military equipment, products of their laboratory research and battlefield experience. The disclosures of both missions were jolting, for they indicated a range of research abroad of which we were entirely ignorant and a superiority in certain technologies of which we were wholly unaware. Particularly impressive were some of the French steels and semi-steels and the developments of French radio apparatus.[30]

Chemicals and steel, forging the weapons of the battle in France, were primary concerns of the Bureau throughout the war. Germany's preeminent dye industry, on which our textile industry depended for 90 percent of its dyestuffs, also made her dominant in explosives, for out of the same coal tar derivatives that built the aniline industry came the phenol for picric acid, the toluol for TNT, and the ammonia for ammonium nitrate.[31] This country's negligible dye industry made us almost wholly dependent on the coking industry for our supply of toluol. When war came that supply was already earmarked for the Allies and other sources had to be speedily developed. In the spring of 1917, at the instigation of the National Research Council, Bureau representatives met with American Gas Institute officials and with Federal, State, and city authorities to study procedures for the recovery of toluol from city gas supplies, as the British were doing, and to determine the adjustments necessary in standards of gas service.[32]

---

[29] NBS M46, "The War Work of the Bureau of Standards" (1921), pp. 11, 172. Hereafter cited as "War Work."

[30] The steel in the French 240-mm. trench mortar, for example, was much better than that in the same mortar made in this country. The French also made a satisfactory processed cast iron (semi-steel) shell that American industry was unable to duplicate until the Bureau established criteria foi its production. See "War Work," pp. 195–196. For the radio equipment of the Allies, see radio section, below. On the other hand, the Bureau discounted the new stainless steel made by the English and even after the war continued to believe it had only limited usefulness. See letter, SWS to Chief of Construction, Navy Department, Dec. 21, 1921 and attached correspondence (NBS Box 12, IMH).

[31] Letter, Secretary of Commerce Redfield to SWS, Feb. 22, 1915 (NBS Box 3, AG).

[32] See Benedict Crowell, America's Munitions, 1917–18 (Washington, D.C., 1919), pp. 107–108.

Constructed on the basis of Bureau recommendations, 21 Government-owned toluol plants were in operation extracting toluol and ammonia from the light oils of coal and water gas in city gas works at the time of the armistice. The reduced efficiency of household gas that resulted from this stripping became a memorable experience of the war as heating values fell off and gas mantles roared as housewives turned them up full to get more light. But along with new coke-oven recovery processes, the plants raised toluol production from the prewar rate of approximately half a million gallons annually to 40 times that amount.[33]

The Bureau also became involved in byproduct coke operations when in the latter part of 1917 the Department of Commerce asked Bureau gas engineers to study the recently developed Roberts coke oven, said to produce a commercial grade of metallurgical coke from the low-grade coals of Illinois and Indiana, as well as large yields of byproducts, including light oils, ammonia, and tar. With Bureau of Mines and Geological Survey representatives, more than 20 members of the Bureau took part in the work and continued the investigations through 1918. The war ended before the Roberts oven was proved, but the investigation indicated that the process had considerable merit. Perhaps more important was the reassessment of the value of some of the midcontinent coals as a new fuel and byproduct resource. Although considered uneconomical to work in peacetime, it seemed possible that new advances in mining technology might make them competitive with established fields.[34]

The most extensive testing undertaken by the Bureau during the war was almost certainly in the chemical, physical, and structural properties of metals—of processed irons for use in shells; of steels and steel alloys for guns, munitions, armor plate, high-speed tools, gages, airplane instruments and engines, helmets and gas masks, horseshoe nails and rivets; of aluminum for metal airplanes and Army canteens; of brass for ammunition. Under the stimulus of war, industry turned out scores of new alloy steels—nickel, chromium, tungsten, zirconium, molybdenum, vanadium, manganese, and cobalt—and sent them to the Bureau for precise determination of their composition and qualities. Ingots of light armor alloy steels (containing zirconium, molybdenum, boron, cerium), made for the Navy at the Bureau of Mines were rolled into plates in the Bureau of Standards mill and thorough tests made of their mechanical, chemical, and thermal properties. And

---

[33] "War Work," pp. 288–293; T117, "Toluol recovery" (McBride, Reinicker, Dunkley, 1918). For the less than cooperative attitude of the gas industry at the time, see letter, SWS to editor, Am. Gas Eng. J., Nov. 17, 1917 (NBS Box 7, ICG).

[34] "War Work," pp. 73–82.

where tests of new alloys warranted it, the Bureau evolved standard test methods and manufacturing control procedures.[35]

At the request of the NACA and the Navy, studies were made of the properties and methods of manufacture of light alloys of aluminum, for the construction of a proposed all-metal airplane, and of duralumin, known to be used in the construction of the German zeppelins.[36] Cooperating with the War Industries Board in its drive to conserve imported tin, the Bureau found cadmium an acceptable substitute in tin-lead solders. It also made recommendations for the reduction of tin in bearing metals, modified the tin content in bronzes, and contributed to recovery processes for tin scrap. Similar research to conserve manganese, in short supply throughout the war, lead to revised specifications of the manganese content in several types of steel.[37]

In these metallurgical investigations the Bureau introduced, in many instances for the first time, new concepts of quantitative measurement in the industry. Under "cookery" methods of manufacture, still prevalent in many plants, adding a variable quantity of manganese, for example, and the necessary fluxes, resulted in a satisfactory steel and industry was therefore content. Bureau laboratory and foundry research showed that even better steel resulted from exact measurement of its ingredients, and besides conserving raw materials this precision made possible greater control over the manufacturing process.

New technologies and the all-consuming nature of the war soon produced shortages never before envisaged. One of these was in platinum, imported largely from Russia. It was needed in large quantities as a catalyst in the manufacture of munitions, was used in the contact points of airplane magnetos, and in the making of chemical laboratory ware. As it grew scarce its price soared, and hunting for platinum ores in this country became as avid a pursuit in World War I as uranium hunting was to be some 25 years later.

Despite its importance to industry, very little was known about the rhodium, iridium, palladium, iron and other metals found as alloys in commerical platinum or about their effect on manufacturing processes. The study of platinum and the platinum metals which began during the war under

---

[35] "War Work," pp. 158–172. A supersteel rumored to be possessed by the Germans and thought to be a zirconium alloy was identified after the war as a uranium alloy, of more propaganda than military or industrial value. See letter, director, Nela Research Laboratory to SWS, July 28, 1917 (NBS Box 11, IM); correspondence in NBS Boxes 10 and 11, IM 1918; interview with Dr. Raleigh Gilchrist, Oct. 30, 1962.

[36] For the Bureau's many years of interest in duralumin (1917–35), see correspondence in NBS Box 384, IM.

[37] "War Work," pp. 154–158, 160–162. See T109, "Conservation of tin in bearing metals, bronzes, and solders" (Burgess and Woodward, 1919).

a special appropriation continued at the Bureau for almost 30 years. The wartime effort was limited to studying the effects of the metals alloyed with platinum when platinum was used for catalytic purposes, assaying the hopeful finds of platinum prospectors—mostly negative—and searching for platinum substitutes. Although Bureau research showed that two gold-palladium alloys known as palau and rhotanium made fairly suitable platinum substitutes in the making of laboratory crucibles and dishes, they were not to be more than wartime expedients.[38]

Since the whole of steel production was preempted for Allied arms and munitions, for war emergency buildings and plants, and for our own weaponry, it seemed for a time impossible to provide sufficient steel to build the transports and merchant fleet this country needed but did not have. Actually, by expansion of existing steel plants and almost total suppression of the automobile industry, the necessary steel plate was made available, but not before a number of wooden ships and even some of concrete came down the ways. It was in the latter program that the Bureau laboratory at Pittsburgh had a considerable role, assisting in the development of a burnt clay aggregate that expanded "like a loaf of bread when it rises," as Stratton said, and yet was strong enough to make concrete ships possible.[39]

Based on designs prepared under the direction of Rudolph J. Wig and Joseph C. Pearson, Bureau members with the Shipping Board, more than 40 concrete cargo ships and tankers were planned. Two experimental ships of 3,500 tons were floated and satisfactorily tested in 1918 and 10 more of 7,500 tons deadweight were completed by 1921. None ever became operational. Although somewhat cheaper and faster to build than steel ships, concrete bottoms by reason of their relative brittleness and reduced cargo space were not deemed likely to replace steel or wood except in an emergency. The same held true of the several concrete barges and concrete freight cars tested by the Bureau.[40]

The months of the emergency disclosed unsuspected gaps everywhere in this country's long vaunted belief in its self-sufficiency. Within weeks of the declaration of war, leather, paper, and textiles went on the list of critical materials and the search for substitutes began. Among leather substitutes produced by industry at the urging of the Council of National Defense and the War Department and tested at the Bureau were fishskin, porpoise, and sharkskin as uppers for civilian and military shoes and a variety of compositions for soles. When it was found that no fishskin would do, the shoe

---

[38] "War Work," pp. 65–66, 159–60; Raleigh Gilchrist, MS, "The scientific activities of Division 5 * * * 1917–61," pp. 15–18 (NBS Historical File).

[39] Hearings * * * 1920 (Dec. 12, 1918), p. 947.

[40] Proc. Am. Concrete Inst. 14, 441 (1918); ibid., 15, 241 (1919); ibid., 17, 284 (1921); "War Work," pp. 86–87, 213; letter, SWS to R. J. Wig, Apr. 23, 1918, and attached correspondence (NBS Box 7, ICP).

industry ceased making high-buttoned shoes, at one stroke solving the problem of civilian uppers and making a genuine contribution, however temporary, to foot comfort and esthetics. On the other hand, at least one of the hundreds of composition soles submitted to the Bureau proved almost as durable as leather under ordinary usage, though unsuitable for shoes destined for hard wear overseas.[41] The infantry got the leather.

Bureau tests of paper substitutes and the search for new uses for paper were more successful, resulting, in a critical area, in partial replacement of tin cans by impregnated paper containers for shipping greases and soaps, and paper barrels for shipping pitch or asphalt. A paper made in the Bureau mill from jute and manila rope stock appeared especially promising. An exceedingly strong paper, it was intended as a substitute for the linen fabrics used to cover airplane wings. But it came too late. The substitute actually used for scarce linen was a mercerized cotton fabric developed in the textile section of the Bureau. It was adopted by this country and also by England, whose inadequate supply of flax for linen had made the research necessary.[42]

Faced with the fact that 65 percent of our raw wool came from abroad, that shipping was scarce and uncertain, and that millions of uniforms and blankets would be needed for the American armies coming into being, the Quartermaster Corps and Ordnance Department appealed to the Bureau for help. To find out what characteristics a wool substitute must have, the Bureau sent inquiries to textile manufacturers concerning the nature of the raw stock and woolen compositions. The answers disclosed that neither here nor abroad had manufacturers ever made clothing materials, woolen or otherwise, with specifications that could be quantitatively measured. Wool was wool, as cotton was cotton, whatever the quality or properties of their ingredients. When the industry protested Bureau proposals to define wool compositions and set up specifications, Stratton began negotiations for a small experimental wool manufacturing plant to make the necessary tests. Working the raw materials with available laboratory equipment, the Bureau found that the heat-retaining properties of wool, as well as other textiles, depends less upon the intrinsic properties of their fibers than on their arrangement, and that a lightweight cotton could be made into almost as warm a fabric as wool.[43] The Bureau thus learned that, as in some areas of the steel, glass, and other industries, the textile industry worked with little understanding of its fundamental principles.

---

[41] "War Work," pp. 143–144.

[42] "War Work," pp. 198–202, 282; correspondence in NBS Box 15, IST. For other leather, paper, and textile substitutes (wooden soles for shoes, cotton currency, transparent silk for airplane wing coverings, etc.), see NBS Box 15, files, ISL, ISP, and IST. Also letter, SWS to National War Savings Committee, June 11, 1918 (NBS Box 6, IC).

[43] "War Work," pp. 283–284.

As with so many of the wartime investigations, the war ended before much of the research in substitutes could be translated into new products. In the emergency, the quickest solution was often elimination, as in the case of uppers on shoes. Wool simply disappeared from shops and stores and went into uniforms. Felt, too, went off the market and into canteen cases and helmets, splints, and shell packing. Silk went into powder bags. But elimination alone was not enough. To continue to supply the Allies and at the same time clothe, feed, and equip our military forces demanded an end to traditionally wasteful practices and a hitherto unknown degree of standardization. Thus, perhaps the most important result of the search for new sources or substitutes for materials in critical supply was not the substitutes themselves but the fact that both Government and industry were forced to establish specifications for materials and insist on greater standardization of products.

The drive for standardization and elimination of waste in commercial and industrial practices had its beginning in the Commercial Economy Board, organized in the Council of National Defense in March 1917. Renamed the Conservation Division, it was transferred in May 1918 to Bernard Baruch's War Industries Board, soon to regulate the manufacture of some 30,000 articles of commerce.[44]

In the year and a half of the war the Conservation Division and its predecessor effected enormous savings of manpower and materials in over 250 industries by reducing the number of styles, varieties, sizes, and colors, by eliminating services and certain materials and products altogether, by substituting plentiful for scarce materials, and by standardizing sizes, lengths, widths, and weights. The clothing industry was revolutionized from the skin out as steel for corsets, weighted silks, and heavy woolens disappeared from the market. Fabric was saved by shortening men's coats, eliminating outside pockets on suits, and restricting suit styles to 10 models. Shoe lasts were reduced in number and shoe colors restricted to black, white, and one shade of tan.

Newsprint for papers and magazines was cut as much as 20 percent. Colors of typewriter ribbons shrank from 150 to 5 and were sold in heavy paper instead of tinfoil and tin boxes. Buggy wheels were reduced from 232 sizes and varieties to 4, plows from 326 to 76 sizes and styles, and automobile tires from 287 types to 9. Brass pens were abolished, pocketknives

---

[44] At the same time, Herbert Hoover's Food Administration began fixing food prices, to forestall hoarding and profiteering, inaugurated "meatless" and "wheatless" days, campaigned for other food economies in the home, and acted to stimulate food production. "Hooverizing" enabled the United States to export almost three times her normal amounts of breadstuffs, meats, and sugar in 1918. Mark Sullivan, Our Times: The United States, 1900–1925. V. Over Here, 1914–1918 (New York: Scribner, 1933), pp. 383–384, 418–422.

cut from 6,000 to a hundred varieties, and steel pens reduced from 132 to 30 styles. Mail order catalogs best reflected the new austerity as their customary bulk fell away by more than half.

As a result of simplification and standardization, labor savings in the manufacture of products from clothing to coffins reportedly reached as high as 35 percent. Savings over prewar consumption of materials in some instances rose to 50 percent as simplicity ruled and plentiful wood, paper, zinc, and cotton replaced the steel, tinplate, copper, brass, bronze, pig tin, nickel, and raw wool consumed by war.[45] The country had experienced nothing like it before, and the impact of this husbandry of resources reached into every home, every office, factory, institution, and government agency in the Nation.

Reviewing the wartime economy drive shortly after the armistice, the Bureau had to admit that despite more than a decade of testing of Government purchases,

> no very pronounced demand for standardization among * * * the different Government departments * * * had existed prior to the war. Large as the orders for * * * materials had been in normal times, the necessity for complete standardization was not very evident. When, however, as a result of the war many Government bureaus [began] buying goods of about the same kind at the same time, it soon became necessary to have some sort of standard specifications.[46]

It must be admitted that in the case of the military departments, which had been left free to develop their own purchasing procedures, the new order of the day, for all its intrinsic value, permitted a latitude of interpretation that sometimes worked mischief. Specifications arbitrarily arrived at often defeated their purpose, as when General Electric complained to the Bureau that it frequently received greatly differing specifications for identical items of electrical apparatus ordered by the Army and Navy.[47] Asked at a congressional hearing why the Government had requirements or specifications that manufacturers found all but impossible to meet, Stratton replied that these were not Bureau specifications. New department or bureau heads, particularly in the War Department, who suddenly became "specification-minded" were apt to set up standards for materials on their own initiative

---

[45] Grosvenor B. Clarkson, Industrial America in the World War: The Strategy Behind the Line, 1917–1918 (Boston: Houghton, Mifflin, 1924), pp. 209–231; Bernard M. Baruch, American Industry in the War: A Report of the War Industries Board (1921), edited by R. H. Hippelhauser (New York: Prentice-Hall, 1941), pp. 65–69.

[46] War Work, pp. 151–152.

[47] Letter, General Electric to NBS, Mar. 10, 1917 (NBS Box 7, IE). For a note on the Standardization Section of the General Staff, set up in August 1918, see NBS Annual Report 1919, p. 52.

that could be produced only at high cost. The tensile strength established for one kind of steel wire, for example, had proved clearly beyond the requirements and wholly impractical to make. In another case the Bureau found that a cement specification so limited the magnesium content that it cut off the most important cement-producing district in the United Sates.[48] And in at least one instance the War Industries Board had to act "to kill a general standardization suggestion that evolved in the War Department during an attack of unusually severe standardization fever. To have reduced all machine tools to uniform standards [as recommended] would have stifled production for many months." [49]

Despite the follies committed in the name of standardization, the practice emerged from the war as an indispensable consideration in the coming age of mass production. The war demonstrated not only the usefulness to manufacturers of specifications and standards, as the Bureau had long and patiently pointed out, but their inescapable necessity. For the Bureau to have supplied in those few months the thousands of standards asked for by agencies and industries in the grip of war was out of the question. The major effort of the Bureau was restricted to an attempt to codify Government procedures and to formulate, where it could, responsible and comprehensive specifications for materials and products it was equipped and staffed to deal with.[50]

The hope of the Bureau that the impulse toward conservation, toward sensible husbandry of resources through standardization, might continue in the postwar period was soon dashed. Industry no sooner turned from war production to the consumer market again than it reverted to all its former wasteful practices. It was brought up short by the severe postwar depression that struck late in 1920. Under the leadership of the Department of Commerce and the National Bureau of Standards, industry was again instructed in its wartime lesson. Conservation and standardization became key words of the decade.

THE AIRPLANE IN THE LABORATORY

So rapid was the wartime development of air power and air strategy that by 1917 some at the Bureau seriously believed that "victory was likely to go to the side having the largest and most effective types of machines.[51] Yet in no aspect of scientific, technological, or industrial capability was America so utterly unprepared as it was in aviation. The airplane that first

[48] Hearings * * * 1920 (Dec. 12, 1918), pp. 929, 945.
[49] Clarkson, Industrial America in the World War, p. 454.
[50] "War Work," p. 16.
[51] Ibid.

flew at Kitty Hawk had continued to evolve in Europe, where the early years of the war saw successively improved military planes and power plants—the enemy and Allied artillery spotters, scouts, pursuit craft, and great lumbering bombers—whose designs were carefully withheld from neutrals. In the same decade and a half after the Wright brothers' flight, the military forces of this country had acquired just 2 flying fields and 55 planes. Every one of those planes was either obsolete or obsolescent by European standards and had little or none of the instrumentation in the aircraft then flying in France.[52]

With our entry into the war, the Allies at once made their airplane designs available. On the other hand, because this country was supplying parts, some of their engine and instrument difficulties had arrived here earlier, through the war missions. Reports from abroad in 1916 indicated a number of shortcomings in their new high-powered planes. The spark plugs in use were said to limit better engine design, engine fuels were erratic in performance, and the lubricating oils often congealed at high altitudes. Bombers, fighters, and reconnaissance planes all required more refined instrumentation and, more important, improved wing fabrics and dopes, to reduce their vulnerability to fire. Other questions laid before the Bureau through the National Advisory Committee for Aeronautics and the Bureau of Aircraft Production in the Signal Corps included determination of the rate of flame propagation and of pressure cycles in aviation engine cylinders and better design of engine radiators.

Bureau ignition experts found that besides the high carbon deposits that frequently formed on the American-made spark plugs used by the Allies, sudden extremes of heat and cold at high altitude (10,000 to 30,000 feet) sometimes cracked the porcelain insulators, or the high heat alone caused the insulators to become conductors of electricity, resulting in the engine sudddenly cutting out in flight.[53] The Bureau discovered that these failures occurred principally because of poor materials or poor workmanship, and sent to manufacturers of ignition equipment the data it had collected, along with new specifications and standard test methods to insure a better product. Before the war ended the Bureau's electrical and ceramic divisions had devised a much improved arrangement of engine circuits and produced a better type of porcelain for aviation spark plugs.[54] The work continued

---

[52] Leonard P. Ayres, The War With Germany: A Statistical Summary (Washington, D.C., 1919), p. 85.

[53] Letter, General Electric to Chief Signal Officer, Nov. 22, 1917 (NBS Box 9, IEP), declared: "If we are correctly informed, the spark plug, as at present developed, is one of the weakest points in the equipment of the modern aeroplane."

[54] Silsbee, "Ignition work at the Bureau of Standards," Automotive Industries, nv, 1294–1299 (June 12, 1919); "War Work," pp. 24–30.

The instrument panel in the De Havilland–4 of 1918. Most of the instruments shown were of European origin, all modified by the Bureau before adoption as U.S. Army standard for the De Havilland.

after the war in a new power plant section set up in the heat division at the Bureau.

All of the altimeters, airspeed indicators, tachometers, and other aeronautical instruments that came to the Bureau for examination and testing were based on European prototypes. Many were still in an elementary stage and underwent considerable modification in the laboratories prior to their adoption as standard by our Army and Navy. Successive modifications of the inclinometer or banking indicator led to an almost wholly new instrument. The same was true of the rate-of-climb indicator, whose inherent defects could not otherwise be eliminated.[55]

If instrumentation and engine problems were to a degree overcome by the end of the war, time militated against getting the highly publicized "cloud" of American planes into the air. When in July 1917, the Signal Corps was directed by Congress to design and build a fleet of 22,000 planes, neither the military services nor American industry had developed a single modern airframe or engine. A year was simply not time enough to acquire the necessary skills or experience, and the Government's overambitious program resulted in fewer than 700 planes. These were chiefly flying boats and observation planes, the latter principally a redesigned De Havilland–4, called by the American pilots who took them up, the Flying Coffin.[56]

---

[55] "War Work," pp. 11–16, 38–40; NBS Annual Report 1919, pp. 186–187.

[56] George C. Reinhardt and William R. Kintner, The Haphazard Years: How America Has Gone to War (New York: Doubleday, 1960), p. 80.

Except for the pioneer work of the Wright brothers, Langley, Chanute and a few others, serious study of the scientific fundamentals of flight began in this country only after the NACA requested the Bureau in 1915 to undertake an investigation of aviation aerodynamics. The Bureau was to play an important part in this research before the NACA acquired facilities of its own.

In January 1918 the Bureau transferred its aerodynamic studies from the library and laboratory to a new wind tunnel building recently constructed under the direction of Dr. Lyman J. Briggs. Dr. Briggs, a Department of Agriculture physicist lent to the Bureau several months earlier, recalled that soon after he arrived Dr. Stratton asked him to design and build a wind tunnel balance. Asked whether he knew what that was, Briggs answered that he presumed it was "to measure forces on an airfoil." "Right," said Stratton, "and while you're about it, you'd better design a wind tunnel to put it in." [57]

The wind tunnel that Briggs designed housed a 9-foot propeller that produced air speeds of 90 miles an hour. In it he installed recording apparatus and began his measurements on airfoils and on airplane and dirigible models. In almost continuous operation, the wind tunnel was also used to make studies of wind stresses, to test airspeed indicators and similar instruments, and to determine the flight characteristics of aerial bombs.

While the aircraft program as a whole lagged for lack of time, knowledge, and experience, aviation engine production, utilizing the Nation's automotive industry, quickly went into high gear. Both as a matter of national prestige and practicality, an American-designed engine was considered crucial from the start. Although an aircraft commission sent to Europe in the spring of 1917 examined more than 80 different engines in use or under development by the Allies, none was deemed sufficiently powerful to meet future requirements or, what was more important, lend itself to mass production methods or materials.[58]

Design work on both 8-cylinder and 12-cylinder engines was started that June by a group of Packard Motor Car engineers quartered at the Bureau. They had begun the preliminary paperwork in the Washington hotel where they were staying and were ready to start on the detailed manufacturing drawings when they phoned Dr. Stratton one midnight and told him they needed more space. He promptly made available the whole of the new Chemistry building and the use of any other facilities at the Bureau they might need. The engineers moved in the following morning.[59]

---

[57] Interview with Dr. Briggs, Nov. 1, 1961; NBS Annual Report 1918, pp. 127–128.
[58] Redfield, With Congress and Cabinet, p. 227; Paxson, American Democracy and the World War, II, 112.
[59] Crowell, America's Munitions, 1917–18, p. 270.

The Bureau's second wind tunnel as set up in Northwest building late in 1919. The honeycomb at the entrance of the 3-foot wind tunnel steadied the incoming flow of air. The maximum wind speed that could be established was about 150 miles per hour, more than enough to determine the air resistance of bombs, projectiles, airplane models, and for calibrating instruments.

The 12-cylinder Liberty engine mounted for testing in the Bureau's altitude chamber. When both concrete side doors (one open here) were closed, the air pressure and temperature inside could be lowered to correspond to any desired altitude, making it possible to test the engine under simulated flying conditions.

The exhaust from the engine and the air in the chamber were withdrawn by an electric-driven centrifugal exhauster. The pressure could thus be reduced as low as one-third of an atmosphere, corresponding to an altitude of approximately 35,000 feet.

But so rapidly was aviation history moving that 1 month later, when the first 8-cylinder engine arrived at the Bureau for testing, it was declared inadequate. Pershing had cabled that the planes he would need for his operations in 1918 must have 12-cylinder engines. Exactly 2 months after, in September 1917, the "12," putting out over 300 (later more than 400) horsepower, as against the 225 horsepower of the "8," had arrived and successfully passed its 50-hour test. Originally named the "United States Standard 12-cylinder Aviation Engine," it was rechristened the "Liberty engine" as it went into production 4 months later. Up to the armistice, the Packard, Lincoln, Ford, Cadillac, Buick, and Marmon factories built 13,574 Liberty engines, of which fully a quarter went overseas to the AEF and the Allied air services.[60]

In preparation for tests of the Liberty engine, special dynamometer and altitude laboratories were erected on the Bureau grounds for performance studies of the engine under simulated flight conditions.[61] (The temporary structures were later combined in a permanent Dynamometer Laboratory, built adjacent to Northwest building.) Construction of the altitude laboratory, in which conditions of low air pressure and cold encountered at great heights could be established, was a tremendous engineering feat, and for a time the chamber was the only one of its kind in existence.

Liberty engines, as well as Rolls-Royce, Hispano-Suiza, Fiat, Bugatti and other engines made by the Allies underwent endless tests and measurements of the effects of altitude on carburetor performance, on radiators, fuels, lubricating oils, and on supercharging devices designed to enable planes to attain higher altitudes.[62] Of considerable importance at the time were the Bureau studies in its chemical and altitude laboratories on the conservation

---

[60] Crowell, pp. 273, 277, 280; Ayres, The War With Germany, p. 90.

Stoutly defending what some claimed was "a cooperative monstrosity," Secretary Redfield said that Liberty engines after the war went into the planes of the airmail service inaugurated by the postal service in 1921, powered the transatlantic flight of the Navy NC–4 (Halifax to Lisbon) in 1919, and held all transcontinental record flights and world's altitude, speed, and endurance record flights up to 1923 (Redfield, With Congress and Cabinet, pp. 298–299). Stratton, too, thought it a fine engine, pointing out that it had 200 fewer parts than European equivalents and developed 475 hp., where the most powerful European engine had less than 300 hp. Letter, SWS to Airplane Engineering Department, Signal Corps, June 7, 1918, and attached correspondence (NBS Box 16, ITA).

[61] Fourth Annual Report, NACA, 1918, pp. 483–498; NBS Annual Report 1917, pp. 110–111.

[62] "Lubrication presented its problems, because the engineers believed that no other lubricant possessed all the advantages of castor oil," and the Army Signal Corps called for the planting of 100,000 acres to the castor-oil bean in this country. Paxson, American Democracy and the World War, II, 269; letter, Director, Aircraft Production to SWS, Oct. 11, 1918, and attached correspondence (NBS Box 16, ITAL).

of petroleum. They yielded the first quantitative data reported anywhere on the power-producing qualities of gasolines, and resulted in liberalizing the excessively rigid specifications set by the French for the aviation gasoline we were sending them, and incidentally were using ourselves.[63]

Designing an engine to lift the vast Government airplane program off the ground was only half the task. New woods or wood substitutes had to be found for airframes and materials for covering wings and fuselages. Spruce, considered most suitable for airplane construction, became scarce through oversea demands even before we entered the war. In exhaustive tests of proposed substitutes, more than 20 other kinds of wood, shaped as ribs, beams, and struts, went under the impact- and fatigue-testing machines of the Bureau. Although a laminated spruce, made of the waste in solid-beam construction, proved satisfactory, it was considered too costly, and only beams of fir showed practical promise.

The spruce shortage and the desirability of building a nonflammable, or at least fire-resistant, plane led to a great deal of work on metal airplane parts. Several sheet metal companies even proposed an all-metal plane, similar to the German Fokker introduced early in 1918. The companies were far from encouraged when the wings on one all-metal mockup sent to the Bureau for testing proved to have a low safety factor. The plane went back for redesign.[64]

Metal wing and fuselage frames seemed more promising, and numerous alloy steels were tested before attention finally centered on aluminum. Weight for weight, some of the structural beams of aluminum ranked well above Sitka spruce in strength tests, and in test flights an experimental plane with wing beams and ribs of aluminum demonstrated "the possibility of the successful manufacture of airplanes with metal-wing frames." [65] Only the discovery of a satisfactory nonflammable or fire-resistant wing and fuselage covering remained, and this problem had still not been solved when hostilities ceased.

The development of an acceptable mercerized cotton fabric and even a strong paper of jute and manila rope stock as substitutes for linen in airplane wing construction has already been mentioned. No form of glue or adhesive, however, could be found that would fasten either cotton or paper to the frame and at the same time render them waterproof and fireproof. For this purpose, better airplane dopes had to be found.

A cellulose acetate made in Germany by Bayer was the dope usually applied to the fabric on wing and fuselage, in order to shrink the material,

---

[63] "War Work," pp. 16–24, 30–32; NBS Annual Report 1919, p. 26.

[64] "War Work," p. 33. For another all-metal design turned down by the Bureau, see letter, SWS to NACA, July 27, 1918 (NBS Box 13, INM).

[65] "War Work," p. 34.

make it impermeable to wind and moisture, and improve the flight characteristics of the plane. In the turmoil of designing an American plane and engine, the subject of dopes was somehow overlooked, and when late in 1917 the first acetate orders went out, its raw materials had already been commandeered by other Government agencies.

With acetate gone, nitrate (guncotton) dopes were used for a time, until Eastman Kodak provided a small supply of acetate from cuttings and scraps of nonflammable motion picture film. (Why the airplane program was left with cuttings and scraps is not recorded. True, the research came late in the war and remained in the experimental stage. Possibly, too, the supply of motion picture film was limited and was needed by the services and for the spate of propaganda films made for domestic consumption.) Meanwhile, the Bureau was testing scores of new solutions proposed as dope substitutes, establishing specifications for those that seemed to have some value, and making studies of their application to fabrics. Only a few "fire-proofed" nitrate dopes of the many so-called fire-resistant solutions submitted proved acceptable, and then only when the fabric itself was also fireproofed.[66]

American scientists never wholly overcame the problem—nor did anyone else. The need for fireproofing was real even though in aerial combat, tracer and incendiary bullets rarely ignited the fabric of planes. It was the engine of World War I planes that was most susceptible to fire. Occasionally a pilot was able to execute sideslipping maneuvers and keep the engine flames from igniting the fabric. Where that failed, the plane was consumed as it fell.

OPTICAL GLASS AND OPTICAL INSTRUMENTS

Although Dr. Stratton never actively took part in the optical research at the Bureau, his work with Michelson on light at the University of Chicago was the impulse for his years of personal direction of the optical division.[67] The men he brought in—Bates in polarimetry, Coblentz in radiometry Priest in colorimetry, Peters in interferometry, Meggers in spectroscopy—were topnotch, and he zealously followed with them every development in the field of optics both here and abroad. Yet as numerous as were the military applications of optics, it was a crisis in supply that shaped the principal wartime effort in optics at the Bureau.

---

[66] "War Work," p. 56.

[67] Explaining the interferometer and its use in standardizing gage blocks to a congressional committee on one occasion, Stratton said that "interferometry is the field of measurement in which I am personally interested, and in which I was engaged when called to take charge of the bureau" (Hearings * * * 1924, Nov. 16, 1922, p. 191).

Stratton had long expressed concern over the foreign monopoly in high-grade optical glass and the fact that this country had to import every quality optical instrument it used. Because the glass for the optical systems of telescopes, microscopes, field glasses, navigation and surveying instruments, cameras and similar instruments was expensive to make and the market limited, American optical firms imported their quality glass and confined their manufacturing to spectacle glass, a product midway between optical and plate glass.[68] They had made little effort to learn for themselves German formulas and techniques and were content to have high-grade instruments manufactured abroad.[69] The war in Europe abruptly cut off the supply of both optical instruments and optical glass.

In the fall of 1914 Stratton ordered furnaces and apparatus for the Pittsburgh laboratory, where investigation of American clays and ceramics was already going on, and set it to work studying the manufacture of optical glass. A year later the Bureau began supplying its data to experimental optical glass plants organized at Bausch & Lomb, Keuffel & Esser, Pittsburgh Plate Glass and other firms that had been urged to take on this work. But development of good optical glass was a slow process, artisans in precision grinding were hard to find, and few outside the Bureau seemed to sense the emergency. When America entered the war in 1917 the industry had progressed little beyond the experimental stage.[70] In desperation, urgent appeals went out across the Nation begging private owners to lend their binoculars and field glasses, in whatever condition, to our military services.

Optical glass, a mixture of silica and chemicals melted in a clay pot, was highly susceptible to contamination from deterioration of the pot material under high heat. The initial problem of the Bureau was to find a suitable mixture of American clays as pot materials, capable of resisting the corrosive effect of fluid optical glass. The first satisfactory pot made was based on a

---

[68] Spectacle glass came under scrutiny during the war, too, when the cost of eyeglasses skyrocketed. Secretary of War Newton D. Baker complained to Commerce, and Stratton was asked to investigate. The war had "nothing to do with the increase in prices," the manufacturers told Stratton. Their price on lenses was a few cents each and they had increased it less than 10 percent. But the jobbers had raised their profit by 25 to 33⅓ percent and retailers by 200 to 500 percent. Letter, Secretary of Commerce to Secretary of War, July 18, 1918, and attached correspondence (NBS Box 14, IPO).

[69] Quality optical glass, unlike glass for electric light bulbs, bottles, and window panes, must have a high degree of chemical homogeneity, freedom from physical imperfections, and be of varied compositions to insure a wide range of refractive index and dispersion. For its prewar status, see Science, 41, 788 (1915); George W. Morey, The Properties of Glass (New York; Reinhold, 1938), p. 26; Samuel R. Scholes, Modern Glass Practice (Chicago: Industrial Publications, 1946), p. 59.

[70] Robert M. Yerkes, ed., The New World of Science, p. 108; Secretary of Commerce correspondence, 1917, NARG 40, file 67009/43; MS, "Development of optical glass at the Bureau of Standards" (NBS Box 482, PA).

kaolin-clay mixture. After more than a year's work on this and other compositions, Dr. Bleininger produced a superior porcelain pot unlike any previously known in this country. Widely acknowledged in the industry as an original contribution to the technique of glass manufacture, it proved one of the Bureau's most notable accomplishments in the war effort.

Drawings and specifications of the potmaking equipment were furnished to the commercial glass companies, as were data on annealing, optical constants, polishing processes, and inspection tests and methods devised by the Bureau. Bleininger's crucible or melting pot and the glass data came none too soon, for in May 1918, as the shortage became critical the War Industries Board ordered an all-out effort to achieve large-scale manufacture of optical glass.[71]

The early glassmaking experiments at Pittsburgh were conducted with pots holding about 30 pounds of glass. Compositions and methods of treatment of the different kinds of optical glass were first studied in these 30-pound melts, with laboratory personnel from the optical firms and representatives of the Geophysical Laboratory of the Carnegie Institution in Washington present as observers. In the winter of 1916–17 a larger furnace holding a 1,000-pound pot was built, and in this was made the first large melt of commercial borosilicate, as well as successful melts of crown and prism glass. Altogether, eight types of glass were made during the war in Bureau furnaces, totaling 15,000 pounds, of which more than 3,000 pounds comprised first-grade binocular glass. Only efforts to make dense barium-crown glass of the type used for photographic lenses were not wholly successful, and work on this continued after the war.[72]

Late in 1918, after producing almost 300 melts of optical glass, the Pittsburgh glass plant was transferred to the new Kiln building, with 8 melting furnaces, going up on the Bureau grounds in Washington. The importance of the Bureau's war work on refractories and glassmaking assured continuance of this research all through the 1920's and 1930's, and during World War II glass production at the Bureau was again undertaken on a full-scale basis.

In addition to the exhaustive testing of optical glass samples produced in the Pittsburgh furnaces, the optical laboratories in Washington were on constant call to advise on the design, construction, and testing of almost every optical instrument made for the Signal Corps and for Army and Navy Ordnance. Special test devices had to be constructed and frequent factory conferences were necessary since many of the instruments were being

---

[71] The pot composition was described in NBS Annual Report 1919, p. 266. See also Clarkson, Industrial America in the World War, pp. 470–471; Crowell, America's Munitions, pp. 139–140, 577; A. V. Bleininger, "Recent developments in ceramics," Chem. Met. Eng. 19, 467 (1918).

[72] Redfield, With Congress and Cabinet, p. 209; "War Work," pp. 183–185.

After the optical glass mixture has gone through the melting process and solidified under slow cooling, the pot is broken away from the 1000-pound melt. The glass cannot be removed from the pot in a molten or plastic condition or bubbles and cords will form.
Although the chemical composition of good optical glass had been mastered by World War I, a satisfactory pot material had not, and the special kaolin-clay mixture developed by the Bureau proved a real contribution to the industry.

manufactured in this country on a large scale for the first time. This was particularly true of binoculars, but also included periscopes, range finders, military and naval gun sights, bomb sights, and aviators' goggles. Important assistance was given as well in the manufacture of mil scales for military binoculars and in the development of the 37-mm gun sight, the panoramic machine gun sight, a new tank-gun sight, and a periscopic alidade.

The alidade, an angle-measuring device, illustrated how our armed services acquired some of their new optical instruments. The AEF sent back a French model, asking the Army Engineers to copy and supply it to our forces. The Bureau took it apart and from the data supplied, the Engineers prepared the blueprints for an instrument manufacturer. Samples of the American-made alidade then came back to the Bureau and with a few minor changes the device was approved for production.[73]

An interesting adaptation of peacetime optical research to wartime needs occurred in the case of military photography. Some years before the war, the spectroscopy section had carried out an extensive program of measur-

[73] "War Work," p. 188.

ing standard wavelengths of light, particularly in the spectra of neon, helium, and iron, by photographic means. Making these observations required a broad knowledge of the underlying complex elements of photography. It also drew attention to the fact that highly sensitive plates capable of photographing the wavelengths of red and infrared light could not be purchased commercially. Preparing their own plates, Bureau spectroscopists under Dr. Meggers made a systematic study of the spectra of some 50 of the chemical elements, and in 1917 began photographing stellar and solar spectra to determine their composition.

With the war, the spectroscopy section turned to military problems of aerial photography. By then physicists both here and abroad were using plates at least four times as sensitive and fast as the best commercial orthochromatic (sensitive to blue, green, and yellow) and panchromatic (sensitive to all colors) plates in use by the military. The Bureau phyicists were also using new dyes of British manufacture, devised to replace German aniline dyes, and following a series of experiments offered their adaptation of these dyes to the Air Service, for use in photographing battle terrain through haze and smoke and detecting military works under camouflage.

Extensive experiments with the red-sensitive plates were carried out at Langley Field in the spring and summer of 1918, but because of the fixed idea of the military that the Bureau plates were still in an experimental stage, they were never used overseas. Before the war ended, however, their practical use had been completely demonstrated, and with the design and construction of new photographic lenses for use with red light, the importance of red-sensitive plates in military photography was fully acknowledged.[74]

Bureau scientists also designed a new airplane camera using film instead of plates, and at the time of the armistice had under construction for Ordnance a special camera that photographed the inside of machine-gun barrels to determine their degree of deterioration—a piece of technology enormously important in gunmaking and maintenance.[75] Sharing its laboratory space, the Bureau provided facilities to the Engineers, the Geological Survey, and the Navy for camera and lens designing and testing and for camera mechanism testing by the Signal Corps. Among the guest scientists in the optical laboratories was Albert A. Michelson, Stratton's former superior at Chicago, who came on his first visit to the Bureau to work on new long-range binoculars he had devised for the Navy, and later returned to test the optics of the short-

[74] "War Work," pp. 202–207; NBS Annual Report 1918, pp. 83–84; Annual Report 1919, pp. 115–118; letter, SWS to Capt. Edward J. Steichen, Air Service, SOS, France, Dec. 3, 1918 (NBS Box 14, IPO).

[75] "War Work," pp. 186–187; NBS Annual Report 1919, pp. 141–142.

base Michelson rangefinder, another instrument he had designed for the Navy.[76]

It was a time of crash programs, of improvisations, of hurried application of basic principles, of hastily contrived instruments and equipment. In optics as in other areas of research the Bureau worked in largely untried ground. Some of its efforts saw service, some came too late. The same experience befell the scientists and technicians in the nearby radio laboratories.

"NEW THINGS IN RADIO COMMUNICATION"

When the war came, the Bureau radio laboratories under Dellinger and Kolster, as well as the adjacent Navy radio laboratory and that operated by the Signal Corps, were still relatively small affairs and for the most part more concerned with basic radio phenomena than with their practical applications. How far behind other nations the United States was in radio communications became known when the French scientific mission that arrived in the spring of 1917 left with the Bureau some of the scientific apparatus in use overseas. Included was a great variety of radio equipment developed around the electron tube.

Although the electron or vacuum tube amplifier was the invention of Fessenden and De Forest in this country, its use was practically unknown to our military departments, which still used damped wave apparatus that limited them to code telegraph.[77] A decade of patent litigation centering around the vacuum tube had blunted the growth of radio here at home. (It happened again with color television in the 1950's and 1960's.) The French, on the other hand, with government control of rights to the vacuum tube, used it in all their radio apparatus, in wire telephony, and in their radio telephone.

Outraged by the stifling consequences of the litigation, Strattton exclaimed to Congress: "It is time we should be working out the new things in radio communication instead of depending on foreign countries for scientific developments." [78] But even the Bureau had been helpless as the experimental

[76] Letter, SWS to Chief, Navy Bureau of Ordnance, Aug. 8, 1918 (NBS Box 4, AGC). Report attached to letter, SWS to War Production Branch, Mar. 5, 1919 (NBS Box 15, IRG), also notes an optical striae investigation made by Michelson at the Bureau. See NBS S333 (Michelson, 1919).

[77] Southworth, Forty Years of Radio Research, p. 38; "War Work," p. 233.

[78] Hearings * * * 1919 (Jan. 25, 1918), p. 978. For an account of the litigation involving De Forest's audion tube, the British and American Marconi Companies' Fleming valve, the General Electric audion of 1913, and Western Electric's audion of 1917, see Schubert, The Electric Word, pp. 126–131.

and commercial exploitation of the vacuum tube remained locked in the courts.

The impasse was broken on April 7, 1917, when by Presidential proclamation all commercial radio, comprising some 60 stations serving maritime commerce, was handed over to the Navy Department, and all other stations, amateur and privately owned, were closed down for the duration. The Navy, long anxious to secure better equipment for its ships, its coastal stations, and the radio chain it operated across the Pacific, immediately assumed all liability for patent infringements, and companies sprang up overnight to manufacture radio equipment, vying with the big three, General Electric, Westinghouse, and Western Electric, already in the field.

That event, together with the visit of the French commission and the requirements of the Army Signal Corps and the Navy, provided the major stimuli for the attack on the wartime radio problems facing this country: the training of technicians, civilian and military, in a complex and rapidly changing subject; the establishment of a high-powered transatlantic radio system (clearly of foremost importance not only for itself but in the event the enemy cut the telegraph cables); the development of low-powered radio equipment for battlefield communication; radio means for locating enemy radio stations, airplanes, ships, and submarines; equipment for communication with submarines when submerged; and portable radio apparatus.[79]

In the Navy laboratory at the Bureau, Dr. Austin, who in his long-distance transmission research had recently begun an investigation of the reenforcement of signals from the upper layer of the atmosphere, now took up the development of new radio apparatus for his service. In the Bureau laboratories the most immediate consideration was the training of thousands of men in radio communication for the Signal Corps to meet battlefield needs. To update available training material and set up better courses of radio instruction, a conference of university representatives was called at the Bureau in late December 1917. Following the conference, a Bureau group under Dr. Dellinger rushed preparation of a treatise on radio principles, measurements, and theory—subjects not covered by any publication then available—to supplement Signal Corps training pamphlets. Circular 74, "Radio instruments and measurements," with 318 pages of text, a bibliography, index, and 224 illustrations, came off the presses in March 1918, as a much needed reference book for radio instructors in the Army and Navy schools and the universities. It appeared later in hard covers as a commercial publication and its continued usefulness led the Bureau to issue a revised edition in 1924. Frequent reprints made this bible of radio engineers and amateurs available through the next two decades.

[79] "War Work," pp. 223–225.

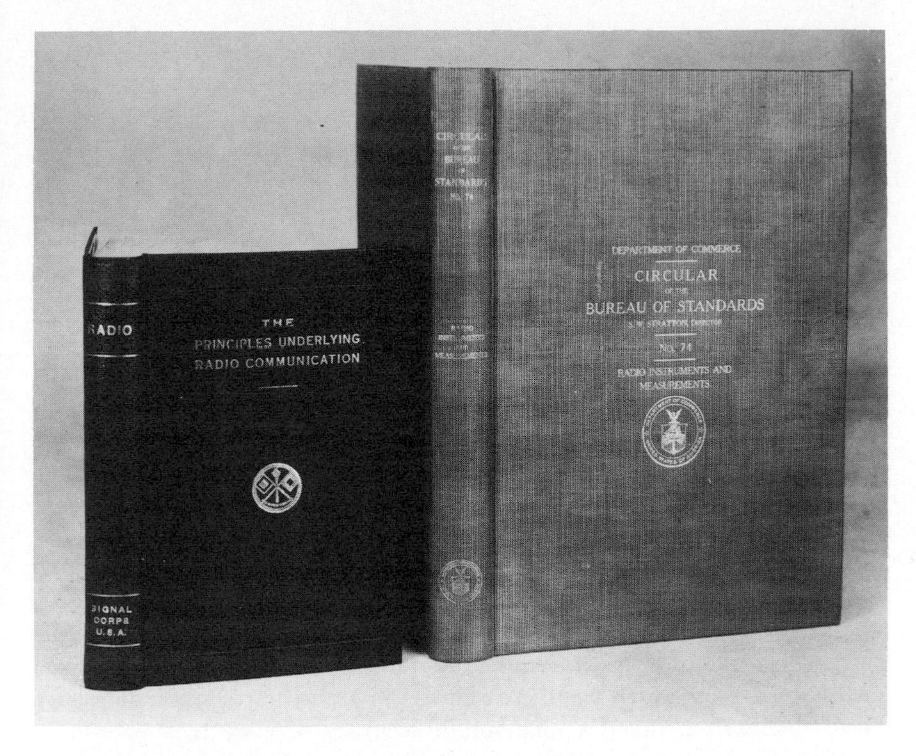

Two famous books, on radio communication and on radio principles, theory, and measurements, were written in 1917–18, making widely available the unpublished results of radio research carried out in the Bureau laboratories.

Circular 74, on measurements, was a radio reference book, the first which based radio theory on straight alternating current theory, giving damped waves only minor and separate treatment. The volume on principles was an elementary textbook, originally designed to accompany Signal Corps radio apparatus issued in the field, but used for many years as both reference and textbook.

Soon after Circular 74 came out, the Signal Corps requested an elementary textbook for enlisted men, as background for its training pamphlets, to cover in nonmathematical language the fundamentals of electricity and dynamoelectric machinery, as well as radio circuits and apparatus. Six college faculty members were invited to the Bureau to work with the radio staff on the book. They completed the 355-page text of The Principles Underlying Radio Communication in just 3 months. (Because of its joint authorship, it did not appear as a Bureau publication.) Press difficulties prevented the Signal Corps from issuing the book until March 1919, and instead of the planned 50,000 only 6,000 copies were printed. Admired by Thomas Edison as "the greatest book on this subject that I have ever read," it was reprinted when Army and Navy schools and a number of colleges later adopted it as a standard radio textbook.[80]

From the beginning of hostilities, the Bureau and the military services were bombarded with ideas for using radio as a weapon of war. Most notable perhaps was Thomas Edison's proposal to establish a transmitting station near Ostend, in British-held Flanders, to interfere with radio communication between German submarines and their bases. The Bureau had to tell him that a single station probably would not be sufficient. And even if it were, interfering signals sent out from even that one station in Flanders might well spread along the whole of the Western Front and confuse all radio communication there.[81]

A more practicable approach to the U-boat menace seemed possible through Kolster's radio direction finder, still in the experimental stage when we entered the war.[82] With the incorporation of a French electron tube amplifier and a new coil aerial, replacing the former antenna, a more compact unit with greater range of usefulness at once became possible. It was seen not only as an aid to air and sea navigation but as a potential means of locating enemy radio sending apparatus and, therefore, the enemy himself, whether in the trenches, in the air, or under the sea. Essentially a simple rotating coil that detected transmitted radio waves and then narrowed down the direction from which they were sent, the improved direction finder under ideal conditions achieved a pinpointing accuracy of close to 1 percent.

One application of the radio direction finder, largely the work of Kolster's technical assistants, Willoughby and Lowell, appeared particularly significant. So far as was known, no navy had developed a radio system for use in submarines, in the belief that sea water could not be penetrated by radio waves.[83] Before its first underwater tests, the Bureau had determined that with exceedingly sensitive amplifiers the coil aerial of the finder might act as both a transmitting and receiving device. Next, the Bureau began underwater tests of the coil and found, surprisingly, the signals almost as strong as with the coil in the air. Experiments on cruising submarines followed, and in final tests off New London in June 1918, the apparatus picked

---

[80] See chap. III, p. 138. Southworth, Forty Years of Radio Research, pp. 36–38; "War Work," pp. 227–229.

Still another Signal Corps publication prepared at the Bureau was Vacuum Tubes: Theory and Use, a compilation of all available information on the subject for the use of Army and Navy radio engineers. NBS Annual Report 1918, p. 47.

[81] Letter, SWS to Thomas Edison, Dec. 7, 1917 (NBS Box 10, IEW).

[82] The basic idea of the direction finder was an Italian invention, to which the British secured rights in 1912. Kolster's invention appears to have been an independent discovery and sufficiently different to raise no question of patent infringement. Schubert, The Electric Word, pp. 139–140; conversation with Percival D. Lowell, Mar. 4, 1963.

[83] War Work, p. 231.

The submarine at New London, Conn., equipped by the Bureau with special antenna for underwater radio reception and transmission.

In place of the large antenna used in his original direction finder, Kolster found that with the more sensitive amplifiers that had become available, a simple coil aerial was equally effective for receiving and transmitting radio waves.

Neither here nor abroad had navies developed a successful radio system for underwater use when late in 1917 one of Kolster's direction finder coils was tested, first under water, then in a submerged submarine, and in both instances picked up clear signals from as far away as Europe and our own west coast.

up clear signals transmitted from Germany, from Paris, Rome, and California. Still later tests proved it possible to transmit as well as receive radio messages in a submerged submarine, although the sending range, about 12 miles, was short.[84]

Experiments with the radio direction finder as an aid in aviation began in 1918 soon after the Post Office Department started a daily airmail service between New York and Washington. Night flights of the mail were still 3 years away, but presenting an immediate and comparable hazard was the problem of flying in daytime rain and fog. The pilot's compass guided him toward his landing field but gave him no indication when he was over it. At the request of the Post Office, the Bureau took up the problem and made two adaptations of the direction finder that answered it, one employing magnetic induction, the other a radiofrequency current. Either of these enabled the pilot to hear a signal when he was directly over the field. A crude device and effective only at altitudes up to a mile, it was nevertheless the forerunner of modern instrument landing techniques.[85]

No invention factory, the Bureau was drawn into these and other experiments as the organization best equipped to handle such problems for other Government agencies.[86] In radio research, its mission of providing and maintaining basic measurements was better exemplified in the constant and careful reassessments made of its standards of inductance and capacitance on which standards of radiofrequency or wavelength were based,

---

[84] War Work, pp. 229–232.

[85] Letter, SWS to Postmaster General, Nov. 29, 1919 (NBS Box 10, IEW); "War Work," pp. 232–233; NBS Annual Report 1919, pp. 66–67.

[86] One of the prime functions of the Bureau, the solution of problems relating to measurement, inevitably led to a number of patentable materials, processes, and products. From about 1910 on, members of the Bureau were granted a steady stream of patents for new or improved instruments and devices, including a new type of thermopile by Coblentz (1913), Kolster's decremeter (1913), Schlink's improvements in weighing scales (1916), Kolster's radio direction finder (1916), Whittemore's element for airfoils (1918), Willoughby and Lowell's submarine radio (1919), Bleininger's porcelain for spark plugs (1919), Priest's inferential dilatometer (1919), Ingberg's fire-resistant column cap (1920), and Emley's plastic gypsum (1920). A more complete list appears in NBS Box 71, AB–2105.

Although other Government agencies permitted and even encouraged their employees to take out patents in their own names and exploit them, under Stratton it was an unwritten but inviolable policy of the Bureau that patents of its employees were to be assigned to the use of the Government and the free use of the public. (Letter, SWS to Commissioner, Bureau of Navigation, May 21, 1913, and letter, SWS to W. D. Shoemaker, Patent Office, Aug. 28, 1919, in NBS Box 4, AGP.) No evidence appears in Bureau records that industry ever objected to this policy, but Bureau inventors were not always happy with it and on occasion rebelled. See Coblentz, From the Life of a Researcher (New York: Philosophical Library, 1951), pp. 141–143, and footnote ch. VI, pp. 348–349.

the standards themselves "handled with a care and reverence that was comparable with that given to the prototype platinum-iridium standard meter bar." [87] Basic too was the Bureau work on the new electron or vacuum tube.

With patent litigation suspended, radio manufacturers turned out large numbers of these tubes as generators, detectors, amplifiers, and modulators of radio waves and other electrical currents. (Some of the early tubes were as large as the wall telephones then in use.) Most of them went into the radio communication apparatus constructed in the Signal Corps and Navy radio laboratories at the Bureau and produced in quantity for these services by the electrical industry.[88] The Bureau measured the characteristics of both experimental and production tubes, devised test methods and apparatus, standardized certain types of tubes, and made studies of their behavior in a variety of circuits.[89]

Of special importance in its work with vacuum tubes were the first Bureau studies of such phenomena as the effects of diurnal fluctuations, solar activity, and atmospheric electricity on radio communication. Out of this work in the postwar years came wholly new concepts of the dimensions of radio, as well as new standards of radio measurements.[90]

Wartime research on the electron tube, which had previously been little more than an artifact of the radio experimenters in this country, made possible reliable long-distance wire telephony, as well as speech communication between ground stations and airplanes. Incorporating the vacuum tube in the direction finder made it a convenient and portable apparatus that was to prove as useful in detecting transmitting stations violating radio laws as it was in guiding planes and ships through fog. In its role as an amplifier, the vacuum tube permitted for the first time very small antennas, and by greatly extending the range of radio communication ushered in the age of radio.

That age did not, as might have been expected, begin with the armistice. It was delayed first by the threat of Government ownership and then by renewal of the patent wars of the radio industry. Under the widely held

---

[87] Southword, Forty Years of Radio Research, p. 34.

[88] For the wartime Navy research at the Bureau in long-distance communication, see report of L. W. Austin in J. Franklin Inst. 193, 437 (1922), and NBS Letter Circular (LC) 194 (Mar. 10, 1926).

[89] A discovery made at that time in the idiosyncrasies in vacuum tubes, since known as the "Miller effect," was first published in John F. Miller's "Dependence of the input impedance of a three-electrode vacuum tube upon the load in the plate circuit" (S351, 1919). See also NBS Annual Report 1919, pp. 65–66, and F. Langford Smith, ed., The Radiotron Designer's Handbook (Sydney, Australia: Wireless Press, 3d ed., 1940), pp. 46–48.

[90] "War Work," pp. 233–242.

The use of the three-electrode (triode) electron tube was practically unknown to our military forces prior to 1917, and all of their apparatus was of the damped-wave type. The Bureau began testing electron tubes, as shown here, a month after we entered the war, and reported testing 467 of them up to mid-1919.

assumption that radio was essentially an instrument of navigation and of national defense, and therefore must be under Government control, as it was in Europe, bills to that end were offered in Congress on behalf of the Navy Department in January 1917 and again late in 1918. On both occasions Congress, ever fearful of outright Government control or ownership of anything, tabled the proposals.[91]

Rebuffed, yet concerned for the development of its radio system, the Navy Department urged General Electric, largest of the radio manufacturers, to buy out the British-backed Marconi Co. whose commercial radio system had been taken over by the Navy in 1917 and was, with the end of the war, to be returned. The result was the formation in October 1919 of a General Electric subsidiary, the Radio Corporation of America, which at one stroke became owner of virtually all the commercial high-power radio facilities in the country.[92]

---

[91] Secretary of Commerce Redfield and Dr. Stratton both favored Government control, either under the Navy or, better, under Commerce. See Hearings * * * 1920 (Dec. 12, 1918), p. 946, and correspondence in NBS Box 10, IEW 1918–20.

[92] W. Rupert Maclaurin, Invention and Innovation in the Radio Industry (New York: Macmillan, 1949), p. 99.

But the moratorium on patent litigation also ended with the war, and since no one had an important infringement-free radio patent, the expectations of commercial radio were checked. Except for laboratory experimentation, the wartime work on vacuum tubes, radio circuits, and transmission apparatus remained out of reach to all. Until that impasse was breached in 1921, no radio manufacturer could safely make anything but crystal sets for the public. The Bureau continued its research and waited.[93]

FROM GAGES TO GAS MASKS

The mass production of guns, ammunition and other ordnance material, with components made in almost 8,000 plants across the country, reached a scale in World War I never before attempted in any machined product. The manufacture of interchangeable parts and components in widely separated factories depended upon the accuracy of hundreds of thousands of gages, and of the master gages on which they were based. Construction of a single round of artillery ammunition, for example, required gaging of 80 dimensions, necessitating the use of over 500 different gages. To standardize these shop gages required 180 master gages.[94]

The work of standardizing and testing master gages, begun under an urgent deficiency appropriation of June 1917, soon outstripped the facilities Stratton had set up 2 years before at the Bureau, and branches were established in New York, in Cleveland, and at Bridgeport. The 4 laboratories handled over 60,000 gages used in making America's munitions.[95] The magazine Science was to say that "The national provision for master-gauge standardization was one of the most important contributions of the war." [96]

At the height of its activity the Bureau gage section numbered 225 engineers, physicists, master gage experts, inspectors, toolmakers, technical assistants, and administrative aides. Besides testing and calibrating gages, the section trained gage inspectors for Ordnance plants, Navy yards, arsenals, and commercial manufacturers. It also carried out an extensive salvage

---

[93] Memo, SWS for Secretary of Commerce, Sept. 21, 1921 (NBS Box 10, IEW).

[94] Crowell, America's Munitions, pp. 25, 124–125. Including the gages used by Government inspectors, almost 800 gages were necessary in the manufacture of a single complete round.

[95] These comprised plain gages (plain plug, snap, and ring gages), profile gages (templets, chamber and fixture gages), and screw-thread gages. Originally set up in the Stucco building (erected early in 1918 for the testing of building materials), the gage laboratory moved to larger quarters in Northwest building later that year. Of more than $4 million spent by the War Department for gages in 1917–18, Stratton reported, over $550,000 came to the Bureau (Hearings * * * 1921, Jan. 2, 1920, pp. 1583–1584).

[96] "The work of the Bureau of Standards during 1918," Science 39–40 (1919).

program as large numbers of gages in Ordnance factories became obsolete when designs were changed or wore out. The Bureau shops rebuilt nearly a thousand gages for serviceable use again and constructed almost 500 new master and inspection gages as replacements.[97]

The invention that perhaps contributed most to the manufacture of interchangeable parts was the famous set of precision gage blocks made by the Swedish engineer Carl Edvard Johannson in 1904. For many years these were the only satisfactory standards of their kind available for the manufacture and inspection of closely machined parts. Prior to the war their sole source was Sweden, and so exquisite was their workmanship that production never kept up with demand.[98] When this country began tooling up, they were not to be had at any price.

Late in 1917 an inventor, William E. Hoke, came to the Bureau proposing a method for the mechanical manufacture of precision gage blocks that promised to be near equivalents of the Swedish blocks. Persuaded that their manufacture was feasible, the Bureau obtained the sum of $375,000 from the Ordnance Department to make them and after several months produced a satisfactory set of the blocks. Altogether, 50 sets were made, each comprising 81 blocks, ranging from 0.05 inch to 4 inches, and each block accurate to within 0.000005 inch. Their value, apart from the fact that nothing comparable could be had, Stratton declared, far exceeded the amount of the allotment made for their production.[99]

Allied with the gage work was that of the National Screw Thread Commission, established by Congress in July 1918 with nine members from the War, Navy, and Commerce Departments, the American Society of Mechanical Engineers, and the Society of Automotive Engineers, under the chairmanship of Dr. Stratton. The Commission sought to simplify the variety of threads, sizes, types, and systems then prevailing in industry, and standardize those having the most extensive use and utility. Among other things, standardization of threads (and hence interchangeability) would facilitate repair or replacement of machines and their parts, as well as of all machine-made threaded products from nuts and bolts to hose couplings.

---

[97] "War Work," pp. 116–117; report, Van Keuren, "Progress of munition gage testing at the Bureau of Standards" [ca. Sept. 1918], in NBS Historical File.

[98] Joseph V. Woodworth, Gages and Gaging Systems (New York: Hill, 1908), p. 229, described the first set of Johannson's blocks seen in this country. Combinations of the blocks, ranging in thickness from 0.1001 to 4 inches, made possible at least 80,000 sizes. For Johannson's description of the blocks, see NBS Standards Yearbook, 1931, pp. 14–15. (Johannson was then an engineer with the Ford Motor Co.)

[99] Hearings * * * 1920 (Dec. 12, 1918), p. 952; letter, SWS to Ch, Inventions Section WD, Dec. 23, 1918 (NBS Box 19, IWG); NBS Annual Report 1919, pp. 37, 148–149; interview with Irvin H. Fullmer, Mar. 23, 1962.

The Hoke precision gage blocks used in the manufacture of closely machined parts, shown here being used to determine the dimension of a limit gage. Any desired dimension can be obtained by combining various sizes of blocks, as in the three used here to test the limit gage in the jig.

It was an almost impossible task to undertake in the midst of war. Congress twice extended the term of the Commission, to 1920 and then to 1927, in order that it might implement its plans to "reduce the variety of screw threads in general use, facilitate manufacture in case of war, make the best use of labor in our industries in time of peace, increase the safety of travel by rail, steamship, and aeroplane, and in general * * * increase the dependability of all mechanisms." [100] It would take the coming of another war before progress became visible.

Besides its work on threads and gages and the extensive investigations in substitute materials, in aeronautics, optical glass, and radio, the Bureau responded to calls for help with literally hundreds of other wartime problems submitted by industry and the sciences. Only mention can be made of the almost continuous testing carried out on protective coatings, from experiments in electroplating techniques to tests of bituminous materials, varnishes, enamels, fire-retarding paints, and special paints for projectiles.[101] The Bureau established safety standards for military plants and factories. It

[100] NBS M42, "Progress report of the National Screw Thread Commission" (1921), p. 5.
[101] "War Work," pp. 66–67, 208–220.

investigated the protective properties of goggles and glasses for laboratory workers and those used by oxyacetylene cutters and welders against injurious ultraviolet and infrared radiations.[102]

It made studies in the use of radium and other self-luminous materials for illuminating aircraft instruments, gunsights, marching compasses, watches, and navigation instruments. In addition, almost 500 preparations of radium, for use in surgery and dermatology, were measured and certified in the Bureau's radium laboratory. An investigation of X-ray protection in this laboratory for the Surgeon General's Office demonstrated that many of even the most expensive X-ray shields then on the market were practically worthless. And with the X-ray apparatus acquired for these studies, the Bureau also began its preliminary study of techniques for the radiographic detection of flaws in aluminum and steel, which were to succeed where in many cases magnetic testing failed.[103]

The Bureau developed an improved blasting machine for the Corps of Engineers, worked on rockets and illuminating shells with the Trench Warfare Section of Ordnance, and helped design signal lamps for daylight transmission of messages in the trenches or between planes in flight.[104] The colorimetrists and photometrists of the Bureau supplied scientific data for a high-priority searchlight investigation made by the Engineers. Dr. Harvey L. Curtis spent much of the war devising and operating his complex electrical circuits for measuring velocity and other ballistic characteristics of projectiles for the Navy.[105]

Investigations of sound-ranging and sound-detecting equipment, for locating distant or concealed enemy guns, began soon after the French mission brought to this country some of the apparatus in use overseas. Designing and constructing improved sound-ranging apparatus, as well as geophones and seismicrophones, to detect enemy mining operations in the trenches, and special microphones for the detecting of underwater sounds, occupied the Bureau's electrolysis (sic) section until well after the armistice.[106] The only death of a Bureau staff member on the battlefield occurred in this group. Dr. Ernest E. Weibel, who with Dr. Eckhardt and Burton McCollum made important developments in a new sound-ranging device, entered the Army as a captain in the spring of 1918 in order to take the equipment overseas and test it in the trenches in the British sector near Ypres. In a mustard-gas

---

[102] "War Work," pp. 261–263, 246; NBS Annual Report 1918, p. 103.

[103] "War Work," pp. 251–255, 298–299; NBS Annual Report 1918, p. 52; Annual Report 1919, p. 74.

[104] "War Work," pp. 107–112, 124–127.

[105] Crowell, America's Munitions, pp. 389–391; "War Work," pp. 263–265; NBS Annual Report 1918, p. 41; Curtis, Recollections of a Scientist, pp. 39–51.

[106] Crowell, America's Munitions, pp. 384–387; "War Work," pp. 265–271; NBS Annual Report 1918, pp. 67, 104–105.

attack on that front in April he was badly gassed and died of complications several weeks later.[107]

Almost the whole of the legacy of science and technology that seemed so rich in promise at the turn of the century was, in that holocaust in Europe, reworked into weapons and agents of war. None was more frightening than the chemical poisons first introduced on the battlefield in 1915. Although it is difficult to believe, America entered the war 2 years later knowing little or nothing about the gas war in Europe. The Bureau first encountered its challenges when a special mission arrived with models of the protective gas masks then in use in France. Besides its investigations for American gas masks, the Bureau also worked with the Bureau of Mines, the Chemical Warfare Service, the Geophysical Laboratory, and the universities on a number of tests and experiments preliminary to this country's production of war gases and smokes.[108]

Two new gases were introduced in the field by the Germans as the AEF arrived in France in the summer of 1917. The first was mustard gas, for which no satisfactory defense was ever devised, the other, diphenylchloroarsine, a sneeze gas. The arsenical sneeze gas—actually not a gas but an irritant smoke—even in minute quantities readily penetrated all gas masks then in use, producing uncontrollable coughing and sneezing, and forced removal of the mask, to expose its wearer to the lethal gases that were fired simultaneously with the sneeze gas.[109]

In the Bureau paper mill and at a commercial mill a group under Dr. Philip V. Wells made numerous special crepe paper filters to prevent mask penetration of the smokes, testing them in a gas chamber erected on the grounds. But the filter, added to others already in the mask, so increased the difficulty of breathing while wearing the mask as nearly to immobilze the soldier. As a result, neither this country nor the Allies produced more than a handful of cannisters incorporating this paper, and sneeze gas casualties continued high to the end of the war.[110]

Hardly a day passed during the war years but a new problem in detection or a solution to an old one was presented to the Bureau. None

[107] Redfield, With Congress and Cabinet, pp. 222–223. Lt. Arthur J. Fecht, member of the Bureau with Weibel, survived the gassing and served in the sound-ranging section of the 29th Engineers to the end of the war. Interview with Dr. Silsbee, Nov. 27, 1962.

[108] Crowell, America's Munitions, p. 405; NBS Annual Report 1918, pp. 104, 159; Annual Report 1919, p. 149.

[109] Studies of chemical substances in suspension were carried out in the Bureau's dispersoid section set up in the optical division.

[110] Letter W. K. Lewis, Research Division, CWS, to SWS, July 31, 1918 (NBS Box 6, IC); "War Work," pp. 72, 199–200. Almost a third of AEF battle casualties resulted from gas, most of them from mustard gas or phosgene, following concentrations of sneeze gas. See Col. H. L. Gilchrist, A Comparative Study of World War Casualties From Gas and Other Weapons (Washington, D.C., 1931), p. 19.

certainly exercised the scientific and inventive talents of the Nation more when we entered the war than did the menace of the U-boat. Submarine detection was widely held to be "the most pressing of all problems" that fateful spring as month by month the toll of merchant tonnage sent to the bottom steadily rose. It was estimated that for a time one-quarter of the leading physicists in this country were working on the submarine problem, and Edison's proposal to interrupt German submarine radio communication was but one of thousands of solutions suggested.[111] As obvious aids in sub hunting, and most capable of rapid development, the National Research Council urged the Bureau to devise special goggles, colored lenses, and special binoculars for better visual detection of submarines and their periscopes. But before these and more complicated means of detection got beyond the experimental stage, the convoy system with destroyer escort had been inaugurated and shipping losses began to abate.[112]

As pressing as enemy submarine detection was detecting the presence of dangerously combustible gases, hydrogen in particular, in our own submarines. Elmer R. Weaver of the gas chemistry section pioneered the development of thermal-conductivity measurements for the detection and analysis of such gases that later became the basis for a multimillion-dollar instrument company.[113]

Thermopiles or bolometers, for the detection of ships and planes by the radiation of heat from the smokestacks and exhausts, and electrical inductance devices, for detection of metallic mines laid by the enemy, were endlessly tested. None proved practical. Out of the work, however, came a device employing the thermopile principle that made it possible to send out infrared rays as signals without fear of detection. The Bureau felt it might have far-reaching applications, since these signals, unlike radio signals at the time, could be directed and could be operated without interference.[114] The device was a forerunner of the World War II snooperscope,

---

[111] Interview with Dr. Dellinger, Jan. 26, 1962. Even Dr. Stratton offered a device, based on a series of wire hawsers suspended from ships' sides that would offer sufficient resistance to deflect torpedoes from their course. Letter, SWS to Ch, Bur. Const. and Repair, Navy Department, May 23, 1917 (NBS Box 11, IG).

[112] "War Work," p. 273. Some of the "target-finding torpedoes," one-man submarines, and electrical devices suggested to the Bureau for locating or destroying U-boats, often reached, Dr. Rosa said, into the realm of superscience. See correspondence in NBS Box 7.

[113] S334, "New forms of instruments for showing the presence and amount of combustile gases in the air" (Weaver and Weibel, 1919); T249, "Thermal-conductivity method for the analysis of gases" (Palmer and Weaver, 1924); Science, 126, 161 (1957).

[114] "War Work," pp. 133–139, 247; NBS Annual Report 1918, p. 146; letter, Millikan, Chief of R&D Division, NRC to SWS, Jan. 25, 1918 (NBS Box 14, IPR).

Dr. Goddard obtained his first rocket patent in 1914, in 1919 stated the principle of multistage rockets, and in the next decade developed liquid fuels and gyroscopic stabilizers for his rockets. His recoilless launcher demonstrated for the Bureau in 1918 fired a two-foot-long powder loaded rocket.

The historic liquid-fueled rocket of the 1920's, pictured above, rose only 41 feet. With stabilization and better fuel the rocket flew 7,500 feet up just a decade later. Goddard's interest was not in weaponry but in methods of raising recording apparatus beyond the range of sounding balloons, in order to explore the upper atmosphere.

which was to detect reflections from infrared light projected by the scope itself.

At least two inventions that came to the Bureau in World War I proved to be 20 years ahead of their time. Late in 1916, Dr. Robert H. Goddard, a physics professor at Clark University, Worcester, Mass., went to Dr. C. G. Abbot, Secretary of the Smithsonian and head of the Astrophysical Laboratory, with an idea for a rocket device theoretically capable of firing shells "far outdistancing rifled cannon."

The principle of the rocket was of course centuries old, and in modern times its "red glare" had illuminated the bombardment of Fort McHenry, in the port of Baltimore. By increasing its thermodynamic efficiency and incorporating new power principles, Goddard believed he had found a way to control and enhance the flight characteristics of the rocket. Dr. Abbot agreed and called in Dr. Edgar Buckingham, the aerodynamics specialist at the Bureau. After studying Goddard's data they concurred on "the probable great military value of this rocket" and recommended that the Bureau assign $5,000 of its Signal Corps funds for development.

By January 1918 two models of Goddard's rocket gun had been designed, one with a potential range of 7 miles, the other of 120 miles. Buckingham reported that a working model of the former, preliminary to large-scale production, might be readied within 3 months if the work was pushed, and Stratton, with Abbot's accord, assigned another $10,000 for its construction. Goddard, meanwhile, had designed still other rocket weapons: a launching device for firing a sequence of rockets, a rocket trench mortar, and a "hand-supported recoilless gun"—prototype of the bazooka—capable of firing shells from a 5½-foot tube for distances of 400 to 700 yards.

Reports of the first tests of the rocket gun in July 1918 were good, but Dr. Stratton's efforts to find scientists and technicians through the Smithsonian to assist Goddard with further development were unavailing. Other wartime projects, with more immediate prospects of utilization, occupied every trained man in sight.[115] Goddard's project was shelved.

Destined for the next war too was the automatic rifle invented by John C. Garand. Originally submitted to Thomas Edison's Naval Consulting Board, the model was referred to Army Ordnance who sent it to the Bureau "to look over" in the summer of 1918. As received, it was "exceedingly crude and inoperative," Stratton said later, but its conception was sound, it had been made by "an excellent mechanician," and Stratton himself took personal charge of its development. After more than 6 months of work in the Bureau shops, the rifle was successfully fired. At that point litigation over the patent rights arose and with the war over the War Department lost interest. The Bureau returned the rifle to Mr. Garand.[116]

Day-to-day life at the Bureau during the war was hectic and dominated by a sense of urgency, but the brevity of this country's involvement and the distance from the battlefield prevented rise of the tensions that were to mark life in the Second World War. Except for the hush-hush designing of the Liberty engine, of Dr. Briggs' stable-zenith device for the Navy (to synchronize the training of big guns, independent of the pitch and roll of the ship), and of some aspects of sound-ranging apparatus, the Bureau was concerned with few classified projects. Apart from observing routine security measures, the Bureau staff and visitors came and went with a minimum of surveillance.

Although the Bureau had an officer of the day and a watch, the absence of vigilance was illustrated in an unscheduled visit made by the President and Mrs. Wilson, accompanied by Secretary Redfield, out Connecticut Avenue one Sunday afternoon to see the novel all-metal airplane sent to the Bureau for structural tests. The doors of West building where it sat were locked,

---

[115] Letter, C. G. Abbott to SWS, July 25, 1918, and attached correspondence (NBS Box 10, IG). See Goddard's classic monograph on rockets, "A method of reaching extreme altitudes," Smithsonian Miscellaneous Collections (Publ. 2540), 71, 1–69 (1919).

[116] Memo, SWS to Secretary of Commerce, Mar. 25, 1921, and attached correspondence (NBS Box 12, IN).

but the Secretary found an unfastened window and all three climbed in to see the plane.[117]

And the Bureau found time to play. An avid reader of detective and mystery novels, the President one morning sent a messenger to the Bureau with an envelope bearing his seal. He had read the night before that such a letter could be opened and resealed without any sign of tampering. Could the Bureau do it too? A day later the President had his sealed letter back, apparently intact. Inside was a note and the lead disks from which the fraudulent seal replacing his seal had been made overnight.[118]

THE BUREAU AND THE METRIC SYSTEM

The war not only forwarded the Bureau's efforts to induce American industry to accept scientific measurements and methods in its operations; it also for a time brought hope that its long endeavor to secure general adoption of the metric system in this country might at last succeed. To its proponents the simplicity of the metric system in common measures and its advantages in scientific mensuration were overwhelming; to its opponents the cost to industry of conversion and the inconvenience to the public seemed insuperable. For years, a band of ardent antimetricists, supported by representatives of engineering and textile interests and by a merchant-minded Congress had repeatedly defeated metric legislation. Their success convinced Dr. Strattton that only through education of the public might sufficient pressure be generated to sway the lawmakers. The war offered an unexpected opportunity to further that education.

On January 2, 1918, a War Department General Order announced that the General Staff of the AEF in France had adopted the metric system and that guns, munitions, and certain other materials produced in this country and destined for the AEF would conform to metric measurements:

> The metric system has been adopted for use in France for all firing data for artillery and machine guns, in the preparation of operation orders, and in map construction. Artillery and machine-gun material intended for service abroad is being graduated accordingly. Instruction in the metric system will be given to all concerned.[119]

Alerted by the War Department, the Bureau at once ordered reprints of a descriptive pamphlet of the international metric system and of a large graphic wall chart derived from this pamphlet, both published by the Bureau

[117] Redfield, With Congress and Cabinet, pp. 98–99.
[118] Letter, Secretary of Commerce to President Wilson, Jan. 26, 1918 (NBS Box 10, IG).
[119] War Department G.O. 1, Jan. 2, 1918, was based on AEF G.O. 65, Nov. 21, 1917.

some years earlier.[120] A circular prepared in 1914, "Units of weights and measures: definitions and tables of equivalents," went to press again, as well as a 30 cm (12-inch) comparison scale, printed on paper, that permitted direct visual translation from centimeters and millimeters to inches and fractions of the inch. Large numbers of each of these were soon on the way to the technical services of the military here and abroad for instruction purposes.[121]

The most widely distributed metric aid was a soldier's manual, especially prepared at War Department request shortly after the general order appeared. A 16-page booklet, precisely 10 by 15 cm in size, small enough to fit the pocket, and issued as NBS Miscellaneous Publication No. 21 was pointedly entitled: "Metric manual for soldiers—The soldier's primer of the metric system—An international decimal system of weights and measures adopted as the legal standard by France and thirty-three other nations, and in world-wide use."

The manual described the rapid wartime progress of the metric system, particularly in industry, and its "necessity for efficiency in warfare." It offered graphic examples of the units, showing the length of the meter in terms of the soldier's 1903 or 1917 rifle, cited dimensions of other objects familiar to the average soldier, and included a sketch of the origin of the metric system, brief tables of equivalents, and a glossary. After printing and distributing over 100,000 copies for military personnel here and abroad, the plates were made available to the Army and Navy for printing special editions.[122] With the American armies indoctrinated and a considerable segment of American industry working in metrics, the long-deferred legislation seemed at last in sight.

The interest of the Bureau in promoting the metric system went back to the act of 1866 that legalized its use in this country and the subsequent ratification of the Metric Convention in 1878, making the United States party to the creation and support of the International Bureau of Weights and Measures. Yet legislation to put the metric system into general and commercial use had not followed. Despite our decimal system of coinage, the fact that our common measures derived from the meter and kilogram, that almost all scientific measurement was based on the metric system, and that it was the only system of weights and measures specifically legalized by the U.S. Congress, opposition had arisen at once and could not be overcome.

---

[120] NBS M2, "The international metric system of weights and measures" (1906); M3 (chart, 1908). Over 10,000 copies of the M2 had been distributed since 1906 and 22,000 copies of M3 between 1908 and 1915.

[121] Between 1915 and 1917, 10,500 copies of NBS C47 were printed; another 15,000 were issued in 1918. For printing data, see Annual Reports, Bureau of Publications, Department of Commerce.

[122] "War Work," pp. 220–221.

Beyond all practical considerations—and they were many but not insuperable—the opposition appeared bound as much by emotional principles as by practical ones: the common measures were soundly Anglo-Saxon in origin; they had mystic biblical connotations; above all, they were a kind of badge of our isolation from the affairs of Europe.[123]

The leading advocates of the metric system were of course the scientists and scientific institutions of this country. Three times at the turn of the century, in 1896, 1901, and 1903, they had mobilized to support metric legislation introduced in Congress, only to see it fail.[124] During the hearings in 1900 that led to the establishment of the National Bureau of Standards, the subject of metric legislation came up but fortunately was not pressed. As Dr. Stratton confessed not long after, had Congress known that the proposed bureau was favorable to the adoption of the metric system, a great many there would have opposed its establishment.[125]

Evidence of Bureau interest in the metric system—and perhaps as a demonstration of its application in the construction industry—appeared in the seeming irregular dimensions (that is, in terms of feet and yards) of North and South buildings and their laboratories, which resulted from their computation in metrics.[126] Regrettably, no correspondence has been found to indicate the reaction of either the architects or the builders to fitting conventional materials to unaccustomed dimensions.

From its very beginning, the Bureau took an active part in supporting metric legislation. It secured the cooperation of those who had assisted in

---

[123] Two of the most dedicated of the antimetricists in the early century were Frederick A. Halsey and Samuel Dale, spokesmen for the textile industry and authors of one of the ablest of the antimetric books, The Metric Fallacy (New York: Van Nostrand, 1904).

For the considerable correspondence of Samuel Dale with the Bureau in the period 1904–23, see NBS Boxes 20, 21, 55, 58. Typical of the temper of antimetricists was the remark of Samuel Russell, clerk to Senator William H. King of Utah, who wrote in an 8-page letter on the subject: "Metricitis, like socialism and Christian Science, is a mental Aberration" (letter to Secretary of Commerce Hoover, Apr. 8, 1921, NBS Box 20, MS).

[124] Letter, SWS to Secretary of Commerce and Labor, Apr. 4, 1904 (NBS Box 21, MS). See also Hearings before Committee on Coinage, Weights, and Measures, Jan. 30, 1896 (L/C: QC91.U46), and Annual Report, Secretary of the Treasury, 1899, p. lxxvii.

A good account of early metric legislative efforts appears in William Hallock and Herbert T. Wade, The Evolution of Weights and Measures and the Metric System (New York: Macmillan, 1906), pp. 133–134. Still the most authoritative general work available on weights and measures, it devoted more than half its 300 pages to the origin, development, and uses of the metric system.

[125] Hearings before the Committee on Coinage, Weights, and Measures, May 3, 1900, pp. 7–8; letter, SWS to E. L. Corthell, Minister of Public Works, Buenos Aires, Argentina, Aug. 16, 1901 (NBS Box 21, MS).

[126] See Rosa, "Plans of the new buildings * * *," Science, 17, 137 (1903); Coblentz. From the Life of a Researcher, p. 131.

establishing the Bureau and it participated in the hearings in the House and Senate. On one occasion, early in 1902, Dr. Stratton spoke before a congressional committee for over an hour on behalf of a metric bill then under consideration.[127]

Altogether, nine measures relating to the metric system or to some other "decimal" system were introduced in Congress in the first decade of the century, but even with the strong support of such international luminaries as Lord Kelvin and Alexander Graham Bell, none could be enacted.[128] Although Dr. Stratton participated in every metric hearing in that decade and the next, he did not always support the measures proposed. Some he felt were not well drawn, some were too drastic. He was aware of the difficulties of any sudden or complete conversion of systems and once declared that the Bureau "never advised or favored the introduction of any bill making the metric system compulsory for all purposes." It was the Bureau's position that it was "desirable to work toward a decimal and international system of weights and measures * * * [and] gradually extend the metric system into common work." [129]

The qualification was ignored by critics of the Bureau, who saw any effort on behalf of the metric system as a threat to all domestic tranquility. It was indictment enough that "the Bureau of Standards under the administration of Dr. Stratton has been the seat of metric propaganda for many years. The doctor himself is known as a hobbyist, not to say lobbyist, for the metric system." [130]

Upon the entry of the United States into the war, committing our armies in France to the metric system, hope rose that metric legislation might finally be passed. War fervor and the AEF requirement were believed to have weakened the resolve of many former objectors. New industries, like munitions and aeronautics, and older ones, like the electrical industry, were working with the metric system in supplying the Allies and other nations

---

[127] Hearings on H.R. 2054 * * * before the Committee on Coinage, Weights, and Measures, Feb. 6–Mar. 6, 1902, pp. 151–165 (L/C: QC91.U48).

[128] Kelvin's testimony appeared in supplementary hearings before the Committee on Coinage, Weights, and Measures, Aug. 24, 1902 (L/C: QC91.U481); Bell's appears in his article, "Our heterogeneous system of weights and measures," National Geographic, 17, 158 (1906).

[129] Letter, SWS to editor, American Industries, Aug. 10, 1920 (NBS Box 20, MS). Dr. Burgess reaffirmed this position on the metric system in NBS Annual Report 1923, pp. 25–27. Stratton was confident, as he told Congress, that American industry would sooner or later "have to come to it" because of foreign trade. He "always felt that the request [for general use] should come from the public [and not be initiated in Congress], and that the public should be educated more into the system before it was introduced." Hearings * * * 1921 (Jan. 2, 1920), p. 1594.

[130] Letter, Samuel Russell to Secretary of Commerce Hoover, Apr. 8, 1921 (NBS Box 20, MS). Hoover replied (Apr. 23, 1921) that he was "inclined to favor the metric system as the only possible substitute for our present system."

abroad, and Stratton predicted with confidence that it would be in common use "in a comparatively short time." [131] He was not a good prophet.

In support of the first metric bill presented after the war, General Pershing himself attempted to set at rest public fears by reporting that the troops overseas "were able readily to change from our existing system of weights and measures to the metric system." He urged its adoption "to the greatest extent possible * * * [as] the only system with a purely scientific basis." [132] Again the measure failed. Said a disappointed Stratton, "The opponents of the metric system see to it that every Congressman is reached, and Congress does not see that it originates practically from a single source." [133] Almost certainly he referred to the American Institute of Weights and Measures, founded in 1917 by the antimetricists Samuel Dale and Frederick A. Halsey. With the support of the National Association of Manufacturers and less than a dozen other trade organizations, Dale had founded the institute for the sole purpose of opposing metric legislation—and had succeeded.[134]

Another metric proposal followed a year later, but the era of normalcy was at hand and Stratton had to admit that the political climate was no longer favorable. Moreover, past experience had shown that neither inducing prominent personalities to appear before Congress, soliciting petitions, nor lending the Bureau's own prestige were sufficient. More was needed. The Bureau must adopt a policy of wider education and secure the conversion of members of Congress through their constituents.

Between 1920 and 1930, 23 metric bills were introduced in Congress. Science in industry and industry itself, with an eye on foreign trade, inclined more and more to the metric system.[135] But the great depression saw foreign

---

[131] Remarks of SWS reported in minutes of meeting, Standards Committee, Society of Automotive Engineers, Feb. 16, 1917, pp. 3–4, 20 (NBS Box 20, MS).

[132] Letter, John J. Pershing to W. Mortimer Crocker, Nov. 24, 1919, transmitted to SWS (NBS Box 20, MS).

[133] Confidential letter, SWS to Fred R. Drake, Drake & Co., Easton, Pa., Dec. 29, 1920 (NBS Box 20, MS).

[134] See miscellaneous documents of the A.I.W.M. in L/C: QC81.A347 and A349. The counterpart of the American Institute is the British Weights and Measures Association, active since its founding in 1904 in opposing introduction of the metric system "as a British standard."

[135] NBS C593, "The Federal basis for weights and measures" (R. W. Smith, 1958), p. 19.

How "vital and timely" the subject seemed just after World War I is evident in the special report prepared by the National Industrial Conference Board, The Metric versus the English System of Weights and Measures, Research Report No. 42 (New York: Century, 1921).

In support of a metric bill introduced in 1921, Stratton reported 102,842 petitions received at the Bureau, 15,501 of them from engineers and manufacturers, and 98.87 percent of the total number favorable (memo, SWS for Secretary of Commerce Hoover, Oct. 29, 1921, NBS Box 20, MS).

trade fall away and a growing sense of isolation fill the Nation. In the decades after, interest in the metric system was revived periodically but the tide of congressional and public sentiment remained against conversion.

"THE LEGACY LEFT TO US"

On this side of the Atlantic it seemed that the war ended as abruptly as it began. Newspaper accounts of the fighting in France all through October 1918 indicated no weakness in the German armies anywhere. After the first week of the Meuse-Argonne battle, AEF advances were measured in meters as, under simultaneous pressure from the French and British to the west and north, the German armies gave ground slowly. Military intelligence reported that they were probably withdrawing to their prepared Meuse-Antwerp line, where they would hold through the winter.

Pershing's plans for a renewal of his offensive in the spring of 1919, with victory that summer, were summarily shelved upon the sudden political collapse of Germany in early November. Here at home, industry, finally coming into full-scale production after a year's preparation, awoke to find the war over. Production lines stopped, contracts were canceled, and all war emergency measures suddenly came to an end.

On November 20, 9 days after the armistice, Secretary of Commerce Redfield wrote Stratton asking him what activities of the Bureau would be discontinued as military and naval operations ceased, and what reduction in force might be expected as a result. Neither discontinuance nor reduction was contemplated, Stratton replied. On the contrary, as a result of the wartime experience, he expected greater demands than ever to be made on the Bureau by the military services, both for specifications and increased standardization of their purchases and for the development of new devices and materials. "One of the great lessons taught by the war," said Stratton, "is the need for engineering and scientific work in connection with our defenses." Such research must never again be left until we were at war. Furthermore, the development of substitute materials and the rise of new industries called for expanded Bureau assistance: "There was never a time when the need for industrial research was greater than the present." And he asked Secretary Redfield for help in persuading Congress to lend assistance both to the military and civil departments of the Government and to industry for this research.[136]

Dr. Burgess, concerned with the fact that War Department funds for research automatically terminated within 6 months of the end of hostilities, proposed further action by the Director:

[136] Letter, Redfield to SWS, Nov. 20, 1918, and reply, Nov. 30 (NBS Box 2, AG).

> With the curtailment of military appropriations to the Bureau by Congress, it becomes necessary for the military bureaus to provide funds for the investigations in which they are interested.

He asked Stratton to seek special funds from Navy Ordnance to continue the Bureau investigation of light armor plate steels and Army Ordnance funds to continue the study of machine gun corrosion.[137] A score of other investigations would need similar financing.

The Bureau thus sought help through a wartime measure, the Overman Act, passed by Congress on May 20, 1918.[138] In the interest of economy and greater efficiency, the act authorized, among other things, the transfer of funds from one Government agency to another, where an agency with funds but lacking the staff or facilities for an investigation, survey, or other service that it required, might turn the necessary funds over to the investigating agency. Under the act the military services had transferred well over half a million dollars to the Bureau in 1917 and 1918 (apart from military funds directly appropriated by Congress to the Bureau), to carry out wartime research for them.

The device of interagency fund transfers, although never officially sanctioned before the Overman Act, had prevailed for a number of years among Government agencies. Stratton had not approved of it. Seeking additional funds from Congress at a hearing in 1910, he rejected a suggestion that he avail himself of this custom, insisting that the Bureau "should not be under obligation to any individual or any department when it undertakes testing." [139]

Now suddenly the Bureau was alarmed. It had a plant more than twice its prewar size. The end of hostilities left it stranded with many investigations for the services far from completed. Particularly important, the Bureau felt, was its research on radio vacuum tubes and coil aerials for the Signal Corps, its testing of rubber compositions and tires for the Motor Transport Service, structural materials testing for the Navy Bureau of Yards and Docks, and the work on airplane fabrics and aviation engines. Upon strong pleas by Stratton, President Wilson on March 4, 1919, authorized the transfer of $100,000 from unobligated funds of the Quartermaster Corps to the Bureau to complete some of these investigations.[140]

---

[137] Memo, Burgess for SWS, Nov. 25, 1918 (NBS Box 5, FPG).

[138] For passage of the Overman Act, possibly the most important piece of legislation enacted for the prosecution of the war, see Paxson, American Democracy and the World War, II, 225–226.

[139] Hearings * * * 1912 (Dec. 2, 1910), p. 273.

[140] Letter, Secretary of War to Secretary of the Treasury, Mar. 4, 1919; letter, Secretary of Commerce to Secretary of War, Apr. 10, 1919, and attached corrrespondence (NBS Box 5, FPG). Further correspondence on tranferred funds appears in NBS Box 7, ICG 1918–22.

As appropriations to the military plummeted after the war, the Bureau's transferred funds fell to $62,000 in 1921 and $3,000 in 1922.[141] But the precedent for transferred funds had been established and with no alternative Stratton accepted it. "We would rather handle [all research] * * * as far as possible, on our regular funds," he told the House Appropriations Subcommittee, "but I see no objection [under the circumstances]. * * * I believe it would be a good thing." A paragraph on transferred funds that Stratton prepared and read to the committee was, with minor changes, accepted for inclusion in the Bureau budget. Appearing in the appropriation act of May 20, 1920, and repeated annually thereafter, it stated that—

> the head of any department or independent establishment of the government having funds available for scientific investigations and requiring cooperative work by the Bureau of Standards on scientific investigations within the scope of the functions of that Bureau and which it is unable to perform within the limits of its appropriations, may, with the approval of the Secretary of Commerce, transfer to the Bureau of Standards such sums as may be necessary to carry on such investigations.[142]

Dr. Stratton's successors were often to find it easier to interest other Government agencies in supporting research at the Bureau than to obtain increased funds from Congress.[143] Not Stratton, whose Bureau could not wait for proffered funds. At the second postwar hearing before the House Subcommittee on Appropriations, he requested what one of his auditors protested as "practically double the appropriation asked for last year." It was over a million dollars, Stratton admitted, but actually represented only a 60 percent increase. Item by item he explained his needs, and most of the request was granted.[144] The appropriation bore witness not only to the powers of Stratton's persuasion but to the esteem the Bureau had won for itself in Congress.

By far the largest item in the new Bureau budget was for industrial

---

[141] These sums apparently represent direct transfers of funds for other departments. The blow was softened, however, by the transfer of additional departmental funds through congressional action in 1921, 1922, and 1923, and are included with special appropriations to the Bureau. See app. F and NBS Annual Reports for those years.
[142] Hearings * * * 1921 (Jan. 2, 1920), p. 1598. The provision as enacted in 41 Stat. 683, is cited in Weber, The Bureau of Standards, p. 73. See also letter GKB to Air Service, WD, June 22, 1923 (NBS Box 41, FPG).
[143] Transferred funds to the Bureau rose from $60,870 in 1923 to approximately $418,600 in 1930, or almost 15 percent of total funds. They maintained the 1930 level until World War II. After World War II, transferred funds at times constituted as much as 85 percent of total Bureau working funds.
[144] Hearings * * * 1921 (Jan. 2, 1920), p. 1525.

research, unconnected, as it had been earlier, with Government testing. Back of Stratton's arguments for this research was the realization, crystallized by the wartime experience, that the recent alliance of science and industry was certain to continue in the postwar years. Nor had it escaped notice that most of the wartime triumphs in physics and chemistry were of European origin. In the coming years the great industrial organizations of this country must, to remain competitive, increase their research activities, and in doing so would make unparalleled demands upon the Nation's scientific resources.

Foreseeing this, in 1918 the National Research Council and the Rockefeller Foundation had raised the question of establishing a permanent research institution devoted to pure research, to which industry after the war might look for leadership in the physical sciences. "Is the Federal Government," George E. Vincent, president of the Rockefeller Institute, wrote to Robert A. Millikan of the Council, "in a position to create a separate institution on the analogy of certain research units in the Department of Agriculture and in the Geological Survey? Is the Bureau of Standards capable of extension into a national research institution?" [145] The questions remained, but hope of implementing them ended with the armistice as Congress turned its back on war and all its prerogatives and the wartime organization of science and scientists melted away.

Although Stratton, as an executive member of the National Research Council, certainly knew of the questions under consideration, no correspondence has been found to indicate what part, if any, the Bureau took in them. Quite apart from the interest they must have aroused, it is more than likely that Stratton had already determined on the postwar course of the Bureau. As nothing else could have, the war opened to the Bureau new vistas of its role in the Nation's commerce and industry. When first called on to meet the Nation's war needs, industry had shown itself both fearful and resentful of Government interference.[146] Within months, as the magnitude of the task stood revealed, industry came to realize that only the Federal Government could mobilize and marshal the Nation's resources and command the scientific assistance that industry must have to produce the materials of war. And it discovered in the Bureau not only technical assistance and

[145] Letter of Feb. 5, 1918, quoted in The Autobiography of Robert A. Millikan, pp. 180–181. See also Dupree, Science in the Federal Government, pp. 323–325.

[146] Clarkson in Industrial America in the World War (pp. 318, 427, 449), speaking of the early efforts of the War Industries Board to harness industry to the war needs of the country, said the Board repeatedly found that "business and patriotism were confined to separate compartments." Besides industry's foot-dragging in meeting specifications, Government war purchases for a time were attended by "a saturnalia of high prices."

necessary measurements but a source of the scientific principles upon which its operations must depend.[147]

The Bureau itself realized for the first time what could be done when its 2- and 3-man sections became 50-man sections and were supported with adequate funds and equipment. It was no more than a glimpse, for Bureau accomplishments, by comparison with the tasks laid before it, seemed few. There had hardly been time to state the problem, acquire the equipment, or find the staff before the armistice came. But it was a turning point in the outlook of the Bureau. If it could not be the hoped for center for pure research, the Bureau would undertake the applied research for industry that industry could not do for itself.

As Stratton and Secretary Redfield told the House subcommittee late in 1918, "Practically all of the military work [conducted by the Bureau] has an industrial value," and that research must be continued and expanded on behalf of industry.[148] Other nations realized the extraordinary role science in industry had played in the conflict, and as a result Canada, Japan, and Australia were already planning national laboratories to look after their industrial development. In beating swords into plowshares, Stratton told Congress, the Bureau must continue its research on airplane engines and instruments and take up much needed studies of automotive engines as well. The study of problems raised by the war in optics and optical instruments, in radio, and in acoustics had only begun.[149]

Much of the proposed peacetime research that Stratton and Redfield outlined to Congress was to be carried on, the latter said, in "the legacy left to us," the Bureau's great Industrial building, clearly destined to become "the center and home of the scientific studies of the Government for the

---

[147] A historian-scientist in the glass industry was to say twice within 20 pages of that period: "Much of [the subsequent] increase in knowledge was the direct product of the enforced extension of the optical glass industry during the war. [There was] * * * an awakened realization by the glass industry * * * that the soundest foundation for a strong industry is the understanding of its fundamental scientific principles." George W. Morey, The Properties of Glass, pp. 5, 26.

[148] Hearings * * * 1920 (Dec. 12, 1918), p. 958. A year later Stratton noted that the Bureau "has gotten practically 100 percent salvage value out of all of its scientific research for the War Department." Hearings * * * 1921 (Jan. 2, 1920), p. 1531.

The new emphasis on research for industry and standardization in industrial production, manufacturing, and distribution were subjects of many articles shortly after the war, among them G. K. Burgess, "Science and the after-war period," Sci. Mo. 8, 97 (1919); E. B. Rosa, "The Bureau of Standards and industrial standardization," Am. Federationist, 25, 1029 (1919); "Work of the Bureau of Standards during 1918," Science, 49, 39 (1919)); P. G. Agnew, "The work of the Bureau of Standards," Ann. Am. Acad. Polit. Soc. Sci. 82, 278 (1919); "The Bureau of Standards and the war," Nature, 103, 197 (1919); C. H. Claudy, "Science in the war," Sci. Am. 120, 653 (1919).

[149] Hearings * * * 1920 (Dec. 12, 1918), p. 957.

benefit of the industries of the country." [150] **There the Bureau would con-** tinue to foster the new industries born of the war, the manufacture of scientific instruments, of aeronautical instruments, of automotive power plants, and the science of electrodeposition. Redfield pointed to three others that had grown out of recent Bureau investigations: The making of chemical porcelain, never before produced in this country; the making of hard-fired porcelain, for which we had been wholly dependent on Germany, Austria, and Great Britain; and the making of pyrometer tubes, polarimeters and other scientific instruments, previously obtained from Germany. In applying science to industry, declared Redfield, "We have begun to do the thing that Germany did 35 years ago." [151]

Still other industries in which research had just begun included the making of precision gages, dyes and chemicals, petroleum products, the rare sugars, the platinum metals, rubber, paper, leather, and ceramics.[152] The fields of metallurgy, photographic technology, and construction and building materials must be examined anew. And Redfield promised that "we will put in [the Industrial building] a small woolen mill, a cotton mill, etc.," to investigate some of the basic problems in cloth manufacture that engaged so much effort during the war and found little solution.[153]

But the real legacy left to the Bureau was not a building or a program but a series of intangibles: the closer relation that had arisen between the Bureau and industry; the beginning of recognition of what scientific methods could contribute to industrial technology; and perhaps more important, the realization by industry that fundamental science, which seemingly produced nothing, might have far-reaching consequences at some future time. Industries that had set up their own laboratories before the war doubled and

[150] Ibid., p. 958.
[151] Ibid., pp. 932–933, 940. Redfield's remark is quoted in letter, Elizabeth Minor King, "New York Evening Post," to Redfield, Mar. 22, 1919 (NARG 40, Box 119, file 67009/63).
[152] In a memorandum to the Bureau of Foreign and Domestic Commerce, Dec. 16, 1918, Stratton listed as new things produced on a commercial scale since 1915, in many instances with Bureau help: manganin, a special alloy for use in electrical work; high-grade volumetric glass apparatus; high-grade optical glass; four types of photographic dyes; fused quartz of optical quality; chemical glassware (Pyrex); oxygen control apparatus; improved design in aeronautical instruments; burned shale aggregates for concrete ships; cotton airplane fabric; photographic paper; cigarette paper; and fine grades of artifical abrasives (NBS Box 10, IG).
[153] Hearings * * * 1920 (Dec. 12, 1918), p. 958. Acquired in 1918, the wool and cotton mills were moved into the Industrial building upon its completion early in 1920. See letter, Textile Research Co., Boston, Mass., to SWS, June 7, 1919, and attached correspondence (NBS Box 4, AP). The woolen mill was never set up. Realizing its need for scientific assistance, the textile industry, working in close cooperation with the Department of Agriculture and the Bureau, organized its own research laboratories in the 1920's. About 1930 the cotton mill, no longer necessary, was dismantled. Conversation with William D. Appel, Mar. 4, 1963.

tripled their scientific staffs, and others that had formerly considered research an expensive frill now made room for the scientists and engineers they began to enlist.[154]

For the Bureau's industrial research, Stratton asked a special congressional appropriation of $363,000, half again as much as the combined sums requested for its previous largest programs, structural materials testing and the testing of Government materials. In addition, he asked for more than four times the past year's appropriation for public utility investigations. The war had put enormous pressure on the utilities, dramatizing, he said, their "engineering and economic problems." Not only gas and electric companies, but telephone and telegraph companies had been overtaxed by the service demands of the war industries, war workers, and military camps. Hardest hit, the telephone company in the District of Columbia had been forced to file a petition for both traffic and financial relief.[155] "The public utilities of the country are trembling in the balance," Redfield told Congress, and if the Bureau did not undertake the necessary research to provide practical standards and scientific data on their behalf, then each of the 48 States would have to establish separate laboratories to do this work.[156] Congress agreed that it was a Bureau responsibility.

For a peacetime America, it was an immense and expensive program the Bureau projected. With the increase in staff, statutory salaries for Bureau test and research personnel had gone up from less than $300,000 in 1916 to nearly $500,000 for fiscal year 1920. In the same period, special appropriations, which included salaries for the additional staff, rose from $300,000 (for 9 projects) to $1,310,000 (for 25 projects). Of the projects under special appropriations, four alone—industrial research, public utilities, structural materials, and testing of Government materials—accounted for well over half the total of special appropriations and more than one-third of total Bureau income. Convinced of the peacetime worth of these investigations begun with public or military funds during the war, Congress made cuts in some but voted to continue them all. Their benefit to industry was beyond question.

A year after Vincent and Millikan raised the question of extending the functions of the Bureau of Standards on behalf of industry, Dr. Stratton, in the introduction to his annual report for 1918–19, accepted the challenge in a significant restatement of Bureau policy. The relation of the Bureau's work to the public, to the Government and to science remained unchanged,

---

[154] Where in 1920 there had been 300 industrial research laboratories in this country, a decade later there were 1,625, staffed by more than 34,000 people. Dupree, Science in the Federal Government, p. 337.

[155] "War Work," pp. 274–276.

[156] Hearings * * * 1920 (Dec. 12, 1918), p. 941; NBS Annual Report 1918, pp. 52–53.

but henceforth the Bureau declared itself "fundamentally concerned, either directly or indirectly, with the improvement of methods of production or the quality of the output" of industry. It thus occupied "somewhat the same position with respect to the manufacturing interests of this country that the bureaus of the Department of Agriculture do to the agriculture interests." [157] Such was the intention of the Bureau when, with the incoming Harding administration, Herbert Hoover became the new Secretary of Commerce.

[157] NBS Annual Report 1919, p. 21.

The Exchecquer standard wine gallon of Queen Anne, 1707.

The Physikalisch-Technische Reichsanstalt at Charlottenburg, Germany. It was, said Dr. Rosa after a visit there, "an illustrious example of how much can be accomplished where research and testing are combined in one institution." (*MS speech in NBS Box 22, PRA 1901–03.*)

THE TIDE OF COMMERCE AND INDUSTRY (1920–30)

CHAPTER V

THE POSTWAR WORLD

The United States emerged from its brief participation in the war by far the world's richest and most powerful Nation. Disillusioned with the chronic sickness of Europe and rejecting the power a world in chaos offered, America deliberately turned its back and set about building a national structure of self-sufficiency and plenty on the broad industrial base and the techniques of mass production it had acquired during the war. In the mid-1920's a social historian spoke simple truth when he said that "A dynamic history of the period might give a volume or two to the automobile and a foot-note to affairs of state." [1]

New industries born of the war were soon to make the Nation independent in nearly every manufactured necessity. The revolution in the coking industry and the confiscation of German patents upon our entrance into the war made possible the production of many of the dyes, medicines, and industrial solvents formerly obtained from Germany, and led to such important new industries as the making of synthetic plastics and fibers.[2] The new chemistry and advances in metallurgy joined with electric power to revolutionize the extraction and refining of copper and iron ores, the cracking of petroleum, and to make giants of the automobile, motion picture, radio, and telephone industries. With the introduction of the closed car at popular prices in 1922, the automobile by itself almost created a new industrial revolution through its mass consumption of steel, nickel, lead and other metals, plate glass, leather, textiles, rubber, gasoline, and oil, and its demand for roads and highways, gas stations, garages, and roadside accommodations.

Surpassing even the growth of the automobile and electrical industries in the decade after the war was the building and construction industry. Government construction of streets, highways, and public buildings alone are

[1] Robert L. Duffus, "1900–1925," Century, 109, 488 (1925).

[2] Preston W. Slosson, The Great Crusade and After: 1914–1928 (New York: Macmillan, 1930), p. 18. The Trading-with-the-Enemy Act of Oct. 6, 1917 permitted the President to license the use of German patents by American firms, under the administration of the Federal Trade Commission. Frederic L. Paxson, American Democracy and the World War, II, 132.

said to have "used more capital and employed more men than in any single line of private enterprise." [3] At the same time, private construction, consuming vast quantities of brick, steel, stone, tile, cement, lumber, hardware, and plumbing supplies, changed metropolitan skylines and pushed up row houses and apartments along ever-lengthening radii out of the cities.

Technology and the plant facilities to make consumer products were far in advance of demand. "For every hundred people in American cities in 1920 there were only thirteen bathtubs and six telephones. One American in every thirteen had an automobile, but not one in ten thousand had a radio. Almost no farmhouses, and but one in every ten city homes, were wired for electricity; only in such homes, therefore, were there potential customers for washing machines, vacuum cleaners, refrigerators, floor lamps, incandescent bulbs, fans, and flatirons." [4] In city and suburb, technology thus stood ready to invade the home as the automobile, radio, telephone, bathroom plumbing, and kitchen appliances became essentials of the good life. Wages rose steadily, but not fast enough to sustain the buying power needed by the pace of mass production, and advertising and installment buying became giant adjuncts of industry to maintain mass consumption.[5] The promise of the decade appeared in the extraordinary boom that followed the end of wartime controls as industry, enriched by research and mechanization, sought to satisfy pent-up demands.[6] There was to be a severe postwar depression but it was delayed until late in 1920.

---

[3] Thomas C. Cochran and William Miller, The Age of Enterprise: A Social History of Industrial America (New York: Macmillan, 1942), p. 298. Highway, road, and street construction expenditures, for example, rose from just over a half billion dollars in 1920 to a billion in 1921 and close to two billion by 1928. U.S. Bureau of the Census, Historical Statistics, p. 382.

[4] Ibid., p. 309. All these appliances, as well as air conditioners, electric ranges, water heaters, and garbage-disposal units, though some were yet crude and costly, were on the market before the end of the decade.

In the 28 million homes in the United States at the end of 1928, it was estimated that 19 million were wired for electricity, 17 million had an automobile outside the door, 13 million had a telephone, 13 million a phonograph, and 9 million had factory-built radio sets. Dellinger, "Radio," in A. B. Hart and W. M. Schuyler, eds., The American Year Book, 1929 (New York: Am. Year Book Corp., 1930), p. 460.

[5] Between 1900 and 1920 the volume of manufactured products went up 95 percent while population increased only 40 percent. Duffus, "1900–1925."

[6] In its haste to convert to peacetime production, industry often neglected new materials or sources developed during the war. Pointing specifically to the renewed but now unnecessary importation of German clays for glassmaking, Dr. Stratton deplored the "tendency on the part of manufacturers to revert to the old order of things just as soon as they could * * * [following] the path of least resistance and of the least financial risk." Letter, SWS to A. V. Bleininger, Feb. 3, 1919 (NBS Box 14, IR).

At the National Bureau of Standards the boom seemed for a time more like disaster. With the war over, it expected the exodus of the scientists detailed from other Government agencies and those on leave from colleges and universities. But it found irreplaceable its loss of regular Bureau members to the siren call from industry for trained investigators. Attracted by salaries which in many instances were twice those available at the Bureau, over 78 percent of the total force of appointed staff members left in the 7 months following the armistice. Some positions had a succession of occupants; in others replacements simply could not be found.[7]

Subprofessionals (aids, apprentices, and mechanics) entered the Bureau at as little as $720 a year and could hope for no more than $2,740. Most, with any length of experience, were caught in the $1,140–$1,240 bracket. Professionals with degrees and experience came in at $1,440. Some among the key members were getting as little as $2,240, most were at $4,000, and only a few of the division chiefs had attained the maximum possible, $4,800.

This was at a time when a bookkeeper in downtown Washington could make $100 a month, "with meals." University salaries were sufficiently higher than those paid by the Government for Dr. E. W. Washburn to turn down the maximum of $4,000 that the Bureau had to offer. (He came 6 years later, in 1926, at the division chief level.) Industry paid close to twice the Bureau salary at every level of training and experience.[8]

The cost of living in 1920 was relatively high and left little for amenities. A Bureau apprentice making $65 a month before taxes could find room and breakfast within a mile of the laboratories for $20 a month. Not far away, a front room rented for $25, and meals were another $30. For a family, a four- or five-room furnished apartment with steam heat and electricity could be found on the way downtown for $110, or 2 miles north of the Bureau, in Chevy Chase, for $100.

Men's suits were fairly expensive, running from $25 to $85 for all wool and $15.50 to $25 for Palm Beach or mohair, with tropical worsteds in between. Hats were $4 to $8 and shoes $7 and up. Although probably 15 or 20 on the Bureau staff owned a car by 1920, it was seldom driven except on weekends and almost everyone still rode a bicycle to work or

[7] NBS Annual Report 1919, p. 279. For a list of the physicists who left the Bureau for industry in the 1920's, see letter, LJB to Secretary, American Institute of Physics, Feb. 24, 1936 (NBS Box 395, ID-Misc.).

[8] Interview with Dr. William Blum, Oct. 15, 1963. By the end of the decade, salaries at the Bureau had gone up by almost one-third. Living costs (a room with two meals a day was $45 to $55 a month) had risen only slightly. See NBS M94, "Scientific and technical positions in the NBS" (1929).

came by streetcar. Some of the prices for new automobiles that year read like Bureau salaries. While the Ford runabout was only $395, the sedan cost $795. The Dort "fourseason" sedan was $1,870, the Auburn sedan $2,775. Nor could used cars have been very popular when a 1919 Chevrolet cost $550 and an Overland $1,000. For the sporty youth on his own, however, there was that Stutz 6-cylinder roadster, vintage not given, going for $375.[9] Few below the scientific grades in the laboratories could afford any of them, just as few could afford to stay at the Bureau.

A loyal nucleus that included most of the key members of the staff remained, even though many of those in the lower grades who elected to stay were, Dr. Stratton said, being paid "less than a living wage." In its search for replacements, all that the Bureau had to offer was "a reasonably good entrance salary to young men just out of college." [10] With industry bidding for them, too, even recent graduates could not be found in any numbers and the Bureau staff fell from 1,150 members in July 1919 to 981 a year later, and 850 by 1921. Few eligibles appeared on the civil service registers and answers to advertising appeals grew meager. The Bureau turned to industry itself in an effort to restaff its laboratories.

Dr. Stratton some years earlier had warned that the schools were not turning out even a tenth of the scientific and technical men needed in industry, and as a consequence industry raided the Bureau in its search for trained men. In 1916, as industry expanded to feed the war machines in Europe and Bureau losses of skilled workmen went up, Stratton proposed to Congress that in order to relieve the pressure on his staff the Bureau make its facilities available to industrial specialists, technical experts, and researchers, and by setting them to work on problems in which both they and the Bureau were interested, "train them up for the industries." He cited as example a linoleum company which had recently asked to send a chemist to the Bureau who after 6 months' training would return and set up a laboratory in the plant where he worked. Without authorization or funds for this type of employment, the Bureau had to deny the request.[11]

Although he brought up the matter at hearings each year thereafter, Congress said no. By the summer of 1919 what Stratton had previously called "more or less a notion of mine" had become stark necessity, and he turned to the trade associations served by the Bureau, proposing that where they needed specific researches on important problems affecting their industry, they send qualified men to the Bureau to do this research. It was

[9] Advertisements in the "Washington Evening Star," April and October 1920.
[10] NBS Annual Report 1920, p. 279; Annual Report 1921, p. 272.
[11] Hearings * * * 1918 (Dec. 1, 1916), p. 483.

agreed that these "research associates" would be paid by industry, and since their work was for the industry at large, rather than for any single company. the results would be published by the Bureau and so made available to all.[12]

Two years later, in 1921, six associates in metallurgy were appointed by the Director. By 1923, 21 associates, representing 18 industries, were at the Bureau, and by 1925 a total of 61 associates, maintained by 36 organizations, were at work, most of them sponsored by trade associations but also among them a number from private research firms, science foundations, and Government agencies.[13]

At the heels of the staffing crisis came the brief but severe depression of 1920–21. Overnight at the end of the war, President Wilson's War Industries Board and other emergency regulatory agencies had been dissolved, ending nationwide Government control of the economy. For a time unfettered business boomed, but as prices soared out of sight, production and employment fell off and thousands of new companies, notably in the automobile industry, collapsed. Soon there was widespread criticism of the high cost of living, which since 1916 had seen the dollar reduced in purchasing value to 45 cents; of the new income tax and surtaxes, seriously felt for the first time since their imposition in 1913; and charges of inefficiency, extravagance, and overdevelopment throughout the Government.[14]

Reacting to "the avalanche of disapproval" aimed at the Wilson administration, Congress lashed out at "the army of clerks * * * and crocheting stenographers" said to be infesting every department of the Government, and at appropriations hearings hacked away funds, research and operating alike. The cuts that could not be compromised were annoying but not deep. The Bureau closed several of its branch offices and began saving its cinders to make cinder-concrete paths between the buildings. As Stratton

---

[12] Hearings * * * 1919 (Jan. 25, 1918), p. 984; letter, SWS to Managing Director, National Industrial Conference Board, June 26, 1919 (NBS Box 10, IG). Most responsive were industries which had small research laboratories or none at all, and had less to fear from patentable discoveries, as in dental materials, terra cotta, tile, and other building materials, pottery, textiles, and color research.

[13] NBS Annual Report 1921, p. 240; Annual Report 1923, pp. 4–5; NBS C296, "Research associates at the Bureau of Standards" (1925). The plan further solved staffing difficulties when a number of the research associates subsequently left industry and came to work for the Bureau, among them Dr. Paul D. Merica, Dr. John R. Cain, R. G. Waltenberg, Dr. I. G. Priest, N. S. Osborne, Dr. H. F. Stimson, N. D. Booth, J. A. Dickinson, Dr. Deane B. Judd, Dr. F. G. Brickwedde, T. S. Sligh, Jr., and Dr. A. V. Astin (see list of associates in C296).

[14] The top rate of tax on personal income, set at 7 percent in 1913, was slightly reduced during the 1920's. By 1932 it was up to 25 percent, and during the depression years it reached a high of 63 percent.

later reported to Congress, "In the program of economy adopted, some retrenchments were made." [15]

Stirred by the debates in Congress and the attacks in the press and periodical literature on Federal spending, Dr. Rosa, with Dr. Stratton's approval, cleared his desk and began work on a series of studies in the cost and efficiency of the Federal Government, in answer to the outcry. For their view of the question of science in Government, particularly as it affected the Bureau, some of Rosa's arguments in these papers are worth summarizing.

Pointing to the wartime exhaustion of raw and manufactured materials, the rising demand for consumer goods in short supply, inflation of currency and credit, and postwar profiteering as among the causes for continued rising prices, Rosa declared that more Government, not less, was necessary to protect the public. He warned of "economic and political disturbance or even disaster," asserting that the Government must again, as it had during the war, induce the Nation "to economize in the use of staple commodities and luxuries, reduce the waste of raw materials, make use of cheaper materials, increase the efficiency of men, of machines, and of processes, on a nationwide scale and at an early date." [16] By "more" Government Rosa made clear he did not mean reimposition of wartime controls but better education of the public in the cost of Government, more efficient operation of Government, and greater assistance to those Government agencies whose recognized function it was to work directly in the public interest.

Answering the charge of extravagance in Federal spending, Rosa showed that in the budget for 1920 interest on the national debt as a result of past wars consumed 67.8 percent of Federal income, the military services received 25 percent, the cost of running the Government came to 3.2 percent, public works 3 percent, and research, education, and development 1 percent.[17]

---

[15] Hearings * * * 1922 (Dec. 20, 1920). p. 1235; Hearings * * * 1923 (Feb. 1, 1922), pp. 424, 425, 452.

In a letter in March 1920 to a former Bureau member who had gone into industry, Stratton discussed the coming economy wave: "I personally know most of the leaders of the party in control and the chairman of the committees directly interested in our work." They had initiated the economy program and intended to push it, said Stratton, and there were no exceptions. Nevertheless, he was "working with the Senate committee and hoped to persuade it to restore some of the more important funds" (Letter, SWS to F. C. Clarke, Mar. 17, 1920, NBS Box 10, IG).

[16] Rosa, "The economic importance of the scientific work of the Government," J. Wash. Acad. Sci. 10, 342 (1920).

[17] J. Wash. Acad. Sci., pp. 346–349. The percentages were based on total revenues of approximately $5.68 billion. (Between 1914 and 1921, the national debt rose from $1,188 million to $23,976 million.)

In his final study, "Expenditures and revenues of the Federal Government," Ann. Am. Acad. Pol. Soc. Sci. 95, 1–113 (1921), Rosa included revenue and expenditure data for

He rivetted attention on that 1 percent, representing little more than 50 cents out of the approximately $50 per capita [18] collected by the Government from all sources, for it was the key to industrial recovery and to reduction in the high cost of living. Out of that 50 cents, agriculture received 62 percent; education, public health, and labor bureaus received 25.6 percent; the Bureau of Mines and Geological Survey 5 percent; and the Bureau of Foreign and Domestic Commerce, Bureau of Standards, Bureau of Fisheries, and Coast and Geodetic Survey together 10.5 percent or little more than 5 cents per capita. Considering these facts, said Rosa, the distribution of Government income left little room for extravagance.

The charge of inefficiency in Government, on the other hand, was more valid, largely because Government pay, based as it was on a statutory salary scale established prior to 1914, failed to attract and hold experienced and competent people. Federal employees from scientists and administrators to clerks and laborers shared the same scale proportionately. As the Secretary of Commerce was to point out to Congress, leading physicists in universities and industrial laboratories were getting between $8,000 and $25,000 a year, while top physicists at the Bureau of Standards could make no more than $4,800.[19] The consequence was an inordinate turnover of personnel at every level.[20] The remedy was revision of the civil service system and its wage scale, to make Government employment more attractive; and establishment of a budget bureau that would plan and coordinate the work of the Government and its agencies, to assure the best use of its employees.[21]

Returning to the subject of Federal research, Rosa pointed out that where the expenses of the Department of Agriculture amounted to about $1.50 for every $1,000 of the national value of agricultural and animal products, those of the Bureau of Standards came to $0.15 for every $1,000 worth of manufactured products, and less than half that amount was spent by the Bureau for the development of manufactures. Agriculture might still be "the most important industry in the Nation," but revival of the economy depended on the recovery of manufactures, by more efficient utilization of raw materials and labor and expansion of production.[22]

---

the years 1910–19. His adjusted figures for 1920 did not materially change the validity of his conclusions and the earlier figures are therefore used here.

[18] Based on a 1920 population of approximately 110 million.

[19] Hearings * * * 1923 (Feb. 1, 1922), p. 14.

[20] Address by Rosa before ASME, "The scientific and engineering work of the Government," Dec. 2, 1920, p. 20 (NBS Historical File). It required at least a year to train a laboratory assistant at the Bureau, yet almost everyone hired in the postwar period left for better positions after 1 to 3 months. NBS Annual Report 1920, p. 30.

[21] Ann. Am. Acad. Pol. Soc. Sci., pp. 73, 88, 90, 94.

[22] J. Wash. Acad. Sci., pp. 342, 350–352.

Unlike agriculture, industry spent generous sums of money on research, but only for its own commercial advantage. Bureau research, on the other hand, reverted to the advantage of the public, for it led directly to decreased costs of commodities, improved service, better quality and performance, and reduced misrepresentation and exaggeration, all "constructive and wealth-producing contributions to the economy." Rosa declared that raising the per capita share of the Bureau appropriation by a single cent would yield returns a hundredfold, and raising it fivefold "would accomplish wonders." [23]

Among the many studies at the time in the causes and cures for the depression, Rosa's analysis was one of the most thorough and was widely studied.[24] The Bureau of the Budget which he urged and which had been under discussion for almost a decade was formally established in June 1921. Much-needed civil service reform, including a slight upward adjustment of salaries, came in July 1924. And Rosa's "wonders" in the national economy were to be accomplished, but in ways and to a degree he could not have foreseen.

A new and fabulous era in the Nation's history was about to begin. The early years of President Wilson's administration had seen a continuation of Federal efforts, begun under Roosevelt and Taft, to curb corporate monopolies and give a measure of Government back to the people. That reform impulse had ended with the war, and the disillusionment of the postwar period, climaxed by the severe depression, led to a massive rejection of the age of idealism, of political experimentation, that swept the President and all his policies off the scene.

The period of Republican ascendancy that followed, it has been said, represented not the high tide of laissez faire but of Hamiltonianism, the deliberate pursuit by Government of policies favorable to large business interests.[25] The trusts of the early century were to rise again in the mergers of the twenties, and the soaring wealth of the Nation reflected kiting of values as often as it did new capital investment. The consolidation of industries and utilities, moreover, exercised measurable control over prices and production, so that the cost of living, after a slight decline from its awful peak in 1920, was to hold steady to the end of the decade.[26] Salaries in the middle-

[23] J. Wash. Acad. Sci., pp. 373–374; Ann. Am. Acad. Pol. Soc. Sci., p. 107.

[24] See "New York Times," May 30, 1920, sec. VII, p. 4. John F. Sinclair, in the "Washington Evening Star," Mar. 19, 1924, p. 6, called Rosa's reports "the most comprehensive and most intelligent survey from the plain citizen's viewpoint of Government finances which was ever undertaken."

[25] Leuchtenburg, The Perils of Prosperity, 1914–1932, p. 103.

[26] The cost of living index, based on 1913=100, had by 1920 reached 286. By 1926 it had subsided to 241 and remained at that approximate level to the end of the decade. Historical Statistics, p. 127.

income bracket went up, and installment buying and liberal credit terms became new measures of personal wealth. But the farmer, the professional man, and the laboring man, unless he was in the automobile or radio industry, had small share in the new wealth.

If the aura of prosperity of the golden twenties resulted principally, as management was to claim, from increased mechanization of industry, greater efficiency through scientific management, industrial research, and the rising output of workers, no Federal Government ever before provided more assistance to industry or a happier climate for free enterprise. Economies in Government spending, a balanced budget, lower taxes, a high protective tariff, and a supremely able and energetic Department of Commerce all acted to accelerate the tide of commerce and industry.

HERBERT HOOVER AND THE BUREAU OF STANDARDS

The most capable man that came in with the Harding administration was the new Secretary of Commerce, Herbert Clark Hoover. Considered by many for a time the best man for the Presidency itself and tentatively claimed by both parties, Hoover, by his efficient handling of the wartime Food Administration and of Belgian relief had made his name a household word. His enginering background and knowledge of industry were needed as the Nation slid into depression. But by nature autocratic, often dogmatic, and almost wholly apolitical, he was not the man party leaders sought.

When he subsequently accepted the Cabinet post it was with reluctance and only on his own terms. His friend Oscar Straus, Commerce and Labor Secretary from 1907 to 1909 under Theodore Roosevelt, once told him that the office required only a couple of hours of work a day and "no other qualification than to be able to put the fish to bed at night and turn on the lights around the coast." [27] Hoover thought otherwise. He was quoted in the press as saying that the department, composed of uncorrelated scientific and semiscientific bureaus, had too long "been a Department of Commerce in name only." [28] With Harding's promise to stand behind him, he intended to expand foreign commerce through organized cooperation with industry, aiming at lower production costs; and to assist domestic commerce in im-

[27] Eugene Lyons, Our Unknown Ex-President (New York: Doubleday, 1948), p. 219. Cf. The Memoirs of Herbert Hoover: the Cabinet and the Presidency, 1920–1933 (New York: Macmillan, 1952), p. 42. (Hereafter designated as vol. II of the Memoirs.)
[28] "New York Times," Feb. 25, 1921, p. 1.

Herbert Hoover as Secretary of Commerce, it was predicted, would make his department "second only to that of the Secretary of State." He did just that, and by making all interests of commerce and industry the province of the Bureau, further expanded its scope of activities and range of research.

proving its industrial processes, abolishing waste, establishing better labor relations, and better business methods. With his knowledge, experience, and driving power, the "New York Times" editorialized, Hoover seemed destined to make his office in the Cabinet "second only to that of the Secretary of State." [29] The "Times" may have overestimated the position but it underestimated the man.

The Department of Commerce in 1921 comprised the Bureaus of Foreign and Domestic Commerce, Lighthouses, Navigation, the Coast and Geodetic Survey, the Bureaus of the Census, Standards, and Fisheries, and the Steamboat Inspection Service. In 1922 Congress was to add a Building and Housing Division to Commerce, and in 1925 Hoover secured by Executive order the transfer from Interior of the Bureau of Mines and the Patent

[29] "New York Times," Feb. 25, 1921, pp. 2, 10. The editorial spoke of Hoover's "dictatorial temper."

Office.[30] In 1926 a congressional act added an Aeronautics Division and in 1927 a Radio Division to Commerce.

On taking over the Department, Hoover seems to have been under the impression that "the Bureau of Standards had hitherto been devoted mostly to formal administration of weights and measures," and that, as he later said in his Memoirs, by greatly enlarging its research not only in "abstract knowledge but * * * [in] its application in industry," the Bureau under his direction became "one of the largest physics laboratories in the world." [31] In all fairness, the Bureau under Stratton had already achieved that eminence. It is true that in the period 1921-28 it expanded from 9 divisions with a total of 68 sections to 13 divisions with 85 sections, but staff and appropriations actually increased very little in those 7 years, from 850 to 889 members and from $2,209,000 in operating funds to $2,540,000.[32] As for any limitation on Bureau research interests, it was quite otherwise. Under Stratton and Rosa, little that was measurable in the home, in the market, in commerce, industry, science, or Government but had at one time or another become a subject of investigation at the Bureau, and as often as not a sustained investigation.[33]

By 1920, in addition to several score investigations and test programs conducted under statutory funds, the Bureau had some 16 other investigations going with special congressional appropriations. That year Stratton secured more special funds to begin another nine studies. Three were short-term investigations, in industrial safety standards, Government materials testing, and platinum and rare metals research. The other six, metallurgical research, high temperature studies, railroad scale testing, sound research, standardization of equipment, and a new huge industrial research

[30] The transfer of the Bureau of Mines to the Commerce Department concentrated the oil testing and ceramics work of Mines and Standards in the latter bureau, with a heavy clay products section located in Columbus, Ohio. The transfer added 52 employes to the Bureau staff. NBS Annual Report 1926, p. 44; Annual Report 1927, p. 2; NBS Blue Folder Box 3, file AG–138c.

[31] Memoirs of Herbert Hoover, II, 73.

[32] See apps. F and H. "In retrospect Hoover was proud of the fact that despite its increased activity the department grew little in size or cost under his charge." Dupree, Science in the Federal Government, p. 340.

[33] So reported a committee of electrical manufacturers appointed by Hoover in 1922 to advise the Bureau on electrical research. The committee, apparently piqued by some of the current public utility recommendations of the Bureau, called "attention to the fact that the Bureau's activities have been very widely extended into various fields not contemplated by the act creating the Bureau, through the medium of * * * special Congressional appropriations, and * * * we [are] not ready to accept this means of enlarging the Bureau's sphere of activities as a safe procedure, and especially since it is apparent that when an activity of this kind is initiated by such appropriation it is apparently considered a function of the Bureau from that time forward." Letter, Chairman, Electrical Manufacturers Council, Committee on the Bureau of Standards, to Secretary Hoover. Oct. 2, 1922 (NBS Box 2, AG).

program, were to continue for more than a decade before being merged in the regular work of the Bureau.[34]

The nine were among the last of the special appropriations made to the Bureau. Coming into office on an economy wave, Hoover in a public announcement declared: "This is no time to ask for appropriations to undertake new work. It is the time to search for economy and reorganization, for effective expenditure on essentials, the reduction of less essentials, and the elimination of duplication." [35] The same regimen held true for the general economy. Recalling the scene of widespread unrest and unemployment as he took office, Hoover was later to say: "There was no special outstanding industrial revolution in sight. We had to make one." His prescription for the recovery of industry "from [its] war deterioration" was through "elimination of waste and increasing the efficiency of our commercial and industrial system all along the line." [36]

To do this, Hoover divided the direction of his bureaus between two special assistants, "except Foreign and Domestic Commerce and Standards, which I took under my own wing." [37] These two bureaus represented ideal instruments for jogging a lagging economy and putting industry back on its feet. The "wing" actually proved to be Assistant Secretary J. Walter Drake, brought to Washington from the Detroit automobile industry. But Hoover himself was to give Bureau interests his wholehearted support, and in his annual encounters with Congress at the side of Dr. Stratton pled the Bureau's need for better salaries and for its research funds.

Where to commence jogging the economy was not difficult to see. Wholly inadequate as a result of the war and beset by excessive costs, home construction offered the most immediate means of reviving the greatest number of industries and providing work for the largest numbers of unemployed. Because its stimulation would depend upon personal organization and massive publicity, Hoover organized the division of building and housing in

[34] See app. G.

A member of Great Britain's National Physical Laboratory, visiting the Bureau in 1921, found it "very considerably larger" in every sense than the Teddington plant, its chemical, spectroscopic, and metallurgical work particularly on "a totally different scale than anything at NPL." Impressed by the ceramics, refractories, and optical glass work at the Bureau, the visitor reported that the effort at NPL in these fields, by comparison, "becomes almost insignificant." NPL Annual Report 1922, pp. 197–199. For a comparison of the Bureau with the German PTR in the 1930's, see ch. VI, p. 310.

Another comparison with NBS research, made by a member of the Bureau's National Hydraulic Laboratory after a year's study of hydraulic programs in the laboratories in Europe, appears in a report attached to letter, LJB to Martin A. Mason, June 28, 1939 (NBS Box 430, ID—Misc.)

[35] "New York Times," Mar. 11, 1921, p. 3.

[36] The Memoirs of Herbert Hoover, II, 61.

[37] Ibid., II, 42.

his own office. The necessary scientific, technical, and economical research, simplification and standardization of building materials, and revision of municipal and State building codes required by the program he made the responsibility of the Bureau of Standards, where a division similarly named was activated.

At the end of 1921, with the housing program well launched, Hoover established a division of simplified practice at the Bureau, on the model of Baruch's wartime Conservation Division, to work with and encourage the technical committees then operating in most trade and industrial associations to eliminate waste in industry. Like the former Conservation Division, simplified practice aimed at reduction of varieties and sizes in commodities and greater standardization of materials and products. Further extending these aims, two more units, a specifications division and a trade standards division, were set up at the Bureau to reinforce and promote the demand anticipated for standardized and simplified products.

The new divisions insured the fullest exploitation of Bureau plans for industrial research, but to Dr. Stratton's dismay, their direction was centered in the Commerce building downtown. Although the whole of the scientific and technical research required by the housing and standardization programs was to be financed out of Bureau appropriations, the administrative staffs of the four divisions were under Secretary Hoover's personal direction.[38] It may be guessed that the divided control and responsibility rankled.

Outwardly, relations between Dr. Stratton and Secretary Hoover were cordial and even close, as correspondence between them and Stratton's letters to members of Hoover's family make abundantly clear.[39] Although Hoover is said to have visited the Bureau rarely, he kept in close touch and consulted Stratton frequently on Department matters; and as the senior administrator in the Commerce Department, Stratton often spent afternoons downtown when the Secretary was out of the city, signing Department correspondence as Acting Secretary of Commerce.[40]

Just when Dr. Stratton first thought of leaving the Bureau is uncertain. It was doubtless an accumulation of events that occurred in that 20th year of the Bureau's founding. On the afternoon of May 17, 1921, Dr. Rosa, not quite 60, died suddenly at his desk in East building. Two months later Stratton's long-time chief of weights and measures, Mr. Fischer, died at his

---

[38] The roles of the divisions at Commerce and their counterparts at the Bureau are distinguished in memo, Secretary of Commerce Hoover for GKB, May 23, 1923 (NBS Box 40, AG).

[39] See correspondence in NBS Box 10, IEW–1922; letter, Mrs. Hoover to SWS, Sept. 1, 1922, and other correspondence in Stratton Papers at MIT. See also Dr. Stratton's speech at 25th Anniversary of the NBS, Dec. 4, 1926 (NBS Blue Box 3, APN–301c).

[40] Interview with Dr. Lyman J. Briggs, Nov. 1, 1961; communication to the author from the Hon. Herbert C. Hoover, Dec. 14, 1962 (NBS Historical File).

home, and 8 months after, Dr. Waidner, chief of the heat and thermometry division, was gone. The deaths of three of his division chiefs within less than a year affected him profoundly. They had been with the Bureau since its establishment, had been his most intimate associates, and understood his ways. Other division chiefs, coming later and without the bond of the early years, sometimes found Stratton's autocratic ways difficult and his concern with the minutiae of every laboratory and Bureau operation excessive. With the loss of his closest associates and amid a faint undercurrent of unrest, of which he could not be unaware, Dr. Stratton may have felt that the Bureau might never again be the same.[41]

There were other considerations, too. In the 20 years that he had been Director, Dr. Stratton's salary had risen from $4,000 to $6,000, the maximum permitted for the position under civil service rules, even though the staff he directed had increased more than sixtyfold. As Secretary Hoover told an appropriations committee, it was a ridiculous sum by comparison with salaries paid outside the Government. The work and responsibilities of the position, said Hoover, were fully equivalent to those of a university president receiving $25,000.[42]

Although a bachelor, Dr. Stratton had heavy expenses. In an age more sedulously social than our own, he delighted in entertaining members of the staff and his circle of friends in Washington. His elaborate Christmas and summer parties for the children of the staff became festive traditions.[43] Entertainment of visiting scientists and businessmen and his colleagues from the national laboratories abroad he had long met out of his own pocket, as he had the expenses of membership in the social and scientific clubs required by his position.

Besides his lifelong interest in his private workshop at the Bureau, which entailed some personal expense, Stratton as a result of his frequent official trips to Europe developed a collector's interest in tapestries, fine crystal, polished glassware, instruments, and ingenious mechanical devices which he found in the shops abroad. The interest was constrained, for many of these things were far beyond his means and likely to continue so. He was in his 60th year, had no private income or other prospect but his

---

[41] A brief rebellion of some of the staff several years earlier against certain Bureau administrative policies is recorded in letters from six Bureau members to Stratton, Mar. 29, 1917, and letters from 19 members to Secretary Redfield, Jan. 25 and Feb. 7, 1918, with attached correspondence (NARG 40, Secretary of Commerce file 76694). The Secretary recommended appointment of an assistant director at the Bureau to lighten the Director's administrative burden, and this was done (letter, Redfield to SWS, Mar. 19, 1918, and attached correspondence, NARG 40, file 67009/66).

[42] Hearings * * * 1923 (Feb. 1, 1922), p. 14.

[34] A good characterization of Stratton and of life at the Bureau at that time appears in G. K. Burgess, "Dr. Samuel Wesley Stratton," Tech. Eng. News (MIT) 3, 146 (1922).

meager retirement pay. Nor, in 1922, did it seem likely that Congress would remedy the salary scale anytime in the foreseeable future.

Dr. Stratton may well have voiced these feelings to his friends at the Department of Commerce, and when Secretary Hoover told him that the Massachusetts Institute of Technology at Cambridge, which had been without a President for more than 2 years, had approached him to recommend a candidate, Dr. Stratton consented to the recommendation.[44]

Stratton had had similar offers before, but he had been building the Bureau then and could not be tempted. In 1913 the Russian Imperial College at St. Petersburg had sought him for an executive post at a large salary and under his own conditions. And in 1916 he was offered an administrative position at Columbia University at $10,000 a year. He had turned both down.[45] This time he accepted the invitation, and on September 19, 1922, the Executive Committee of MIT appointed Dr. Stratton as its ninth president. He took office on January 1, 1923.

In his notice to the press of Dr. Stratton's departure, Secretary Hoover sounded a recurring complaint of Government department heads:

> While the Massachusetts Institute of Technology is to be congratulated on securing Dr. Stratton, one cannot overlook the fact that the desperately poor pay which our Government gives to great experts makes it impossible for us to retain men capable of performing the great responsibilities which are placed upon them. The Massachusetts Institute of Technology, an educational institution, finds no difficulty in paying a man of Dr. Stratton's calibre three times the salary the Government is able to pay him.
>
> Dr. Stratton has repeatedly refused large offers before, but the inability of the scientific men in the Government to properly support themselves and their families under the living conditions in Washington, and to make any provision for old age makes it impossible for any responsible department head to secure such men for public service at Government salaries.[46]

The severance was softened by Secretary Hoover's appointment of Dr. Stratton to the Visiting Committee to the Bureau, succeeding Dr. Joseph S.

---

[44] Communication from the Hon. Herbert C. Hoover, Dec. 14, 1962.

On the death of President McLaurin of MIT in 1920, Hoover himself was sought for the position. See "New York Times," Feb. 1, 1920 (letter to editor), sec. III, p. 1, and May 27, 1920, p. 2.

[45] The Imperial College offer is referred to in a pencil notation on letter, Frederic A. Delano, Smithsonian Institution, to SWS, Jan. 10, 1928 (offering Stratton the secretaryship of the Smithsonian); and the Columbia offer is in letter, Treasurer, Columbia University, to SWS, May 5, 1916, both letters in Stratton Papers at MIT.

[46] "Boston Herald," Oct. 12, 1922, p. 1; "New York Times," Oct. 12, 1922, p. 14.

Ames of the Johns Hopkins University. The appointment was to become effective on the date of his termination of service as director.[47]

In a very real sense, Dr. Stratton never left the Bureau. As he told a Bureau member who wrote to him soon after his arrival in Cambridge, "* * * I can never cease to be a member of the Bureau which has been practically my life work, and I shall never hesitate to give counsel and support whenever the opportunity may afford itself." [48] Both as member of the Visiting Committee and as creator of the Bureau, Stratton's counsel and concern were to be frequent and voluminous and continued so throughout his tenure at MIT. Most of his correspondence was with Dr. Burgess, apprising him of details of Bureau operations, advising on Bureau procedures in cooperating with industry and Government agencies, and forwarding inquiries sent to him at MIT. Planning to buy a radio set in the fall of 1923, Stratton wrote asking about the latest radio developments at the Bureau. He recommended new members for the Visiting Committee, and was active in securing lecturers for the Bureau, writing Burgess on one occasion that he had invited the Danish physicist, Niels Bohr, to come to the Bureau. In turn, Dr. Burgess discussed problems of Bureau appropriations with Stratton, sent him new publications for comment, and frequently mailed slides and other material for lectures and addresses Stratton planned.[49]

An able administrator at MIT, Stratton nevertheless seems to have regarded the Institute as another Bureau of Standards, or as an extension of the Bureau. In training scientists and technologists for industry, the Institute offered complementary services to those of the Bureau. Stratton had exchanged one campus for another. Within a year after assuming the presidency, he began work on a reorganization and expansion program at Cambridge, much of it closely modeled on the Bureau, which undertook to establish at the Institute new departments of aeronautical engineering, automotive engineering, building construction, fuel and gas engineering, hydraulics, physical metallurgy, municipal and industrial research, public health engineering, and ship operation.

Throughout his tenure at Cambridge, Stratton's addresses and talks were filled with his memories of the Bureau. In the several score manuscripts and reading copies that survive, mention of the Bureau by name seldom occurs, but striking to anyone acquainted with its activities is the

---

[47] Letter, Hoover to SWS, Nov. 1, 1922 (NARG 40, Secretary of Commerce, file 67009/5).
[48] Letter, SWS to Walter A. Hull, Jan. 5, 1923 (Stratton Papers at MIT).
[49] Correspondence from 1923 on between Stratton, Burgess, and the assistant director, Fay C. Brown, will be found in NBS Boxes 42, 43, 46, 48, 52, 54, 55, 56, 57, 61, 62, 64, 70, 75, 81, 82, 174, 184, 185, and 214, and in NBS Blue Folder Boxes 4 and 8.

frequency with which Bureau investigations and undisguised Bureau experiences were drawn on for illustrative material. At the banquet he attended in Washington in 1926 to celebrate the 25th anniversary of the founding of the Bureau, he said, "I think of you still as members of my staff." [50]

GEORGE KIMBALL BURGESS

In his letter in November 1922 appointing Dr. Stratton to the Visiting Committee, Hoover asked that Stratton at once take up with the Committee the question of his successor, "as I'd like to have their advice on the subject." Stratton offered two names to his future colleagues on the Committee, that of Dr. Lyman J. Briggs, recently promoted from the aviation physics section to chief of the engineering physics division, succeeding Stratton himself who had held that position; and of Dr. George K. Burgess, chief of the metallurgy division.[51]

Although as chief physicist and senior in point of service and experience Dr. Burgess seemed the logical choice, both the Visiting Committee and the Secretary of Commerce, in deliberations that seem less than flattering, delayed decision.[52] For almost 4 months, until April 21, 1923, Dr. Fay C. Brown, technical assistant to Dr. Stratton, served as acting director of the Bureau. On that date President Harding's appointment of the new Director, Dr. Burgess, became effective.[53]

Dr. Burgess (1874–1932), who on the death of Dr. Rosa became the chief physicist at the Bureau, was born in Newton, Mass., and graduated from the Massachusetts Institute of Technology. He went abroad for graduate training, receiving his D. Sc. in physics with highest honors from the Sorbonne in 1901. His thesis was on a redetermination of the constant of gravitation, but courses he took under Le Chatelier in high-temperature measurements aroused a greater interest and led him to translate his teacher's classic work on the subject. A decade later, as a result of his own investiga-

[50] Speech, Dec. 4, 1926 (NBS Blue Folder Box 3, APW 301c). A brief biographical sketch of Dr. Stratton appears as app. M.

[51] Letter, Hoover to SWS, Nov. 1, 1922, and interview with Dr. Briggs, Nov. 1, 1961.

[52] Announcement of Dr. Burgess' appointment in Am. Machinist, 58, 680 (1923), said it "followed several months of futile search on the part of Secretary Hoover for an outstanding physicist who had not been connected with the Government service, with sufficient means to allow him to make the sacrifice of income * * * [in accepting] a Bureau directorship."

[53] In his letter of congratulation to Dr. Burgess, Prof. Joseph S. Ames, director of the Physical Laboratory at Johns Hopkins, wrote: "I heard with interest of your silent and theatrical way of announcing your appointment, by quietly sitting down in the Director's chair" (letter, Apr. 25, 1923, NBS Box 43, IDP).

Unlike Stratton, Dr. George K. Burgess, second Director of NBS, is said to have administered the Bureau from his desk and seldom toured the laboratories. The Bureau, "a vertiable city of science," had grown, he felt, too large for intimate supervision and he liberally delegated his authority over its detailed administration.

tions in the field of high temperatures, he rewrote the book completely, making extensive revisions and additions.[54]

In 1903, following a year as instructor at the University of California, Dr. Burgess came to the Bureau as an assistant physicist in the heat and thermometry division. His first assignment was an investigation of the use of optical pyrometers in industry. Not long after, he began the work with Dr. Waidner, chief of the division, that was to lead to the present internationally adopted Waidner-Burgess standard of light. In 1913, soon after the Bureau undertook its investigation of railroad track and wheel failures—largely a problem in the physics of metallurgy, concerning the thermal behavior of metals in the manufacturing process—Dr. Burgess organized the Bureau's division of metallurgy. It pleased him later to say that he had never had a course in metallurgy in his life, which was quite possible, since it was so new a field that there may not have been half a dozen metallurgists in the United States at that time.[55]

Ten years after the establishment of the division, Dr. Burgess, as a result of more than a hundred technical papers on heat measurement and metallurgy, had won international recognition. His staff comprised some 50 experts, largely trained by him, inquiring into almost every aspect of modern metallurgical technology, from the melting and casting of metals and alloys to their physical and chemical testing.

Few men ever came to know Burgess intimately, either as division chief or Director of the Bureau. A sociable man in working hours, he was nevertheless reserved, and as impeccable in manner as he was in dress. He has been described by those who worked under him as "quiet," "warm-hearted," "very pleasant," "a nice person," yet a man "you couldn't get to know." [56] Recreation is said to have meant to him a good book—preferably a good detective or mystery story—and a plentiful supply of tobacco, or a long drive in an open car.[57] Of his private life little more was known. In 1901 he had married, in Paris, the daughter of a French Protestant family, but neither he nor his wife was gregarious and seldom entertained. They had no children.

---

[54] Lyman J. Briggs and Wallace R. Brode, "George Kimball Burgess, 1874–1932," Natl. Acad. Sci., Biographical Memoirs, 30, 57 (1957). See Henri L. Le Chatelier, High Temperature Measurements, tr. G. K. Burgess (New York: J. Wiley, 1901); rev. and enl. 2d ed., 1904; rewritten as G. K. Burgess and H. Le Chatelier, The Measurement of High Temperatures (Wiley, 1912).

[55] Letter, Burgess to president, Carnegie Institute of Technology, Mar. 21, 1924 (NBS Box 77, IDP).

[56] Natl. Acad. Sci., Biographical Memoirs, above; interviews with Dr. Briggs (Nov. 1, 1961), Mrs. William Meggers (May 8, 1962), and Dr. Kasson S. Gibson (June 1, 1962).

[57] L. J. Briggs, "George Kimball Burgess," Science, 76, 46 (1932).

If Dr. Burgess was perhaps less impressive in figure or manner than Stratton, he was considered a better scientist. Yet as he saw the need for better technology in the field of metallurgy, he turned increasingly to the practical application of his earlier research.[58] As Director he was to be as concerned as Stratton in promoting Bureau cooperation with industry in solving its scientific and technical difficulties.

To the surprise of many, Dr. Burgess in the Director's chair displayed a marked talent for enlightened management. Unlike Stratton, who found it difficult to believe that the growth of the Bureau had put it beyond a personally directed operation, Dr. Burgess delegated authority widely. He worked from his office and his desk, but his door was always open. Dr. Hobart C. Dickinson, who succeeded Dr. Waidner as chief of the heat division, was to say that the Bureau under Dr. Burgess "became a democracy * * *. Meetings of the Division Chiefs for the free exchange of ideas under [his] skillful chairmanship * * * became the order of the day. Appointments, promotions, and salaries became matters of common knowledge. The needs and welfare of the individual employees became more and more important as compared with those of the institution as a whole."[59]

At the same time, the Bureau seems to have become a somewhat more rigid institution under Burgess. Stratton's encouragement of individual initiative and of new projects had permitted the wide latitude of research that characterized the work of Rosa's division. Similarly, when Dr. Paul Foote and Dr. Fred Mohler, members of the heat division, became interested in spectral phenomena in atomic physics, Stratton let them forget about pyrometry and pursue their research in a section set up in his own optics division. And Raymond Davis, who came to the Bureau in 1911 to establish a photographic service, after devising on his own time a number of ingenious photographic instruments, was rewarded with a new section, photographic technology. It was generally understood that if you had a good idea you could go ahead with it, even if it wasn't your particular job.[60]

Burgess on the other hand was inclined to be a stickler for academic orthodoxy, venerated the graduate degree and its symbol of competence, and had a strong sense of propriety. Despite the success of his own enterprise that had led to the metallurgy division, as Director he tended to dis-

---

[58] References to important research results of Burgess and his group appear in H. M. Boylston, An Introduction to the Metallurgy of Iron and Steel (New York: John Wiley, 2d ed., 1936), pp. 416, 492n, 517, 543n, 544.

[59] Natl. Acad. Sci., Biographical Memoirs, above; MS, memorial address, H. C. Dickinson, "Dr. George Kimball Burgess" (Feb. 8, 1936), p. 18 (NBS Historical File).

[60] Interview with Dr. Mohler, Oct. 9, 1962; interview with Raymond Davis, Dec. 1, 1961. As Dr. Coblentz (From the Life of a Researcher, p. 132) said, Dr. Stratton gave promising men of his staff "an opportunity to pursue research unhampered, and with a freedom beyond all expectations."

courage ventures of staff members outside the field in which they had been trained. Though never spelled out, it was a policy that Burgess seems to have felt made for greater stability in the organization, greater efficiency and concentration of effort, and better research results.

To some extent, of course, both the looser rein and the check on adventuring stemmed from Dr. Burgess' initial unfamiliarity with the administration of the Bureau in general and with the work and scope of its divisions. Sedentary by nature and singleminded, as division chief he had seldom strayed far from his laboratory. And since there was no procedure—not even anything like a briefing handbook—for turning over the Director's office to a successor, Burgess for many months after moving into office had to grope his way through the complexity of Bureau operations left by Stratton. The Bureau correspondence of that period, heavily penciled with Dr. Burgess' "Who?" and "What?", seems to corroborate the degree of unfamiliarity.[61]

Besides the fact that the Bureau had outgrown the need for the highly personal and centralized leadership so effective in its formative years, certain recent events were to have a marked influence on Burgess' administration.

> The time-honored custom of a Chief of [a] Bureau going to the committees of Congress directly with his problems and need for funds had been replaced by a Budget Bureau * * *. No longer could an urgent need, or even a fancied urgent need, be presented by the Director in person and, sponsored by good friends, lead to an appropriation for some important new line of work for the Bureau.[62]

The Director continued to justify his budget to the House Appropriations Subcommittee each year, but it was no longer a budget subject to negotiation. Furthermore, under a succession of Republican administrations intent on economy in Government spending, the Director came to depend increasingly on funds transferred from other Government agencies. In this Dr. Burgess was encouraged by the Secretary of Commerce. And as the Bureau became a more integral and vital part of Commerce, "this led further toward limiting the actions of the Director." [63]

If Burgess could not negotiate with Congress for extension of Bureau research activities as Stratton had, he found a way to impress both Congress and the Bureau of the Budget with the value of Bureau research. The device

---

[61] Dr. Burgess was candid at his first meeting with the National Screw Thread Commission: "You will find that I shall be an impartial chairman because I know absolutely nothing about this subject." Minutes of meeting, May 10, 1923 (NBS Box 64, ST).

[62] MS, Dickinson (Feb. 8, 1936), p. 17.

[63] Ibid., p .18.

was to result in small but steady increases in Bureau appropriations throughout his tenancy. Apparently acting on a hint provided by a member of the House Subcommittee, who had requested that the Director include in his presentation a list of Bureau publications of the previous year, Burgess at his first confrontation with Congress early in 1924 deluged it with statistics. Annually thereafter he compiled imposing catalogs of Bureau operations, Bureau economies effected on behalf of other Government agencies and of industry, and current scientific and technological accomplishments of the Bureau, some of his presentations running to a hundred pages or more and much of it in fine print.[64]

One other influence on Bureau operations may be noted, that of the Visiting Committee, invigorated by the presence of Dr. Stratton.[65] The Committee had originally been set up to keep the Secretary of Commerce informed of "the efficiency of * * * [the] scientific work [of the Bureau] and the condition of its equipment." Perhaps to reassure Congress, or even with the thought of extending the influence of the Committee, Stratton had said soon after the first visitors were appointed: "The visiting committee we shall make an advisory board." [66] In the 1920's, more than ever before, the Committee became that board.

By 1923 the staff and plant of the Bureau of Standards made it the largest physical laboratory of its kind in the world. Dr. Burgess was fully conscious of the enormous responsibility over which he presided. He intended no further expansion of functions or of avenues of research. He was content to carry on the work of Rosa and Stratton. A cautious man, his was to be, as Dr. Briggs said, "a wise administration." [67]

---

[64] Still other tabulations included the 82 advisory committees on Bureau research, the 56 conferences held at the Bureau in the past year, and a selection from a single random day's mail that comprised almost a hundred specific requests for services of one kind or another. Altogether, the tabulations spanned pp. 209–319 of Hearings * * * 1925 (Feb. 12, 1924). A year later Burgess included work-in-progress as well as accomplishments of the divisions, section by section, and added an impressive chart of the total value of products produced by each industry served by the Bureau, arranged according to Bureau appropriations for its work in those industries. Hearings * * * 1926 (Jan. 5, 1925), pp. 157–159.

[65] Few references to the Visiting Committee appear in the annual reports prior to 1924. With NBS Annual Report 1925 (p. 38) and its announcement of the forthcoming NBS M63, "Report of the Board of Visitors * * * Nov. 1924," the recommendations of the Committee became a matter of public record. But the same economy that reduced the Bureau's annual report from 330 pages in 1923 to 38 pages in 1924 also ended the separate Visiting Committee report, and summaries of its recommendations thereafter appeared only in the Bureau's annual report.

[66] Hearings * * * 1903 (Jan. 28, 1902), p. 146.

[67] Interview with Dr. Briggs, Nov. 1, 1961; Briggs, "George Kimball Burgess," Science. 76, 46 (1932).

The Visiting Committee of the Secretary of Commerce to the Bureau in the mid-1920's.
Left to right: Dr. Stratton, president of MIT; Ambrose Swasey, founder of Warner & Swasey; Dr. Burgess, Director of NBS; W. R. Whitney, director of research, General Electric Corp.; W. F. Durand, professor of mechanical engineering at Leland Stanford University and president of the American Society of Mechanical Engineering; and Gano Dunn, president of J. G. White & Co.

Within a year after the war most of the research projects diverted or laid aside in 1917 had been resumed. They were increased now by continuing weapons research for the military, by the optical glass and gage work, investigations on behalf of industry and the public utilities, and the programs in housing technology, specifications, and simplified practice recently established by the Secretary of Commerce.

In certain areas, as in textiles, automotive engineering, and utilities, Bureau plans for research were to be modified as the decade progressed, owing to the organization or expansion of industrial research laboratories as the trade association movement grew, to increased research by public utilities, and to the rise of private research organizations.[68] Where this occurred, the Bureau entered into cooperative investigations with technical committees set up by the associations. Further assistance was rendered by accepting increasing numbers of research associates to work in the Bureau laboratories.

Despite its steady expansion of interest in industrial research, the Bureau both before and after the war carried out considerable basic research, much of it in determination and refinement of physical constants,

[68] NBS Annual Report 1924, p. 22, was to say that the ceramic industry, for example, had begun doing much of its own plant development and practical research, permitting the Bureau to pay "more attention to the fundamentals required by the industry."

Dr. Paul R. Heyl of the mechanics and sound division making observations for his redetermination of the constant of gravitation, probably in the block house constructed behind West building for the project.

and often of more immediate interest to science than to industry. Such was the work of Vinal and his associates from 1912 to 1916 which resulted in more precise knowledge of the limitations in accuracy of the silver voltameter (the reference standard for defining the International Ampere), requisite to the later absolute determination of the ampere.[69] A fine achievement also was Heyl's redetermination of the Newtonian constant of gravitation (G) and later of the value at Washington of the local acceleration of gravity (g), completing as it did a "true weighing of the earth."[70] Significant too were Buckingham and Dellinger's work on a method of computing the constant of Planck's equation for the radiation of a black body,[71] Gibson and Tyndall's determination of visibility factors of radiant energy,[72] and Coblentz's new standards of thermal radiation, also involving Planck's equation, the latter published in a 75-page report on which Coblentz worked from 1909 to 1912. The values of those standards remain unchallenged to the present day.[73]

Although astronomers at the time, as Coblentz, said, would have seriously questioned the possibility of detecting "the heat of a candle 52 miles away," the series of highly sensitive radiometers which he devised for his research made possible new measurements of the heat of stars and planets. His instruments were destined to extend the fields of spectroscopy and colorimetry and find application in the biological and agricultural sciences.[74]

In one investigation Burgess joined Coblentz, when both became interested in the international research going on in the high-temperature optical-pyrometer scale and the laws of radiation upon which to base such a scale.

---

[69] S218 (Vinal and S. J. Bates, 1914); S285 (Vinal and Rosa, 1916).

[70] The work spanned almost 20 years. See letter, SWS to Superintendent, C. & G. S., Feb. 20, 1917 (NBS Box 2, AG); NBS Annual Report 1923, p. 200; Annual Report 1927, p. 6; RP256 (Heyl, 1930); RP946, "The value of gravity at Washington" (Heyl and Cook, 1936).

[71] S162 (1911). Other work at the Bureau involving Planck's constant was reported in S259 (Foote, 1916), S287 (Dellinger, 1917), S304 (Roeser, 1918), and Foote and Mohler, J. Opt. Soc. Am. 2, 96 (1919).

Planck had modified the earlier Wien equation for black-body radiation to better fit the experimental data of Rubens, Coblentz and others. It was his search for a theoretical explanation of this equation which led to his famous postulate of the energy quantum, hv, which laid the foundation for his quantum theory. His equation involving the constant c_2 gives the spectral energy distribution of the heat radiation emitted from a so-called black body at any temperature. Among many applications, the constant can be used to predict the light output of incandescent lamps, cooling time of molten steel, heat dissipation of a nuclear reactor, the energy radiated from the sun, or the temperature of the stars.

[72] S475 (1923).

[73] S204 (1913) and S227 (1914); Coblentz and Stair, "The present status of the standards of thermal radiation maintained by the Bureau of Standards" (RP578, 1933).

[74] Coblentz, From the Life of a Researcher, pp. 148, 154, 168–173.

"A certain amount of prestige and glamour surrounded the [work] in this field," Coblentz wrote later, and there was a good deal of friendly competition with the investigations in progress in the national laboratories abroad.[75] Certain phases of this research were to lead to the establishment of the present-day International Practical Temperature Scale.

The international scale had its inception in 1911 when the national laboratories of Great Britain, Germany, and the United States proposed that they adjust the minor differences in the temperature scales each was maintaining and that, in place of the practical values in use, they establish absolute values for their points. More than a decade passed. The absolute temperature scale they sought proved experimentally difficult to achieve. Finally, in 1927 the three laboratories proposed adoption of an "international temperature scale" that might be more readily realized than the absolute—a practical scale ranging from the temperature of liquid oxygen to that of luminous incandescent bodies—that would at least serve the immediate needs of industry. Agreement on the basic fixed points and the series of secondary reference points on this scale was reached a year later. For the first time it became possible to certify temperature measurements for a wide variety of industrial purposes.[76]

The early work on the temperature scale coincided with an investigation that began in 1913, to provide scientific data to the refrigeration industry in this country for the better construction of its cooling plants and machinery.[77] The Bureau's success in determining the specific heat of ice, the properties of ammonia, and other physical constants required by the industry led Stratton to request a special appropriation from Congress to continue Bureau research in physical constants. For a time Stratton dreamed of an American "Landolt," as a new and more practical engineering reference book of physical constants than was currently available in the German work by Landolt and Börnstein.[78] The appropriation was small and short-lived; the research was too fundamental for Congress. Using statutory funds the

---

[75] Ibid., pp. 134–135.

[76] Burgess, "The International Temperature Scale" (RP22, 1928); Science, 68, 370 (1928). Cooperation and exchange of information with national standard laboratories abroad and with the International Bureau of Weights and Measures has been continuous throughout the existence of the Bureau. Except in particular instances, the history of that exchange is not elaborated in the present work. The scope of cooperation is to be found in the annual reports of the Bureau. That for 1930, for example (pp. 3, 7, 9, 10), describes NBS exchanges of information and equipment relative to new intercomparisons of meter bars, the international temperature scale, standards of capacitance, resistance standards, and standards of candlepower during the previous year with the IBWM, NPL, PTR, and Japanese and Russian standards laboratories.

[77] See ch. III, p. 130.

[78] Letter, SWS to W. R. Whitney, General Electric, Jan. 6, 1920 (NBS Box 10, IG). For Stratton's first proposal, see Hearings * * * 1917 (Feb. 2, 1916), pp. 986–987.

Bureau nevertheless continued limited research on physical constants all through the 1920's and into the thirties, improving its ammonia tables, publishing steam tables for turbine engineering, petroleum tables, a series of papers and a book on the properties and constants of water in all its phases, and establishing new points on the international temperature scale.[79]

A note of considerable interest to physicists appeared just before the first of the airplane ignition troubles arrived in the electrical division in 1917 when Dr. Silsbee published a salient observation he had made on electrical conduction in metals at low temperature. It was well known that resistance to electrical current vanishes in certain metals at very low temperatures, resulting in electrical superconductivity. In 1911 the Dutch physicist, Kamerlingh Onnes, had found in separate experiments that this phenomenon of superconductivity was destroyed if the current exceeded a critical value, and was also destroyed if an external magnetic field of more than a critical value was applied.

Dr. Silsbee saw that these two effects were not independent. The result was the Silsbee hypothesis, "that the effect of electrical current on the critical temperature of a superconductor is caused by the magnetic field produced by the current"—a valuable clue to a more satisfactory theory of the superconductive state and of metallic conduction in general.[80]

Two publications illustrated the progress of 8 years of Bureau research in polarimetry and saccharimetry under Frederick J. Bates. The seven-page circular of 1906 on the simple verification of polariscopic apparatus became a 140-page work by 1914, establishing the basic principles of modern polarimetry.[81] In that period the sugar industry acquired through the Bureau a variety of improved instruments, better apparatus, and a wealth of fundamental data; and Bureau investigations of the rare sugars, in critical supply during the war, were to lead to a wholly new industry in this country—of which more later.

For almost a century before the founding of the Bureau, analysis of chemical elements through their emission spectra had been the subject

---

[79] (1) C142, "Tables of thermodynamic properties of ammonia" (1923). (2) RP691, "Tables for the pressure of saturated water vapor in the range 0° to 374°" (Osborn and Meyers, 1934); NBS Annual Report 1939, p. 53. (3) RP1105 "Supercooling and freezing of water" (Dorsey, 1938); Dorsey, Properties of Ordinary Water-Substance (New York: Reinhold, 1940). (4) C57, "U.S. standard tables for petroleum oils" (1916); M97, "Thermal properties of petroleum products" (Cragoe, 1929). (5) RP-1189, "International Temperature Scale and some related physical constants" (Wensel, 1939).

[80] S307 (1917); interview with Dr. Silsbee, May 21, 1963. For later studies in superconductivity, see NBS Annual Report 1948, p. 207, and ch. VIII, pp. 466–467.

[81] C12 (1906) and C44 (1914; 2d ed., 1918). By 1942 the latter circular had been superseded by C440, a tome of 810 pages.

of studies in Europe. It was well known that each chemical element or combination of elements has distinctive spectra, either by emission or absorption, that are as characteristic of the element as the fingerprints of humans. Yet in that time practically none of the spectra of the elements had been completely described, although their importance, both theoretical and practical, was increasing more rapidly than the knowledge of them advanced. Except in astrophysics, there had been little application of spectroscopy, and in analysis the "wet" chemists continued to reign supreme.

Upon his arrival at the Bureau as a young laboratory assistant in 1914, Dr. William F. Meggers began the measurement of wavelengths of light and their application to an understanding of the spectra of chemical elements. By the sheer weight of accumulated evidence he was to establish standards of spectrographic measurement that were to gain worldwide acceptance. Some of the masses of spectrographic data that he and his assistants compiled over the next three decades for the analysis of chemical elements and compounds, noble gases, common and rare metals and their alloys, had to await the development of electronic computers for their resolution and final form. Out of the routine analyses made in the Bureau's spectroscopic laboratory of the thousands of samples of materials submitted for testing came new methods of quantitative analysis, some of them sensitive to amounts of impurities so small that they completely escaped detection by chemical methods.

The publication in 1922 of Dr. Meggers' paper with Kiess and Stimson on "Practical spectrographic analyses" drew attention to the simplicity and practicality of making chemical identifications and quantitative determinations by spectroscopic means. That paper, Dr. Meggers was to say, "finally put applied spectroscopy on its feet." [82] The tool of science became a tool of industry, owing much to Dr. Meggers' continuing research in improved methods of spectrochemical analysis. At the same time, he was to contribute materially to atomic physics studies going on at the Bureau through his search for better description of atomic and ionic spectra.

A chance assignment first launched the Bureau into areas of atomic physics well beyond its early investigations of radium and radioactivity when Professor John Tate, physicist at the University of Minnesota, came as a guest worker in the heat division during the war. Professor Tate had recently returned from Europe where he learned about the exciting work being done at Göttingen in the spectral analysis of mercury and other metal vapor atoms. At the Bureau he aroused the interest of Dr. Paul D. Foote and Dr. Fred L. Mohler, two youngsters in the heat division, in this work that appeared to support Bohr's theory of atomic processes.

[82] S444 (1922) and interview with Dr. Meggers, Mar. 13, 1962. Today there are more than 3,000 spectrometrical laboratories in the United States alone.

Although it was entirely outside the scope of the division, Stratton allowed Foote and Mohler remarkable freedom (though no funds) to pursue this atomic research. Their studies—described in the annual report of 1918 as "investigations in electronics" [83]—in experimental phenomena of the quantum theory of spectra, that is, the excitation and ionization potentials of simple molecules and photoionization of alkali vapors, culminated in their book published in 1922, The Origin of Spectra, a survey of recent experimentation in atomic physics as related to atomic theory.

The year the book came out, Stratton set up an atomic physics section, consisting of Foote and Mohler, in the optics division, where it remained until after World War II.[84] All through the 1920's, Dr. Mohler, with Dr. Foote and later with Dr. Carl Boeckner, continued their electrical and spectroscopic measurements of critical potentials of atoms, ions, and molecules. In the 1930's, as chief and sole member of the section, the smallest at the Bureau, Dr. Mohler began his pioneer investigations in the then sparse field of plasma physics, a field that was to have far more meaning three decades later than at that time.

The quiet islands of fundamental research at the Bureau in physical constants, in radiometry, spectroscopy, and atomic physics, particularly in the years immediately after the war, were in marked contrast to the din of industrial research going on almost everywhere else at the Bureau.

BUILDING AND HOUSING

Ready with a program more appropriate to the Chief Executive than to the Secretary of Commerce, Hoover entered office determined to recover the Nation, singlehandedly if necessary, from its wartime splurge, its consequent depletion of resources, and the general economic demoralization into which it had plunged. Recovery, by raising as rapidly as possible the level of productivity, was the first essential; reconstruction would follow.

Hoover's plan for recovery, in order to open employment offices again and start up the wheels of industry, was to stimulate building and housing, lend direct assistance to both new and established industries, and minister

[83] NBS Annual Report 1918, p. 70. This appears to be one of the earliest uses of the word "electronics," although not in its present connotation. It did not come into general use until just before World War II.

[84] Apparently challenged to justify such research, Stratton in the annual report for 1922, pp. 85–86, declared that a thorough understanding of the nature of collisions between atoms and electrons might well lead to the development of more efficient illuminants, better "radio-bulb" design, and extension of the range of X-ray spectroscopy. Foote and Mohler's first acquisition of equipment, including an ionization chamber, a beta-ray chamber, electroscopes, and a 1,500-pound electromagnet, waited until 1925 (NBS Annual Report 1925, p. 36).

to the new aviation and radio industries. Reconstruction, providing long-range benefits to the economy, aimed at a progressive elevation of the standard of living, principally by a campaign to eliminate economic wastes.

Although the building trades themselves badly needed reconstruction, they offered the most likely means of achieving immediate and massive results in reviving depressed industry and providing maximum employment across the Nation. The housing shortage as a result of the war was estimated at more than a million units. Stimulate homebuilding, and the brick, lumber, glass, hardware, plumbing, appliance, textile, and furniture industries and all that served and supplied them would revive.

Poor home designs, high labor and material costs, antiquated and obstructive building codes and zoning regulations, and tight mortgage money were among the targets of the division of building and housing set up by Hoover under Dr. John M. Gries in the Department of Commerce on July 1, 1921. Dr. Gries also headed the administrative unit (subsequently raised to divisional status) at the Bureau, to take advantage of its experience with municipal and State codes and to coordinate its numerous investigations useful to the building industry in the electrical, heat, chemistry, structural engineering, metallurgical, and clay products divisions.

A whirlwind campaign was planned, in which the Bureau's role was to publish material on the economics of home building and home ownership, and recommend revisions making for greater uniformity in local building and plumbing codes and city zoning regulations. The Bureau was also to urge adoption of standards of building practice looking to better construction and workmanship, and seek simplification and standardization of building materials and dimensional varieties in order to reduce costs.[85]

The program was launched amid nationwide publicity. Chambers of commerce, women's clubs, and better homes and gardens organizations throughout the country participated, and Secretary Hoover himself headed the national advisory council of the Better Homes in America movement that was organized in Washington early in 1922. Volunteer committees crusaded for Better Homes in every State of the Union. At Commerce, the housing division consulted with building officials, architects, fire chiefs, engineers, building material experts, and the professional societies and associations connected with the building industry. It amassed information and statistics, and acted as liaison between Hoover's advisory committees on building, plumbing, and zoning codes, and the technical divisions at the Bureau.[86]

---

[85] The Memoirs of Herbert Hoover, II, 92–93; NBS Annual Report 1922, p. 260; Hoover remarks at Hearings * * * 1924 (Nov. 16, 1922), pp. 171–73.

[86] NBS Annual Report 1923, pp. 304–305.

The spring of 1922 witnessed the first surge in home construction, and the Bureau issued its first publication in the campaign, on "Recommended minimum requirements for small dwelling construction." [87] Plumbing, zoning, building code, and city planning primers followed. A Bureau investigation of the seasonal irregularities in building activity, which kept building trades workers unemployed for 3 or 4 months out of each year, disclosed that most of the lagging resulted more from custom than climate, as generally believed. Slowly the custom began to yield to the campaign of publicity and persuasion launched against it.[88] The number of new homes built that year, more than 700,000, was almost double that of the previous year.

"How to own your home," a Bureau handbook for prospective home buyers, appeared in the fall of 1923 and sold 100,000 copies the first week and more than three times that number by the end of its first year. It was reprinted in magazines and serialized in newspapers across the country.[89] Eight years later its inevitable companion piece, "Care and repair of the house," came out and was similarly serialized.[90] In the fore-

---

[87] Building and Housing publication No. 1 (BH1, 1922).

[88] NBS Annual Report 1924, p. 26. A survey of the Bureau's building and housing activities appears in the series of articles by Delos H. Smith, "Our national building standards," House Beautiful, 1926–27.

[89] BH4, superseded by BH17 (1931). The "New York Sun" serialization, for example, spanned January and February of 1932. A supplement to BH4 appeared as BH12, "Present home financing methods" (1928).

[90] BH15 (1931). LC366, LC381, and LC383, all in 1933, covered "Bringing your home up to date."

NOTE.—Letter circulars, numbered from LC1 (1921) to LC1040 (1961), have been reproduced at the Bureau to make information available to the public prior to formal publication, to supplement information in formal reports prior to their revision, to supply information too brief for publication, or to excerpt material from Bureau publications for which there was a continuing or voluminous demand. In some instances LC's also reproduced information from reports of the American Society for Testing Materials and the American Standards Association.

Until recently when mimeographed lists of publications (LP) began to appear, perhaps the largest single category of LC's were bibliographies of the published work of Bureau sections (e.g., LC5, "List of communications of the gage section") or of special areas of research, whether done at the Bureau or elsewhere (e.g., LC35, "Publications pertaining to petroleum products").

Some of the subjects that have eluded formal publication include "Good gasoline," "Cellophane," "Color harmony," "Neon signs," "Motorists' manual of weights and measures," "Dry ice," "Metric and English distance equivalents for athletic events," "Matches," "Horology," "Porcelain and pottery," "Abrasives," and "The legibility of ledgers." Others are cited elsewhere in the present history.

The only known complete set of these ephemeral letter circulars, as well as LP's, is presently located in the Office of Technical Information and Publications at the Bureau.

word to Vincent B. Phelan's 121-page handbook, Secretary of Commerce Lamont impressed on the reader that its data came "from the people's own science laboratory, the National Bureau of Standards." The accolade in no way lessened the howls that went up from the service trades at the idea of Government encouragement of do-it-yourself repairs. But the twenty-cent handbook, which sold over half a million copies between 1931 and

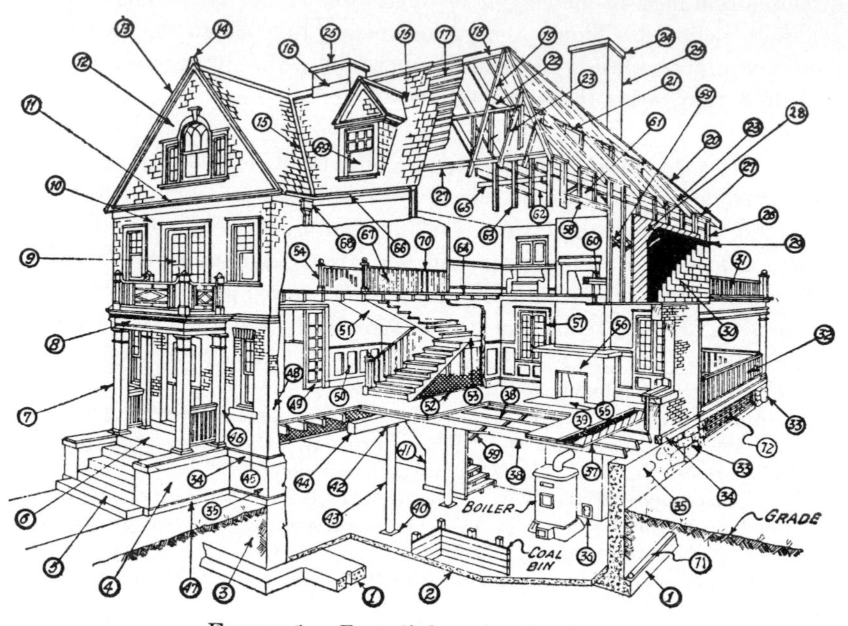

FIGURE 1.—*Essential parts of a house*

1. Footings.
2. Basement floor.
3. Foundation wall.
4. Buttress.
5. Steps.
6. Platform.
7. Porch column.
8. Porch cornice.
9. French doors.
10. Frame wall.
11. Eaves cornice.
12. Gable end.
13. Rake cornice.
14. Finial.
15. Valley.
16. Chimney flashing.
17. Shingle battens.
18. Ridge board.
19. Common rafter.
20. Hip rafter.
21. Purlin.
22. Collar beam.
23. Jack rafter.
24. Chimney cap.
25. Chimney.
26. Corner post.
27. Plate.
28. Diagonal sheathing.
29. Sheathing paper.
30. Shingle.
31. Balcony.
32. Veranda.
33. Piers.
34. Water table.
35. Underpinning.
36. Clean-out door.
37. Subfloor.
38. First-floor joists.
39. Finish floor.
40. Column base.
41. Plaster partition.
42. Column cap.
43. Iron column.
44. Girder.
45. Window sill.
46. Pilaster.
47. Ground course.
48. Brick wall.
49. Sliding door.
50. Wainscoting.
51. Stair soffit.
52. Metal lath.
53. Platform.
54. Newel post.
55. Hearth.
56. Fireplace.
57. Casement window.
58. Rough head.
59. Bridging.
60. Rough sill.
61. Truss over opening.
62. Ceiling joists.
63. Studding.
64. Second-floor joists.
65. Ribbon board.
66. Gutter.
67. Balustrade.
68. Leader head.
69. Dormer window.
70. Handrail.
71. Drain.
72. Lattice.

The first pages of the publication, "Care and repair of the house," took the owner on an inspection tour of the essential parts of his dwelling. It was a fine lesson in terminology but an exhausting tour, and the potentialities for repair were guaranteed to awe any home owner with the responsibility he had assumed.

1940, remained available to the public until the early fifties, when a new reprinting threatened sales of similar commercial publications in the bookstores.[91]

Construction of new homes reached a peak in 1925 when 937,000 units were completed. At the start of the program it had been estimated that a minimum of 450,000 homes a year would be necessary to overcome the postwar shortage. New construction in the 8 years of the program, through 1929, actually averaged 750,000 homes annually.[92]

The housing emergency long past, the building division at the Bureau became an early casualty of the depression. By June 1933 the staff, which had numbered 36, was down to 2. In 1934 its code sections and the safety standards section in the electrical division were merged with the Bureau's specifications division and transferred from Commerce out to the Industrial building at the Bureau.[93] There the regrouped division continued the research that was to serve the New Deal low-cost housing program organized in the late 1930's.

"THE CRUSADE FOR STANDARDIZATION"

In 1920, while President of the Federated American Engineering Societies, Hoover initiated a survey to determine the extent of wasteful use of materials and wasteful operations in industry. Twenty-five percent of the costs of production could be eliminated, the report disclosed, without affecting wages or labor. In six typical industries, wasteful practices accounted for almost 50 percent of materials and labor.[94]

If waste was most prevalent in industry, industry had no monopoly on it. Owing as much to long-established custom as to the wake of war, it was to be found throughout the economy. The great reconstruction program that Hoover proposed upon taking over the Department of Commerce had for its objectives: (1) Elimination of waste in transportation; (2) elimination of waste of natural resources; (3) husbandry of fuel and labor

---

[91] The service trades had some justification, for upon its publication in 1931 the Bureau distributed posters and other advertising matter for the handbook to hardware and paint dealers and put up displays at trade conventions. See monthly reports, Div. XI, 1931 (NBS Box 334, PRM). The trades also had to contend with Doubleday, Doran's publication for Better Homes in America of a hard cover edition of "Care and repair" that same year, 1931. For the outcome of the handbook, see ch. VIII, pp. 481–582.

[92] The Memoirs of Herbert Hoover, II, 96.

[93] NBS Annual Report 1934, p. 73; Annual Report 1935, p. 83.

[94] Waste in Industry (New York: McGraw-Hill, 1921), briefed in H. P. Dalzell, A. B. Galt, and R. M. Hudson's "Simplification data for survey of 'Recent economic changes'," July 2, 1928 (NBS Box 253, PA). See also NBS Commercial Standards (CS–O), 1930, p. 2.

through greater electrification; (4) curtailment of the swing of business cycles and of seasonal unemployment; (5) improvement of the distribution of agricultural products; (6) reduction of waste arising from litigation and from labor disputes, and two areas within the special province of the Bureau,

> [The] reduction of waste in manufacture and distribution through the establishment of standards of quality, simplification of grades, dimensions, and performance in non-style articles of commerce; through the reduction of unnecessary varieties; through more uniform business documents such as specifications, bills of lading, warehouse receipts, etc.,

and through

> Development of pure and applied scientific research as the foundation of genuine labor-saving devices, better processes, and sounder methods.[95]

Certain that industry and commerce succeeded best when acting in their own interests, Hoover sought no enforcement legislation. The Commerce Department would supply guidance, information, and assistance, but compliance would be voluntary. Alarmed by the depression, industry expressed itself eager to cooperate.

"Elimination of waste," as a phrase, did not lend itself to slogan-making as did the word "standardization," but with some loss of clarity and even objectives, they became synonymous. Long advocated by the Bureau, made imperative during the war by the necessity for mass production, and now elevated to something close to national policy, "the crusade for standardization," [96] became a three-pronged attack on waste in commerce and industry. It comprised *standardization* of business practices and of materials, machinery, and products; *specifications* to insure good quality of products; and *simplification* in variety of products.[97] Where the wartime effort had been to achieve mass production through standardization, the postwar effort sought to achieve standardization by establishing mass production techniques—as Henry Ford was doing in the automobile industry—in every field of commerce and in the company office no less than in the shop or factory.

---

[95] The Memoirs of Herbert Hoover, II, 29, 62–63. Hoover was to single out Dr. Stratton for his assistance in organizing the program and Dr. Burgess for his contributions to its achievements (ibid., pp. 62, 185).

[96] The phrase first appeared in Burgess' article, "Science and the after-war period," Sci. Mo. 8, 97 (1919). It is the title of Hoover's article in National Standards in a Modern Economy (ed., Dickson Reck, New York: Harpers, 1956).

[97] Norman F. Harriman, Standards and Standardization (New York: McGraw-Hill, 1928), pp. 78, 116–17, 129. NBS Annual Report 1922, p. 6, described the phases of standardization as those of nomenclature, of variety or simplification, of dimension or interchangeability, and of specifications.

The machinery for committing industry to standardization had been set up in 1919 upon the reorganization of the American Engineering Standards Committee. Associated with the Bureau since its establishment in 1909, the AESC learned during the war how vital standardization was to production and how little had been accomplished up to that time. The War Industries Board, dealing with businessmen through their trade associations to simplify enforcement of its rules, had also demonstrated the need for greater cooperation between Government and industry.[98]

In the spring of 1919, therefore, Stratton, Rosa, and Burgess proposed to the AESC that it become the central agency required to "provide a better connection * * * between the agencies of Federal, State and municipal government and the technical and commercial organizations concerned with engineering and industrial standards." Securing the agreement of the technical societies, trade and business organizations, and professional organizations it spoke for, the AESC that fall adopted a new constitution, broadened to include representation of government agencies and other national organizations.[99]

As its executive secretary the AESC chose Dr. Paul G. Agnew, a member of the electrical division of the Bureau since 1906, and as assistant secretary, Frederick J. Schlink, former technical assistant to Dr. Stratton. Dr. Agnew had been the Bureau representative at the meetings of manufacturers and industrialists that had wrestled with the technical aspects of Gov-

---

[98] Beginning with the formation of the National Association of Manufacturers in 1895, trade organizations by the thousands arose throughout industry. Each acted for the mutual benefit of its particular industry by collecting and distributing information on prices, methods of production, standardization, shipping problems, credit ratings, public and employee relations and the like, by setting up codes of fair practices, and by lobbying on behalf of State and National legislation affecting its industry.

Although frequently charged with monopoly and restraint of trade in the age of reform, when war came the trade associations proved indispensable to the war effort, providing central agencies through which whole industries could be reached. The favorable climate of the 1920's saw over 400 new associations formed, so that by the end of the decade there were almost 7,000 in the country. See Paxson, American Democracy and the World War, II, 123–24; John D. Hicks, The Republican Ascendancy, 1921–1933 (New York: Harper, 1960), p. 50; Bining, The Rise of American Economic Life, p. 586.

[99] Rosa, "Reorganization of the Engineering Standards Committee," Eng. News-Record, 82, 917 (1919); and the symposium on the new AESC in Ann. Am. Acad. Pol. Soc. Sci. 82 (1919).

Among the organizations then associated with the AESC were the American Society for Testing Materials, the American Institute of Electrical Engineers, the Society of Automotive Engineers, the Illuminating Engineering Society, the Institute of Radio Engineers, the Electric Power Club, the American Society of Mechanical Engineers, the American Society of Chemical Engineers, the American Society of Mining and Metallurgy, the American Chemical Society, and the American Railroad Association.

ernment purchases during the war and became the leading spirit in urging the reorganization. He was to serve the AESC for almost 30 years.[100]

The American Engineering Standards Committee thus became the national clearinghouse for engineering and industrial standardization throughout the country. Officially accredited to the Committee by 1927 were representatives of 365 national organizations—technical, industrial, and governmental—including 140 trade associations and 60 or more agencies in the Federal Government. Its title long since a misnomer, in 1928 the AESC was renamed the American Standards Association.[101]

By then, standardization had become "the outstanding note of this century," its influence pervading "the remotest details of our industrial regime," tapping "all sources of scientific knowledge and [affecting] every phase of design, production, and utilization." So trumpeted the opening paragraph of the "Standards Yearbook," a new Bureau publication first issued in 1927, to furnish key information on standardization to manufacturers, industrialists, engineers, and governmental purchasing agencies. Its 392 pages described the fundamental and working standards of the United States, the organization and work of the Bureau, of the national and international standardization agencies abroad, those of the executive departments and independent establishments of the Federal, municipal, and State governments, the central agencies for industrial standardization in this country, and those supported independently by technical societies and trade associations. Succeeding issues of the "Yearbook" detailed the annual accomplishments of all these agencies and described their current activities.[102]

The rage for standardization in the 1920's was not confined to this country. It swept every nation with any degree of industrial development, as the Bureau's compendious "Bibliography on Standardization" bears wit-

---

[100] NBS Report 6227, "American Standards Association, Inc." (December 1958), app. I.

[101] P. G. Agnew, "Work of the AESC," Ann. Am. Acad. Pol. Soc. Sci. 137, 13 (1928). By 1941, according to NBS M169, "Standardization activities of national technical and trade associations," issued that year, more than 3,000 national and interstate trade organizations and 450 technical societies were carrying on standardizations and simplification activities.

[102] The "Yearbook" was issued as NBS M77 and revised annually for the next 6 years as M83 (1928), M91 (1929), M106 (1930), M119 (1931), M133 (1932), and M139 (1933). The brief notice of consumer testing in the "Yearbook" was expanded in M90, "Directory of commercial testing and college research laboratories" (1927), superseded by M125 (1936), M171 (1941), and M187 (1947). A similar need for better coverage prompted M96, "Organizations cooperating with the NBS" (1927)—there were a total of 212. A decade after the last "Yearbook," a revision of its most generally useful sections appeared as M169, "Standardization activities of national technical and trade associations" (1941).

ness.[103] In most countries abroad standardization was Government-directed; here it was largely an industrial effort, the work of technical committees in each industry determining as a matter of profit and loss where standardization of processes and products and adherence to specifications most benefited them.

Among the earliest results ascribed by the Bureau to standardization was the reduction in price of incandescent lamps from $1.30 to $0.16, and reduction of the cost of Army and Navy shoes from $7 to $8 to $3 or $4.[104] Another kind of standardization, said to have been hailed by the building trades, established a new standard for an inch board. Where formerly it had varied anywhere from 7/8 to 1 1/4 inches, by industrywide agreement, a dressed board was set at a uniform 25/32 of an inch.[105] Despite the misnomer, it was at least a consistent "inch board."

As fundamental as standardization itself were specifications of quality, first established by the Bureau in 1909 in its standard samples of metals, minerals, and chemicals. The first official U.S. Government specification, authorized by Presidential order, was published as a Bureau circular in 1912 and applied to portland cement, which then as later constituted probably the largest volume purchase of a single item by the Federal Government. Often revised, the original specification declared that an acceptable cement must take an initial set in 45 minutes and after 7 days possess a tensile strength of 500 pounds per square inch. An earlier specification, in 1907, for incandescent lamps purchased by Government agencies, ruled that any lot in which 10 percent of the lamps was found with defects in workmanship or service threw out the lot. The specifications for weighing and measuring devices, published in 1916, permitted, among other things, a deficiency of no more than one-eighth ounce in a pound or 4 drams in a quart. And those for oils and paints, in 1919, set minimum percentages each of pigment, oil, thinner, and drier in their composition, as determined by quantitative analysis.

One of the first acts of the Bureau of the Budget upon its establishment in 1921 was to create the Federal Specifications Board, to unify specifications already available to some 40 Government purchasing agencies and effect greater economies in the quarter of a billion dollars worth of

---

[103] M136 (1932).

[104] General Electric's simplified line of "bread and butter" lamps (standard household sizes) set up in 1925 made it possible to reduce the price of the 100-watt lamp from $1.10 (1920) to $0.50. By 1942 it was $0.15. The single bulb shape in 6 voltages replaced 45 different types and sizes. Paul W. Keating, Lamps for a Brighter America (New York: McGraw-Hill, 1954), pp. 143, 145, 191.

[105] Hearings * * * 1923 (Feb. 1, 1922), p. 521; Hearings * * * 1925 (Feb. 12, 1924), pp. 6–7.

supplies bought annually by the Government. Thereafter, Bureau of Standards specifications accepted by the Board became official standards, binding on all departments of the Federal establishment.[106]

In immediate charge of Federal specification work at the Bureau was Norman F. Harriman. In an adjacent office Dr. Addams S. McAllister maintained liaison with the AESC, through whose offices drafts of Federal specifications went out to industry and differences of opinions on requirements were ironed out. Between 1921 and 1924 the Bureau alone prepared 72 specifications. Among them was one for fire hose, insisting it contain 75 percent of new wild or plant rubber. That for pneumatic tires required at least 70 percent new rubber on their tread. Glass tumblers had to withstand 6 hours in boiling water. Threads on wood screws were to extend two-thirds of their length. Red ink was given fixed proportions of crocein scarlet to distilled or rain water. Bull and buffalo hides could not be used in sole leather. And precise proportions of ground cork, burlap, and binder were fixed for light, medium, and heavy battleship linoleum.

Preparing specifications and revising those already promulgated became so extensive an effort at the Bureau that it soon proved "a serious drain on nearly all of the appropriation units of the Bureau." [107] The drain continued as the Bureau between 1925 and 1928 prepared over 150 new specifications, covering supplies as diverse as huck towels and cheesecloth, pneumatic hose and wire rope, asphalt and firebrick, quicklime and chinaware, ice bags and friction tape, plumbing fixtures and builders' hardware.

In September 1925 the Bureau, in cooperation with the AESC and associated industrial representatives, issued its "National directory of commodity specifications," 3 years in the making, listing 27,000 specifications for 6,650 commodities. This was Hoover's "Buyers' Bible," as he called it,

---

[106] Memo, N. F. Harriman, "Organization and work of the FSB," Oct. 29, 1923 (NBS Box 42, ID); report, Burgess to Secretary Hoover [1924], p. 11 (NBS Box 96, PRA); NBS Annual Report 1926, p. 3; Burgess, "Relation of public purchases to the national standardization movement," MS report, 1925 (NBS Box 116, IDS–AESC). Another Burgess report dated Jan. 9, 1925 is in Box 139, PA.

The Federal Specifications Board, consisting of representatives of the 10 executive departments, the Panama Canal authority, and the General Supply Committee, with Dr. Burgess its ex officio chairman, utilized the staffs of the Bureau of Standards, Bureau of Mines, Bureau of Chemistry and other Federal and civilian scientific agencies for the preparation of its specifications. By 1924 the Board had 65 technical committees engaged in their preparation, 24 headed by members of the Bureau of Standards.

[107] Letter, GKB to Secretary Hoover, Sept. 13, 1924 (NBS Box 72, FPE). A list of commodity experts at the Bureau, responsible for almost 200 commercial products, is attached to letter, GKB to Assistant Secretary of Commerce, Oct. 27, 1923 (NBS Box 41, AP).

intended to systematize both industrial and Federal purchasing.[108]

Because its results were most readily understandable and lent themselves to impressive statistics, the aspect of the standardization program that captured the greatest public interest was simplified practice. A Bureau study made in the spring of 1921 found "many sizes and styles of material and devices [in use], not through any real demand for such a variety * * * but through the undirected natural expansion of * * * business." The collective waste in commerce and industry from this source alone was said to represent an annual "loss of 30 percent of America's energies." [109]

Under Ray M. Hudson and later Edwin W. Ely, the division of simplified practice, organized in December 1921, got some startling results. The first 2 recommendations issued reduced paving bricks from 66 to 7 sizes, and metal and wood beds from a score or more varieties to 4 widths of one procrustean standard length.[110]

Begun with a congressional appropriation of $52,000 made in 1920 for "the general standardization of equipment," by 1925 the simplified practice program alone was spending twice that amount annually. Adopted recommendations had reduced hotel chinaware from 700 to 160 varieties, files and rasps from 1,351 to 496 types, milk bottles from 49 to 9 different designs, and book and magazine paper from 267 to 11 sizes.[111] Recommendations on the verge of acceptance ranged from warehouse and invoice forms to paintbrushes and paper bag sizes. Totting up the rewards as leaders in the crusade, representatives in nine important industries cooperating with the division estimated that their annual savings through simplification already exceeded $293 million.[112] The figure, rounded off to $300 million, received wide publicity.

---

[108] Hearings * * * 1925 (Feb. 12, 1924), p. 216. The "bible" was M65, superseded by M130 (1932) and M178 (1945), the latter a volume of 1,311 pages. It was followed by a subject index to U.S. Government master specifications, issued as M73 (1926), superseded by C319 (1927), C371 (1928), and C378 (1929). Three volumes of a planned multivolume "Encyclopedia of Specifications," covering products of wood-using industries (1927), nonmetallic mineral products (1930), and metals and metal products (1932) came out before the project was canceled. NBS Annual Report 1926, p. 39; Memoirs of Herbert Hoover, II, 67.

[109] NBS Annual Report 1921, pp. 22–23; Annual Report 1922, p. 265.

[110] NBS Annual Report 1922, p. 266. NBS Simplified Practice Recommendations run from R1 in 1923 through numbers above R250 in the 1960's.

[111] Science, 57, 649 (1923), reported that simplified practice in the American instrument industry had eliminated 1,800 of 3,200 items in its apparatus catalogs, including 99 out of 227 items of chemical porcelain, 123 of 190 forms of gas analysis apparatus, 70 of 148 types of gas burners (some of them over 50 years old), and 107 of 199 sizes and types of funnels.

[112] NBS Annual Report 1925, pp. 23–24; Dalzell, Galt, and Hudson, pp. 42–43; pamphlet, "Simplified practice: what it is and what it has to offer" (Washington, D.C., 1924); "Saving millions by standardization," Lit. Digest, 98, 62 (1928).

A year later, in 1926, a total of 3,461 individual acceptances of recommendations, involving more than 60 commodities, had been received from trade associations, manufacturers, and distributors. Special surveys made in 12 commodities that year indicated an adherence to published recommendations of 79.5 percent.[113] This was a matter of some congratulation, for it was expected that some people would insist on longer beds than the standard, and there were always bound to be manufacturers reluctant to discard a serviceable form or die.

By 1928 acceptances had almost tripled as the program spread from large manufacturers and distributors to smaller firms, to hotel, hospital and other institutional supply firms, and to city, county, and State purchasing agencies. Manufacturers reported savings in reduced inventories, in interest charges, in reduced obsolescence, and in payrolls among the benefits of simplified practice, and in at least two reported instances (concrete blocks and shovels), prices to the trade had been reduced by as much as 25 percent.[114]

The culmination of the standardization program came with Hoover's establishment in 1927 of the division of trade standards at the Bureau. Its purpose was to consolidate Bureau activities relating to standards, extend to the commercial specification field the cooperative methods of simplified practice, and make more readily available to industry the results of the Federal Specifications Board.[115] Where specifications formulated by industry up to that time had principally served the needs of individual industries, the commercial standards published by the trade standards division were to be specifications with industrywide application.[116]

To facilitate the use of Federal specifications and commercial standards by Government purchasing agencies, the Bureau compiled lists of more than 3,000 "willing-to-certify" manufacturers. But industry sought more than Government approval. What industry also wanted was certification

[113] NBS Annual Report 1927, p. 35. The next year adherences reached a high of 86.86 percent in 31 commodities surveyed. Annual Report 1941, p. 83, reported the peak number of commodities affected, over 130.

[114] NBS Annual Report 1928, p. 32; Annual Report 1929, p. 38; Dalzell, Galt, and Hudson, p. 30. LC504 (1931), "Variety reduction * * * by simplified practice," included 7 pages in fine print of such reductions.

[115] It had another purpose too. "The necessity to detach the Division of Simplified Practice from the Office of the Secretary [of Commerce] and * * * align it with the permanent organization of the Bureau of Standards is a major reason for the Commodity Standards group." Memo, Hudson to GKB, Feb. 3, 1928 (NBS Box 231, ID–CS).

[116] NBS Annual Report 1927, p. 42; CS–O, "The commercial standards service and its value to business" (1930), p. 3; chapter on NBS in [Robert A. Brady], Industrial Standardization (New York: National Industrial Conference Board, Inc., 1929).

of grade and quality of certain of its products, such as clinical thermometers, surgical gauze, fuel oils, textiles, and metal products, for greater consumer acceptance. Manufacturers wanted labels to identify or guarantee commodities complying with the standards they had adopted, and consumers wanted the information and protection thus provided. The labeling was approved and by the early thirties over a hundred trade associations were utilizing labels to identify products that conformed to commercial standards.[117]

If there was substance to the idea that standardization would contribute to a new industrial revolution, as Secretary Hoover hoped, it was attenuated by its voluntary nature. The reluctance of even a few members in a trade group was sufficient to bar any consideration of joint agreement, and as often as not carefully worked out programs suddenly collapsed at the point of success.[118] Moreover, despite unsparing publicity and the exertions of such trade-wide organizations as the National Association for Purchasing Agents, gaps in agreement and compliance spread.

The flaw in the standardization program appeared early, and of all places at the Bureau itself. Ray Hudson, setting up the simplified practice division at Commerce, requested Royal typewriters with elite type for his staff. Dr. Burgess demurred, pointing out that more than 20 years before the Bureau had settled on the L. C. Smith, for its superior construction, and pica as the most legible type. This machine was standard throughout the Bureau. Badgered for over a month by Hudson, Dr. Burgess at last gave in and signed Hudson's purchase order. On an attached note he wrote: "Your office is the only one in the Bureau of Standards that appears to insist

---

[117] M105, "Certification plan significance and scope: its application to federal specifications and commodity standards" (1930) ; NBS Annual Report 1931, p. 38. Commercial standards run from CS1, "Clinical thermometers" (1928) through current numbers above CS260.

Earlier proposals by industry to certify its products, particularly those for export, are reported in NBS Box 21 (1909) ; NBS Annual Report 1915, p. 147; and Hearings * * * 1917 (Feb. 2, 1916), pp. 989–990.

[118] Dalzell, Galt, and Hudson, pp. 24–27.

So consuming had the Bureau's standardization work for the Government become by the middle of the decade that a member of the Visiting Committee queried Burgess about the real aims of the Bureau. Was its purpose supporting new and first-class scientific work, as the PTR was doing abroad, or "standardizing old products"? The VC report to the Secretary of Commerce in 1926 expressed concern over the demands on the Bureau for this standardization testing, saying it was crowding out work on basic standards and research, "especially the determination of constants and the discovery of new laws and relations, which may be applied by scientific workers and more particularly by industry." Letter, W. R. Whitney to GKB, Nov. 20, 1925, and report, VC to Secretary of Commerce, Dec. 4, 1926 ("General Correspondence Files of the Director, 1945–1955," Box 6).

on non-standard makes and sizes of types. I am sure you are interested, with us, in the simplification of varieties." [119] The flaw, of course, was in the consumer, at the far end of the production line, who wanted variety in type styles, and a choice in the design of beds.

While the Bureau felt that through the standardization program "the ultimate consumer [was] getting better quality and better service, in some instances, at lower cost, and * * * [enjoyed] greater protection against unfair trade practices," high wages, the high cost of raw materials, and the increasing cost of doing business tended to operate against him as the decade progressed. At the same time, with increasing prosperity, consumer demands for more styles and varieties became an increasing obstacle to simplification. Inevitably, too, the restoration of confidence also increased the reluctance of business and industry to cooperate with Government, lest it lead to regulation or control and ultimately to Government prosecution of one kind or another.[120]

The great depression ended the crusade for standardization as appropriations plummeted and staffs shrank. But there was no thought of wholly abandoning the standardization work of the Bureau. Just before leaving office in 1932, Hoover asked Burgess to take the Commerce Department groups concerned with specifications and trade standards out to Connecticut Avenue. They were installed alongside the simplified practice unit, brought to the Industrial building in 1929, and there they remained until after World War II.[121] In 1950, following the postwar reorganization of the Bureau, they were transferred back to the Department of Commerce.

---

[119] Memo, GKB to Hudson, Oct. 31, 1924, and attached correspondence (NBS Box 72, EI).

[120] Dalzell, Galt, and Hudson, pp. 66, 70–72, 80–81. Perhaps the most notable arguments of industry against standardization were those presented on behalf of General Electric in John H. Van Deventer's "Extreme variety versus standardization," Ind. Management, 66, 253 (1923).

Inevitable were the early excessive hopes for standardization, the warnings against its excesses, and finally the revolt of the intellectuals, as reported in F. C. Brown, "Standardization and prosperity," Am. Rev. 2, 396 (1924) ; G. K. Burgess, "What the Bureau of Standards is doing for American industry," Ind. Management, 70, 257 (1925) ; P. G. Agnew, "A step towards industrial self-government," New Republic, 46, 92 (1926) ; N. F. Harriman, "The sane limits of industrial standardization," Ind. Management, 73, 363 (1927) ; Carl Van Doren, "The revolt against dullness," Survey, 57, 35 and 152 (1926) ; and "Standardization," Sat. Rev. Lit. 3, 573 (1927). Popular accounts of the controversy appeared in the Saturday Evening Post, May 11, 1928 and Dec. 21, 1929, under "These standardized United States" and "Standardized and doing nicely."

[121] Dr. Briggs summed up the status of standardization as World War II began: "It appears to me that the standardization which was accomplished during the last war has to a considerable extent been lost sight of and that the whole subject has again to be subjected to a searching study." Letter to Secretary, SAE, May 29, 1940 (NBS Box 445, IG).

RESEARCH FOR INDUSTRY

Spurred by Hoover's campaign against waste in industry, the Bureau seized the opportunity to extend its investigations in the utilization of raw materials, the quality of manufactured articles, and the quest for new uses for the by-products of industry. By 1922 work in progress included research on automobile engines to find ways to increase their operating efficiency, studies of electric batteries, of power losses in automobile tires, and reclamation of used lubrication oil. New public utility studies looked to improved efficiency of gas appliances and, for electric service, improved methods of measuring dielectric losses as indicators of insulation quality or deterioration. Under way in the construction field were stress studies of building materials, which for lack of scientific data were often used in excess amounts, and studies of fire resistance properties of building materials. With the expertise acquired in the wartime work on sound, the Bureau also began studies of sound transmission in structural materials—the scientific shushing of noise.

Other studies sought to determine heat flow in structures and in structural materials, thermal conductivity of materials at high temperatures, spectroscopic analyses of metals, elimination of gases in metals, uses for low-grade cotton, utilization of American clays in the manufacture of paper, utilization of flax straw and tow in making paper, utilization of refuse molasses, and recovery of waste sugar.[122]

Some account of one or two of these investigations may serve as representative of Bureau research for industry in the 1920's. The work on gas appliances, for example, had important results both for the public and the industry.

Without any specific legislative directive, but using funds first granted by Congress in 1915 for the "investigation of public utility standards," the study of gas appliances began as a result of the sharp rise in the cost of household gas after the war. About half the cities and towns in the United States which were supplied with gas used natural gas, the ideal and cheapest fuel, but like petroleum, widely believed to be in limited supply. The Bureau investigation, therefore, centered on its conservation. It soon traced the greatest waste of natural gas, estimated as costing consumers a million dollars a day, to faulty or poorly installed domestic appliances. Hoping to ameliorate some of the worst conditions found, the Bureau pre-

---

[122] NBS Annual Report 1922, p. 8; Hearings * * * 1923 (Feb. 1, 1922), pp. 501–508. A summary of NBS research for industry, 1921–27, appears in letter, GKB to Exec. Council, Amer. Eng. Council, July 5, 1928 (NBS Box 253, PA).

pared a circular for householders on "How to get better service with less natural gas in domestic gas appliances." [123]

With the rising cost of gas, a rash of inventions appeared, so-called gas-saving devices, to be used on the top burners of gas ranges. Tests showed their claims of economy to be worthless and, where manufactured gas was used, proved that some of these devices created hazards even greater than those in the appliances themselves.[124] But the real problem was the poor design of most of the gas appliances then on the market.[125]

The appliance makers were naturally reluctant to change their products and charged that the Bureau was prejudiced and favored the electrical industry. Bureau suggestions of better design for greater thermal efficiency and safety in gas cooking stoves, water heaters, and room heaters, therefore, met with little acceptance by the industry. Then, in the winter of 1922–23 an unusually large number of deaths occurred in many parts of the country from gas poisoning.

Upon Bureau inquiry of the health departments it was learned that New York had had 750 carbon monoxide deaths during the previous year, Chicago 500, Baltimore 42, Cincinnati 13, and Los Angeles 24. Because the industry tended to attribute all reported fatalities by gas to suicide, the last two cities were of particular interest since they were supplied with natural gas, which does not contain carbon monoxide, and therefore cannot be used successfully for suicide.

The investigation made by Bureau engineers with the cooperation of Baltimore's Consolidated Gas & Electric Co. and city public health officials confirmed the previous findings of badly designed or badly adjusted gas appliances. When the results were published, the president of the American Gas Association came to the Bureau and demanded that further publication be withheld. More forward-looking members of the industry realized the value of the research and persuaded the association to support a research associate group at the Bureau to assist in the work. Little more than a year later the association set up its own laboratories, hired away a Bureau gas engineer as supervisor, and shortly after established a seal of approval and inspection system that quickly brought the appliance industry into line. Two years later, deaths in Baltimore traceable to faulty gas

---

[123] C116 (1921). Antiquated plant equipment and inefficiency also contributed to the waste, Stratton told Congress, and these were compensated for by the industry through periodic increases in the rates. Hearings * * * 1921 (Jan. 2, 1920), pp. 1560–1561.

[124] NBS Annual Report 1922, p. 71. LC397 (1933) and C404, "Cautions regarding gas-appliance attachments" (Eiseman, 1934), summed up more than a decade of investigation of these "gas-savers."

[125] See T193 (1920) and C394 (1931) on the design of gas burners for domestic use.

appliances fell to 1 or 2 instead of 40, and the next year no such deaths occurred at all.[126]

Considerably more complex is the history of Bureau research in the rare sugars, said to be the first new industry created in the United States by the war.[127] Cut off from German sources, the sugar technologists of Bates' polarimetry section undertook to prepare and supply small standard samples of pure sucrose (ordinary sugar) and dextrose (corn sugar) for use in standardizing saccharimeters, testing the heat value of fuels, and for the differentiation of bacteria in medical laboratories. So obscure were the manufacturing processes as described in German patents that reconstruction of the sugars required almost completely original research.

The preparation of dextrose and other rare sugars (arabinose, raffinose, xylose, rhamnose, melibiose, ribose, dulcite, mannite) in the few industrial laboratories willing to undertake such work was, therefore, both difficult and expensive, some of the sugars costing from $10 to $500 per pound. Even so, the products were not wholly satisfactory, for lack of even the most fundamental data on their properties. On behalf of the industry the Bureau undertook a systematic study of the whole group, looking to purer forms than the manufacturers could achieve. If ways to reduce the cost of the sugars could also be found, it might well increase their commercial importance.[128]

In 1917 Dr. Richard F. Jackson, a member of Bates' group, solved the problem of producing hard refined dextrose. Two years later the theoretical and technical work for large-scale manufacture of an almost chemically pure low-cost dextrose was completed by W. B. Newkirk, another member of the Bureau's carbohydrate group, for the Corn Products Refining Co., and a new industry was launched.[129]

Although the Bureau produced experimental quantities of many of the rare sugars, it chose to concentrate on levulose, as a sugar potentially acceptable for diabetics. The sweetest of all sugars, it was also the most

---

[126] NBS Annual Report 1923, p. 78; T303, "Causes of some accidents from gas appliances" (Brumbaugh, 1926); memo, Crittenden for A. V. Astin, Apr. 10, 1953 (NBS Historical File); Elmer R. Weaver, MS, "History of the Gas Chemistry Section, NBS, 1910–1957," pp. 35–36 (NBS Historical File).

[127] Letter, GKB to Executive Secretary, Am. Eng. Council, July 5, 1928 (NBS Box 253, PA).

[128] NBS Annual Report 1919, p. 120–121; Annual Report 1921, p. 112.

Many of these naturally occurring rare sugars are of interest to chemists and bacteriologists for their biological function in the human body and have, as well, industrial applications. Some are also necessary as starting materials for the preparation of synthetic sugars.

[129] S293 (Jackson, 1917); S437 (Jackson and C. G. Silsbee, 1921); LC500 (1937); interview with Dr. Horace S. Isbell, Apr. 23, 1963.

difficult to isolate and purify, and therefore, one of the most costly. Found in honey and fruits, levulose was equally available in the common dahlia and in the jerusalem artichoke, the latter a prolific weedlike plant whose bulbous roots contained an abundance of the raw material.[130]

The year was 1920 and the wheat farms of the West, their wartime markets gone, were in distress. If large-scale commercial production of refined levulose proved economically feasible, wheatfields could be converted to growing artichoke tubers and so ease the Nation's surplus wheat problem. Under that impetus the Bureau investigation lasted almost 20 years.

As an ideal solution for a major surplus crop, the program had the full approval of the Harding, Coolidge, and Hoover administrations. The Bureau set up a special laboratory. In cooperation with the Bureau of Plant Industry of the Department of Agriculture, successively improved types of jerusalem artichokes were grown in the West under contract and shipped to the Bureau for processing. In 1929 a pilot plant for the production of crystalline levulose went up in the Industrial building, and there sirups of 99-percent purity, yielding crystallization of 75 percent of the sugar, were finally achieved.[131] A semicommercial plant for the development of a continuous process approached completion when in 1933 the depression brought the program to an end.

The years of reseach made the Bureau probably the greatest repository of sugar technology in the country but they left unsolved the problem of wheat surplus. Nor were levulose, ribose, mannose, raffinose, xylose or any other rare sugar produced at the Bureau ever to compete economically with dextrose, the corn derivative, which was equally satisfactory for scientific and medical purposes.[132] The wheat surplus continued.

The drive in the early twenties to utilize waste materials and products activated other investigations in the sugar laboratories, some brief, some lasting through the decade. One inquiry had its inception when the sugar industry called on the Bureau for help with the impurities in cane and beet molasses. While working on a method to minimize the deleterious effect of the waste molasses on sugar crystallization, the Bureau became aware of other uses for the waste besides fertilizer and cattle feed. German patents described many valuable chemical compounds produced both from waste

[130] NBS Annual Report 1920, p. 119.

[131] S519 (Jackson, C. G. Silsbee, and Proffitt, 1925); Hearings * * * 1926 (Jan. 5, 1925), pp. 121–123; NBS Annual Report 1926, p. 25; Annual Report 1933, p. 53. As a sugar for diabetics, chemical saccharine eventually proved better than any of the rare sugars.

[132] Continued Bureau research on ribose eventually resulted in an improved method of manufacture that reduced its cost from $40 to $2 per gram, but was still more expensive than dextrose. NBS Annual Report 1937, p. 66.

molasses and the waste waters of sugar manufacture. Despite an intensive search, the Bureau to its surprise found little or nothing on the subject in the scientific literature, in any language.

A closely guarded commercial secret, the processes for recovering amines, ammonia, cyanides, nitrogenous nonsugars, potash, alkalies, and miscellaneous products such as glycerine, esters and fatty acids from sugar wastes, were carefully buried in the patent literature. More than a thousand of these processes were found in German patents alone. As was true of German dye, drug, glassmaking, rare sugar and other patents confiscated at the outbreak of the war, it was unmistakable "that every legitimate means had been used by foreign patentees to create as many difficulties as possible in the trailing of patents." [133]

After considerable research, the Bureau compiled a "Summary of the technical methods for the utilization of molasses" and made these findings available to the industry.[134] Before the decade was out much simpler and far less expensive processes for producing industrial chemicals were to be developed by the petroleum industry, and waste molasses substantially remained an ingredient of cattle feed.

The early promise of the levulose and waste molasses research suggested to the Bureau and the Secretary of Commerce that gums, sugars, and cellulose products of great economic value might well be recovered from such farm wastes as cornstalks and straw, and that this research warranted Government initiative and support.[135] Under a special congressional appropriation to investigate the "utilization of waste products from the land," the miscellaneous materials division of the Bureau was reorganized as the division of organic and fibrous materials and Warren E. Emley was brought from the Pittsburgh laboratory as its chief.

Before long a stream of products issued from the new division, including a stout wrapping paper made from the waste fibers in manila rope manufacture; wall, insulating, and pressed board from cornstalks; fertilizer from cotton burrs; and textile sizing from sweet potato starch. With the hope of utilizing the fifty million tons of cereal straws wasted on American farms annually, the Bureau developed a satisfactory kraft paper from wheat and rye straw pulp. Shortly before the program was transferred to the Department of Agriculture in the midthirties, the group developed a process for making a high-grade cellulose from cornstalks, oat hulls, and straw. Together

---

[133] NBS Annual Report 1920, pp. 121–122; Annual Report 1922, pp. 109–110.

[134] C145 (1924).

[135] NBS Annual Report 1926, p. 44. Industry and Government were anticipated in this type of research by George Washington Carver, famed chemist at Tuskegee, who by 1920 had evolved over 145 byproducts from the peanut, including face powder, coffee, wood stains, and relishes.

with the gums, pentoses, and lignins separated in the process, recovery totaled more than 80 percent of the substance of some of these farm wastes.[136]

A group brought into the fibrous materials division upon its organization in 1927 began a rival investigation to the levulose research going on in the optics division. Where the levulose group concerned itself with planted crops, Hudson, Isbell, and Acree, working with farm wastes, sought to convert cottonseed hulls, corncobs, and peanut shells into useful industrial chemicals. Attention centered for a time on the considerable quantities of the rare sugar xylose available in these cellulose wastes, which had important medical uses and also might, if economically extracted, be readily converted to organic acids useful to the tanning industry.

Within 2 years a process had been developed for the production of 100 pounds of 99.99-percent-pure xylose per day.[137] But as both levulose and xylose approached the commercial development stage, interest in them waned. Their high cost repelled industry and Congress refused further research support as an invasion of industry's domain. Nor were efforts to utilize farm wastes to survive their relatively high cost of conversion or the avalanche of chemicals from petroleum distillation in the 1940's. In the depression years the Bureau turned from its technological development of specific rare sugars to the chemistry of carbohydrates and later to the study of labeled (radioactive tracer) carbohydrates, extensively used in current biological and medical research.[138]

The investigation of paper made from waste materials was but one of more than a dozen paper studies going on in the Bureau's fibrous materials division. Some were continuations of the wartime search for new sources and substitutes, others wholly new research, looking for fundamental data in the properties and performance of paper. Elsewhere in the Industrial building similar lines of search went on in rubber, leather, and textiles. In the electrical division the investigation of electroplating, which began with studies of zinc-, lead-, and nickel-coating protection for military supplies, broadened to include fundamental studies for the industry, particularly the silverware and printing trades. And when chromium plating became commercially feasible in the midtwenties, some of the first scientific data on this process was produced at the Bureau.[139]

By 1921 pyrometric control stations in heavy industry had become "nearly as intricate as a telephone central station," a far cry from the days when high temperatures were estimated by visual observation. At the re-

---

[136] NBS Annual Report, 1933, p. 61.
[137] NBS Annual Report, 1929, p. 41; Hearings * * * 1934 (Dec. 12, 1932), p. 179; NBS Annual Report, 1933, p. 61; interview with Dr. Gordon M. Kline, May 7, 1963.
[138] Interview with Dr. Horace S. Isbell, Apr. 23, 1963.
[139] NBS Annual Report, 1925, p. 13. See ch. III, p. 128.

quest of the industry, the Bureau made a compilation of almost 20 years of its research data on the industrial applications of pyrometry. The original printing of 2,000 copies of the 326-page manual, the first book on the subject in this country, was exhausted within 2 months.[140]

Not only pyrometers and thermocouples but hundreds of other instruments, military and nautical, optical and aeronautical, were being made in this country largely as a result of Bureau research and Bureau encouragement of the instrument industry. "We now manufacture over 85 percent of our industrial and scientific instruments and appliances," Burgess reported to the Secretary of Commerce in 1924, "where before the war over 80 percent of these were imported." [141] Among the optical instruments alone made in this country were spectrometers, spectroscopes, refractometers, interference apparatus, and spectrophotometers, colorimetric and optical pyrometers, polarimeters and saccharimeters, microscopes and binoculars, astronomical telescopes and heliostats, surveying instruments, and military instruments. Most glass volumetric apparatus was American made, as were hydrometric and thermometric instruments and fire-resistance and automotive-test instruments.[142]

Long interested in fostering new industries, the Bureau took even more satisfaction in the changing attitude of established industry. "Not long ago," Burgess noted in his annual report for 1923, "it was a matter of considerable difficulty to obtain the cooperation of industrial groups in the small amount of research then carried on [for them] by the Government." Now,

---

[140] T170, "Pyrometric practice" (Foote, Fairchild, Harrison, 1921); NBS Annual Report 1921, p. 92.

Another compilation for heavy industry was made when in 1920 the Smithsonian asked the Bureau to assist in revising its physical tables. They appeared in C101, "Physical properties of materials" (1921). Twenty years later the original 20-page circular had become the 480-page C447, "Mechanical properties of metals and alloys" (1943).

[141] Letter, Sept. 13, 1924 (NBS Box 72, FPE). Similarly optimistic was Science, 57, 649 (1923), but it pointed out that scarcity of skilled labor, high labor costs (75–80 percent of the cost of constructing a delicate analytical balance went for labor), and the American penchant for mass production would act to retard the young instrument industry.

Seeming confirmation appears in a recent report that in the period 1948–56 "imports of laboratory balances and analytical weights increased 1,096 percent, microscopes 671 percent, and other scientific instruments basic to military victory 131 percent," all "strategic 'tools' of atomic research, public health, and scientific education." James R. Irving, The Scientific Instrument Industry. Vocational and Professional Monograph Series No. 98 (Cambridge, Mass.: Bellman Publ. Co., 1958), p. 13 (L/C: TS500.I7). Cf. Frederick A. White, Scientific Apparatus (University of Michigan dissertation, 1960), p. 65 ff. L/C: Microfilm AC–1, No. 59–3296.

[142] Letter, GKB to U.S. Tariff Commission, May 10, 1923 (NBS Box 52, IPO); NBS Annual Report 1935, p. 65.

he said, problems were brought to the Bureau by almost every industry in the country.[143] Large corporations, some with research organizations almost the size of the Bureau, were "as insistent as the small manufacturers in their demands on the Bureau for research and standardization." [144]

The field of research at the Bureau in which undoubtedly the greatest variety of industries and interests had a vital concern was the standardization of color. As early as 1912, to settle disputes raging at the time, a cottonseed oil firm and representatives of the butter and oleomargarine industries called on the Bureau for help with the color grading of their products. The search for answers opened a whole new branch of physics for investigation. Three years later Irwin G. Priest, brought into the Bureau in 1907 to take charge of spectroscopy and applied optics, became head of a new colorimetry section set up in the optics division.

By then color problems collected in Bureau correspondence ranged from those of glass (in signal lamps, headlights, and spectacles for eye protection), of petroleum oil, turpentine, rosin, paper, and textiles to flour, sugar, eggshells, egg yolks, dyes, and water (as an index of purity). Still other queries asked for color measurement of chemical solutions, paints, portland cement, tobacco, porcelain, enamels, and even blood and human skin—the latter of concern to biologists and anthropologists.[145]

Available to Priest and his group were the Lovibond color scale (dating back to 1887), used in the color grading of vegetable oils, and the recently published (1915) Munsell color system, both of them excellent but of narrow application and uncertain foundation.[146] The Bureau made plans to estab-

---

[143] Simply by reason of its limited staff and facilities, not every problem could be handled at the Bureau. Many inquiries involved testing that could be done as well by commercial testing laboratories. LC209, "General policy of the NBS with regards to testing" (Dec. 2, 1926), distinguished between permissible and nonpermissible testing. The Bureau accepted material or products for testing where it had equipment, technicians, or was able to provide scientific data not available elsewhere, and where, as a central and unbiased agency, it was in a position to act as arbiter or final authority in the settlement of technical disputes.

In the "Standards Yearbook," 1927, pp. 284–285, the Bureau distinguished between its fundamental tests (of standards for industry and science), routine tests (of measures, devices, and materials, principally for Government agencies), referee tests, and cooperative tests (where the results might be of mutual concern to industry and the Bureau). The testing program alone, said the "Yearbook," consumed approximately half the Bureau's resources each year.

[144] NBS Annual Report 1920, p. 121; Annual Report 1923, p. 4.

[145] NBS Annual Report 1915, p. 75.

[146] The years of Bureau work on these systems culminated in two papers: Newhall, Nickerson, and Judd, "Final report of the OSA subcommittee on the spacing of the Munsell colors," J. Opt. Soc. Am. 33, 385 (1943); and Judd, Chamberlin, and Haupt, "The ideal Lovibond color system," J. Res. NBS 66C2, 121 (1962).

lish a broad scientific basis for color specification, color standards, and color grading.

Limited during the war to color and light investigations for the military and to the development of spectrophotometric methods of color analysis, Priest became convinced as a result of the latter work that "the keystone of the whole structure" of color and color standardization was a rigidly defined and accurately reproducible "white light." [147] But color standards were not to depend on this single factor, which is as much psychological as it is measurable, as Priest thought.

The breakthrough came in 1921 in a pioneer report published by the Optical Society of America, to which Priest contributed, pointing out that definition of a standard white light solves but one of the three conditions or functions that had to be satisfied in the measurement of color. In addition to specifying the characteristics of the light source, the report declared it also necessary to specify those of the object (by its spectral-reflection curve), and those of the observer who is to view it (specified by three color-matching functions).[148]

The major step on this psychological front during the decade was the experimental determination of the luminosity curve, which serves as one of the three color-matching functions. Along with the work of Gibson and Tyndall on the visibility of radiant energy, assembled data from over 150 persons of assorted ages and both sexes yielded a curve truly typical of human eyesight. The curve shows for radiation of a given energy at any wavelength how much sensation of light is produced in the human consciousness. The diplomatic skill of Dr. Crittenden secured adoption of this standard curve by the International Commission for Illumination in 1924, and it remains the cornerstone of all photometry and colorimetry to this day.[149]

With this basis laid, exploration and application of the new color-matching functions, along with efforts to standardize nomenclature, occupied the Bureau colorimetrists through the next three decades. The result was the Bureau's dictionary of colors and color names.[150]

Bureau research in dental amalgams, begun late in 1917 at the request of the Surgeon General of the Army when he was suddenly confronted with an army of teeth in disrepair, disclosed a mass of confusion and conflicting data in this and other areas of dental science. In 1922, upon the urging of the dental industry and the profession, Dr. Wilmer S. Souder and Dr. Peter

---

[147] S417 (Priest, 1921); NBS Annual Report 1921, pp. 129, 132; Annual Report 1922, pp. 119–120.

[148] Leonard T. Troland, chm., "Report of the Colorimetric Committee of the OSA, 1920–21," J. Opt. Soc. Am. 6, 547 (1922).

[149] S475 (Gibson and Tyndall, 1923); interview with Dr. Deane B. Judd, Nov. 26, 1963.

[150] C553, "The ISCC–NBS method of designating colors and a dictionary of color names" (Kelly and Judd, 1955).

Hidnert of the Bureau expanded their initial investigation of dental inlay materials and dental techniques.

Assisted by research associates from private laboratories and practicing dentists representing the American Dental Association, the Bureau physicists studied the physical and chemical properties of inlay materials, amalgams, plasters, and waxes, and began to establish specifications and standards for dental testing laboratories and manufacturers of dental materials.[151] Prior to this research, rejection of dental materials tested at the Bureau for the Government had run as high as 50 percent or more. One Bureau report about to be made public, disclosing that 6 out of 10 dental amalgams available to the profession were unsatisfactory, and only 4 out of 10 would stay in any appreciable time if used as fillings, was suppressed by the Commerce Department lest it result in loss of public confidence.[152]

By the early 1930's rejections amounted to less than 10 percent. Before long it became "possible for dentists to use amalgam fillings that [would] not shrink and drop out, cements that [would] not dissolve, bridgework that [was] practically permanent, and gold inlays lasting [far beyond the] 3 to 5 years as was the case a short time ago." [153]

A persistent difficulty encountered with certain types of metallic alloys used for fillings was their tendency to become deformed in use and require replacement. Interferometry studies disclosed that, extending over a period of 1 to 4 days, the expansivity of some amalgams was about four times that of the teeth. For many years the trouble was attributed, in the absence of other discernible causes, to variations of the alloy from package to package.[154] The source of the difficulty, at least in amalgams containing zinc, was eventually traced to the dentist's office, in the moisture added to the filling by his palming or hand mulling of the amalgam. The moisture and salt contamination from the hand, acting on the trace of zinc in the amalgam, formed hydrogen gas, and in a short time out came the filling.[155]

Research for the textile industry in the 1920's covered basic investigations into the physical and chemical properties of fibers, yarns, and fabrics, the conservation of textiles (for the peace of mind of dyers and cleaners), utilization of low-grade cotton and of waste silk materials, estab-

---

[151] T157 (Souder and Peters, 1920); superseded by C433 (Souder and Paffenbarger, 1942), the latter a résumé of dental research at the Bureau since 1919.

[152] Letter, P. J. Crogan, Bureau of Foreign and Domestic Commerce to F. C. Brown, Aug. 25, 1926 (NBS Box 179, PA).

[153] NBS Annual Report 1931, p. 43; Annual Report 1936, p. 62; Science, 92, 527 (1940).

[154] NBS Annual Report 1919, p. 148; Annual Report 1922, p. 174; T157, p. 9.

[155] Schoonover, Souder, and Beall, "Excessive expansion of dental amalgam," J. Am. Dental Assoc. 29, 1825 (1942).

lishment of standard tests for color fastness, of textile specifications, and standardization of textile products, from hosiery to cordage.[156]

In textile research, as in many other fields, it was through research associates, trained men from industry itself, that the Bureau rendered its most direct assistance to industry. Every division had its associates, the largest numbers in the metallurgy and building materials laboratories of the Bureau. They were to be found alongside Bureau staff members in almost every investigation into the manufacture of iron and steel, in the heat, optical, mechanical laboratories of the metallurgy division and in its experimental foundry, studying foundry sands, rail steel, high-speed tool steel, and the spectrographic analysis of atomic composition in metals.[157]

Investigations for the building and construction industry ranged all over the Bureau, from the elevator safety code work of the electrical division to fire-resistance studies in the heat division. Almost 100 projects in the chemistry, mechanics and sound, structural engineering, and ceramic divisions were on behalf of heavy construction or the homebuilding program of the twenties. One device, made in the mechanics division for an investigation of riveted joints in the construction of Navy ships, was to have wide application. This was Tuckerman's optical strain gage, devised in 1923, which gave consistent readings sensitive to two-millionths of an inch of deformation. It proved as reliable in measuring strains in the duralumin members in the framework of dirigibles, in concrete models of dams, or in steel and cement models of building structures, as in ship construction.[158]

While industry was for the most part highly cooperative, particularly where the Bureau dealt with problems of research or standardization beyond the capabilities or resources of industry, it could be stubborn on occasion. A case in point was the resistance to the idea of uniform screw threads. The war had amply demonstrated the need for uniformity but the cost of retooling and fear of competition prevented any real agreement. As the Bureau reported in 1922: "The manufacturing world is not yet fully awake to the advantages of this type of standardization." [159]

Throughout the twenties the National Screw Thread Commission, the American Engineering Standards Committee, and the Bureau continued to urge standardization and unification of screw threads and adoption of a consistent series of allowances and tolerances for greater efficiency in inter-

---

[156] NBS Annual Report 1923, pp. 230–231. H. T. Wade, "Textile research laboratory," Sci. Am. Supp. 2, 153 (1920). Some 20 current problems of the cotton industry were sent to the Bureau in letter, president, National Association of Cotton Manufacturers to Director, NBS, Feb. 4, 1920 (NBS Box 15, IST).

[157] NBS Annual Report 1923, p. 262; LC197, "Work shops of science" (May 2, 1926).

[158] NBS Annual Report 1923, p. 210; Annual Report 1928, p. 15.

[159] NBS Annual Report 1922, p. 42.

changeable manufactures. Yet not until the very end of the decade was there sufficient general acceptance to warrant extending this line of research at the Bureau.[160]

Because of the technical difficulties, relatively small market for the products, and ease of obtaining an adequate supply from Europe, efforts to turn over to industry the making of optical glass met with little response.[161] To assure sufficient glass for scientific purposes, the optical plant behind the Industrial building continued its operations with annual appropriations from Congress. Besides its research in optical and other types of glass for the industry, the Bureau yearly melted approximately 30,000 pounds of optical glass for the production of optical blanks, most of them going to the military services. Allowing for wastage and imperfections, the yield of serviceable glass from this weight of melt approximated 20 percent or 6,000 pounds.

The most ambitious undertaking in the history of the Bureau glass plant was its casting of a 69.5-inch disk for the mirror of a large reflecting telescope. At the time there were not more than 10 optical glass plants in the world, all abroad, capable of making such a disk. The two largest in this country, the 40-inch at the Yerkes Observatory and the 100-inch at Mount Wilson, had both come from Europe. Challenged by the lack of information on methods of making glass for a large telescope reflector—it was of course a trade secret—the Bureau borrowed on its own experience and began to experiment.

The first great disk was poured in 1924. It cracked during cooling. So did the next three. Trying still another method, the Bureau cast a fifth one in May 1927. Cooled in the first weeks at the rate of only 1° per day and at no time more than 10° per day, in January 1928 the great disk, some 10.5 inches thick and weighing 3,800 pounds, was pronounced a success. Polished and silvered elsewhere, the mirror was subsequently presented to the Perkins Observatory at Ohio Wesleyan University.[162]

---

[160] M89, "Report of the National Screw Thread Commission" (rev. ed., 1928). The Commission was placed on a permanent basis by Congress in 1926, abolished as an economy measure by Executive order in 1933, and reestablished as an agency of the War, Navy, and Commerce Departments in 1939.

[161] Of the firms that began making optical glass during World War I, all but Bausch & Lomb ceased production with the armistice. Hearings * * * 1922 (Dec. 20, 1920), p. 1248.

[162] NBS Annual Report 1927, p. 23; Annual Report 1928, p. 21; RP97, "Making the glass disk for a 70-inch telescope reflector" (Finn, 1929); Harlan T. Stetson, "Optical tests of the 69-inch Perkins Observatory reflector," J. Opt. Soc. Am. 23, 293 (1933); conversation with Clarence H. Hahner, May 20, 1963.

Prior to the casting of the 200-inch mirror for the Hale telescope at Palomar, the largest disk the Corning Glass Works had attempted was 30 inches. With the Bureau experience as guide, work on the 200-inch, 15-ton disk began in 1931. For 2 months after the

Prof. Clifford C. Crump, director of the Perkins Observatory and Dr. Burgess examining the Bureau's 69.5-inch telescope disk after an 8-inch hole had been drilled through its center for mounting. The disk after polishing was set up in the observatory at Ohio Wesleyan University.

If the most ambitious project of the optical glass section was the telescope disk, perhaps one of its greatest pieces of craftsmanship was the construction in 1926 of the Bureau's first standard of planeness. This standard of straightness, as well as planeness, in the form of highly polished disks of clear fused quartz, was the work of John Clacey, a remarkable self-trained hand craftsman of fine lenses who came to the Bureau in his 54th year back in 1911 and worked with Michelson during the war. The disks he shaped a decade and a half later, three in number in order to provide a self-checking standard, proved when tested interferometrically to have an accuracy of five-millionths of an inch. Aside from its application in testing the plane-

successful cast in 1934, the temperature was held at 1,200° F. The mirror was then cooled at the rate of 1° a day for 8 months. It was shipped to Palomar in 1936 to be ground and polished, but interrupted by the war the work was not completed until 1947. Six and a half million dollars went into the making of the mirror. The Corning Glass Center (Corning, N.Y., 1958), pp. 6, 8; Frederick A. White, American Industrial Research Laboratories (Washington, D.C.: Public Affairs Press, 1961), pp. 47–48.

ness of surfaces, the straightness of edges, and the limiting surfaces of end gages, the Bureau's standard plane was to serve as a basis for producing standard angles and for calibrating instruments that measured curvature.[163]

All the major industries reached new peaks of development and production in the twenties, and in the glass industry few so spectacularly as the manufacturers of automobile windows and windshields. But the three giants, and the symbols of the age, were the automobile, aviation, and radio industries.

AUTOMOBILES AND AIRCRAFT

Between 1920 and 1930 the number of cars registered in the United States leaped from 9 to 26.5 million, well over half of them Henry Ford's Model T. With them came the first officially numbered highway, the first automatic traffic light, the first concrete road with banked curves, the six-lane highway, one-way street, parking problem, tourist home, and tourist cabin.[164] Enclosing the tonneau in glass and canvas or in steel and installing more efficient and more powerful engines converted the car from a family horseless carriage to a family locomotive. With moderate prices and installment payments, the acquisition of an automobile moved rapidly from luxury to convenience to necessity. But it might not have happened if the geologists had been right.

Bureau research on the automobile and airplane, in adjoining laboratories in West building and in the dynamometer chambers, began on a pessimistic note: the Nation's supply of gasoline and oil must be conserved. Depletion of this country's known petroleum resources was said to be as little as 10 years away. The need for conservation was unquestioned.[165] A secondary problem, partly resulting from the producers' efforts to conserve the supply, was the poor quality of much of the gasoline on the market. If, by improvement of combustion through better knowledge of fuels, ignition, lubrication, and carburation, the Bureau reported, it could assist "in lowering the gasoline consumption of automobiles only 10 percent for a given mileage, it [would] represent a saving to the country of something like

---

[163] C. A. Skinner, "Making a standard of planeness," Gen. Elec. Rev. p. 528 (1926); "John Clacey—Optician," Pop. Astron. 38, 1 (1930); NBS Annual Report 1937, p. 65.

[164] Frederick Lewis Allen, The Big Change, p. 110.

[165] Hicks, The Republican Ascendancy, pp. 27–28. As late as 1926, "the dwindling supply of crude oil" still marked the "urgent necessity for rigid economy in the use of fuel." Hearings * * * 1927 (Jan. 25, 1926), p. 107. The Bureau was to lose 8 or 10 of its best young physicists to industry in the search for oil in the 1920's, including Karcher in 1923, McCollum and Eckhardt in 1926, and Foote in 1927 (interview with Dr. Paul D. Foote, July 23, 1963).

$100 million per year." [166] The phrasing was in terms of consumer savings, but the objective was conservation.

Working largely with funds transferred from the Quartermaster Corps of the Army, with the assistance of research associates from the Society of Automotive Engineers, and the cooperation of the American Petroleum Institute, the Bureau issued a series of papers establishing the most efficient characteristics of motor engines, fuels, and oils. Among other considerations, it became evident that more knowledge of engine starting factors was necessary as use of closed cars over the new network of paved roads greatly increased winter operation of automobiles. (The Bureau refused to recommend any of the dozens of antifreeze solutions that appeared, finding none better than plain alcohol and water.) [167] Previously given little attention, extensive studies were made of fuel-air ratios, jet size, spark advance, fuel volatility, throttling and choking, and air and water temperatures in the engine.[168]

When Bureau technicians learned that laboratory and road performances of automobiles and trucks often differed widely, they constructed an ingenious array of complicated apparatus that automatically recorded 18 different measurements of the performance of the engine and the vehicle itself in operation. A Bureau investigation of brakes and brake linings for the Army Motor Transportation Corps, begun as better engines and roads made speeds above 25 miles an hour common, was used by the automobile industry to induce parts manufacturers to improve these products. Out of this work came the Bureau's recording and inspection decelerometer that measured the braking ability of cars, and the Bureau's famous study of the reaction time of drivers, as well as minimum stopping distances, when brakes were applied on automobiles, trucks, or busses. A chart showing these

[166] NBS Annual Report 1922, p. 8; Annual Report 1936, pp. 62–63. Inevitably, almost as many "gasoline-savers" as there were household "gas-savers" came on the market, the most spurious a device that was built into a Hudson Super Six touring car and alleged to give 54 miles to a *quart* of gasoline. It proved to be a series of concealed spare gas tanks. Memo, GKB for Department of Commerce, Sept. 17, 1923 (NBS Box 58, PA).

[167] NBS Annual Report 1920, p. 162; H. K. Cummings, "Anti-freeze solutions and compounds," J. Soc. Auto. Eng. 19, 93 (1926).

[168] NBS Annual Report 1925, p. 8.

It was while making an acceleration test at low temperature and atmospheric pressure on a Ford engine using aviation gasoline—part of a Bureau investigation "to determine the grade of gasoline for cars that would best utilize our petroleum resources"—that on Sept. 20, 1923 a gasoline leak resulted in an explosion and fire in the altitude chamber that caused four deaths and injured six among the test staff. Science, 58, supp. 12 (1923); file in NBS Box 40, AG.

Freighted with apparatus designed and constructed at the Bureau, this touring car was ready to measure and record 18 points of performance of its engine and operating equipment on the road.

The instrument mounted on the running board measured wind speed and direction relative to the car. The apparatus on the floor of the front seat measured and recorded graphically the instantaneous rates of gasoline flow to the carburetor. The equipment in the rear seat recorded 16 separate measurements of various factors in engine and car performance on a moving strip of paper.

To measure a Bureau motorist's reaction time in applying his brakes, his car was rigged with two pistols. When the first pistol under the running board was fired it made a mark on the roadway. The sound was the signal for the driver to apply the brakes, the application of which automatically fired the second pistol, making another mark on the road. The reaction time was obtained by dividing the car speed by the distance measured.

reaction times and stopping distances at speeds up to 45 m.p.h. was widely publicized and found its way into many drivers' manuals. A Bureau member recalls that the chart continued to appear in at least one of these manuals as late as the early 1950's, long after high-speed cars had made the data dangerously obsolete.[169]

Besides engine research, the Dynamometer Laboratory was also used to make studies of the durability of tires—of which there were more than a hundred makes and sizes available. Together with the tire data acquired during the war, these tests enabled the Bureau to prepare its first Government master specifications for pneumatic and solid tires and inner tubes.[170] The specifications brought no special joy to the industry.

The center of rubber investigations was in the Industrial building, where Holt and Wormeley were testing rubber goods of all kinds. Until the rubber section was set up at the Bureau about 1911 there had been almost no rubber research in this country. Making rubber and rubber products was an art, with closely guarded trade secrets, and with wide ranges in quality as a consequence. The exhaustive testing of rubber products at the Bureau constituted some of the first real research in the field, and the successive editions of the Bureau circular on testing rubber products that first appeared in 1912 became the bible of the industry.[171]

By the mid-twenties the Federal Government alone was spending almost a million dollars a year on tires, and much of the Bureau work in

---

[169] NBS Annual Report 1925, p. 9, cites a report in preparation on "The maximum possible deceleration of an automobile." The report seems not to have been published, but a chart of braking distances, showing speeds up to 20 m.p.h. and possibly prepared for that report, appears in Standards Yearbook, 1927, plate 36. The brake work was consolidated in M107, "Safety code for brakes and brake testing" (1930), its chart on braking distances based on a maximum speed of 45 m.p.h.

Dr. Hobart C. Dickinson, chief of the heat and power division and automobile enthusiast, personally directed the many braking studies made by the Bureau. He was most proud of his paper with C. F. Marvin, Jr., on "What is safe speed?" (J. Soc. Auto. Eng. 17, 81, 1925) that recommended a "clear course principle" in place of fixed speed limits for safe driving. Several States adopted its conclusions, he reported in the paper, as well as its splendid formula, $v=\int(2as+a^2t^2)-at$, in which v represented the safe speed, a the rate of acceleration, s the clear course ahead, and t the time lag of the driver.

[170] C115 (1921; 2d ed., 1925).

[171] C38 (1912; 5th ed., 1927). Another aspect of rubber research occurs in a Bureau letter of 1944 asserting that so great was the difference between Government and industrial salaries for rubber technologists that for 25 years the Bureau had not employed a single chemist for that work who had had any previous rubber training or work. Letter, A. T. McPherson to War Manpower Commission, Aug. 3, 1944 (NBS Box 493, ISR).

rubber was concerned with their construction, quality, care, and use.[172] In the late twenties, as British control of natural rubber resources in the Far East shot prices sky high, the Bureau extended its product testing to more basic research, including comparative studies of natural, reclaimed, and synthetic rubbers.

Attention first turned to the possibility of growing natural rubber in Mexico and California, and some progress was made at the Bureau in producing from the guayule bush a sheet rubber that compared favorably with the latex from plantation rubber.[173] A preliminary investigation was also made in the chemistry of synthetic rubber, a project abandoned in the depression thirties when rubber prices fell with everything else. Work on synthetic rubber was not resumed until the eve of World War II.[174]

All through the 1930's rubber manufacturers stoutly maintained the merits of reclaimed rubber, which was being used in larger and larger proportions in the making of tires. Bureau tests of tires and other products from reworked scrap and waste rubber indicated little basis for the manufacturers' claims. The reduced quality and durability of the tires, said the Bureau, actually made them more costly than tires from high-priced new rubber. Not until natural rubber became available again with victory in the Pacific did the tire industry admit that the Bureau had been right all along.[175]

Investigations in 1917–18 of storage batteries used in the electric trucks and tractors of the Army, in submarines, submarine mines, and airplanes resulted in numerous improvements in their construction, the data appearing in a circular issued shortly after the war.[176] Scarcely any of the improvements, however, found their way into the batteries offered to the general public. As a result, few products were more deficient electrically and mechanically or stood in greater need of standardization and reduction in sizes and kinds than the storage batteries used for starting and lighting automobiles.[177] Working with the standards committees of the American Institute of Electrical Engineers and the Society of Automotive Engineers, Dr.

[172] NBS Annual Report 1926, p. 31. The tire research was reported in T283 (1925), T318 (1926), C320 (1927), C341 (1927), all by Holt and Wormeley, and J. Walter Drake, "The automobile: its province and problems," Ann. Am. Acad. Pol. Soc. Sci. 116, 1 (1924).

[173] T353 (Spence and Boon, 1927).

[174] C427 (Wood, 1940).

[175] T294 (Holt and Wormeley, 1925). C393 (McPherson, 1931), p. 17, said that reclaimed rubber at 7 cents per pound cost the consumer more per unit of abrasion than new rubber at 20 cents or even 40 cents.

[176] C92 (Vinal and Pearson, 1920).

[177] NBS Annual Report 1920, p. 86.

George W. Vinal of the electrochemistry section sent out a stream of research and test results to the manufacturers. Automobile batteries slowly improved. Simplification, in that highly competitive field, was more difficult, but a start was made in 1922 when the Bureau, on behalf of the Army, prepared specifications limited to 17 of the some 150 sizes of batteries available.[178]

A sequel to a battery study made for the Navy in the late spring of 1921 was to vex the electrochemists at the Bureau off and on for the next 30 years. The Navy came to the Bureau reporting trouble with the negative plates of its submarine batteries. Chemical and spectroscopic tests of the battery electrolyte and plates traced the repeated battery failures to impurities in the electrolyte. While studying electrolyte impurities, Vinal also tested a new jelly electrolyte that had come on the market, as well as several patent electrolytes, all being sold "with extravagant and impossible claims [of extending the life of storage batteries] at relatively high prices." Where these battery additives did not contain substances actually harmful to storage batteries, as most did, Dr. Vinal reported, they were useless.

The results of the Bureau tests were used "both as a basis for specification for [battery] acid and in published warnings widely circulated to protect the public from fraud." [179] The warnings went unheeded. Before the decade was out, dozens more of the additives appeared on the market, and at the request of Government transportation agencies, the Post Office, and the Federal Trade Commission, were tested by the Bureau. The answer to the claims made for them, again made public, was still a resounding no.[180] The continued encouragement by a credulous public of the manufacture of these spurious additives was some years later, as we shall see, to make headlines from coast to coast and imperil the reputation for scientific integrity of the Bureau.

Another long-term study in applied electrochemistry begun during the war centered on the dry cell batteries used in telephones, flashlights, and radios. In the subsequent standardization crusade specifications for their construction and operating life were prepared and under simplified practice a successful effort was made to reduce the multitude of sizes and shapes that

[178] Letter, SWS to Secretary of Commerce, Dec. 14, 1921 (NBS Box 8, IEB); Hearings * * * 1923 (Feb. 1, 1922), p. 519.

[179] NBS Annual Report 1921, pp. 70–71; Annual Report 1923, pp. 83–84; Annual Report 1925, p. 5; NBS TNB No. 94 (Feb. 10, 1925), p. 1.

[180] LC302, "Battery compounds and solutions" (May 15, 1931). Later Bureau letters to motorists included LC512, "Automobile costs" of owning and operating a car (1938), superseded by LC520 (1938), and for travelers, LC517, "Motorists' manual of weights and measures" (1938).

had proliferated. The annual tests of hundreds of samples of dry cells by the Bureau, on which Government purchases of millions annually were based, served to keep manufacturers on their toes and thus led to improvement in the quality of the billions of dry cells sold to the public.[181]

Apart from the conservation and consumer studies of the Bureau, the automobile industry before long took over most of its own research. But aviation remained a fledgling, of interest principally to the National Advisory Committee for Aeronautics, the Army Air Service, the Navy Bureau of Aeronautics, and, after 1927, the aeronautics branch of Commerce. All of these agencies transferred funds to the Bureau of Standards for their research. Besides engine research, to improve power and fuel economy of aircraft engines at high altitude, investigations continued in ignition, aviation metallurgy, instrumentation (including radio), and the aerodynamics of flight.

The military in the 1920's displayed some interest in better plane design but, inherently conservative and on reduced appropriations, was to express only passing interest in such innovations as the helicopter and jet propulsion. Back in 1917 the National Physical Laboratory at Teddington had sent the Naval Consulting Board, at its request, a two-foot model propeller for a proposed helicopter. Asked to look it over, the Sperry Gyroscope Co. sent it on to Dr. Edgar Buckingham at the Bureau to work out its aerodynamic equations. It seemed promising to him. Within the limits set by the model, Buckingham reported, a small one-man helicopter was entirely practicable. The only "real problem [was] motor stoppage." And, indeed, in view of the unreliability of aircraft engines at that time, Buckingham was probably right.[182] Twenty years passed before Heinrich Focke, in Germany, demonstrated the successful achievement of vertical flight. Two years later, in 1939, Sikorski's helicopter made its first flight in this country.

Jet propulsion fared even less well in the twenties. In the spring of 1920 Dr. Robert H. Goddard, father of rocket engineering, who had proposed the use of rocket weapons during the war, published the first of his papers on "ejectors and new systems of propulsion" for airplanes. Both the National Advisory Committee for Aeronautics and the Army Air Service, aware that jet propulsion was being worked on in Europe, offered the Bureau funds to study its principles and possibilities. As it happened, Buckingham, knowing of the work in Europe, had for some time been studying the aerodynamics involved.

---

[181] A brief history of dry cell testing, beginning with NBS C79 (1918), appears in H71, "Specification for dry cells and batteries" (1959).

[182] Letter, SWS to Elmer A. Sperry, Aug. 18, 1917 (NBS Box 12, INA).

From a theoretical point of view, he said, fuel consumption would be so much greater than that with the motor-driven screw that there was no prospect of using jet propulsion. (The petroleum industry was still experimenting with the cracking of oil, and Buckingham could not foresee better fuels than those available.) Moreover, said Buckingham, in what seems now masterly understatement, no further fundamental work on the subject was needed, since the principles of jet propulsion were "all well known." Only the engineering problems remained, and these could be better done by the Air Service than by the Bureau.[183]

A member of the Bureau who followed Buckingham's work at the time has a distinct impression that "jet motors may not have got off the ground because the idea of airplanes spouting 2,000° F flames on an airport was a far from welcome thought."[184] Even into the next decade top-flight engineers considered jet propulsion impractical, in the belief that no material but fire brick could be used for facing the combustion chamber of a jet engine. The weight alone would keep it earthbound.

The real interest of the military in the 1920's was not so much in airplanes as in lighter-than-air craft. Bemused by Count Zeppelin's invention and totally undismayed by their poor record of survival—of some 80 built by the Zeppelin Co. during and after the war, 66 were destroyed by enemy action, burned, broke up in flight, or smashed in landings—the Army began building its RS series of semirigid airships, the Navy its nonrigid dirigibles and ZR series of rigid airships. Considerable research for these ships, especially in instrumentation, was supported at the Bureau with NACA and Navy funds. Designed originally for ship navigation but adaptable to dirigibles and airplanes as well was the earth inductor compass invented in 1922 by Dr. Paul Heyl and Dr. Lyman J. Briggs. Equipped with this compass, the navigator after presetting his compass course had only to keep the galvanometer needle of the earth inductor at zero to stay on course. In an airplane, the compass, an armature driven by a cup propeller projecting through the fuselage and responding to the magnetic field of the earth, was housed in the rear of the fuselage, its indicator in the cockpit. But the career of the compass

---

[183] Letter, SWS to Engineering Division, Air Service, Dec. 2, 1920, and attached report by E. Buckingham, June 28, 1920 (NBS Box 12, INA). Even stronger was Buckingham's conclusion in a restudy of jet propulsion made 2 years later, in which he said that publication of his calculations by the NACA might "prevent engineers or inventors from attempting impossibilities" (NBS Annual Report 1922, p. 168). Cf. George W. Gray, Frontiers of Flight: The Story of NACA Research (New York: Knopf, 1948), p. 276. The fuel problem is discussed in NBS TNB 189, 10 (1933).

[184] Interview with Howard S. Bean, Apr. 24, 1962.

was brief, giving way to improved magnetic compasses, simpler in design and operation.[185]

The enthusiasm of the military for the zeppelin as a hovering gun platform throve on adversity. The dirigible ZR–2, built for the Navy in England in 1921, broke and exploded on its first trial run. The Army's *Roma,* a 410-foot semirigid built in Italy, crashed over Virginia in February 1922 on its fourth flight. A month later the NACA recommended that Germany's Zeppelin Co. build the next ship, as part of war reparations. This was the 670-foot ZR–3, christened the *Los Angeles* upon her arrival in 1924.[186]

Meanwhile, the Navy, using German plans, began construction of the ZR–1, the 680-foot *Shenandoah,* using in its framework the same lightweight alloy, duralumin, that the Germans had developed for their zeppelins. Although fatigue tests made at the Bureau of sheet duralumin members were not wholly satisfactory and the Bureau expressed itself as reluctant "to draw general conclusions," the Navy believed the duralumin ship indestructible, particularly since it was to be filled with helium and not the explosive hydrogen used abroad.[187]

All the dirigibles proved constitutionally fair weather vessels when brought out of their hangars. In a winter storm in 1924 the *Shenandoah* tore loose from her mooring mast and rode the gales for a night and a day before she could be brought home. Less than 2 years later, in September 1925, while cruising over Ohio, she broke apart in a squall and crashed.

Structural specimens from the wreckage, sent to the Bureau for examination, revealed widespread corrosion, yet insufficient, it seemed, to cause her destruction. American-made duralumin was found to have a fatal flaw: with time it became brittle. "Embrittlement by corrosion," the Bureau described it.[188] Experimentation indicated it could be made durable by apply-

---

[185] Letter, Engineering Division, Air Service to Director, NBS, Feb. 13, 1922 (NBS Box 12, INA); NBS Annual Report 1922, p. 162. The earth inductor compass, often reported as the only navigation instrument in Lindbergh's *Spirit of St. Louis* in 1927, was not that of Heyl and Briggs but a similar, and simultaneous, development of the Pioneer Instrument Co. of St. Louis. In his memoir of the flight, Lindbergh said this earth inductor compass developed trouble shortly after the takeoff and he had to rely solely on his "liquid compass" for bearings. Lindbergh, The Spirit of St. Louis (New York: Scribner, 1954), pp. 135, 337, 349; conversation with Dr. William G. Brombacher, June 19, 1963.

[186] For Bureau development of new gas cells for the *Los Angeles,* see Annual Report 1928, p. 40.

[187] NBS Annual Report 1922, pp. 172–73.

[188] T270, "An analysis of the deformation of the mooring spindle of the *Shenandoah*" (Tuckerman and Aitchison, 1925); editorial, "Deterioration of duralumin in the *Shenandoah,*" Eng. News-Record, 95, 1000 (1925); NBS Annual Report 1926, pp. 8–9; Annual Report 1927, p. 41.

Testing a duralumin girder from the wreckage of the Shenandoah *in 1925. The girder is shown ready for combined column and transverse tests in the 2,300,000-pound capacity Emery testing machine at the Bureau. The verdict was "embrittlement by corrosion."*

ing a protective coating of aluminum, but the last two U.S. dirigibles were not to survive long enough to prove the coating. Although the German-built *Los Angeles* flew for 9 years before it was decommissioned in 1932, neither the Navy's 785-foot *Akron* (ZR-4), completed in 1931, nor her sister ship the *Macon* (ZR-5), ready in 1933, lasted 2 years beyond their maiden flights.[189]

Reacting as much to the *Shenandoah* disaster as to the unpopular court-martialing of air-power enthusiast Brig. Gen. William Mitchell, who believed in planes, not dirigibles, Congress in 1927 raised the Army Air Service to corps level and authorized assistant secretaries for aeronautics in the War, Navy, and Commerce Departments. Design was standardized to enable industry to build up a reserve of war planes. And in support of civil aviation, the National Bureau of Standards, designated the research agency of Commerce's new Aeronautical Division, was directed to accelerate

[189] See John Toland, Ships in the Sky (New York: Holt, 1957), passim. Germany's *Graf Zeppelin* lasted almost 10 years before it was decommissioned in 1938, but the explosion of the *Hindenburg* while landing at Lakehurst that same year put an end to further investment in sky queens.

its work on the radio direction beacon, ground-to-air radiotelephony, and develop a marker beacon system both to guide and track planes in flight.[190]

If the recent war saw the development of specialization in planes, better planes and engines, sturdier airframes, wind tunnel research, and aerial photography, postwar spurs to aviation were to include the experience gained in flying the U.S. mails and inventions like the radio beacon, radio compass, gyroscopic automatic pilot, streamlining, development of the monoplane, and of retractable gear. The glamor of the dirigible was only to be exceeded by the headline performances of the planes that crisscrossed the skies in the decade that began with Lindbergh's flight to Paris.

"POLICING THE ETHER"

The cross-licensing agreements of General Electric, Western Electric, and Westinghouse in 1920–21, involving some 1,200 radio patents, ended the long patent war in radio. For the first time since its discovery in 1907 the three-element vacuum tube was free from danger of infringement and could be manufactured and sold to the general public. It was exempt from Government monopoly, and there were no taxes on receiving sets, as in Europe The radio boom was on.

In 1920 Westinghouse's experimental station KDKA at Pittsburgh made history by broadcasting the election returns to a radio audience estimated at less than a thousand. By the end of the first year of the patent peace there were 508 broadcasting stations in the United States for the hordes of crystal set and vacuum tube enthusiasts. The great radio craze really began after Armstrong's superheterodyne, with its superior reception, came out in 1922.[191] Whereas in 1921 there were probably not more than 7,000 privately owned sets in the Nation, by 1928 there were nearly 10 million, not counting home-made sets.[192]

As much as anyone, the Bureau fired up a nation of do-it-yourself addicts by issuing a series of mimeographed letter circulars in the spring of 1922 on how to construct a simple crystal detector set for $10; [193] a two

[190] NBS Annual Report 1927, p. 40. See below, pp. 295, 297.

[191] Armstrong's modification in the heterodyne introduced another oscillation with the incoming high frequency signal which produced a third "beat frequency." This lower intermediate frequency could be amplified much more effectively, permitting very high selectivity of the original signal.

[192] Schubert, The Electric Word, pp. 212–214.

[193] Not to be outdone by the Bureau's radio engineers, Clarence A. Briggs of the gage section built a crystal set with coils on cardboard that, except for the antenna and telephone receiver piece, cost 60 cents, and on which, without amplification, he picked up Schenectady, 300 miles away. Letter, H. G. Boutell to Assistant to Sercetary of Commerce, May 23, 1922 (NBS Box 21, PAC).

circuit crystal set capable of picking up stations beyond 50 miles, at a cost of $15; and an electron-tube set, reaching out a hundred miles, for between $23 and $37, including the tube ($5) and the storage battery ($15–$20). Other Bureau letter circulars that spring and summer furnished sources of elementary radio information to amateurs and described auxiliary condensers, loading coils, and an audiofrequency unit for receiving sets.[194] Even before these letter circulars appeared as formal publications, they were widely printed on the new radio pages introduced by newspapers everywhere.[195] Altogether, in that first year of the radio boom the Bureau issued almost a hundred reports, most of them typewritten or mimeographed, to meet the demand for radio data and instruction of radio technicians.[196] Available too was the Bureau's compendious Circular 74, "Radio instruments and measurements," an encyclopedia of the theoretical and practical aspects of radio measurements. Less than a year after the boom started so many types of radio sets were on the market that the Bureau urged that a national movement be launched for the standardization of radio apparatus and service.[197]

The proliferation of radio receivers attracted thousands of hopeful station owners into the potentially lucrative broadcasting field, and for every one that succumbed, two stood ready to take his place. But there was more to it than building a station and selling air time even in those days. Of fewer than a thousand channels or noninterfering wavelengths in the then utilizable radio wave spectrum, only 89 were available to American broadcasting. Interference between stations as some 500 of them competed in these wavelengths raised immediate difficulties, and became insufferable when, in order to drown out competition and reach more people, stations that could afford it increased their power.[198]

Since radio had long been used almost exclusively by ships, the Federal Radio Law of 1912 had made the Bureau of Navigation in the Department of Commerce responsible for licensing stations and assigning wavelengths. It was a toothless law, for Commerce could not deny or revoke a license, and bills proposed by Commerce for "policing the ether" repeatedly

---

[194] LC43 (Feb. 15, 1922) described the crystal set, LC48 (July 26, 1922) the vacuum tube set. The other letters were LC39, LC44, and LC46.

[195] C120, C121, C122, and C133 were published in 1922; C137 and C141 in 1923. Two commercial publishers not only reprinted C120, on the crystal set, but copyrighted their booklet, and had to be enjoined. NBS Progress Report, May 1922 (NBS Box 24, PRM)

[196] NBS Annual Report 1922, p. 56.

[197] LC66 (June 1922) offered a partial list of almost 275 manufacturers and distributors of radio receiving equipment.

[198] As late as 1928 most stations still operated on 500 watts, with some up to 1,000 watts. The most powerful, 50,000 watts, had a radius of less than 500 miles. Schubert, The Electric Word, pp. 223–224.

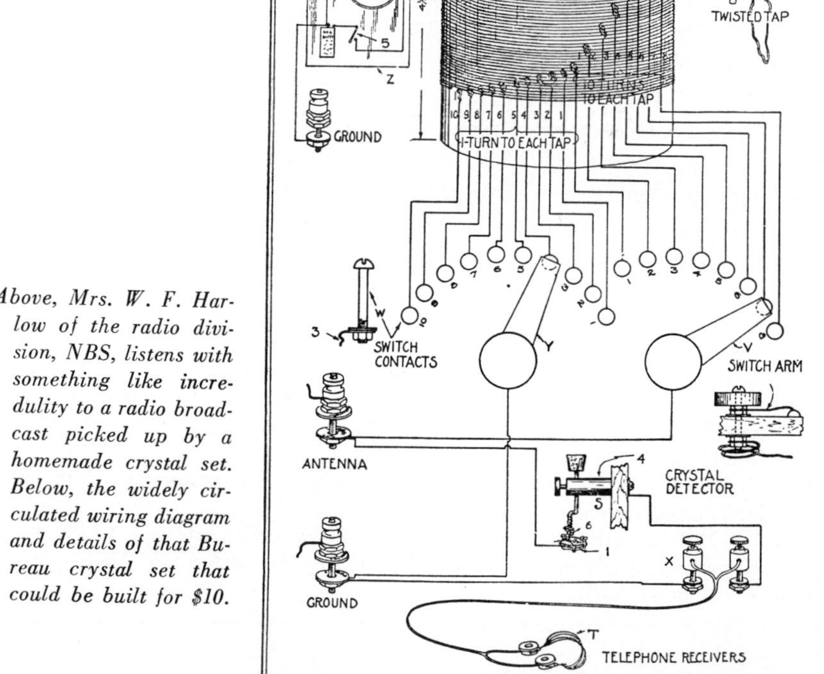

FIG.3. WIRING DIAGRAM AND DETAILS OF RECEIVING SET

Above, Mrs. W. F. Harlow of the radio division, NBS, listens with something like incredulity to a radio broadcast picked up by a homemade crystal set. Below, the widely circulated wiring diagram and details of that Bureau crystal set that could be built for $10.

died in committee.[199] Without the least power to regulate a licensee, Commerce could only propose solutions and seek the compliance of the stations.

At a conference called in March 1923, the Department and the stations agreed to abolish the term "wavelength" for that of "frequency," the latter representing the number of oscillations of the radio wave per second, expressed in kilocycles per second.[200] The band of frequencies between 550 and 1350 (later 1500) kilocycles was to be set aside for commercial broadcasting, and by dividing the country into 5 radio zones and setting station frequencies 5 kilocycles apart, 570 broadcasters could be accommodated in the 89 available channels.

Stations continued to proliferate and the air waves grew crowded again. Conferences in 1924 and 1925 moved ship traffic out of the broadcasting band, and by duplication on the east and west coasts, room was found for an additional 30 stations. By 1926, another 155 new stations raised the total on the air to more than 730 and the chaos had become complete. The radio industry begged to be regulated and Congress had to oblige. On February 23, 1927, the Federal Radio Commission (to become the Federal Communications Commission in 1934), with policing power over its decisions, established public ownership and regulation of the air waves. The boom and battle of the stations came to an end.

Members of the radio section of the Bureau participated as technical advisers at all the early radio conferences, chief among them Dr. J. Howard Dellinger and Dr. Charles B. Jolliffe, who laid the groundwork for the formation of the FRC. As brilliant and sound in radio research as he was in planning and directing its research by others, Dellinger become the first chief engineer of the FRC. He was to leave his name in radio terminology a decade later with his discovery of the simultaneous occurrence of visible solar eruptions and semi-worldwide sudden radio fadeouts, a phenomenon known as "the Dellinger effect." [201]

Jolliffe, who joined the Bureau radio group on getting his doctorate at Cornell in 1922, succeeded to the Commission post when Dellinger returned to the Bureau in 1930. A researcher and organizer himself, Jolliffe moved on the the RCA Laboratories in 1935, later becoming executive vice president and technical director of the company and its laboratories.[202]

In order to learn about radio transmitting at first hand, the Bureau itself became one of the first of the broadcasters, antedating KDKA by several months, when in 1920, at the request of the Bureau of Markets in the

---

[199] Herbert Hoover, "Policing the ether," Sci. Am. 127, 80 (1922).
[200] NBS Annual Report 1923, p. 71.
[201] See ch. VI, p. 351.
[202] Correspondence on the FRC work of Dellinger and Jolliffe appears in NBS Box 234, IEW (1928); Box 296, AP; Box 303, IEW; and Box 321, PRM.

The phonograph playing into the high-power radiotelephone transmitter may be the experimental "broadcast station" pioneered by the Bureau. The date of the photograph is September 1920.

Department of Agriculture, it pioneered an experimental radio market and crop report service. Even before that the Bureau had successfully transmitted music and speech for short distances over its station, but—such was the novelty of broadcasting—for the sake of reliability the Bureau resorted to Morse telegraph for the market reports. After operating the service for 4 months, the Bureau turned it over to the Post Office, whose stations already served the air mail.[203]

It was not transmission but reception that harbored the real gremlins of radio communication. The first of the technical difficulties that came to the Bureau as commercial broadcasting began was that of fading or variations in the intensity of received signals. A statistical study conducted by the Bureau traced still other forms of interference to their source in amateur equipment, radiating receiving sets, and powerlines, arc lights and other non-radio electrical equipment.[204] Although queries about fading and noise began arriving at the Bureau in 1921, little was done about them at the time because of the even greater obstacle to reception, the interference between stations in the overcrowded air.

---

[203] NBS Annual Report 1921, p. 69; letters, SWS to Secretary of Agriculture, May 17 and Sept. 7, 1921 (NBS Box 10, IEW).

[204] Dellinger and Whittemore, "Radio signal fading phenomena," J. Wash. Acad. Sci. 11, 245 (1921); LC182, "Electrical interference with radio reception" (September 1925).

If simple restriction on their proliferation, as the obvious solution to station interference, impinged on free enterprise, a degree of order seemed possible if the stations would operate exclusively on the frequency assigned to them, use as small power as was required to reach the necessary distance, and use waves as sharp as possible. The first two remedies were outside the realm of the Bureau, and it therefore concentrated on the measurement and control of the radio waves emanating from the stations, since the fluctuations in their width determined their capacity for interference.[205] Typical was the experience of a listener in Baltimore who reported interference between two broadcasting stations, one in Cincinnati, the other in California. The interference arose, the Bureau learned, because one of the stations was off its assigned frequency by one-half percent.

Bureau development of new and improved types of wavemeters, wavemeter scales, and devices for rapid radiofrequency measurements gave the Radio Inspection Service of Commerce better instruments for detecting and monitoring broadcasting frequencies.[206] Then in 1923, in order to provide means of self-policing, by enabling broadcasting and other stations to hold exactly to their assigned frequencies, the Bureau set up a standard of frequency and began sending out precise signals over its laboratory transmitter, WWV, set up at Beltsville, Md. The frequency signals were transmitted in groups each day so that the range from 125 to 6000 kilocycles was covered every 2 weeks for all stations within range of the Bureau signal. The obvious advantage of the service soon led to more frequent transmission of the signals and to their broadcast over a nationwide system of standard frequency stations.[207]

Holding to an assigned frequency was not always enough in the noisy crowded air at that time. In January 1924 when the dirigible *Shenandoah* tore loose from her mast at Lakehurst during a winter storm and with only a skeleton crew aboard was lost for almost 20 hours, all New York broadcasting stations went off the air to keep from interfering with her messages.[208]

An enormous improvement on the original frequency standard—a tuning fork device—was the piezo oscillator which used a quartz plate vibrating at a radio frequency.[209] As modified by the Bureau, it furnished an

---

[205] NBS Annual Report 1923, pp. 64–65.

[206] Dellinger, "The Bureau of Standards lends a hand," Radio Broadcast, 2, 40 (1922).

[207] Letter, Acting Director, NBS, to Department of Electrical Engineering, Pennsylvania State College, Jan. 26, 1923 (NBS Box 46, IEW); NBS Annual Report 1923, pp. 66–69; Southworth, Forty Years of Radio Research, p. 40; LC171 (1925), superseded by LC280 (1930).

[208] John Toland, Ships in the Sky, p. 85.

[209] The piezo or pressure electricity effect on quartz was first identified by Pierre Curie in 1880. Its application to radio stations was described in LC223, "Use of piezo oscillators" (1927).

Dr. J. Howard Dellinger examines the continuous recording of super-power tests of station WGY, Schenectady. In 1926 when this picture was taken, WGY had been granted permission to broadcast regularly twice a week on 50,000 watts. WGY assisted the Bureau for a number of years in both its studies of radio interference and its compiling of radio propagation data.

extraordinary selective, precise, and portable frequency standard both for the use of radio inspectors and for the stations themselves. The remarkable accuracy of about 0.01 percent attained with the oscillator closely agreed with that of the national laboratories abroad, as comparison tests disclosed, but it was not enough for the Bureau. Mechanical ingenuity and capital had already created a far more acute situation in broadcasting in this country than abroad. The Bureau therefore aimed at absolute frequency values with a certainty of 0.001 percent. It achieved them before the decade was out.[210]

Upon formal adoption by the Federal Radio Commission in 1927 of frequency standards for broadcasting stations, the Bureau was made responsible for their testing. New allocation of broadcasting channels and station restrictions imposed by the Commission, as well as the improved instruments, equipment, and filtering devices that had become available, ameliorated the problem of station interference for the time being. The

[210] Dellinger, "The status of frequency standardization," Proc. IRE, 16, 579 (1928). That certainty, to within 1 part in 100,000, was exceeded in 1930 when the Bureau devised a primary frequency standard with an error of 1 part in several million (NBS Annual Report 1930, p. 22; RP759, 1935). By 1960, with frequency standards based on atomic radiation beams, reliability was in the range of parts in 10 billion. (Dellinger, MS, "Fifty years of radio in the NBS," 3 March 1961, p. 6, NBS Historical File.)

Bureau turned again to the study of radio fading—"the vagaries of radio wave propagation," in the Bureau's blanket term—that by the mid-twenties had come to be considered "the principal obstacle to radio development."[211]

A survey several years before had dispelled the belief that increasing transmitter power would overcome fading, or that high power itself contributed to the fading phenomenon. It was learned that appreciable fading occurred as close as 8 miles distant from a broadcasting station and that the irregularities in reception resulted in part at least from the multiplicity of paths followed by the wave from the station to the receiving set. The primary sources of fading seemed associated with the ionized air of the Kennelly-Heaviside layer, a radio-wave conducting surface identified with the ionosphere, some 60 miles up.[212]

Aware that the task of measuring even some of the phenomena of radio fading was beyond its powers, the Bureau group under Dellinger secured the cooperation of 23 university, industrial, and commercial radio laboratories in recording fading data. General Electric's station WGY and the Westinghouse station KDKA provided the transmission. It took more than a year to sort out the collected data, but the figures seemed to establish a number of facts that had previously been only surmises.

Fading was greatest from 60 to 125 miles from the broadcasting stations, and was almost certainly due to variable absorption of the transmitted waves in the upper atmosphere. The phenomenon occurred between the ground-transmitted wave and the wave that returned from the ionosphere. While there seemed no consistent correlation between fading and weather conditions, day and night variations in the degree of fading were consistent, and during the solar eclipse that occurred in 1925, the fading phenomenon mimicked the day and night fading pattern.[213]

Although fading was quite pronounced on the shorter wavelengths of high frequency transmission, the Bureau was to learn that it presented even greater difficulties at very high frequencies. Except for Austin's work in the Navy radio laboratory at the Bureau,[214] the possibilities of shortwave (very high frequency) radio communication had been neglected in the excitement of the work in broadcasting. The shortwave spectrum had been briefly explored in 1922 when the Army Air Service complained to the Bu-

---

[211] NBS Annual Report 1926, p. 19. Dellinger discussed the scope of the problem in "The International Union of Scientific Radio Telegraphy," Science, 64, 638 (1926).

[212] The first suggestion of ionized or "electrically conducting strata" in the upper region of the atmosphere in connection with radio wave propagation was reported simultaneously by Sir Oliver Heaviside in England and Arthur H. Kennelly in this country at the turn of the century. See Kennelly in Elec. World & Eng. 39, 473 (1902), and account in S476 (Dellinger, Whittemore, and Kruse, 1923).

[213] S561 (Dellinger, Jolliffe, and Parkinson, 1927); NBS Annual Report 1928, p. 8.

[214] Described in LC194 (Mar. 10, 1926).

reau of increasing interference in its radio reception. Dellinger's group found at that time that in the narrower band of frequencies utilized by radio telephony interference was greatly reduced. Although uncertain of the practicability of using that band, the Bureau developed apparatus transmitting and receiving on a frequency of 3000 kc for the Air Service. The two-way tests between Washington and Pittsburgh proved successful, with materially less broadcast interference as well as less atmospheric fading.[215]

By 1925 the vast and previously untrammeled range of frequencies between 1500 and 23,000 kc had come into extensive use by transocean communication companies, in ship telephony, and airplane-to-ground communications, and by the military services, amateurs, and broadcast relay stations using it to set up the first radio networks. Three years later, the high frequency channels, as yet unallocated and in common use by all nations, were as congested as the broadcast channels had been. Moreover, real knowledge of the high frequency spectrum was still meager, use of high frequencies was admittedly still in the experimental stage, and despite early optimism it was now known that they were "subject to greater vagaries than radio waves of lower frequency." [216]

Many of the questions raised by these preliminary observations on radio wave propagation and the phenomena of fading would, as Dellinger reported, require years of research and development. He might better have said "decades," for the quest goes on to this day, increasing in scope as knowledge increases.[217] In applied radio, where Federal agencies continually sought new radio equipment for their air and sea commerce, progress was more rapid.

From its very beginning broadcast radio raised hob with the Bureau's radio direction finder (radio compass) on ships trying to pick up signals from the shore stations along the coast. No sooner had the Bureau designed

---

[215] NBS Annual Report 1923, p. 66, and correspondence in NBS Box 10, IEW.

[216] Dellinger, MS, "The high frequency spectrum," Jan. 17, 1928 (NBS Historical File). Of interest is Dellinger's report in the American Year Book for 1928, p. 462, of the first transmission by broadcasting and high frequency stations "of pictures and of moving pictures and television [via rotating discs and photoelectric cells]. * * * The received moving images were crude silhouettes or barely recognized faces." Television remained a laboratory novelty as late as 1940, the year radio reached the peak of its popularity, with 45 million sets in 33 million homes, serviced by 882 broadcasting stations. William Kenney, The Crucial Years, 1940–45 (New York: Macfadden-Bartell Corp., 1962), p. 116.

[217] The American Telephone & Telegraph laboratories began studies of the ionosphere in the 1920's, in the interest of long-distance radio communication, but "later recognized that this type of work should be carried out by more centralized bodies [i.e., the Carnegie Institution's Department of Terrestrial Magnetism and the National Bureau of Standards] for the benefit of the whole industry." Maclaurin, Invention and Innovation in the Radio Industry, pp. 161–162.

a special high-frequency radiotelephone for a new fleet of patrol boats put in service by the Coast Guard than the Bureau was asked to convert their radio compasses to similar high frequency reception. The new radio compass, using a frequency of 2100 kc led next to a portable unit that the Bureau of Navigation sought for shipping, with a useful range of 90 to 7700 kc.[218]

While the radio compass was useful for locating a radio signal source, acting as a radio beacon to guide ships at sea or planes in flight, Federal aviation, when it added passengers to its mail flights and extended its operations, required greater safeguards than the compass could provide.[219] (European aviation was to rely entirely on radio direction finders for another two decades at least.) Shortly after the establishment of the Aeronautical Division in Commerce, the Bureau was asked to begin work at once on better air navigation aids.

The Bureau's first crude radio guidance system for aircraft was tested in 1921, when a pilot flew along a course designated by signals sent from two transmitting coils on the ground. The prototype radio beacon produced 2 years later for the Army Air Service was put aside for further work on the radio compass. Without passengers, flying the mail was high adventure and the pilots liked it that way. Work on a beacon was not resumed until 1926.[220]

It was the inventive talents of Harry Diamond, who came to the Bureau in 1927, that resulted 2 years later in the first visual-type radiobeacon system anywhere, enabling a pilot to keep on course and know his approximate position at all times while in flight.[221] Incidental to the system, the Bureau constructed receiving sets of special design for use in planes and improved shielding against interference from the engine ignition. A year later, in 1930, a 15-pound unit that Diamond added to the radio range beacon

[218] S428 (Kolster and Dunmore, 1921); NBS Annual Report 1922, p. 57; S525 (Dunmore, 1926); S536 (Dunmore, 1926).

[219] By 1924 regular day and night mail service had been established between New York and San Francisco via Chicago and Cheyenne. By the end of 1928, 48 airways covering 20,000 miles linked 355 cities in the United States. Slosson, The Great Crusade and After, p. 401; Aircraft Year Book, 1929 (New York: Aeronautics Chamber of Commerce of America, Inc.), p. 103.

[220] NBS Annual Report 1921, p. 68; S480 (Engle and Dunmore, 1923). Letter, Harry Diamond to Leland Jamieson, Nov. 16, 1939 (NBS Box 431, IEW), credits P. D. Lowell of the Bureau with the suggestion for the radio range beacon about 1922, the experimental work carried out under his guidance in 1922–23 by Engel and Dunmore.

[221] RP159 (Dellinger, Diamond, and Dunmore, 1929).

Born in Russia at the turn of the century, Diamond graduated from MIT and taught for 4 years at Lehigh University before he came to the Bureau as a radio engineer. His electronic genius served the Bureau and the Nation well, notably during World War II. His driving, tireless energy was to bring him to an untimely death in 1948.

A Curtiss Fledgling was equipped in 1931 with the first complete system for blind landing of an aircraft and demonstrated its practicability by an extensive series of hooded landings at College Park, Md., and at Newark Airport.

The dual-pointer landing indicator on the instrument panel gave the pilot a visual indication of his position in space with respect to the approach glide path. Adopted and adapted by the Civil Aeronautics Administration, this NBS radio instrument landing system is basic to the present universally used ILS blind landing system.

and radiotelephone in the cockpit made possible the first blind landing of an airplane entirely by radio guidance.[222]

Blind flying and blind landing—that is, flying under conditions of no visibility—required the pilot to know his position in three dimensions at all times. This was achieved with indicators on his instrument panel which recorded signals from a small direction beacon, giving the pilot his lateral or landing field position; a marker beacon, giving the pilot his longitudinal or approach position; and an inclined ultrahigh frequency radio beam that continuously reported his height. One important difficulty remained. The Commerce Department transmitted weather information to planes on the same frequency it used for ships, while the radio beacon operated on a different frequency. This meant that the pilot had to keep switching his frequencies and also contend with interference from marine radios. The difficulty was solved by adding a device allowing voice communication without interruption to the range service.[223]

Diamond himself operated the radio in the first of the test series of directional and blind flights made between the Bureau experimental air station at College Park, Md., and Newark Airport, the latter chosen because of its heavy traffic—even then. The system proved highly satisfactory, and in 1933 it was turned over to the Department of Commerce.[224]

That same year the Bureau devised a new type of radio direction finder that operated on the radio waves of broadcasting stations. It was designed for the use of itinerant fliers, such as barnstormers and other non-government fliers, who did not have the special equipment necessary to use the radio range beacon.[225]

The twenties witnessed extraordinary developments in radio technology, and extraordinary radio sales. The radio and automobile industries were the bellwethers of that most prosperous-seeming of decades, paying the highest wages and leading the way in mass production and mass consumption techniques. Salaries and the standard of living inched up, goods and groceries were plentiful and relatively cheap, and boom followed boom, real or inflated, in industry, in consumer services, in real estate, and utilities. The Nation speculated, buying stock on margin as it bought appliances. The bootblack and the grocer took fliers, and life savings went into marginal ac-

---

[222] A previous blind landing was achieved in July 1929 when Lt. James Doolittle brought down a hooded plane using a sensitive barometric altimeter, a gyro-stabilized horizon, together with a radio lateral course indicator and marker beacon supplied by the Bureau.
[223] RP238 (Diamond and Dunmore, 1930); RP341 (Kear and Wintermute, 1931).
[224] RP602 (Diamond, 1933); Frank G. Kear, "Instrument landing at the NBS," IRE Trans. on Aeronautical and Navigation Electronics, vol. ANE–6, No. 2, June 1959.
[225] RP621 (Hinman, 1933).

counts. [226] The fever struck the Bureau too, but was to some extent contained. Because of the Bureau's close connection with industry and possible access to knowledge that might be useful, a matter of ethics was involved and speculation was quietly discouraged. But no one was exempt from the consequences of the delirium as the Nation headed for the crash.

---

[226] Not "everyone" was in the market, but active speculators, as distinguished from those who took fliers, probably numbered close to a million, in a nation of 30 million families. John K. Galbraith, The Great Crash, 1929 (Boston: Houghton Mifflin, 1961), pp. 82–83.

The Winchester bushel of Henry VII, a corn bushel, with a capacity of 2,150.5 cubic inches. This was the first English standard measure of capacity of which there is any cognizance.

THE TIME OF THE GREAT DEPRESSION (1931–40)

CHAPTER VI

THE BUREAU IN THE PUBLIC VIEW

The better-homes movement and the standardization crusade of the twenties, fed by fountains of publicity, made the Bureau known to the public as it had never been before. The spate of articles in the Saturday Evening Post, Collier's, Popular Mechanics, Literary Digest, and Everybody's describing how Uncle Sam was saving millions for autoists, homeowners, and the consumer industries acquainted the general public with a helping hand in Washington, available to all, of whose existence many had not previously been aware. The publicity had some remarkable consequences.

The Bureau since its founding had been a high-level information center, an assaying office for inventions and ideas, and a court of appeal, to which Congressmen sent inquiries from their constituents, businessmen their production problems, and inventors their notions for appraisal. The Bureau, after making tests, had politely discouraged citizens of the Great Lakes States who saw their peat and its byproducts as unlimited substitutes for coal and oil, had sent investigators to examine clays, sands, and marls of hopeful economic value on behalf of owners of exhausted farmland, and explained repeatedly to would-be inventors the technical fallacies in their tide motors, and why a hole 12 miles deep, to harness the earth's heat, was impracticable.[1]

Incoming mail at the Bureau surged following the appearance in the early twenties of magazine articles on "Uncle Sam's Question-and-Answer Office" that pointed out that by "Federal law, every government department has to answer every letter which it receives, irrespective of whether the epistles come from lunatics or scientific ignoramuses."[2] The articles cited a dentist's request for a method of measuring wear and tear on false teeth, and a businessman's interest in a motor-driven letter opener to speed clear-

[1] Correspondence in NBS Box 12, IN; Box 13, INM.

[2] George H. Dacy, "Answering a hundred million questions," Illustrated World, 37, 823 (1922); S. R. Winters, "Uncle Sam's question-and-answer office," Sci. Am. 129, 114 (1923).

ance of his morning's mail. A potential voter had written to her Congressman for the recipe she was certain the Bureau of Standards had for a cosmetic to protect her complexion when she played tennis or went bathing.

Some of the queries sent to the Bureau were not as farfetched as they seemed at first glance, as Dr. Coblentz observed in one of his monthly reports:

> That the Optical Division of this Bureau should be called upon to help solve [the problem of increasing the birth-rate of pigs and decreasing the price of bacon] seems comical on first thought. Nevertheless, the question presented by a large forest-products corporation, of the proper windows for hog houses, was a fair one that is worthy of consideration. Perhaps the inquiry should have been turned over to the Housing Commission for more mature consideration. However, having had some experience with problems in solar radiation as well as the farrowing of pigs, advice was given on the proper arrangement of hog-house windows in order to trap and conserve the maximum amount of sunlight.[3]

But many of the inquiries from the public in that decade, whether addressed to the "Natural Bureau of Standards," "National Bureau of St. Andrews," "National Burrough of Standards," "National Brewer of Standards," occasionally the "Department of Science," or by its right name, defied the best minds of the Bureau. Would the Bureau describe "what the average American should be"? Had it a pamphlet on "what the well-dressed person should wear"? Would the Bureau please send its booklets dealing with "protection against the electric influence of radioactive Dictagraphs, the kind that follow people around everywhere * * * and influence * * * hypnotically"? [4]

Newspaper stories in the period announcing somewhat prematurely the imminence of an age of atomic energy aroused interest and apprehension.[5] How, wrote a correspondent, might he "avoid being hit by the 'death ray' "? Another asked whether he ought not to sell his gas and electric stock—to which Dr. Crittenden replied that he had better keep it, since no method was yet in sight to hasten or retard the natural disintegration of radium or other radioactive materials. Nor, wrote the Bureau to another correspondent, was science in a position to release atomic energy by the rapid withdrawal of the magnetic field in a quantity of matter, not even that containing the heavy atom of uranium, thorium, or radium. And to someone who proposed to obtain heat from the oxygen and hydrogen in water,

---

[3] NBS Box 23, PRM, December 1922.

[4] Correspondence in NBS Box 162, IG.

[5] Contributing to the speculations were a series of speeches and articles by a member of the Bureau, Dr. Paul D. Foote. See his "Ancient and modern alchemy," Cml. Age, 31, 337 and 423 (1923), and "The Alchemist," Sci. Mo. 19, 239 (1924).

the Bureau offered the warning that this defiance of the law of conservation of matter, "would upset the whole structure of physics and chemistry." [6]

The Bureau received an average of a letter a month announcing the discovery of a perpetual motion device, and to the invariable request that it be tested, the Bureau answered that it would be delighted, upon submission of a working model. So many letters came asking for devices to locate buried treasure that the Bureau composed a form letter. It was really "cheaper to dig over the suspected region than to attempt to build such equipment," said the Bureau.[7]

Not all was chaff. Publicity given to the beneficial effects of airplane flights on those hard of hearing or even totally deaf led to many requests for treatment in the Bureau's high-altitude chamber. The Bureau always agreed to accept patients with types of deafness that might respond to this treatment, provided medical supervision was furnished.[8] But the medical panacea of the twenties was radium (it had been electric belts and electric accumulators before that), and the Bureau was besieged with requests from firms and factories to verify their radium appliances or certify their radium preparations. Sent to the Bureau for tests, in order to obtain American Medical Association approval, were numerous radium injection preparations, "facial radium applicators," and "radium salves," the latter offered as gangrene and cancer cures. Devices for inhaling radium emanations, a do-it-yourself "hydro-radium activator" for making potable radium salts (guaranteed to induce mental as well as physical stimulation), and "Radithor—the perpetual sunshine drink" found avid markets well into the 1930's.[9]

In 1924 the Bureau discontinued its certification of radioactive preparations, but continued to test them at the request of the Post Office, the Federal Trade Commission, and health authorities. On the basis of their minute or nonexistent radioactivity, the Bureau reported the patented waters, muds, slimes, and other concoctions "no more dangerous than a day out in the sun" and uniformly useless.[10] Radium was known to inflict superficial

---

[6] Correspondence in NBS Box 14, IPXA; Box 41, ICG; Box 45, IEG. See also NBS Box 47, AG; Box 83, IG; Box 119, IG; Box 121, IM.

[7] Letter, GKB to Office of Secretary of Commerce, Jan. 18, 1926 (NBS Box 166, IN); letter, GKB, Dec. 1, 1927 (NBS Box 201, IE).

It may be noted here that by 1923 the Bureau was handling over 244,200 pieces of first-class mail annually or more than 800 incoming, and outgoing pieces each working day (NBS Annual Report 1923, pp. 320–321). A count made in 1939, in a 3-day period chosen at random, showed almost 800 incoming letters requesting technical information, the same number of telephone calls on technical matters, 450 letters asking for publications, and 429 visitors who called at the Bureau for scientific or technical information or help (Hearings * * * 1940, Apr. 21, 1939, p. 154).

[8] Letter, GKB, Feb. 11, 1926 (NBS Box 166, INA).

[9] Letter, SWS to AMA, May 13, 1922 (NBS Box 14, IPXR).

[10] NBS mimographed letter, June 30, 1924 (NBS Box 103, TPX).

burns when applied externally, but that skin lesions had insidious effects was not so well known. Despite this, and the total ignorance of the effects of radium when taken internally, the American Medical Association did not remove radium for internal administration from its list of recognized remedies until 1932.

The standardization crusade that did so much to fix the public image of the Bureau as a "great scientific business [operated] for the common benefit of all the people" acted in yet another way. Consumers and those interested in consumer welfare began asking what precise benefits the public derived from standardization. Critics of the Bureau appeared who saw only too well how its efforts at standardization and simplification saved money for industry but little evidence that those savings were passed on to the householder.

The Bureau was at some fault itself. It extolled its consumer research without making clear the distinction between the "organized consumer," meaning Federal, State, and city agencies and hospital, hotel and similar trade associations which were direct beneficiaries of its research, and the "over-the-counter consumer" or man in the street. Yet the Bureau was sincerely concerned for the individual consumer and assured him in correspondence and publications that he was the ultimate beneficiary of all its research, in better products and better quality.[11] Even more direct aid was available to the consumer through Bureau publications on incandescent

[11] An indirect consumer service of the Bureau was its unpublicized investigations for the Federal Trade Commission, Postal Service, Justice Department, and Treasury Department, particularly in the scientific detection of misrepresentation, fraud, and high crime. Misleading advertising and misrepresentation of products became subjects of Bureau investigation almost from its inception, but interest in crime did not begin until 1913 when Albert S. Osborn, author of Questioned Documents, sent some micrometers to the Bureau for calibration. By chance, the instruments were tested by Dr. Wilmer Souder of the weights and measures division, who became interested in the scientific detection of crime. His laboratory, with Dr. Stratton's encouragement, was for almost two decades the principal crime research center in the Federal Government, long antedating the organization of a crime laboratory in the Federal Bureau of Investigation. The FBI Laboratory acquired its first scientist in 1932.

Assistance from all the Bureau laboratories was available to Dr. Souder, especially the photographic technology laboratory, where Raymond Davis developed a method for photographing and deciphering almost completely charred records when the ordinary camera, the microscope, and chemical reagents failed (S454, 1922). Specializing in the identification of questioned documents, of typewriting, handwriting, bullets, cartridge cases, and firearms, Dr. Souder by the early 1930's was participating in some 50 to 75 Federal investigations a year involving extortion, kidnapping, theft of money orders, raised checks, forgeries, stolen securities, and threatening letters. Bureau testimony in a contract case in 1935 was reported to have saved the Government almost $300,000, and in another instance settled the payment of income taxes on $1 million (NBS Annual Report 1935, p. 66; correspondence in NBS Box 386, IWI).

lamps, on "gas-savers," "fuel-savers," reclaimed rubber, the care of automobile tires, on battery additives, antifreeze solutions, and the characteristics of "good gasoline." Directed wholly to the consuming public too were the Bureau circulars on household measurements, materials, and safety, and on care and repair of the home.

If industry resented this kind of Government research, the consumer protested it was not enough. The criticism came to a focus with the depression. In the considerable reorientation of Bureau research impelled by the economies of the depression, neither side was pleased.

The criticism that began shortly after the war swelled to a storm in 1923 and lasted for a decade. The Bureau was accused of meddling with the rights of private industry. It was said to be producing materials that should be made by industry. It served industry at the expense of the small consumer. It had become an adjunct of the Better Business Bureau. It was an engineering rather than a scientific research agency. It entertained too many interests outside the scope of its organic act. Many of the charges were exaggerated and, taken together, highly contradictory, but they possessed a common element of truth. The empire building of Stratton and Rosa, bequeathed intact to Burgess and maintained by him, made the Bureau vulnerable to the inference of expansionism.[12]

The censure of the Bureau began and, for all practical purposes, ended with the American Engineering Standards Committee (AESC), over whose reorganization in 1919, in order to commit industry to standardization, the Bureau had presided. Much concerned to define the role of the Bureau in the standardization program, an AESC affiliate had pointedly observed that the Bureau "originally dealt largely, if not exclusively, with scientific problems." Was it authorized "to include also engineering standards, that is, problems of applied science"? Stratton's reply, that he "most emphatically had no intention of limiting the activities of the Bureau of Standards exclusively to what you call 'problems of pure science'," was not reassuring.[13] Nor was the published remark of Russell McBride, Bureau gas engineer, calculated to calm representatives of industry, that the Bureau had become "now * * * what is in effect a 'Bureau of Technology,' closely interwoven with, and in some measure superseding parts of, the original 'Bureau of Physics'." [14]

---

[12] Dr. Burgess acknowledged the criticism in a speech on "Policies, problems, and practices of the NBS," dated Nov. 4, 1923 (MS in NBS Box 42, ID).

[13] Letter, SWS to president, Am. Soc. Mech. Eng., Sept. 12, 1919, and attached correspondence (NBS Box 2, AG).

[14] McBride, "The National Bureau of Standards," Chem. & Met. Eng. 27, 1162 (1922). Cf. letter, H. D. Hubbard for Acting Secretary of Commerce to Secretary of State, Sept. 3, 1924: "The Bureau of Standards is primarily a laboratory for industrial research and standardization" (NBS Box 71, AG).

The first serious disagreement with the AESC arose over the degree of Bureau involvement in the simplified practices program, which, the committee asserted, increased the reluctance of some industries to accept the principles of simplification and standardization for which the AESC worked.[15] The establishment in 1927 of the trade standards division at the Bureau, for the purpose of bringing together the standardization, simplification, and specification activities of the AESC and the Bureau, at once met resistance.

In 1928, at the direction of Dr. Agnew, its executive secretary (and former member of the Bureau), the AESC was reconstituted as the American Standards Association (ASA), with authority, through acceptance by concensus of its members, to make standards and validate them as well, and thereby "draw to itself * * * the bulk of standardization and simplification" in industry.[16] Preliminary to the reorganization, the AESC formally requested Bureau withdrawal from all commercial standardization activities. A period of estrangement ensued during which Burgess and other Bureau members ceased to attend ASA meetings.[17]

The resolution was rescinded, but the estrangement continued as the Bureau reported that whole series of projects begun by its trade standards group were being held up or deliberately duplicated by ASA and that the attitude of the association had become antagonistic. Claiming interference and lack of cooperation, ASA retorted that the Bureau was usurping ASA functions and was promoting Federal specifications as commodity standards. As a result, ASA claimed, both producing and consuming industries, fearful of Government interference, resisted the validation by ASA of standards largely determined by Federal agencies.[18] The conflict of interests was not to be entirely resolved for another two decades.

The ASA estrangement was but one manifestation of increasing censure of Bureau research. In 1924 a Baltimore newspaper article, "What becomes of the money you pay in taxes," singled out the Bureau as representative of bureaucratic extravagance, claiming it wasted public funds on testing gas meters, recording the flight of golf balls, investigating fire hazards of motion picture film on ocean liners, testing watches, and making liquid air, all to no purpose.[19] An editorial in the "Washington Post" on "Futile putter-

---

[15] Letter, GKB to chairman, AESC, May 14, 1923 (NBS Box 43, IDP); memo, GKB for Durgin, Simplified Practices Division, Jan. 10, 1924 (Box 71, AG); memo, Crittenden for GKB, Sept. 30, 1925 (Box 141, PM, SSMC).

[16] Eng. News-Record, 99, 291 (1927); ibid., 101, 712 (1928).

[17] Minutes, AESC Executive Committee, Jan. 19, 1928, par. 1923; rescinded in letter, chairman, AESC to GKB, June 15, 1928 (NBS Box 231, IDS–AESC).

[18] Memo, Fairchild for GKB, Sept. 10, 1928 (NBS Box 231, ID–CS); letter, chairman, ASA to R. Hudson, Nov. 15, 1928 (Box 231, ID–SP).

[19] Attached to memo, GKB for Assistant to Secretary of Commerce, Feb. 15, 1924, and Bureau articles, in manuscript, in reply (NBS Box 71, AG).

ers in Washington," which was widely reprinted, rounded on "the paladins of precision" at the Bureau to which Congress had given "a blanket charter to go as far as it likes * * * [investigating] everything under the round and shining sun." Other research agencies of the Government, particularly in the Department of Agriculture, shared in the editorial complaints, but the Bureau was the focus of the storm. The rumbling had been of some duration and apparently had reached Congress. The "Post" editorialist, summing up the questionable research, recommended that in the promised general shakeup of Federal bureaus "this small dust in the balances of government may as well be swept out. It will never be missed." [20]

In this, as in each instance of attack, the Bureau answered with a statement of the need and authority for its research. It was to little purpose. Acting on complaints of industry, the Comptroller General in 1925 informed the Bureau that it had no right to manufacture optical glass for the Navy or to make special castings for the Coast and Geodetic Survey. Transferred funds for those purposes would be withheld. The Bureau replied that it alone manufactured a suitable optical glass in sufficient quantity for Navy requirements, and that its castings, made "in connection with the Bureau of Standard's investigation of such material," were experimental and noncompetitive. Satisfied, the Comptroller General released the funds.[21]

Industry was not alone in its criticism of the Bureau, nor was Dr. Agnew, executive secretary of the ASA, the only Bureau-trained censor. On a wholly different tack was the private war of Frederick J. Schlink, former technical assistant to Dr. Stratton and from 1922 to 1931 the assistant secretary of the ASA. He was to carry his feud with the Bureau into the thirties from the offices of Consumers' Research, Inc., which he founded with Stuart Chase in 1929.

In 1925–27, while an officer of the AESC, Schlink, with Stuart Chase, wrote a series of eminently readable articles for the New Republic (subsequently published as Getting Your Money's Worth) that had as a principal target the Bureau of Standards.[22] The authors estimated that the Bureau, operating on a budget of $2 million, saved the Government better than a hundred million dollars a year through its testing of products. That same

---

[20] The editorial also appeared July 2, 1925 in the "Philadelphia Public Ledger" and "New York Evening Post" (NBS Box 108, AG, and Box 139, PA).

[21] Letter, GKB to Secretary of Commerce, July 21, 1925 (NBS Box 112, FPG); letter, Acting Secretary of Commerce to Comptroller General of the United States, August 3, 1925 (NBS Box 111, FL); letter, GKB to Chairman, Navy BuOrd, June 14, 1926 (NBS Box 170, IRG).

[22] While probably not endorsed by the AESC, the articles and book may have had some support in the AESC's pique with the Bureau at the time. See Getting Your Money's Worth: a Study in the Waste of the Consumer's Dollar (New York: Macmillan, 1927, reprinted 1931), pp. 82, 98.

research and testing, said Schlink and Chase, would save the public at least a billion dollars annually if Bureau test results were made available in a form that the consumer could use. They declared invalid in an agency operated on taxpayers' money the Bureau argument that release of its test results on competitive products, and identifying them by name, would "promote commercial injustice." They proposed a consumers' rebellion, and urged the public to act through Congress to secure release of all Government information of consumer interest, particularly that concealed in the publications and files of the Bureau of Standards and the Department of Agriculture's Bureau of Chemistry.[23]

In a book he wrote in 1929, Dr. Harvey W. Wiley, former chief of the Bureau of Chemistry, father of the Food and Drug Act, inveterate polemicist, and at that time director of research on Good Housekeeping magazine, made one of the most virulent and comprehensive of the attacks on the character of research at the Bureau up to that time.[24] Besides his condemnation of Bureau investigations that encroached on provinces of other research agencies in the Government, he assailed at length, as did Schlink and other consumer-oriented critics, the research associate plan at the Bureau which performed research directly for the benefit of industry at the taxpayer's expense. And he struck at "the expansive activities of the Bureau of Standards," citing its use of transferred funds—

> to investigate oil pollution, radio direction for the Coast Guard, helium recorders, chromium plating, corrosion, fatigue and embrittlement of duralumin, electrically charged dust, optical glass, substitutes for parachute silk, goldbeaters skin, storage batteries, internal combustion engines, fuels, lubricants, photographic emulsions, stresses in riveted joints, machine guns, bomb ballistics, rope and cordage, chemical and metallurgical tests, wind tunnel tests of models, aircraft engines, velocity of flame in explosives * * * caroa fibers * * * and farm wastes

---

[23] The same criticism of the Bureau appeared in Dr. Robert A. Brady's article, "How Government standards affect the ultimate consumer," Ann. Amer. Acad. Soc. Pol. Sci. 137, 245 (1928), and in Schlink's article, "Standards and specifications from the standpoint of the ultimate consumer," ibid. issue.

The Bureau position has been repeatedly pointed out. The creation of a Government laboratory to test consumer goods sounds eminently reasonable. But the Bureau has long been aware how impossibly large and controversial such a project would be. Health hazards may justify the Food and Drug Administration, but to cover all consumer products in order to mitigate merely economic hazards would be a herculean task. Interview with Dr. F. B. Silsbee, Mar. 10, 1964.

[24] The recitation of grievances appeared in a remarkable digression in his History of a Crime against the Food Law (Privately printed, Washington, D.C., 1929), wherein a whole chapter (pp. 281–345) was devoted to the Bureau.

as evidence that the Bureau was in direct competition with private research laboratories such as the Mellon Institute of Industrial Research and Arthur D. Little, Inc. There was no more warrant in the organic act of the Bureau for this commercial research, Wiley declared, than there was for its "architectural excursions" in building pilot plants to manufacture dextrose and levulose. The Bureau, he concluded, was badly in need of policing.[25]

The recurring charge that the Bureau interpreted its authority over weights and measures as a license to investigate literally everything that could be weighed or measured, appeared also in a pamphlet entitled "Why not reorganize the Bureau of Standards?" published in 1929 by William E. Bullock, secretary of the antimetric society, the American Institute of Weights and Measures.[26] If this was simply a random gadfly attack, a letter that same year from Arthur D. Little, president of Arthur D. Little, Inc., was not. It was an ultimatum from industry. Many prominent chemists and chemical engineers, he wrote, were convinced that "the Bureau has extended its efforts far outside its legitimate field," and "threatened to take the whole question before the House Committee on Appropriations."[27]

Provoked by "the four-year furor" over its research in industry, Dr. Burgess submitted the controversy and a statement of the Bureau position and its program of research to the Department of Justice for a legal opinion. Justice ruled that the extension of Bureau activities beyond the organic act, as authorized by a succession of congressional acts, was completely valid.[28]

In the last months of the Hoover Administration, Congress finally held its long-promised investigation of Government interference in industry. (It paid no attention to the equally valid criticism of Federal apathy where the taxpaying consumer was concerned.) Acting on complaints of the U.S. Chamber of Commerce, the National Association of Manufacturers, and the Federation of American Business, Congress appointed a committee on May 31, 1932, to survey "the extensive commercial and manufacturing interests of Government bureaus seriously competing with private industry." Despite all the furor, the Bureau turned out to be the least of offenders.

Congress found that during World War I, owing to the reluctance of private industry to risk short-term, unprofitable ventures, Government agencies had organized a great number of manufacturing plants, factories, foundries, and services, and with the "overreaching zeal of governmental bureaus to retain authority and prestige," had continued to operate them after the war. Heading a list of 17 specific areas of serious competition were

---

[25] Many of Wiley's charges were longstanding. See 12-page letter, GKB to C, Bureau of Efficiency, Aug. 31, 1923 (NBS Box 40, AG).

[26] Pamphlet in Bureau of Budget records, NARG 51, file 86 (Bureau of Standards).

[27] Letter to GKB, Dec. 30, 1929, and attached correspondence (NBS Box 263, AG).

[28] Letter, Dr. Julius Klein, Assistant Secretary of Commerce, to R. O. Bailey, Dec. 30, 1931 (NBS Box 339, AG-Conf. for Dir. only).

Navy Department factories and foundries, Government Printing Office supply plants, Army and Navy clothing and leather factories, the Post Exchange organization, a wide range of Farm Board enterprises, and many of the Federal prison industries.

Nowhere in the 253-page report of the committee was the Bureau of Standards mentioned by name, though it might have answered to the indictment of "overdevelopment of industrial research in Government laboratories," buried in the last pages of the report. Much of that research had been initiated by industry itself, the committee found, but had "grown beyond the original intent or desired objective in many instances."[29] The Bureau might also have answered to the charges that technical specialists in the Government, acting as industrial consultants, thereby competed with professional consultants, and that Government patents taken out by Federal scientists on behalf of the public "prevented exclusive development by industry." Since the congressional committee felt that neither the intention nor extension of Government research for industry could be accurately defined, it recommended only "curtailment by limitation of funds appropriated for such investigations," as a brake on Federal competition.[30]

The report of the committee appeared at the depth of the depression, just as the incoming administration launched its massive drive against Federal expenditures. Curtailment of Bureau funds, and the investigations of Bureau activities that followed, were to end more of its research for industry than industry bargained for.

LYMAN JAMES BRIGGS

It has been said that any Republican could have been elected President in 1928. That the Republican was the incumbent Secretary of Commerce made Hoover the unluckiest President in American history. With the stock market crash, the national income between 1929 and 1932 fell with the value of the dollar from $87.4 billion to $41.7 billion. Unemployment, from an irreducible peacetime low of 1.8 million in 1925 (representing 4 percent of the civilian labor force), reached 4.3 million (8.7 percent) in 1930. In

[29] Report of Special Committee appointed to investigate Government competition with Private Industry (72d Cong., 2d sess., H.R. 1985), Feb. 8, 1933, p. 236 (L/C: HD3616.U45A3).

[30] Ibid., p. 237. The House questionnaire on Government competition, with Bureau answers, appears in letter, LJB to Hon. Joseph B. Shannon, Aug. 24, 1932 (NBS Box 339, AG). For the Chamber of Commerce attack on the Bureau's "overdevelopment of industrial research," see memo, Office of Secretary of Commerce for LJB, Oct. 4, 1932 (ibid.).

the wake of the financial collapse of Europe in early 1931, this country began the steep slide into the great depression.

By late 1932, 85,000 business firms and 5,000 banks had failed and unemployment reached 12.8 million (24.9 percent of the labor force), representing 1 out of every 4 workers in the Nation.[31] With varying intensity, the depression lasted for 10 years, until the vast pool of manpower and industrial capacity was absorbed by war.

Constitutionally opposed to emergency Government measures, President Hoover at first sought, as he had in his recovery program of the early twenties, to prod private enterprise into action by stepping up Federal construction, urging local governments to accelerate their spending, and businessmen to maintain wage rates.[32] By 1931, as State and city treasuries emptied and business and industry acknowledged their helplessness, the administration was forced to act. Much against his will, Hoover brought large areas of the economy—the banks, railroads, insurance companies, farmers, and finally the unemployed—into the Federal orbit. A Reconstruction Finance Corporation was set up to lend money to States and municipalities for self-liquidating public works and a Federal Home Loan Bank Act was passed to prevent home foreclosures. A "public works administration" was proposed to promote expansion of Government construction. In the presidential campaign of 1932 these and other measures intended to shore up the financial and industrial structure, relieve unemployment, and restore balance were rejected by the Democratic opposition as rampant socialism, encroachment of the Federal Government on States' rights, and radical spending of public funds.[33] By the summer of 1932 Hoover's influence was gone and a vast apathy, born of confusion and despair, settled over the Nation.

The Bureau gave no sign that it was in any way aware of the stock market crash of 1929. Its first recognition of "reduced industrial activities" occurred in mid-1931, following the collapse of Europe, with the note that "every effort [is being] made to operate economically." Still, the Bureau exhibited no alarm. That year in his annual report Dr. Burgess counted 525 projects under 22 research appropriations made to the Bureau, the largest number of projects ever. Both public and Government demands for tests continued to increase each year, and it was expected they would ac-

[31] Historical Statistics, p. 73. By comparison, at the height of the 1920–21 depression, unemployment did not rise above 5.01 million or 11.9 percent of the labor force.

[32] Leutenburg, The Perils of Prosperity, 1914–1932, p. 251; Dixon Wecter, The Age of the Great Depression, 1929–1941 (New York: Macmillan, 1948), p. 17.

[33] Arthur M. Schlesinger, Jr., The Age of Roosevelt: Crisis of the Old Order, 1919–1933 (Boston: Houghton Mifflin, 1957), pp. 416–417, 423, 433.

celerate "with returning prosperity."[34] Actually, from the viewpoint of appropriations, as Dr. Burgess wrote with great satisfaction to Gano Dunn of the Visiting Committee, 1931 had been "the banner year for the Bureau." Transferred funds and direct appropriations totaled more than $4 million, the largest sum in its history, exceeding even the appropriations of the war years. Besides increases in salaries, special appropriations, and transferred funds, almost a million dollars had been allocated for a new hydraulic laboratory, two radio stations, and some 15 acres of additional land to the north and west of the Bureau quadrangle.[35]

---

[34] NBS Annual Report 1931, pp. 1, 46. This report is the only one ever to state the number of projects carried on under each Bureau appropriation.

No special alarm, either, seems to have been felt at the Physikalisch-Technische Reichsanstalt (PTR), the Bureau's counterpart in Berlin. More interestingly, that year produced the only comparison between the Bureau and the PTR that has been found. Five years earlier, in 1926, Paul D. Foote while in Europe had written Dr. Burgess that from his observations the Bureau, with better equipment, now excelled the PTR in practically every line of work (letters in NBS Box 157, ID and IDP). A German article on the state of the PTR in 1931 confirmed Foote's reports.

By comparison with the NBS and Britain's National Physical Laboratory, the writer said, the PTR "in these past years, has considerably receded into the background." It had become preoccupied with testing to the exclusion of basic physical-technical research, it suffered from lack of team work, and the technically important work it should be doing for industry was instead being done by industry itself.

Where the NBS budget for 1929 amounted roughly to $2.75 million or 11.5 million RM, with a "material" (nonsalary) budget of 8.8 million RM, the PTR budget for 1931 of 1.5 million RM allowed but 400,000 RM for all material expenditures, of which only 170,000 RM were earmarked for research. As for productivity, "The staff of the Reichsanstalt would really have to consist of half-gods * * * to achieve the same results as the Bureau of Standards." J. Zenneck, "Werner von Siemens und die grundung der Physikalisch Technische Reichsanstalt," Munich Deutsches Museum Abh. u. Ber. 3, 13 (1931) L/C: AM101.M9743.

[35] Letter, Mar. 4, 1931 (NBS Box 330, ID). The National Hydraulic Laboratory established at the Bureau was described in Science, 72, 7 (1930), and Civil Eng., 1, 911 (1931).

Surveying the 9 major and 12 minor buildings spread over the Bureau heights, Burgess beheld "a varitable city of science." Outside Washington, the new radio research station on 17 acres at Beltsville, Md., was to be used to send continuous standard frequency signals to broadcasting stations, the station on 200 acres at Meadows, Md., to study upper atmosphere radio phenomena. Aviation engine testing, too rackety for the householders down on Connecticut Avenue, had been moved to a new station at Arlington, Va. Other field stations included that for radio aids to aviation at College, Park, Md., electric lamp inspection laboratories in the New York and Boston districts; farm waste stations at Ames, Iowa, and at Auburn and Tuscaloosa, Ala.; cement and concrete test stations at Northampton, Pa., and Denver, Colo.; cement, concrete, and miscellaneous materials test units at San Francisco, and ceramics research at Columbus, Ohio. Burgess, "The National Bureau of Standards," posthumously published in Sci. Mo. 36, 201 (1933). For an earlier report by Burgess on the Bureau plant, see Hearings * * * 1928 (Dec. 5, 1927), p. 43.

The Bureau was also fully staffed. Not long before, Dr. Burgess observed that "for the first time in many years the Bureau now has a complete administrative and scientific roster.[36] The addition of more than 300 new members in 1931 brought the total Bureau staff to 1,066, despite the recent loss of some of its best people who had left for better pay elsewhere.[37] In order to maintain this staff, Burgess proposed not only to operate as economically as possible but to give special attention to those activities "tending to relieve the business depression and unemployment," that is, industrial research, stimulation of new industries, standardization, and building and housing.[38]

The sense of well-being was brief. In the spring of 1932 Dr. Burgess learned that Bureau funds for the coming year were to be reduced by one-fifth, affecting every item in his budget.[39] But he did not live to see this disaster or the subsequent effects of the depression on the Bureau.

Six months previously, in October 1931, while presiding at a Wednesday meeting of his division chiefs, Dr. Burgess suffered a slight stroke resulting in a partial paralysis from which he recovered after 3 months of care.[40] A second and fatal stroke occurred on July 2, 1932, while he was working at his desk in South building. He had been with the Bureau for almost 30 of his 58 years.

Dr. Briggs, assistant director for research and testing, became acting director upon the death of Dr. Burgess. A week later Secretary of Commerce Robert P. Lamont wrote to the Visiting Committee asking its assistance in recommending a successor to Dr. Burgess. He was, Lamont said, a strong believer in filling vacancies from within the service and for that reason suggested Dr. Briggs's name. Charles F. Kettering, a senior member of the committee, replied that he himself did not know Briggs very well, but it had been his experience that it was often better to bring in someone from outside. The point was discussed in committee correspondence for several months. It was December before the Visiting Committee met and formally recommended Dr. Briggs.[41]

---

[36] NBS Annual Report 1926, p. 1.

[37] Letter, GKB to Office of Department of Commerce, June 11, 1930 (NBS Box 296, AP), named 28 in the professional group at the Bureau who had resigned since mid-1928. Memo, GKB for Secretary of Commerce Lamont, Apr. 16, 1932 (NBS Box 339, AG), told of 8 members of the automotive section, including its chief, who left in 1927 to set up a research department at the Studebaker Corp., at almost three times their Bureau salaries.

[38] Memo, GKB for Administrative Assistant to Secretary of Commerce, May 14, 1931 (NBS Box 331, IG).

[39] Science, 75, supp. 11 (April 1932).

[40] Letter, Lamont to Kettering, Oct. 30, 1931 (Department of Commerce, Visiting Committee file, NARG 40, 67009/5); Briggs at Hearings * * * 1933 (Jan. 8, 1932), p. 212.

[41] Letter, Lamont to K. T. Compton, July 13, 1932; letter, Kettering to Lamont, July 20, 1932; letter, Compton to Chapin, Dec. 1, 1932 (NARG 40, file 67009/5, pt. 2).

Dr. Lyman J. Briggs, third Director of NBS, in his 6th year as chief and 5th year of the New Deal. Under the glass top of his desk is an organization chart of the Bureau. The advice of Satchel Paige may also be under that glass, but this cannot be verified.

Receiving the recommendation from interim Secretary of Commerce Roy D. Chapin, Hoover offered Dr. Briggs's name to the Senate. In view of the imminent change of administrations, the Senate did not act on the appointment. In the patronage scramble of 1933, Roosevelt was pressed to name "a good Democrat" to the office. He is said to have replied: "I haven't the slightest idea whether Dr. Briggs is a Republican or a Democrat; all I know is that he is the best qualified man for the job." On March 27, 1933, Roosevelt renominated Dr. Briggs and on June 13 the Senate confirmed the appointment.[42]

Dr. Lyman J. Briggs (1874–1963), born the same year as Dr. Burgess, grew up on a farm north of Battle Creek, Mich. He acquired his copy of Ganot's Physics at 18, in his third year at Michigan State College. Transferring to the University of Michigan for graduate work, Briggs studied under Dr. Karl E. Guthe, who was to be chief of an electrical section at the Bureau of Standards in its early years. In 1895 Briggs graduated with a master of science in physics.[43] That same fall he entered the Johns Hopkins University, where he worked under Prof. Henry A. Rowland, investigating with him the recently discovered Roentgen rays.[44] But his principal interest had been fixed earlier at Michigan State, in what was then a new science called "soil physics." To learn more of the subject, and to support his approaching marriage, Briggs in June 1896 obtained a position as physicist in the Bureau of Soils of the Department of Agriculture.[45] His Hopkins thesis,

---

[42] Wallace R. Brode, "Lyman J. Briggs * * *," Sci. Mo. 78, 269 (1954).
The delay in acting on the nomination of Dr. Briggs was occasioned by efforts of certain members of the Senate to name a director of their own choice. Their candidate was Winder Elwell Goldsborough of Maryland, electrical engineer, teacher, inventor, businessman, and from 1923 to 1932 director of the Henry L. Doherty Research Laboratories. The impasse that ensued was apparently broken when Secretary Roper informed Goldsborough's sponsors that contrary to their belief "that he is a Democrat and entitled, because of this as well as because of his qualifications, to this position," he was in fact "a consistent Republican" (letter, Secretary Roper to Senators Harrison, Lonergan, and Sheppard, June 10, 1933 [NARG 40, Correspondence of Secretary of Commerce Roper, Box 24–S]). Additional correspondence on Goldsborough's candidacy, dating from September 1932, appears in NARG 40, file 93067).

[43] His thesis was published as Guthe and Briggs, "On the electrolytic conductivity of concentrated sulfuric acid," Phys. Rev. 3, np (1895).

[44] Rowland, Carmichael, and Briggs, "Notes of observations on the roentgen rays," Am. J. Sci. 1, 247 (1896); Rowland, Carmichael, and Briggs, "Notes on roentgen rays," Elec. World, 27, 452 (1896).

[45] At that time, according to Dr. Briggs, there were only three soil physicists in this country, Eugene W. Hilgard at California, Franklin H. King at Wisconsin, and Milton Whitney in the Department of Agriculture. Interview with Dr. Briggs, Nov. 1, 1962.

for which he received his doctoral degree in 1901, was on an aspect of the physical action of moisture in soil.[46]

Dr. Briggs headed the biophysical laboratory of the Bureau of Plant Industry, which he had organized in 1906, when he was detailed by Executive order to the Bureau of Standards upon America's entry into the war and set to work constructing a wind tunnel for aviation research.[47] Two years later he brought into his aviation physics section Hugh L. Dryden, a graduate student from Johns Hopkins, recommended by Professor Ames as "the brightest young man he had ever had, without exception." By then Briggs was wholly won to the study of aerodynamics and formally severed his connection with the Department of Agriculture. Briggs and Dryden were to remain closely associated throughout their careers at the Bureau.[48]

Chief of the mechanics and sound division when Stratton left the Bureau, Briggs had declined the proposal of the Visiting Committee that his name be submitted with that of Burgess for the directorship, saying that he considered Burgess the better fitted at the Bureau for the position. Soon after he became Director, Burgess asked Congress that a position of Assistant Director be established at the Bureau, to take over some of the burden of supervising research and testing. Dr. Briggs was offered the position and declined, but when in 1926 Secretary of Commerce Hoover proposed that Dr. Ray M. Hudson of his office be made Assistant Director at the Bureau, Burgess asked Briggs to reconsider. On September 29, 1927, two Assistant Directors were appointed, Briggs for research and testing and Hudson for commercial standardization.[49]

Dr. Brigg's assumption of the Director's chair after 6 years of supervising research and testing and a year as Acting Director was therefore without incident, except that it occurred at the nadir of the depression. He was already confronted with the task of preserving a working organization in the face of repeated reduction in salaries, staff, and programs, and was about to participate in a series of congressional and special committee inves-

[46] Briggs, "On the adsorption of water vapor and of certain salts in aqueous solution by quartz," J. Phys. Chem. 9, 617 (1905).

[47] The request for the transfer of Dr. Briggs to the Bureau said he was needed "in connection with the organization of a division for the purpose of certifying all gages in the manufacture of munitions." Letter, Secretary of Commerce to Secretary of Agriculture, May 22, 1917 (Department of Commerce records, NARG 40, file 67009/43). The gage work, however, remained a section in the division of weights and measures, and Dr. Briggs went into aeronautics.

[48] Interview with Dr. Briggs, Nov. 1, 1962. Dr. Dryden succeeded Briggs at the Bureau as section chief in 1922, as division chief in 1934, and as associate director in 1946, leaving in 1947, 2 years after Brigg's retirement, to become research director of the National Advisory Committee for Aeronautics.

[49] Interview with Dr. Briggs, Nov. 2, 1962. The positions are described in NBS Annual Report 1928, p. 1.

Dr. Eugene C. Crittenden, who came in 1904 to develop standards in photometry and remained 50 years, was to become the most knowledgeable man about NBS operations and activities and the Bureau's chief diplomat in negotiating national and international agreement on the establishment of new standards.

Dr. Hugh L. Dryden made some of this country's earliest studies of airfoil characteristics near the speed of sound. He was associate director of the Bureau until 1947, when he became research director of NACA, forerunner of NASA, and first deputy administrator of NASA when that agency was created in 1958.

tigations of Bureau operations, ordeals that deeply pained Dr. Briggs's gentle spirit. The time called for a ruggedness and ruthlessness he did not have, and in his later years he preferred not to think of the problems of that troubled era, turning questions about them to peripheral subjects more agreeable.

Unlike Stratton and Burgess, Dr. Briggs was of slight, slender build and of warm, affectionate, and unfailingly kind demeanor and manner. Dr. Stratton, when harassed by demands upon his time and attention or in a stormy mood, often sought out Briggs' company in his laboratory in West building, for as he once said: "You always have something nice to report to me and I appreciate it. These other fellows give me a lot of trouble." [50] The "something nice" was usually a new and ingenious piece of apparatus or testing device, for, like Stratton, Dr. Briggs was strongly mechanical and an inveterate tinkerer. When he came from the Department of Agriculture he brought with him his mechanic, Mr. Cottrell, and for years the two designed and constructed many of the special devices that Briggs used in his measurement studies.[51] His laboratory was a wonderful clutter of apparatus in various stages of assembly, a tangle of piping and tubing and ticking instruments, but it was comfortable and a tranquil spirit filled it.

His serenity of temper was Dr. Briggs's outstanding characteristic, and he was to have need of it under the frustrations of the depression years and the pressures and harassments of security in World War II. Asked after he resigned the direction of the Bureau and returned to his laboratory for the secret of his unfailing patience, he liked to say that the "precepts of that great philosopher and baseball player, Satchel Paige," best summed up his own:

> Avoid fried meats which angry up the blood.
>
> If your stomach disputes you, lie down and pacify it with cool thoughts.
>
> Keep the juices flowing by jangling around gently as you move.
>
> Go very lightly on the vices, such as carrying on in society. The social ramble ain't restful.
>
> Avoid running at all times.
>
> Don't look back. Something might be gaining on you.

The last was the precept he set greatest store by and delighted to quote at interviews.[52]

Dr. Briggs had two outside enthusiasms during his years at the Bureau, scientific exploration and baseball. Succeeding Dr. Burgess on the board of trustees of the National Geographic Society, Dr. Briggs took a highly

---

[50] Interview with Dr. Briggs, Nov. 3, 1962.
[51] Interview with Dr. Dryden, Aug. 26, 1963.
[52] The NBS Standard, April 1963; interview, Nov. 2, 1962.

active interest in its expeditions, and in his laboratory supervised the design and construction of many of the scientific instruments required by the Society. In the 17 years he held the chairmanship of the research committee of the Society, he personally directed or was closely involved in its many expeditions.[53]

Well past retirement age when he left the Director's office, Dr. Briggs spent the last years of his long life in his old laboratory in West building. A baseball player while at Michigan State and avid fan in the stands at Griffith Stadium in Washington, he was in his 85th year when he determined to settle a long disputed phenomenon: scientific proof of the degree a baseball can be made to curve in the 60-foot throw from the pitcher's box to the plate. With the aid of the wind tunnel he designed in 1918 and the pitching staff of the Washington Senators, he made a series of quantitative measurements of the relation of spin to deflection of a pitched baseball at various speeds.

In laboratory tests to measure spin, Dr. Briggs repeatedly projected baseballs, rotated on a rubber tee to provide spin, out of a mounted air gun at a paper target 60 feet away. Air flow phenomena were measured in the wind tunnel, and still other studies with a suspended camera measured the curvature of the ball in flight. Finally, at Griffith Stadium, members of the pitching staff hurled endless balls to which light, flat tapes were fastened, and the number of completed turns in the twisted tape were counted at home plate.

With baseballs thrown at a speed of 100 feet per second, roughly 68 miles per hour, and well within a professional pitcher's capability, Briggs recorded lateral deflections in the 60-foot flight from the pitcher's box of 11.7 inches at 1,200 revolutions per minute and 17.5 inches at 1,800 revolutions per minute as the maximums attainable. The spin rather than the speed of the ball, he found, determined its "break." The feat, reported in every newspaper in the country, was a logical development in the field of mechanics, Dr. Briggs said, closely related to the low-speed ballistics and projectile work of the Bureau. And it had been fun.[54]

As the new Director, Dr. Briggs presided over a temporary eclipse of the Bureau. For several years his paramount concern was to hold on to his scientific staff by all means available and to justify research that was not immediately productive of depression-thwarting results.[55] Throughout the decade he was aware of something less than enthusiasm on the part of the

---

[53] See below, pp. 355–357.

[54] Briggs, "Effect of spin and speed on the lateral deflection (curve) of a baseball; and the Magnus effect for smooth spheres," Am. J. Phys. 27, 589 (1959); interview, Nov. 2, 1962.

[55] Letter, LJB to Secretary of Commerce, Oct. 10, 1932 (NBS Box 339, AG).

Dr. Briggs, Director Emeritus, and Mr. Ossie Bluege, comptroller of the Washington Baseball Club and formerly third baseman and manager, at Griffith Stadium in 1959, measuring the spin of a pitched ball with the aid of a flat measuring tape fastened to the ball.

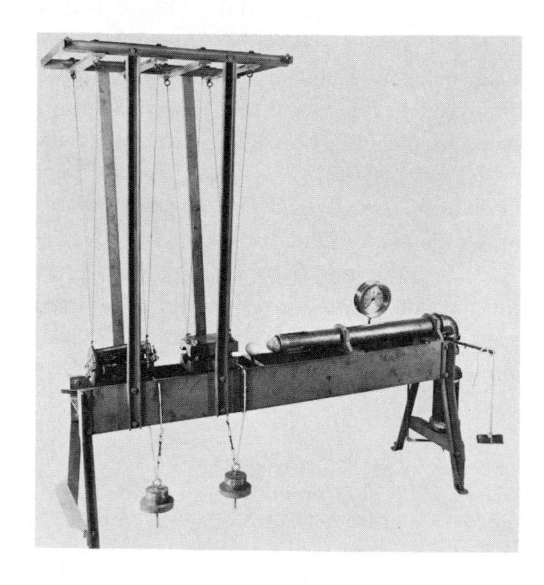

The baseball impact machine constructed at the Bureau for measuring the coefficient of restitution (evidences of liveliness) of baseballs.

new administration toward his organization. The stature of the Bureau in the Department of Commerce and its close identity with industry and commerce linked it with the policies of the Hoover administration and therefore the depression.

Daniel C. Roper, Roosevelt's appointee as Secretary of Commerce, said that his Department, "important under normal conditions, was at this time suffering from the fact that business was in the doghouse." [56] On the other hand, as a living memorial to Herbert Hoover, it was "looked upon by Congress as the 'last stronghold of sanity in the New Deal.' " [57] To the New Dealers the Department, whose body of civil servants continued in office during the greater part of the Roosevelt administration, was anathema. At the very outset of the new administration, Sam G. Bratton, Senator from New Mexico, went so far as to propose a joint House and Senate committee "to consider the advisability of abolishing the Department of Commerce and the transfer of its indispensable services to other agencies." [58]

The threat of dispersal persisted, and some thought it imminent when at the start of his second term Roosevelt proposed legislation to reorganize the departments of the Government. Ignored at Cabinet meetings and unable to gain the President's ear, Roper wrote to his bureau chiefs asking them whether they had "knowledge of any proposed action by other Government agencies or by Congress looking to transfer of your Bureau or any part of it from the Department." [59] The bureau chiefs knew no more than the Secretary. Badgered by rumors at fourth and fifth hand "that there would not be much left of the Department of Commerce after this reorganization," Secretary Roper resigned in December 1939 to make way for Harry Hopkins.[60] The talk of reorganization ended.

Apart from the drastic cuts made in its funds, the Bureau was in no way further endangered by the political trafficking downtown. Yet through-

---

[56] Roper, Fifty Years of Public Life (Durham, N.C.: Duke University Press, 1941), p. 288.

[57] Grace Tully, F.D.R.—My Boss (New York: Scribner, 1949), p. 196.

[58] Congressional Record, vol. 76, pt. 2, 72d Cong., 2d sess., 1933, pp. 1720–1721. The National Association of Manufacturers maintained that "throughout both the New Deal and the war production programs, Commerce was all but ignored. Special agencies and executive offices were created by the dozen to perform functions that should naturally have fallen to this department." Hearings * * * on First Deficiency Appropriation Bill for 1946 (Oct. 25, 1945), p. 320.

[59] Letter, Administrative Assistant to Secretary of Commerce to Heads of Bureaus, June 29, 1938, and attached correspondence (NBS Box 414, AG).

[60] Roper, Fifty Years of Public Life, pp. 347–348.

out the period the recurring tremors had their effect in the office of the Director out on Connecticut Avenue.

TOWARD A REDEFINITION OF BUREAU FUNCTIONS

Out of the welter of emergency measures, experiments, and planned programs of the new administration, three impinged importantly on the Bureau: the initial drive for economy in Federal spending, the effort to define the relations between Government and non-Government research, and the exertions on behalf of the common man in his role as ultimate consumer.

Campaigning on a platform of Federal frugality, Roosevelt on taking office ordered a slash of 25 percent in the funds of every Government department and agency, making it retroactive by impounding current as well as projected appropriations. The 10-percent cut in Government salaries voted by the previous administration in the Economy Act of June 30, 1932, had necessitated an 8-day furlough without pay for all at the Bureau but had not cut the staff.[61] As a result of the new 25-percent slash, almost one-third of the Bureau force was dismissed, and to stretch remaining funds, a second payless 8-day furlough was decreed for those not separated.[62]

In mobilizing the resources of the Nation for recovery, Roosevelt exercised his penchant for creating new agencies, particularly in order to bypass such of his executive departments as seemed to him ingrown and incapable of adapting to the New Deal emergency.[63] His precedents were the all-powerful agencies of World War I, his guide Bernard Baruch's report on the War Industries Board of 1918, which Baruch in 1931 had supplemented with a detailed program for the creation of a central agency to control industrial

---

[61] Letter, Secretary of Commerce Chapin to Visiting Committee, Nov. 10, 1932 (NARG 40, file 67009/5).

[62] Schlesinger, The Age of Roosevelt: Crisis of the Old Order, p. 256; NBS Annual Report 1933, p. 45; Annual Report 1934, pp. 51, 75. Hearings * * * 1935 (Jan. 4, 1934), p. 131.

A startling economy proposed by Roosevelt in late 1932 involved transfer of the National Advisory Committee on Aeronautics to the Bureau of Standards. NACA's Langley Field Laboratory was to be maintained as an independent agency, but considerable savings in the NACA budget of $900,000 were anticipated in consolidating its Washington staff with that of the Bureau. Questioned at a House committee hearing about the transfer, Dr. Briggs admitted he had not been consulted, but he "liked" it, and pointed out that in Britain, aeronautical research had always been under the National Physical Laboratory (Hearings * * * 1934, Dec. 12, 1932, pp. 175–77). NACA, now the National Aeronautics and Space Administration (NASA), which had strong roots in Bureau aeronautics research, was not of course turned over to the Bureau.

[63] Schlesinger, The Age of Roosevelt: The Coming of the New Deal, 1933–1934 (Boston: Houghton Mifflin, 1958), pp. 534–535.

mobilization in the event of war.[64] That war had come, a war of relief, recovery, and reform.

As the major experiments of the New Deal's planned economy, industry was mobilized through the National Recovery Administration (NRA), agriculture through the Agricultural Adjustment Administration (AAA). Science was not included in the planning. As the adjunct of industry, identified with laissez faire and classical economics and divorced from modern economic theory, science was suspect. To find a possible future place for it in the social experiments of the New Deal, however, called for a reassessment of the scientific agencies in the Government and the role of Government in both the physical and social sciences.[65]

To that end, on July 31, 1933, an Executive order created a Science Advisory Board under the jurisdiction of the National Research Council and National Academy of Sciences to study the functions and programs of the principal scientific agencies of the Government and propose a more effective relationship between governmental and nongovernmental research organizations. It was to examine the place of science in the Government structure with a view to establishing a policy both for economic recovery and for future national welfare.[66] As it turned out, the Board at once became more concerned with the current plight of Federal research agencies than with the goal that was sought by the New Deal, namely, to effect a conjunction between the natural and social sciences that would provide solutions pointing the way out of the depression.

The Bureau of Standards came under special scrutiny during the study, since four of the nine members of the Science Advisory Board—its chairman, Karl T. Compton, and Gano Dunn, Charles F. Kettering, and

---

[64] The two Baruch reports were reprinted in a special edition as American Industry in the War: a Report of the War Industries Board, with an introduction by Hugh S. Johnson (New York: Prentice-Hall, 1941). For Roosevelt's great interest in Wilson's wartime administration, see Roper, Fifty Years of Public Life, pp. 320 ff.

[65] Dupree, pp. 347–350.

An extremist point of view then current saw science as a cause of the depression. Notice of the charge that the physicist and chemist made discoveries too rapidly for the good of the world, and did not heed or care what misapplications were made of their discoveries, appeared in Science, 80, 535 (1934) and Science, 81, 46 (1935). For the opposite viewpoint, that this country had succumbed to the depression because it had lived on its resources and had not put science to work for the national welfare or to combat its present difficulties, see Science Advisory Board correspondence in NBS Box 382, ID-Misc.

[66] Science Advisory Board, Report, 1933–34 (Washington, D.C., 1934), pp. 9, 11, 13, 15, 40–42. The Board reported scientific services functioning in 41 Federal bureaus, of which 18, on which the Board focussed its attention, could be called primarily scientific and essential to the national welfare, in agriculture, manufacturing, commerce, health and safety (p. 12).

Frank B. Jewett—were on the Visiting Committee to the Bureau. As it happened, the Visiting Committee was already engaged in a study of Bureau problems. The same four men were also members of the Business Advisory and Planning Council, which had recently been appointed by Secretary of Commerce Roper to survey the program of research of the Bureau and other Commerce agencies in the light of the economies forced on them. Thus, the Bureau entertained simultaneously three investigative groups in 1933–34. Except for details in the reports of the two Commerce committees, the essential findings of all three groups were by agreement embodied in the comprehensive report of the President's Science Advisory Board.

Perceptibly waiving the purpose for which it had been created, at least so far as the Bureau of Standards was concerned, the Board declared that the drastic reductions in its funds "prompted a critical examination of the Bureau's situation and program." [67] The slashes in Bureau appropriations for 1933 and 1934, together with the impounding of funds, amounted to a reduction of 50 percent since 1932. But Bureau testing of materials for Government departments and State institutions, an essential service not specified in the organic act or explicitly provided for in appropriations, represented a fixed charge of 45 percent against Bureau funds. The actual reduction in Bureau funds since 1932 therefore amounted not to 50 percent *but to about 70 percent* [italicized in the Report].[68] In the same period the Bureau staff had been reduced by 200 to 300 members through separation or indefinite furlough.[69] This much the three investigating groups agreed upon, and noted with concern the necessary but serious drain on Bureau time and energies involved in its representation on 825 committees in scientific, engineering, testing, standardizing, interdepartmental, and international organizations.[70]

In its separate study, the Business Advisory group acknowledged the validity of much of the late criticism of the Bureau by industry and urged that the greatest economies be made in some of the more recently acquired functions giving offense. Somewhat more specifically, the Joint Committee recommended curtailment of those projects which were in a

[67] Science Advisory Board, Report, 1933–34, p. 23.

[68] Dr. Briggs described the actual working funds even of the full 1932 appropriation as "only the equivalent of one 3-cent postage stamp during the year for each inhabitant of this country" (Ann. Am. Acad. Pol. Sci. 173, 153, 1934).

[69] The total was 348, out of a staff of 979, according to memo, C. J. Humphreys for LJB, July 31, 1933 (NBS Box 358, ID).

[70] Science Advisory Board, Report, 1933–34, pp. 23, 62–63, 65. By February 1934, with 613 members, the Bureau had the smallest staff since 1917 (letter, LJB to F. J. Schlink, Feb. 3, 1934, NBS Historical File).

measure completed or could be continued by non-Government agencies, and elimination of all others, insofar as they left the basic functions of the Bureau unimpaired. Those functions, vital to the industries of the Nation, must be maintained on an effective basis at all costs.[71]

The Business Advisory group particularly argued against the commercial standards activities of the Bureau as not matters of scientific fact and accuracy but matters of convenience. Every one of these activities had created problems of one kind or another, now made acute by the enforced economy.[72] Similar conflicts had arisen in the Bureau's industrial research, and the Business Advisory group therefore recommended that Bureau research should be strictly limited to the development of fundamental standards for science, medicine, and industry.[73]

The Science Advisory Board, equally concerned about the reduced funds of the Bureau and the necessity for some adjustment in its activities, was both less drastic and more concrete in its recommendations. It urged that official approval be given to a redefinition of Bureau functions it proposed that would formalize current Bureau activities and, of more import, that direct appropriations be made to cover the testing work of the Bureau for Federal agencies.[74]

---

[71] Minutes of the joint meeting of the Visiting Committee of the Bureau of Standards and the Committee on the Bureau of Standards of the Business Advisory and Planning Council, Dec. 5, 1933 (NARG 40, Box 114, file 67009/5).

[72] The report traced the progress of Bureau acquisition of these activities, from the work on safety codes in the early century through building and housing codes, standards and specifications for Federal and State purchasing agencies, and testing of materials purchased by the Government. Closely allied were the trade standards and simplified practices programs for industry.

[73] Report of the Committee on the Bureau of Standards of the Business Advisory and Planning Council, Dec. 9, 1933, pp. 15–16 (NARG 40, file 67009/5).

[74] Science Advisory Board, Report, 1933–34, pp. 67–68. The proposed Bureau functions (ibid., pp. 64–65), harmonizing those of the organic act with those subsequently sanctioned by acts of Congress, were:

1. To maintain the national standards of measurement and conduct research necessary for the development of such standards.
2. To calibrate and certify measuring instruments in terms of the national standards, for the Federal Government and the various States (without charge), and for scientific, engineering and industrial groups and individuals (at cost), in order that accurate and uniform standards of measurement may be used throughout the Nation.
3. To develop improved methods of measurement for use in industry, engineering, and scientific research.
4. To determine physical constants and the properties of materials and physical systems "when such data are of great importance to scientific or manufacturing

Nothing like formal approval of the new functions was considered, although the Board later reported that the restatement was "to a large degree * * * officially approved" by the appropriations act of 1935. That act replaced the 29 specific appropriation items in the budget of the previous year by grouping the work of the Bureau into 4 general funds: (1) for operation and administration, (2) testing, inspection, and information service, (3) research and development, and (4) standards for commerce, the latter to provide for Bureau cooperation in the work of the American Standards Association.[75]

Turning from its extended study of the Bureau and other scientific agencies in the Federal establishment, the Science Advisory Board briefly

---

interests and are not to be obtained of sufficient accuracy elsewhere" [quoted from the organic act].

5. To serve, insofar as is practicable, as a centralized laboratory for physical, chemical and engineering investigations for governmental agencies, thus utilizing effectively the special facilities of the Bureau, avoiding unnecessary duplication among Government agencies and preventing unnecessary development of new laboratories in the future.
6. To conduct investigations looking to broader and more effective utilization of materials and the development of better processes and methods of fabrication, in cooperation and with the financial assistance of engineering societies, trade associations, industrial and consumer groups, provided such investigations are of public and governmental interest.
7. To cooperate with the Federal Specifications Board and national standardizing agencies in the development of (a) specifications for equipment and supplies, and (b) safety and engineering codes; and to conduct research when necessary to provide a satisfactory technical basis for such specifications and codes.
8. To serve as a testing agency for governmental purchases to determine whether purchases of equipment, materials, and supplies meet the purchase specifications.
9. In connection with national standardizing organizations to develop simplified practice recommendations and commercial standards in cooperation with manufacturers, distributors, and consumers, provided such activities are of public and governmental interest; and to encourage the use of nationally recognized specifications by purchasing agencies expending funds derived from taxes.
10. To serve Federal, State and municipal agencies in an advisory capacity on technical matters in the fields of physics, chemistry, and engineering; and to indicate to citizens of the United States, upon request, available technical information relating to these subjects.

[75] Science Advisory Board, Report, 1934–35 (Washington, D.C., 1935), pp. 52–53; letter, LJB to Secretary, SAB, Aug. 6, 1935 (NBS Box 383, IDS–SAB).

The House Appropriations Committee had suggested consolidation of Bureau funds to Dr. Stratton in 1922. But special appropriations had served him well and he hesitated. "On the whole," he had replied, "it is not a bad plan. * * * The best thing from many points of view is to have a lump sum for all purposes to carry on * * * research work, but on the other hand it is good business to have a specific appropriation for a specific thing" (Hearings * * * 1924, Nov. 16, 1922, p. 207). In his annual reports of 1927 and 1928, Dr. Burgess strongly recommended to Commerce consolidation of funds into three or four classes, to simplify office procedure.

considered the relation between governmental and nongovernmental research. The Board saw "no need for the Government to embark upon comprehensive programs on pure science, invention or industrial development." That was the province of industry, the universities, and private institutions.[76] The proper scientific activities of the Government, which alone justified its scientific bureaus, were "scientific services of such wide scope and universal utility that no agency except the Government is competent adequately to handle them" (e.g., the development of scientific and technical standards); those "essentially supplementary to nonscientific governmental activities" (e.g., standards for Government purchases); and those "which hold evident promise of benefiting the public but which are not proper or practical fields for private initiative" (e.g., NACA).[77]

The "social objectives of science," whose consideration had been a prime purpose in the creation of the Board, appeared in a section awkwardly entitled, "Recovery Program of Science Progress." In effect, the Board recommended a new deal for science based on enlistment of "the science and engineering groups in the country in a cooperative effort for the quick success of the National Industrial Recovery Program." But the proposal that a fund of $16 million (subsequently raised to $75 million) be spent over a period of 5 years on research for public works programs, for

---

[76] The discussion of the "place of science in the Government" in the reports of the Science Advisory Board (1933–34, pp. 15–17; 1934–35, pp. 40, 269) reflected the concern of the National Research Council since the end of World War I for fundamental research in this country.

A recurring anxiety voiced in the 1920's was that the war years had used up the basic research of the previous century and it was not being adequately replaced. Industrial research laboratories annually spent almost $200 million on applied science, Secretary of Commerce Hoover wrote in 1925, while funds for all pure research did not exceed $10 million. Yet the applied science laboratories were wholly "dependent upon the raw material which flows from the laboratories and men engaged in pure science. And the industrial investigators are the first to demand more support to pure science."

> It is unfortunately true [Hoover declared] that we can claim no such rank in pure science research as that which we enjoy in the field of industrial research. Instead of leading all other countries in the advancement of fundamental scientific knowledge, the United States occupies a position far in the rear of the majority of European nations. A list of the awards of the Nobel prizes to men of various nationalities reveals the small proportion of first rank minds that we support. Other tests lead to the same conclusion, namely, that the number of first rank investigators developed in the United States is far below what our population, education, and wealth would lead one to expect.

("The vital need for greater financial support of pure science research," an address before Am. Soc. Mech. Eng., Dec. 1, 1925, reprinted by National Research Council [L/C: Q11.N293]). See also Dupree, Science in the Federal Government, pp. 340–343.

[77] Science Advisory Board, Report, 1934–35, p. 15 and n.

conservation, and for the creation of new industries was not apparently what the administration had in mind. The Science Advisory Board was dissolved.[78]

The year 1935 came and the depression persisted. The WPA and other relief agencies were at their peak, giving work to 20 million persons, and Federal employees, numbering 588,000 when the depression began, headed toward the total of 1,370,000 reached in 1941. But across the Nation over 11 million remained unemployed and close to that same number would still be unemployed on the eve of war.[79]

Industry was moving again but cautiously, and consumers, growing wary of the rising public debt, tended to hoard the little they had. To the economists and social scientists of the administration more planning was the answer. To scientists, including Dr. Briggs, who wrote and spoke repeatedly on the subject, new discoveries, inventions, and enterprises were needed to prime the economy, stimulate the consumer, and start up industry again.[80]

Federal agencies, notably the Public Works Administration (PWA), successfully employed tens of thousands in reclaiming and developing the natural resources of the country, completing Boulder [Hoover] Dam in Nevada and the Triboro Bridge in New York, harnessing the Mississippi,

---

[78] Science Advisory Board, Report, 1933–34, pp. 267 ff.; Dupree, Science in the Federal Government, pp. 353–358.

[79] Schlesinger, Coming of the New Deal, p. 294; Wecter, The Age of the Great Depression, p. 82.

[80] Dr. Briggs's promise of "rich returns in employment in new industries" was made repeatedly, in a speech of Mar. 25, 1936 (NBS Box 400, PAC), memoranda for the Secretary of Commerce between July 26 and Nov. 4, 1936 (NBS Box 394, AG; Box 400, PA; Box 401, PRA); letter to the Civil Service Commission, Dec. 22, 1936 (NBS Box 394, AP).

Before the House Appropriations Subcommittee in 1938, Briggs said: "We need more industries in this country; but new industries must have something to work with—new facts, new discoveries which they can develop. To get new discoveries and new facts we must support research" (Hearings * * * 1939, Jan. 31, 1938, p. 139).

Stimulated as much by the need to replenish the stock of pure science as to create out of it new industries that would absorb some of the unemployed, Roosevelt from 1936 to 1941 gave his approval to a number of bills proposed in both the House and Senate designed to support programs of basic research in physics, chemistry, metallurgy, and engineering. In several of the bills the research was to be carried out by the National Bureau of Standards and other nonprofit research institutions, through grants administered by the Bureau and the National Research Council. Other bills proposed basic research stations affiliated with State universities, in cooperation with the Department of Commerce, or engineering experimental stations at the land-grant colleges, on the model of the Department of Agriculture experimental stations. To Dr. Briggs, the most promising was the Lea bill (H.R. 3652), proposed in 1939, which called for almost $60 million to be expended over a period of years, 75 percent of that sum going to research in the natural sciences and engineering. Half of the funds were to be appropriated to the Bureau, the other half to universities for specific research projects. By June 1941, as war approached and debate continued, all chances of enactment ended. See correspondence in NBS Blue Folder Boxes 30, 31, 58.

setting up the Tennessee Valley Authority, and planning hydroelectric power dams such as that at Passamaquoddy Bay.[81] But science proved unamenable to planning. In the latter half of the decade, the National Planning Board and its successors, the National Resources Board and National Resources Committee, all sought, unsuccessfully, to establish a sound Federal relation with scientific research that would harness the scientific resources of the Nation.[82]

As stirring in its implications for the Bureau as the search for the role of Government in scientific research was the revival in the thirties of concern for the consumer. In the national emergency of 1918, Bernard Baruch had shown the possibilities of an economy oriented to "engineered consumption" instead of uncontrolled production for individual profit. A controlling idea in the early years of the New Deal was the plan to shift from a producer economy to a consumer economy. Thus arose "consumerism" as a major remedy for the depression, its mystique in the recent books of Stuart Chase, Schlink, Kallet, and others.[83]

Hope for Government support and direction of consumer interests centered in the National Recovery Administration, Roosevelt's chief prescription for recovery, set up on June 16, 1933, as a cooperative system of industrial self-government under Federal supervision. Under an NRA code system, industry, in exchange for Federal aid in regulating prices, would increase minimum wages and shorten work hours, thereby accelerating consumption. To maintain a balance between the interests of management, labor, and the consumer, NRA was to have the advice of three official boards, an Industrial Board, to secure the cooperation of the trade associations in support of NRA codes; a Labor Advisory Board, to work with the labor

---

[81] Among civic structures whose completion provided much needed employment was the new monumental Commerce Building at 14th and E Streets in Washington, its cornerstone laid on Apr. 5, 1929. Its acres of office space, reported the "New York Sun," were to house all the scattered activities of Commerce "except * * * the experimental gentlemen of the Bureau of Standards—perhaps the most interesing single agency of the Government of these United States" (file in NBS Box 263, AG).

[82] The remarkable "study of Federal Aids to Research and the place of research (including natural and social sciences) in the Federal Government," prepared by the science subcommittee of the National Resources Committee, under Dr. Charles H. Judd, University of Chicago psychologist, made two notable recommendations, destined to be implemented in the vast Federal research programs of World War II and after: That research agencies of the Government be authorized and encouraged to enter into contracts for the prosecution of research projects with * * * recognized research agencies, and that research agencies of the Government extend the practice of encouraging decentralized research in institutions not directly related to the Government and by individuals not in its employ. National Resources Committee, Research—A National Resource. I. Relation of the Federal Government to Research (Washington, D.C., November 1938), p. 2.

[83] Schlesinger, The Coming of the New Deal, pp. 128–130.

unions; and a Consumers' Advisory Board, to represent consumer interests.[84] A brief account of the latter agency as it impinged on the Bureau of Standards is of interest.

The Consumers' Advisory Board was charged with promoting greater use of specifications and labeling in consumer products by recommending such provisions in NRA codes. It was assumed that the necessary consumer standards could be promulgated in existing Government and Government-connected agencies. A committee of the Board, headed by Dr. Robert S. Lynd, professor of sociology at Columbia University, disagreed. In a report made public on December 1, 1933, the committee declared that the American Standards Association, the Bureau of Standards and other available agencies were so strongly oriented to the point of view of industry that they could not be entrusted with the task.[85]

The Lynd report aroused wide interest, but its proposal for an independent consumers' research laboratory wholly within the Government was turned down.[86] During its brief career, the Consumers' Advisory Board, without facilities of its own, had to rely on the Bureau and the ASA for its research and testing. The Bureau reviewed almost 500 of some 830 NRA codes of fair competition involving consumer standards that the Board submitted.[87] ASA, asked to aid in quality labeling of consumer goods, set up its Committee on Ultimate Consumer Goods, on which the Bureau was also represented. But neither agency, nor NRA itself, satisfied the requisites of the Board, and with the death of the NRA in 1935 went its hopes for some kind of Federal department of the consumer.[88]

---

[84] More than 2.5 million firms enrolled under the Blue Eagle and nearly 800 trade associations came to Washington for their codes before enthusiasm for the NRA waned and cynical violations began to vitiate its promise. On May 27, 1935, the Supreme Court declared invalid the NRA as an attempt to control the national economy through regulation of intrastate commerce.

[85] See Paul G. Agnew, "The movement for standards for consumer goods," Ann. Am. Acad. Pol. Soc. Sci. 173, 60 (1934).

[86] Persia Campbell, Consumer Representation in the New Deal (New York: Columbia University Press, 1940), p. 49.
Bolder than Lynd's laboratory was Schlink's proposal for a Federal Department of the Consumer, to be comprised of the oil, gas, coke, and fuel laboratories of the Bureau of Mines, all of the Bureau of Standards, the Office of Education, and the Bureaus of Home Economics, Chemistry, and Entomology in the Department of Agriculture. Schlink, "What the Government does and might do for the consumer," Ann. Am. Acad. Pol. Soc. Sci. 173, 125 (1934).

[87] NBS Annual Report 1934, p. 74; correspondence in NBS Blue Folder Box 19, 669c–CAB.

[88] Helen Sorenson, The Consumer Movement (New York: Harper, 1941), pp. 183–184. Campbell, pp. 54, 172, reported that the influence of CAB recommendations on NRA codes was negligible.

The consumer movement responded to a real public need and persisted as a militant force throughout the decade, but it was unable to present the united front, as did industry, labor, and agriculture, necessary to make a place for itself in the alphabetical agencies of the New Deal.[89] Sparking that movement, Schlink and Chase in 1927 had brought out their Consumers' Research Bulletin, as a mimeographed letter of the Consumers' League of New York. Two years later, upon the acquisition of laboratory facilities, the Bulletin appeared under the imprimatur of Consumers' Research, Inc. In 1933 the Consumers' Council of the Agricultural Adjustment Administration (AAA) inaugurated a biweekly Consumers' Guide, and in 1936 Arthur Kallet's organization, Consumers Union, began publication of Consumer Reports. A number of city and State agencies established consumer laboratories, as did the "New York Herald-Tribune" and the magazines Delineator, Modern Priscilla, and Good Housekeeping. By the end of the decade, as textbooks became available, some 25,000 secondary schools were giving consumer education courses, and in 1937 Stephens College, in Missouri, set up one of the first of the college and university consumer laboratories.[90]

The Bureau, as its extensive correspondence files witness, was never entirely happy in its relations with these consumer groups. It was, by law and organization, oriented to industry, as the Consumers' Advisory Board said. Schlink's avowed objective in setting up his Consumers' Research was "to translate everything that the National Bureau of Standards and the National Physical Laboratory [in England] had done into consumer terms."[91] But except in the most general terms, this was not possible with the technical reports of the Bureau, since its tests centered on the determination of those physical properties and characteristics of commodities or materials which made them most suitable for Government use. Efforts of Schlink and others to obtain useful and authoritative test results from the Bureau by sending consumer products to its laboratories had to be rebuffed. They were referred to commercial testing laboratories.[92]

---

[89] Sorenson, pp. 19, 20.

[90] Wecter, p. 279. Among widely used textbooks were Charles S. Wyand's The Economics of Consumption (New York: Macmillan, 1937), Alfred H. Hausrath and John H. Harms's Consumer Science (New York: Macmillan, 1939), and Leland J. Gordon's Economics for Consumers (New York: American Book Co.. 1939).

[91] Interview with F. J. Schlink, June 7, 1962.

[92] See Consumers' Research General Bulletin, II, 309 (January 1933); public and congressional correspondence with the Bureau, largely incited by Schlink's publication, in NBS Box 356, AG; Schlink's own correspondence with the Bureau, in NBS Box 400, AG; and D. W. McConnell, "The Bureau of Standards and the ultimate consumer," Ann. Am. Acad. Pol. Soc. Sci. 173, 146 (1934).

The Bureau acknowledged that consumer testing might well be a function of the Federal Government and that it ought to be concentrated in a single institution. Indeed, the Bureau frequently expressed itself as willing to become that agency. It doubted, however, whether Congress was ever likely to appropriate the estimated hundred million dollars annually that a really comprehensive program of consumer testing would cost.[93]

Although oriented to research for industry by the nature of its organic act, the Bureau insisted that its ultimate beneficiary was the consumer, whether represented by a public purchasing agency or private citizen. It was therefore in sympathy with the consumer movement and did what it could. Besides its assistance to the Consumers' Advisory Board it advised consumer laboratories on test instruments and equipment and developed new equipment, such as the standard abrasion machine for the American Home Economics Association, to measure the durability of textiles. It revised its directory of commercial laboratories that tested consumer products, issued a letter circular on "the availability to the public of research and testing facilities of the National Bureau of Standards," and issued periodically its list of "publications of interest to household purchasers." [94] Perhaps most widely circulated was the illustrated brochure, "Services of the National Bureau of Standards to the consumer," which went through five printings totaling 15,000 copies between 1937 and 1940. Besides explaining the relation of Bureau testing to over-the-counter buying, the brochure informed readers of the Bureau's useful mimeographed letter, "Aid for over the counter buyers," and of the range of letter circulars and published reports of

[93] Letter, Crittenden for LJB to Prof. Robert S. Lynd, Nov. 15, 1933, and letter, Crittenden to Executive Secretary, Peoples Lobby, Inc., June 16, 1949 (NBS Historical File); Hearings * * * 1939 (Jan. 31, 1938), p. 138.

In a resurgence of interest in the consumer in 1938–39, several bills were proposed in Congress to extend the services of the Bureau to consumer testing, one of them authorizing an initial sum of $250,000 to "provide performance standards in the public interest," and permit the Bureau to grant firms and factories the right to label tested goods as "U.S. Consumer Standard," such standards to be policed by the Federal Trade Commission. Letter, LJB to Secretary of Commerce, June 14, 1939 (NBS Blue Folder Box 19, 669c); letter, Assistant Secretary of Commerce to Gano Dunn, Visiting Committee, Sept. 15, 1939 ("General Correspondence Files of the Director, 1945–1955"); LJB correspondence in NBS Box 430, ID-Misc; letter, LJB to Wm. E. Ames, Jan. 3, 1940, and attached correspondence (NBS Box 445, IG).

[94] M125 (1927), revised 1936; LC490 (February 1937); LC322 (1932), superseded by LC416 (1934), LC586 (1940), LC696 (1942), LC849 (1946). See letter LJB to Department of Agriculture, Aug. 6, 1927 (NBS Box 428, SPD), for a complete listing of Bureau publications of consumer interest.

interest and use in the purchase of hundreds of products from automobiles to window glass.[95]

The failure of national consumer interests to mobilize Government action on their behalf recoiled on the Bureau. Its products testing and its continued association in the specifications, simplified practices, and commodity standards work even after that work was transferred to ASA in 1933 sustained the hopes of consumer groups and kept the Bureau in something of a bind for the next two decades. As late as 1952 the Bureau still found it necessary to maintain a form letter explaining the limitations inherent in its testing of products for Government and industry and why it could not issue comparative ratings of brand-name commodities.

Despite the alarms, apprehensions, and hardships of the period, many of the seniors at the Bureau later remembered the time of the depression as not unrelievedly bleak. The respite in committee assignments, curtailment of travel, and decline in supervisory duties left welcome time for research. The paper load was further lightened as testing, which had long accounted for almost half of all annual funds and occupied more than half the time of the staff, fell off.

It was a time of moratoriums and petty economies. The annual conference on weights and measures, first postponed in 1932, was not resumed until 3 years later. The Director's annual report was reduced by half and printed with that of the Secretary of Commerce. The master scale depot at Chicago, the farm-waste laboratory at Tuscaloosa, Ala., and the ceramic station at Columbus, Ohio, were closed, and the Bureau's cotton mill in the Industrial building was shut down. Reduction of the building and housing division from 36 to 2 members and the automotive research section from 40 to 13 members had counterparts in almost every building at the Bureau.[96]

Although hiring of technicians and scientists, no matter how available or desirable, was out of the question, large numbers of "clerks," "draftsmen," and "technicians" were offered the Bureau through the Federal Emergency Relief Administration (FERA).[97] A Works Projects Administration

---

[95] The material of the brochure first appeared as an article by Dr. Briggs in Ann. Am. Acad. Pol. Soc. Sci. 173, 153 (1934). In the same brochure series were "Services of the National Bureau of Standards to the home building industry and to the household" (1936) and "Services * * * to governmental purchasing agencies" (1937).

[96] NBS Annual Report 1932, p. 2; Annual Report 1934, p. 73; correspondence in NBS Box 356, AB and AG, and Box 399, IST.

[97] Early in 1935 the President allotted $75,000 of FERA funds to the Bureau, "to assist educational, professional, and clerical persons in a study of materials for low-cost housing." Few of the 189 persons assigned to the Bureau possessed the specified training and were given cleaning and repairing chores. By autumn only half were still at the Bureau, on a part-time basis. The other half had been transferred to other Federal agencies. Report, A. S. McAllister, Oct. 4, 1935 (NBS Box 388, PRM).

(WPA) allotment of $100,000 in 1934, distributed over some 20 projects, made possible long-deferred repairs to walks, walls, storm sewers, wiring, and general enhancement of the buildings and grounds.[98] Several of the abler mechanics and technicians of the Bureau, let go earlier, found their way into these projects and tarried there until they could be restored to the Bureau payroll.

It was a time of petty economies. The most elementary tools and supplies could not be obtained through customary supply channels, and Bureau members vividly recall raiding junk heaps for usable parts, and sending assistants with a dollar to Woolworth's downtown to buy pliers, friction tape, wire, and the like. A small compensation in that period was Dr. Brigg's successful effort to restore the word "National" in the original name of the Bureau. For over 30 years, through an administrative whim, the agency had been simply the "Bureau of Standards." It was "nationalized" again in 1934.[99]

With salaries down and insecurity rife, it was a time of tight money. Across the Nation car sales slumped and nightclubs closed. Theaters gave away dishes and held bank nights. Hobbies of all sorts boomed. A craze for crossword puzzles swept the country and contract bridge became a national pastime. The spirit of speculation found new outlets in card games and the game of monopoly. And satisfying both the speculative and acquisitive impulses at small cost, stamp collecting in the mid-thirties zoomed from a hobby to big business, dignified by a President who was an ardent collector himself, and made profitable by an enterprising Postmaster General, James A. Farley.

The first slight upturn in the depression came in 1935 when the Bureau reported "a distinct increase in * * * requests * * * from industries * * * for scientific and technical data." At the same time, as building activity by Federal and State agencies accelerated, tests and calibration for Government agencies increased fully 15 percent over the highest previous year in Bureau history. That year also brought a small increase in Bureau appropriations, sufficient to rehire some 20 former staff members separated 2 years previously.[100] And the next year, 1936, the consolidation of funds went into effect, greatly simplifying the Director's bookkeeping and his sessions before Congress.[101]

---

[98] Hearings * * * 1936 (Dec. 27, 1934), p. 109; letter, LJB to Secretary of Commerce, Feb. 20, 1936, sub: Emergency funds administered by the Bureau (NBS Box 394, FA). The first group of laborers came under the Civilian Works Administration ($50,000) and NRA ($20,500) in late 1933. Hearings * * * 1935 (Jan. 4, 1934), pp. 134, 137–39.

[99] See ch. I, p. 47.

[100] NBS Annual Report 1935, p. 61. In 1936 half the 10 percent salary cut of 1932 was restored, the remainder in 1937.

[101] Hearings * * * 1937 (Feb. 18, 1936), p. 127.

The first approval of new construction since the turn of the decade occurred in 1938 when Congress agreed to the erection of a high voltage laboratory to replace the obsolete structure built alongside East building in 1913.[102] Up to that time the electrical industry had been content with laboratory measurements in line-to-line voltages in the range of 100,000 volts. By the late thirties the industry, transmitting power at 285,000 volts, was in need of new measurements. At a cost of $315,000, the new laboratory, with a 2 million-volt generator for high voltage work and a 1,400,000-volt generator for X-ray studies, was completed late in 1940.[103]

Reflecting less the upturn than the relentless outpouring of Federal funds into construction projects was the expansion of Bureau branch laboratories in the latter half of the decade. A new laboratory was established in Seattle to test cement for the Grand Coulee Dam. The staff at Denver was augmented for the building of the Austin and Hamilton Dams in Texas and the Conchas Dam in New Mexico, as were the test groups at Riverside, Calif., and Allentown, Pa., for local construction projects.[104]

Despite the relief programs and the massive construction projects, the Nation still failed to recover its normal momentum, a fact the President bitterly attributed to the deliberate machinations of the economic royalists in industry.[105] The answer was more pump-priming, and the administration turned to new efforts on behalf of housing, the railroads, and utilities.

The better homes movement of the 1920's became the low-cost housing program of the 1930's, administered on a series of fronts by the housing division of the Public Works Administration, the Federal Emergency Relief Administration, the Home Owners' Loan Corporation, and the Tennessee Valley Authority. For some time a consultant to these agencies on building materials, the Bureau was now brought directly into the program and provided with special funds for research in low-cost housing. Its studies in the structural and fire-resistant properties of materials for these houses were

---

[102] The original laboratory was not planned but acquired as an alternative to invoking a penalty clause in the construction contract for East building. The structure, Building No. 26, was later converted into a telephone exchange for the Bureau. Interview with Dr. Silsbee, May 21, 1962.

[103] NBS Annual Report 1937, p. 59; Hearings * * * 1939 (Jan. 31, 1938), pp. 146–152; Annual Report 1940, pp. 63–64, 70.

[104] NBS Annual Report 1936, pp. 75–76.

[105] James A. Farley, Jim Farley's Story (New York: McGraw-Hill, 1948), pp. 101, 104. For Morgenthau's diary entry on the "conspiracy" of business, see The Memoirs of Herbert Hoover: The Great Depression, 1929–1941 (New York: Macmillan, 1952), p. 482.

published in a new series, 'Building Materials and Structures Reports' (BMS).[106]

With the approach of war, New Deal sponsorship of the program ended and the special funds for the Bureau ceased. At the urging of the building trades, of engineers, and architects, the work continued under both research and transferred funds and was broadened to include all building construction. Halted during the war, building technology achieved divisional status in 1950 as a necessary and permanent Bureau function.

One other line of research extending earlier work, reactivated in the year of the Great Crash, was that on the permanence of paper and paper records. With funds provided by the Carnegie Foundation, studies were made of the permanence of Government writing papers, the preservation of records, and of library storage conditions. Light, heat, humidity and many other deterioratives of papers and books were assessed, but the principal

[106] NBS Annual Report 1935, p. 84; Annual Report 1938, pp. 90–92. The program, under the direction of Dr. Hugh L. Dryden, was formally launched in 1937. See Arch. Rec. 82, 34 (1937); NBS LC 502 (1937).

The Bureau preserves the Declaration of Independence by air-sealing it in a frame against air pollutants.

enemy of records proved to be the common air pollutant, sulphur dioxide. The investigation, extended to newspaper records, motion picture film, records on photographic film, microfilm, and lamination, culminated in the Bureau's work on the preservation at the National Archives of the originals of the Declaration of Independence and the Constitution of the United States.[107]

After the unsettling events of the early decade, the Bureau made its adjustment to the new limitations on research and working force. Few of the professional staff had taken their imposed furloughs, preferring to work without pay, unhampered by administrative duties. Others, under indefinite furlough, sought on their own initiative, with some success, funds from other Federal agencies, in order to return to their laboratories. Looking back on those years, many at the Bureau were to have the impression that with industrial research at low ebb the period was particularly fruitful in fundamental research.

SOME FUNDAMENTAL WORK ON STANDARDS

The Seventh General Conference on Weights and Measures held in Paris in the fall of 1927, with Dr. Stratton, on leave from MIT, and Dr. Burgess as the American delegates, was later pronounced the most important since that of 1875, when the international prototype meter and kilogram were adopted. The 31 nations attending the Conference established an international temperature scale, accepted the principle of defining the international meter in terms of light waves, instead of the prototype meter bar maintained in Paris, and urged the national laboratories to reach agreement on a new basis for the international electrical units.[108]

Establishment of the international temperature scale was discussed in the previous chapter. Equally gratifying to the Bureau delegates was the adoption by the Conference of the American proposal to define the international meter in terms of the wavelength of the red radiation from the cadmium lamp. Not only were many precision measurements in science and industry then being made in terms of light waves, but acceptance of this definition would greatly increase accuracy in the intercomparison of gage blocks and in determining the subdivisions of the meter and yard. Moreover, it

---

[107] NBS Annual Report 1930, p. 28; Annual Report 1931, p. 26; NBS M128 (1931) and intermittently through M168 (1940), and NBS C505 (1951).

[108] In no danger of being supplanted, as was the international meter, this country's national prototype kilogram was taken to the International Bureau at Sèvres in 1937 and recompared for the first time in 50 years with the international standard. Its mass had changed by only 1 part in 50 million, a reassuring high degree of constancy (NBS Annual Report 1937, pp. 60–61).

was hoped that with acceptance many of the difficulties in the way of international interchangeability of parts in industry might be satisfactorily solved.

No serious competitor of the cadmium red line had been found since Michelson's comparison of that wavelength with the international meter in 1893. Now, in the light of advances in spectroscopy, the search for possibly superior lines was renewed. The arc and spark spectra of the elements krypton and xenon disclosed very narrow lines when subjected to low temperatures obtained with liquid air, though none compared favorably with the cadmium lamp line.[109] For its own purposes, however, the Bureau developed a method for the use of cadmium and krypton wavelengths in the measurement of master precision gage blocks that permitted their certification to an accuracy of 0.000001 inch per inch or three times closer than previously.[110] Not until after World War II were krypton and mercury lamps devised that made possible a redefinition of the light wave to give more precise values for the inch and yard.

Earlier, in 1932, as a matter of industrial convenience, the Bureau and the American Standards Association agreed on a new ratio between the American inch and the millimeter. Arbitrary reduction by 0.00005 millimeter in the American inch made its equivalent to the 25.4-mm inch that was standard in England, and the new agreement put precision measuring in the two countries on the same basis, with consequent advantage to American export industries.[111]

Because the national laboratories both here and abroad had fewer calls on them from industry, the depression years were remembered as a time of international conferences, of many interlaboratory comparisons and exchanges of data and equipment looking to new or improved international standards. Besides the work in thermometry and standards of length, much was done in the standards upon which electrical, heat, photometric, X-ray, and radio measurements depend.[112]

---

[109] NBS Annual Report 1928, pp. 2–3; Annual Report 1929, p. 8.

For the earlier research see S441, "Notes on standard wave-lengths, spectrographs, and spectrum tubes" (Meggers and Burns, 1922); Meggers, "Measuring with light waves," Sci. Am. 129, 258 (1923) and Sci. Am. 134, 258 (1926); S535, "A fundamental basis for measurements of lengths" (Bearce, 1926).

[110] NBS Annual Report 1935, pp. 66–67. The early work on standardization of precision gages was done on the Hoke blocks of World War I (ch. IV, p. 200) and reported by Peters and Boyd in S436 (1922).

[111] Science, 76, supp. 8 (1932). See app. B.

[112] NBS Annual Report 1929, pp. 2–3, marks the first appearance of a series of yearly notes on interlaboratory cooperation and on international visitors to the Bureau.

An excellent review of the fundamental research in the decade appears in Briggs, "The national standards of measurements," Annual Report, Smithsonian Institute, 1940, pp. 161–176.

Meeting in Paris the year after the Conference of 1927, an international advisory committee on electricity proposed the establishment of electrical units based on the fundamental units of mechanical energy, the centigrade-gram-second system, rather than the practical but arbitrary units then in use. To this end the Bureau in 1934 published Dr. Curtis's absolute determination of the ampere and its relation to the accepted international unit, and in 1936 his absolute determination of the ohm.[113] Moreover, the new apparatus constructed for these determinations made it possible to maintain and transfer working standards of the units to other laboratories for purposes of intercomparison.

Anticipating a rapid conclusion to the work, the international advisory committee predicted general agreement on the new electrical values within 2 years and their formal adoption by January 1940. But by 1939, as the laboratories in Europe continued to delay reporting their work, the Bureau had constructed still better apparatus than that used in its original determinations and was working toward even greater precision in its measurements. The adjustment of discrepancies and final agreement with the laboratories abroad were suspended until after the war.[114]

Also deferred by the war was final adoption of new and practical photometric units, based on a scale of color temperatures developed during the 1930's.[115] While the photometric measurements involved psychological factors and could not be put on an absolute basis, the national laboratories subsequently reached agreement on a single, practical, worldwide system of units, in place of the diverse units and standards then prevailing.

The new photometric units were made possible by the adoption of a standard visibility curve, based mainly on earlier work of Coblentz, Emerson, Gibson, and Tyndall,[116] and by the realization of the Waidner-Burgess absolute standard of light, first proposed in 1908 and achieved experimentally for the first time in 1931.[117] Together with absolute units of electricity, international adoption of the photometric units was accomplished at last in 1948.

---

[113] RP685 (H. L. Curtis and R. W. Curtis, 1934); RP857 (Curtis, Moon, and Sparks, 1936).

[114] NBS Annual Report 1936, pp. 58–60; Annual Report 1939, pp. 49–50. In RP1606 (1944), Curtis reviewed the experimental work on the absolute units and in C459 (1947) announced their international adoption, along with the photometric units, effective Jan. 1, 1948. The former electrical units, last adjusted in 1912, were then 50 years old.

[115] The reproducible color temperature scale, consistent with the International Temperature Scale, was reported by Wensel, Judd, and Roeser in RP677 (1934).

[116] S303 and S305 (Coblentz and Emerson, 1918); S475 (Gibson and Tyndall, 1923).

[117] See ch. III, pp. 111–112; NBS Annual Report 1930, p. 10; "A primary standard of light," Science, 72, 109 (1930); RP325 (Wensel, Roeser, Barbrow, and Caldwell, 1931); RP699, "Determination of photometric standards * * * (ibid., 1934); NBS Annual Report 1937, p. 64; Annual Report 1938, pp. 69–70.

Much of the success in securing cooperation and final agreement on these standards was owing to the skill and diplomacy of the Bureau's chief representative over those years, Dr. Eugene C. Crittenden.[118]

In the lull of the depression, Dr. Coblentz found time to reassess his standards of thermal radiation, kept at the Bureau for precise calibration of thermopiles and other radiometers used by industry, and to work on his standards of ultraviolet radiation.[119] Hospitals, as well as many industries, had long been concerned with control of both the beneficial and harmful effects of ultraviolet radiation, and sought means for precise calibration of the photoelectric dosage intensity meters used for measuring radiation. Under study since 1931, about the time ultraviolet lamps first appeared on the market as household health aids, the Bureau standard, consisting of a quartz-mercury arc lamp whose ultraviolet rays were calibrated in absolute units, was ready in 1936.[120]

An even more critical aid to the medical profession than the standard of ultraviolet radiation was the Bureau's standardization of X-ray dosages. The need arose when World War I saw new X-ray apparatus that increased the voltage from 50,000 to 200,000 volts, and soon after the war these new voltages began to be widely used in cancer therapy.

Even after a quarter century of experience hospital technicians and private practitioners still operated their X-ray equipment empirically. Although the early postwar apparatus, unlike previous equipment, had some lead shielding, in cancer therapy the voltage, more or less arbitrarily established at 140,000 volts, presented a tremendous hazard. Patients were relatively safe since exposure times were fairly well known, but cumulative injuries to the operators working constantly with the apparatus were frequent and often severe. The question of these radiation hazards was first raised at the International Congress of Radiology, held at London in 1925. Con-

---

[118] Crittenden, who came to the photometry section of the Bureau from Cornell in 1909, succeeded Rosa as chief of the electrical division in 1921, became Assistant Director of the Bureau in 1933, Associate Director in 1945, and consultant to the Director from his retirement in 1950 until his death 4 years later. As chairman of the personnel and editorial committees of the Bureau for many years, he set the standards for personnel policies and for the high quality of the scientific output of the Bureau. Serving under all five Directors, he came to possess the most complete knowledge of the Bureau at every level of its operation and administration.

[119] RP578 (Coblentz and Stair, 1933).

[120] RP858 (Coblentz and Stair, 1936); NBS Annual Report 1940, p. 71. Two projects dear to Coblentz still unsolved at the time of his retirement were establishment of a unit of dosage of biologically effective ultraviolet radiation and a primary standard meter for measuring ultraviolet solar and sun radiation, for use in heliotherapy. Coblentz, "Reminiscences of the radiometry section," Dec. 9, 1944 (NBS Historical File). Without Coblentz, his group turned to more pressing work in the field of X rays. Interview with Harry J. Keegan, Feb. 12, 1964.

cerned at the time principally with the certification of radium and not with radiation measurement, the Bureau had sent no one to the Congress.

In the spring of 1926 the president of the Radiological Society of North America came to the Bureau and in some desperation asked it to undertake the determination of proper X-ray and radium dosages. At the urging of the society, Congress provided funds for the radiation research, and Lauriston S. Taylor, a young physicist working in X rays and electronics on a Heckscher Foundation grant at Cornell, was brought to the Bureau for the work.[121]

Taylor found the war surplus equipment that had been acquired by the Bureau wholly inadequate for the research to be done and successfully constructed from odd parts new apparatus of 200,000-volt capacity, setting it up in East building. A year later, in 1928, Taylor attended the Second International Congress, which proposed the "roentgen" as the unit of quantity for expressing X-ray and gamma-ray protection. The American counterpart of the councils working on standards in Europe was established with the founding of the National Committee on Radiation Protection and Measurements (NCRP) in 1928, its chairman, Dr. Taylor.[122]

Taylor's work on the absolute measurement of X rays, published in 1929, showed that the roentgen could be precisely measured, and resulted in the first real quantitative data on X-ray dosage standards in this country. Working through NCRP, his X-ray safety code in 1931 established guides for the shielding of operating rooms and of high voltage equipment and for protective devices for patients and operators. The first NCRP handbook on radium protection, prepared by Taylor's colleague, Dr. Leon F. Curtiss, for the use of industry and the medical profession, followed in 1934.[123]

The initial measurements of X rays had been made with heavy and bulky equipment. Construction in 1930 of a portable, guarded-field ionization chamber provided means for a much needed, accurate primary standard in convenient form. With the chamber, intercomparisons were made in 1931 with measurements obtained in the laboratories abroad. The excellence of results led in 1934 to international agreement between the laboratories of England, France, Germany, and the United States on procedures in X-ray

---

[121] Interview with Dr. Taylor, Sept. 24, 1963.

[122] NBS Annual Report 1928, pp. 35–36. The work of the Second Congress was reported in NBS C374 (1929).

Represented on the NCRP was the American Roentgen Ray Society, the Radiological Society of North America, the American Medical Association, X-ray equipment manufacturers, and the Bureau. See Taylor, "Brief history of the NCRP * * *," Health Physics, 1, 3 (1958).

[123] RP56 "The precise measurement of X-ray dosage" (Taylor, 1929); H15, "X-ray protection" (1931), superseded by H20 (1936); H18, "Radium protection" (1934), superseded by H23 (1938).

measurement, using the Bureau method of characterizing the quality of X radiation.[124]

After years of careful compilation of data here and abroad on X-ray and radium effects and "tolerances," NCRP established as a specific maximum permissible exposure level of radiation a value of 0.1 roentgen per week.[125] Any hospital or industrial technician reaching that level had to transfer at once to other work or be furloughed. This "tolerance dosage" appeared in the revision of the X-ray safety code handbook in 1936 and remained in force for 12 years. It was that used by the Manhattan District throughout its operations.[126]

A threat to Bureau measurements appeared in the late thirties with advances in X-radiation therapy. While its so-called high voltage equipment was limited to work between 200,000 and 600,000 volts, hospitals began using higher and higher voltages—up to a million volts—in the treatment of cancer. The gap was closed with the construction in 1940 of the new high voltage laboratory on the Bureau grounds, its 1,400,000-volt constant potential X-ray generator the most powerful that had been built up to that time.[127]

One area in the field of X radiation long overlooked was that of radioactive luminous compounds. A formula for the manufacture of luminous paint, a zinc sulphide-radium mixture (later, mesothorium, a cheap radioactive isotope of radium) was devised in 1915 for application on clock and watch dials. During World War I the paint was extensively used on military instruments and equipment, as well as wristwatches, and at the request of the military services the Bureau made a series of studies of its composition, effectiveness, and possible hazards.

Radium, it is now known, is far more damaging to the body on ingestion than, for example, strontium 90.[128] The amount used on watch dials,

---

[124] RP397 (1932); Radiology, 23, 682 (1934); NBS Annual Report 1934, p. 60; Annual Report 1935, p. 62.

[125] The ambiguity possible in the word "tolerance" led in 1947 to substitution of the phrase "maximum permissible dose."

[126] Taylor, "Brief history of the NCRP." "Because [0.1 roentgen] was not definitely known to be safe, the tolerance dose at the atomic plant at Hanford was set at one-hundredth of a roentgen per day" (Leslie R. Groves, Now It Can Be Told, New York: Harper, 1962, p. 87).

[127] NBS Annual Report 1933, p. 54; Annual Report 1940, p. 70; Taylor, "New X-ray laboratory of the NBS," Radiology, 37, 79 (1941).

The structure and equipment, shared with the electrical division at the Bureau, is described in F. B. Silsbee's "New high-voltage laboratory at NBS," Elec. Eng. 59, 238 (1940). RP1078 (Brooks, Defandorf, and Silsbee, 1938) described construction of an absolute electrometer for direct measurement of high voltages in electrical measurement in the new laboratory.

[128] The "permissible body burden" of radium is considered only one-twentieth that of strontium 90.

though measurable, was and, with some qualifications, still is considered harmless. Ingestion of the radium paint was something else again, yet no one gave any thought to the hundreds of girls who during the war painted the dials, putting the radium-tipped brushes in their mouths to point them. In the early twenties a number of the girls fell mysteriously ill and died. It was 1927 before their illness was identified as radium sickness.[129]

Staff artists on the tabloids drew lurid front-page pictures of young girls in nightgowns glowing in the dark of their bedrooms before full-length mirrors, while captions beneath described this terrifying experience in the night as the initial clue to the sickness. If the drawings were medically unsound, the poisoning was real, and in 1932, after extensive studies of the radium nostrums on the market, the American Medical Association removed radium for internal administration, in any form, from its list of remedies. Bureau research on radioactive luminous compounds, particularly their safe handling in industry, found it way into the handbook on radium protection in 1934 and by 1941 merited a handbook (H27) of its own.[130]

Among other fundamental studies accelerated in the thirties was Dr. Meggers' work in spectroanalysis, leading to the compilation of new and accurate measurements of the atomic emission spectra of chemical elements, rare gases, rare metals, and to analyses of their structures. In a specially equipped laboratory, Meggers began an investigation to standardize the emission spectra of elements, with the intention of developing methods for quantitative chemical analysis by means of partial spectra. The systematic observation of the relation of various spectral lines to atomic structure pointed the way to fundamental factors that were to provide a valuable guide later in the chemical purification of metals, in testing materials of specific purity, sorting scrap metal, and controlling the composition of alloys.[131]

The progress in spectrochemical analysis, increasingly used in both research and industrial laboratories, was mirrored in an index, published by the American Society for Testing Materials, that listed almost a thousand papers on the subject spanning the period 1920–37.[132] Even as the stacks of graph paper with their six- and eight-digit columns of figures mounted in the spectrographic laboratories in Washington, another tabular project of the Bureau, equally ambitious, got under way in New York City.

---

[129] Daniel Lang, "A most valuable accident," The New Yorker, May 2, 1959, pp. 49–92. For Surgeon General—NBS conferences on radium sickness, see memo, L. F. Curtiss for GKB, Dec. 21, 1948 (NBS Box 230, ID–Div IV).

[130] In the 1960's the watch industry began using tritium, a radioisotope of hydrogen, as a substitute for radium in dial paints, its radiation so slight it cannot be detected outside the watch.

[131] NBS Annual Report 1933, p. 53; Annual Report 1937, pp. 64–65.

[132] NBS Annual Report 1939, p. 55.

An indispensable tool of physicists are the mathematical tables of functions, such as exponentials, logarithms, and probability functions, necessary in determining mathematical problems as varied as the diffraction of sound and electromagnetic waves, the potential of radiofrequency transmission lines, and electrical and thermal diffusion. The tables are fundamental in the solution of problems ranging from heat conduction and wave motion, the diffusion of a searchlight beam by fog, and the production of knock in gasoline engine cylinders, to thc oscillations of an ultrahigh frequency radio tube.

Scientists in this country as a rule relied on partial tables made up as needed. In the universities sporadic attempts had been made to formulate more comprehensive tables, but there was nothing comparable to the mathematical services available to scientists abroad, such as that established in the early thirties by the British Association for the Advancement of Science.[133] Then in January 1938 at a conference called by the Works Projects Administration to aid unemployed scientists (it was assumed there must be some, though they had not been heard from), Dr. Briggs proposed that the Bureau sponsor establishment of a central agency for computing fundamental tables of importance in various fields of applied mathematics. Dr. Arnold N. Lowan, Hungarian-born professor of physics in residence at the new Institute for Advanced Study at Princeton and part-time teacher at Brooklyn College, was offered the directorship of the project. That summer the program was set up in a vacant loft building off Columbus Circle in New York.

As it was WPA policy to provide work in its projects for as many unemployed as possible, and as almost no equipment of any kind could be provided, the planning staff assembled by Dr. Lowan devised a self-checking, hand-computing procedure of preparing tables that could be performed in a series of simple, single stages. Over 400 individuals from the relief rolls, with a variety of talents but none of them trained scientists, and in most instances with no mathematical background whatever, were set to work with paper and pencils on the initial basic projects. These were to prepare the 16-place values of natural logarithms, the 15-place values of probability functions, and the 10-place values of Bessel functions of complex arguments. A few desk calculators and adding machines were acquired by the directing staff to check the tabulations and were also used by a select group whose more complex task it was to determine values of polynomials for integral arguments.

Electronic equipment that became available less than a decade later performed in minutes what 400 pencil-computers took months to do, but the

---

[133] Some German tables were available to their scientists but were not in print. The British work was still in progress, and most of the Bureau tables came out before theirs did. Conversation with Miss Irene A. Stegun, Feb. 18, 1964.

procedure devised by the Mathematical Tables Project insured nearly flawless tables that received wide and grateful recognition. Before long universities, industry (General Electric), the Bureau itself, and other Federal agencies (the Bureau of Marine Inspection and Navigation, the Corps of Engineers, the Navy's Bureau of Ordnance) began suggesting or requesting much needed tables for their research. By 1943, 27 book-length tables had been published in the Bureau's Mathematical Tables (MT) series, and as many more short tables had appeared in specialized periodicals. That spring the project staff, reduced to 60 by induction into the Armed Forces or employment in industry, was transferred from WPA administration to that of the Bureau, to continue its work on behalf of the National Defense Research Committee. Four years later the project moved from New York to the National Applied Mathematics Laboratories established at the Bureau.[134]

Another fundamental study begun in the thirties was concerned with the physical constants of pure substances. The Bureau had long been aware of the need for accurately determined constants as offering the best criteria of the identity and purity of many industrially important organic compounds. A new technique in this field had been devised abroad, that of ebulliometry, providing a comparative method for determining the vapor pressure, boiling point, and purity of organic substances by comparison with water as a primary reference standard. In 1935 the Bureau invited Dr. Mieczyslaw Wojciechowski of the Polytechnic Institute of Warsaw, the student of Wojciech Swietoslawski, originator of the technique, to Washington. Under his direction, Bureau chemists began preparation of a number of high purity organic reagents and organic substances, including benzene, dioxane, isoprene, as well as of the aliphatic hydrocarbons and alcohols. The work continued up to the eve of war.[135]

The considerable fundamental research of the depression years, useful alike to science and industry, won wide acknowledgment. Unlike some of the research earlier in the decade, which had found little welcome though it was equally fundamental, none of these new lines of work impinged on or

[134] Lowan, "The computer laboratory of the National Bureau of Standards," Scripta Math. 15, 33 (1949); interview with Mrs. Ida Rhodes, Sept. 10, 1963. For the status of staff and equipment just prior to the transfer of the project from WPA to NDRC auspices, see memo, Warren Weaver, Applied Math Panel, NDRC, Nov. 13, 1942 (OSRD records, NARG 227, file MTP General Correspondence).

[135] NBS Annual Report 1936, p. 67; Annual Report 1941, p. 73; interview with Dr. E. R. Smith, Jan. 14, 1964. Swietoslawski visited the Bureau 3 years later and with Smith published RP1088, "Water as a reference standard for ebulliometry" (1938). See memo, Crittenden for LJB, Aug. 15, 1940 (NBS Box 490, IDM), for a program of standard substances at the Bureau.

threatened to disclose industrial processes. Almost all of them found important uses and applications when war came.

"CURTAILMENT BY LIMITATION OF FUNDS"

In September 1934 Science magazine reprinted an excerpt from the bulletin of the Société Française de Photographie et de Cinématographie concerning an event that had occurred almost a year earlier:

> The budget retrenchments which the Government of the United States have made has forced the Bureau of Standards to close its laboratory devoted to the study of photographic emulsions, a laboratory in which Messrs. Burt H. Carroll and Donald Hubbard have carried on researches the publication of which has for the first time given quantitative information on the preparation of modern photosensitive emulsions. * * * Our society will be honored in awarding to Messrs. Carroll and Hubbard two of its medals, thus expressing its appreciation of their important contributions in a field heretofore mysterious.[136]

Research in photographic emulsions, initiated at the Bureau in 1921, grew out of the need in the spectroscopy laboratory for emulsions sensitive to infrared spectra. Commercial film was not very satisfactory, particularly for spectrographic purposes. Its sensitivity was of a low order, its base of cellulose nitrate was flammable, and it shrank badly. The search for a better infrared emulsion led the Bureau to the study of emulsions in general.[137]

With funds transferred from the Army Signal Corps, which was equally concerned with better film, Dr. Meggers went to Germany and obtained pilot plant machinery for making emulsions. To operate the plant installed in the basement of the Chemistry building, he brought to the Bureau two skilled technicians, Carroll, a chemist from the Chemical Warfare Service, and Hubbard, a recent University of Florida graduate in chemistry.

For 7 years results were largely negative. The first notice of their efforts, now with funds provided by Congress for "industrial research," appeared in the Director's annual report of 1926 and spoke only of the difficulties under which they labored:

> The science of lens design has received a great amount of attention which is almost classical in character. The preparation of photo-

---

[136] Science, 80, 263 (1934).

[137] S422, "Studies in color sensitive photographic plates * * *" (Walters and Davis, 1922); S439, "Sensitometry of photographic emulsions * * *" (Davis and Walters, 1922); interview with Dr. Meggers, Mar. 13, 1962.

> graphic emulsions, on the other hand, is largely a secret and empirical art known to relatively few. There is probably room for ten times more improvement in making emulsions than in making lenses.

That year Carroll and Hubbard had made over 400 batches of emulsion. Under more exact controls, they were turning out emulsions with superior keeping qualities, but the secret of emulsion sensitivity still eluded them.[138] The breakthrough came 2 years later, and they published their first paper, on the sensitization of photographic emulsions by colloidal materials.[139]

In 1933 Carroll and Hubbard published their seventeenth report on the mechanism of photographic hypersensitivity, and their preparation of new "grainless" emulsions.[140] Not only were these emulsions superior to the best commercially available, but disclosure by the Bureau of the method of their preparation threatened to make public vital trade secrets. It was the time of the great depression, and the advisory committees surveying Bureau research and mindful of recent complaints of Government interference with private industry had to recommend retrenchments. The emulsion project was among the first to be terminated in the interest of economy.[141]

The emulsion work was one of seven investigations which the Visiting Committee specifically "questioned whether the Bureau ought to continue": (1) its research in heavy hydrogen, (2) its work on dental cements and alloys, (3) distinctly industrial problems like temperature measurements in the pouring of cast iron, (4) ignition phenomena and flame propagation in internal combustion engines, (5) development of large-scale production methods for levulose, (6) design of a telephoto astronomical objective, and (7) development of special photographic developers.[142]

The precise areas of industrial research terminated or curtailed under the pressure of economy are difficult to identify or document, since they

---

[138] NBS Annual Report 1926, p. 34.

[139] RP20 (1928).

[140] NBS Annual Report 1933, p. 52. The key paper in the group was RP447, "The photographic emulsion: analysis for nonhalide silver and soluble bromide" (1932).

[141] Dr. Briggs' outline of the project and unavailing efforts to interest the Carnegie Institution of Washington in its support appear in letter, Sept. 7, 1933 (NBS Box 361, IPS). Subsequent photographic research at the Bureau was limited to work on the international standardization of photosensitometric methods and, in cooperation with the ASA, preparation of specifications for films and plates. See NBS Annual Report 1940, p. 71.

NOTE.—In 1934 Burt Carroll and his assistant, Charles M. Kretchman, went to Eastman Kodak. Hubbard remained at the Bureau.

[142] Minutes of meeting of the Visiting Committee, Aug. 23, 1934 (NARG 40, 67009/5).

were determined by verbal agreement between Dr. Briggs and the committees to the Bureau. Acting on an earlier House recommendation for "curtailment by limitation of funds," Congress in 1933 made the deepest of its cuts, 54 percent, in its appropriation to the Bureau for "industrial research." It alone affected more than 100 projects.[143]

Notable was the cut in the special fund for the "investigation of auto motive engines." Supporting some 40 projects in 1932, funds for that work a year later were down by 30 percent. Among the investigations abandoned was one on the measurement of the road performance of automobile engines, undertaken at the request of interested Government agencies. The comparative tests made by the Bureau, indicating marked superiority of one make (the new Ford V–8 engine) over all others on the market, understandably displeased the rest of the industry, and termination of the study precluded publication of the test results.[144]

Appropriation cuts, together with impounding of funds, came close to putting an end to all Bureau participation in both the building and housing and the standardization programs. With the initial reduction of 40 percent in standardization funds, Secretary of Commerce Roper, with Dr. Briggs' concurrence, proposed to the American Standards Association that it take over the major role in that program.[145] The work on specifications, simplified practices, trade standards, and building and safety codes was, however, to the advantage to many industries, and at once, through their Congressmen and trade groups, they protested the transfer to ASA, arguing for the Bureau's impartiality and superior facilities.

As a compromise, Commerce agreed that the Bureau would cooperate in ASA standardization "under the procedure of the association," continue

---

[143] NBS Annual Report 1931, p. 37, reported 103 projects under this fund. Dr. Briggs later said that funds for industrial research were finally cut by 88 percent. Hearings * * * 1935 (Jan. 4, 1934), p. 132.

Obviously incomplete was the list in memo, C. J. Humphreys (of the radiometry laboratory) for LJB, July 31, 1933 (NBS Box 358, ID), which noted that besides discontinuance of the specifications, simplified practices, building and housing, and trade standards divisions, and the safety standards work, other projects dropped included soil corrosion, telephone standards, preparation of levulose, testing of commercial aircraft engines, and radio aids to air navigation.

[144] See NBS Annual Report 1931, p. 43; Annual Report 1932, p. 34; interview with Dr. Meggers, Mar. 13, 1962.

[145] Letter, Secretary Roper to Senator A. Lonergan, July 7, 1933; letter, president, ASA to H. S. Dennison, Nov. 2, 1933, and related correspondence in NBS Blue Folder Box 19, 669c, and NBS Box 356, AG. The proposal for complete transfer of the standardization work was reported in Science, 78, 95 (1933).

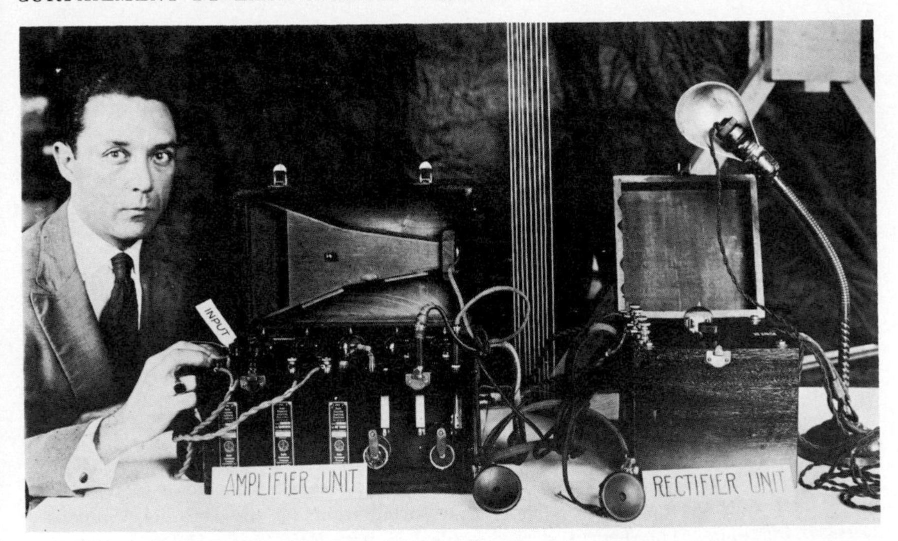

Percival D. Lowell with his invention in 1922 that made it possible to use ordinary house current instead of storage batteries to operate a home radio. For the first time, the 60-cycle alternating current that operated the lights in the house could, with Lowell's rectifier, equally well supply power to the filament and plates of the radio.

its representation on almost a hundred sectional committees of ASA dealing with technical subjects, and sponsor certain projects assigned to it by ASA. When the formal transfer was made, some of the staff members separated earlier by the Bureau were taken on by ASA, to continue their work at the Bureau as ASA employees.[146]

To what extent Bureau research was terminated in areas susceptible of patentable ideas that industry might otherwise discover for itself cannot be determined. Suggestive, however, is the example in radio research, where fundamental investigations in radio transmission phenomena were continued, while the entire group in applied radio research at College Park, Md., involving 20 members, was dismissed in June 1934 and the station closed.[147]

All three committees advising the Bureau on retrenchment and reorganization of its research expressed concern over the current patent policy of the Bureau. Their investigations came at a time when Dr. Briggs was in

---

[146] NBS Annual Report 1934, pp. 52–53; Annual Report 1937, p. 59. Upon consolidation of Bureau funds in 1936, the standardization work remaining at the Bureau was performed under the appropriation for "commercial standards."

[147] Interview with W. S. Hinman, Jr., Dec. 28, 1963. Three of the group, Hinman, Diamond, and Dunmore, were brought back to Washington not long after.

the midst of serious litigation over patents taken out by members of the staff, in defiance of long-standing practice.[148] No solution was offered at that

[148] Traditionally, the Government retained rights to the use of inventions of Federal employees but otherwise left title to them with their inventors. The Bureau of Standards did not follow this policy. For 20 years under Dr. Stratton it was understood that any innovation or invention of a Bureau staff member was to be patented in the name of the Government for the use of the public.

The understanding was not seriously challenged until the summer of 1921 when two members of the radio section, Percival D. Lowell and Francis W. Dunmore, while working on a radio relay project for the Air Corps, conceived the idea of substituting house power for the storage batteries then used with radio apparatus. The method they devised for operating radio on ordinary house current also eliminated the principal obstacle to its use, the hum of alternating current in the radio. Their inventions were only remotely related to the Air Corps project.

In March 1922 Lowell and Dunmore filed the first of three related patents in their own names and in October 1924 granted manufacturing rights to the Dubilier Condenser Corp. of Delaware. The devices were described in NBS S450, June 17, 1922, and in a paper in the AIEE Journal, 41, 488 (1922).

Shortly after filing their first patent, the Government, at the prompting of the Bureau, submitted the case for judgment to the U.S. District Court for Delaware. And on Nov. 2, 1922, in a memorandum to all Bureau employees, Dr. Stratton for the first time formally established as policy the assignment of all patent rights in inventions and discoveries of the staff to the Government (memo in NBS Box 40, AGP).

Almost a decade later, on Apr. 27, 1931, the District Court handed down its decision, deciding against the Government. Although the court declared that the devices of Lowell and Dunmore had been developed on Government time, with Government funds, and with the assistance of other Government employees, the devices had not been a part of their assigned work and therefore the inventions and patents were their property (The United States Daily, May 2, 1931, p. 52). The decision was appealed by the Justice Department.

When on May 24, 1932 the U.S. Circuit Court upheld the decision of the district court, the Government filed a petition in the Supreme Court. No similar case of patent rights had come up at the Bureau in the intervening years, but after the district court decision of 1932 some members of the Bureau continued to assign their rights to the Government, while others were advised that the Bureau would raise no objection to a private patent, pending a final court decision (letter, Acting Director LJB to Secretary of Commerce, Dec. 17, 1932, NARG 40, 67009/5). On Apr. 10, 1933, the Supreme Court, one member dissenting, decreed that in the absence of a specific contractual agreement, all commercial rights to patents belonged to the inventor, whether or not the work was performed on Government time.

Aware of the lack of uniformity in patent policy in Government agencies and the impasse at the Bureau, the Visiting Committee to the Bureau and the Business Advisory Council of the Department of Commerce in their joint report issued on Dec. 5, 1933, suggested that a Government ownership of patents clause be written into the standard employment contract of the Bureau. For unknown reasons, the Business Advisory Council reversed its stand and in a separate report of Dec. 9, 1933, formally recommended that Bureau employees be permitted to patent devices developed at the Bureau, with the warning that exercise of their right must not "interfere with free communication and cooperation time, and Bureau policy, as elsewhere in the Federal establishment, continued vague and uncertain for almost another two decades.

Bureau appropriations between 1932 and 1933, as the Science Advisory Board reported, fell by half, and further diminished by the sums diverted to the testing work of the Bureau, left its research funds reduced by almost 70 percent. Equally imperiled was the fundamental research carried out under statutory salaries and investigations under special appropriations. Among projects in the latter category, two were scheduled for early termination, the whole of the levulose program and all research on utilization of waste products of the land, the second by transfer to the Department of Agriculture.[149] Except in the Bureau's huge industrial research and standardization programs, however, most of the other cuts in special appropriations did not exceed 15 percent. And in the research funds transferred to the Bureau from other Government agencies, slashes ranged between 10 and 50 percent. The necessity for economy was the sole justification offered.

A member of the metallurgy division who had left the Bureau several years before to become director of the Battelle Memorial Foundation wrote

---

between Bureau members or between the Bureau of Standards and industries and other organizations."

Lowell and Dunmore gained little from their revolutionary invention. Granted a license by the inventors to manufacture the device in 1922, Dubilier in turn licensed it to Philco and several other interested makers of radios. Then in 1924 the Radio Corp. of America (RCA), largest of the radio manufacturers, developed a heater type of vacuum tube that performed as well with alternating house current as the Lowell-Dunmore unit. Within a year or two most radios sold to the public were operating on house current with the RCA tube (see "The electric light socket and our vacuum tubes," Sci. Am. 132, 240, 1925.)

Dubilier at once sued RCA for infringement of the patents and won the first round in the Delaware courts. When RCA offered to settle out of court and Dubilier refused, RCA appealed. The case was finally adjudicated in 1937 in favor of RCA when it was decided that the Lowell and Dunmore patents were not valid by reason of priority and the only new element in the invention, the suppression of a.c. hum, was inherent in the RCA tube and constituted no infringement (interview with P. D. Lowell, Nov. 12, 1963).

Stratton's patent policy announced in 1922 continued in force until modified in 1940, when patents were procured by the Justice Department and assigned to the Secretary of Commerce for licensing under terms he prescribed (Hearings * * * 1942, Feb. 11, 1941, p. 219, and policy letter, LJB, Feb. 16, 1944, NBS Box 489, AGP).

The long-accepted Federal policy of permitting employees to retain title to their inventions ended on Jan. 23, 1950, when by Executive Order 10096 it was announced that all rights to any invention developed by a Government employee in the course of his assigned work belonged to the Government (see app. C).

[149] Some cherished research died hard. As late as 1939, Dr. Briggs requested experiments on the possible use of levulose or xylose in the quick-freezing process for preserving fruits and strawberries. Nothing apparently came of the study (memo for F. J. Bates, Dec. 7, 1939, NBS Box 490, IDM).

frankly to Dr. Briggs that he believed the enforced curtailment of Bureau activities a good thing:

> * * * In the course of time there are likely to creep into a long term program, and to stay there because there is always one more thing to try, projects that are not of very great import, or in which the economic condition has passed that once made them important. * * * In the long run the necessity for * * * a clean-cut decision as to the relative importance of the work in hand * * * will improve the patient.

Dr. Briggs, who saw science the handmaid to new industries, with reservations reluctantly agreed.[150]

One area of investigation which felt the knife of economy directed wholly at its applied research was radio. By 1935 staff and funds for radio research were approximately half what they had been in 1932. As a consequence, research was narrowed to the most pressing concerns: The improvement of primary and secondary frequency standards and of Bureau broadcasting of standard radio and audio frequencies for the control of station transmitters; research in the character and cause of variations in radio wave intensity and direction (i.e., radio wave propagation phenomena); and accurate determination of the height and characteristics of the ionosphere layers, the primary factor in long-distance radio transmission.

Outgrowing its radio laboratory and its reliance on commercial and Government broadcasting stations for additional operating facilities, the Bureau in 1932 received funds to establish two experimental stations just outside Washington. One was a transmitting station, in several frame buildings erected on the site of the Department of Agriculture experimental farm near Beltsville, Md.; the other a receiving station for radio wave research, in similar structures on 200 acres purchased near Meadows, Md.[151]

With new and improved equipment at Beltsville, the Bureau continued its transmission of standard radio frequencies to permit stations to calibrate standard oscillators and check their broadcast frequencies, and in 1935 began transmitting standard time intervals in the form of spaced pulses, as well as a standard musical pitch.[152]

Long-distance radio transmission continued to present the greatest difficulties, owing to the character of the ionosphere layers, some 60 miles up. In cooperation with standards laboratories and radio agencies abroad, the Bureau set up automatic equipment at Meadows and began making con-

---

[150] Letter, H. W. Gillett, July 13, 1933, and attached correspondence (NBS Box 356, AG).
[151] NBS Annual Report 1932, pp. 16–17.
[152] The services were described in LC453, "Standard frequencies and other services * * *" (1935), superseded by LC498 (1937), LC565, (1939), and LC591 (1940).

tinuous recordings at varying heights of the critical frequencies of the ionized layers responsible for reflecting radio waves back to earth.

Not a single surface, as originally believed, the ionosphere phenomenon apparently consisted of a series of layers, each affecting differently the distance obtained in radio transmission at various frequencies, at different times of day, different seasons, and even in different years. From "the most complete body of data in existence on this subject," the Bureau reported in 1934, the radio section began the first of its deductions about the roles played in long-distance transmission by reflection and refraction and the relative effects of ultraviolet light, electrons, and heavy ions. The amassed data on sudden fadeouts in long-distance transmission, obtained through cooperative research, led in 1935 to Dellinger's confirmation of their source in sudden eruptions on the sun, a phenomenon subsequently known as "the Dellinger effect." [153]

By 1937 the data at the Bureau made it possible to inaugurate a service of monthly predictions of ionospheric and radio conditions. For the first time Government long-distance stations and commercial air services were provided with information on the selection of radio frequencies for transmission over specified distances at various times of day and year, alternative means of radio communication when sun disturbances interfered with normal communications, and other vital transmission information.[154]

One investigation in the field of applied radio in the 1930's—long before the advent of CONELRAD or EBS (Emergency Broadcast System)—struck a faintly ominous note, when the Federal Bureau of Investigation requested the Bureau to make experiments to see whether voice broadcasting

---

[153] NBS Annual Report 1934, p. 54; Dellinger notes in Science, 82, 351 and 548 (1935); NBS Annual Report 1936, p. 61; RP1001, "Characteristics of the ionosphere * * *" (Gilliland, Smith, and Reymer, 1937); RP1061, "Sudden disturbances of the ionosphere" (Dellinger, 1937).

[154] The service was announced in LC499, "The weekly radio broadcast of the NBS on the ionosphere and radio transmission conditions" (1937). LC565, "Standard frequencies and other services broadcast by NBS" (1939), said the Bureau's ionospheric reports would offer information on vertical-incidence critical frequencies, heights of the ionospheric layers, maximum usable frequencies for radio transmission, and information on ionospheric disturbances, thereby permitting a choice to be made in selecting optimum frequencies for long-distance transmission.

LC614, "Radio transmission and the ionosphere" (1940), was a 22-page description of the new ionosphere observation, reporting, and predicting service of the Bureau, analogous to the Federal weather reporting service.

LC615, "Radio distance ranges" (1940), provided the first detailed data for long-distance radio stations on ionospheric heights and ionization density of ionosphere layers, and determination and control of optimum conditions for long-distance radio for the coming year. This circular was superseded by LC658 (1941), with ranges for the summer of 1941 and winter of 1941–42. It was withdrawn on Jan. 2, 1942, as classified information. The series was resumed after the war.

Recording radio-weather forecasting data as a preliminary to preparing monthly predictions of ionospheric and radio conditions. Systematic measurement of the height and density of the ionospheric layers, the highly electrified region of the upper atmosphere produced by solar radiation and greatly influenced by high-speed particles discharged from the sun, is basic in the predicting of radio weather.

to cover the entire United States was possible from a single station. The Bureau engineers came up with a system that seemed feasible, but whether any part of it was ever tested, and what the FBI proposed to do with it is unfortunately nowhere recorded at the Bureau.[155]

A happier career was promised in two kindred projects first reported in 1935. They grew out of the experimental work in telemeteorography then going on in Germany, France, and Finland, where compact packages of radio equipment were being sent aloft via unmanned balloons to gather upper air weather data and record their transmission on a ground receiver.[156]

---

[155] NBS Annual Report 1936, p. 61.

[156] The principle of telemetry or remote measurement was not new to the Bureau. In 1924 McCollum and Peters devised an electric telemeter for remote reading and recording of strain and force measurements, especially in inaccessible places, for use in testing bridge members and airship girders already in place in units under construction (T247, 1924).

At the request of the U.S. Weather Bureau, Leon Curtiss and Allen V. Astin of the electrical division undertook similar research at the Bureau, to devise a practical system of radiometeorography for the weather service.[157] When the aerological division of the Navy's Bureau of Aeronautics requested a high-altitude weather recording system of its own, a second project was initiated in the radio laboratory under Diamond, Hinman, and Dunmore.

As the Diamond apparatus seemed better suited to both Weather Bureau and Navy needs, Curtiss and Astin, more interested in radiation phenomena than in weather, equipped the radio telemeter they devised with special Geiger counters and began lofting them 20 miles and more into the stratosphere to gather cosmic-ray data.[158] Cosmic rays, the source of high energy particles that impinge on the earth from space, are of interest not only as radiation phenomena but for their effect on radio communication and also as possible keys to the study of atomic structure. The 18 ascensions made with the Curtiss-Astin telemeter confirmed earlier views reported from abroad, that the greater part of cosmic-ray phenomena was apparently caused by secondary effects generated not in outer space but within our own atmosphere.[159]

A year after beginning construction of their unit, Diamond and his group sent up their first model and demonstrated its effectiveness in transmitting continuous data on cloud height and thickness, temperature, pressure, humidity, and light intensity in the upper atmosphere. Effective from ground level to heights of 15 or more miles and at distances up to 200 miles, the radiosonde, as it was called, enormously increased the range and quantity of weather data, previously gathered by observing devices strapped to kites, zeppelins, or the wings of airplanes. By 1940 the radiosonde had become an integral part of U.S. weather and meteorological services and some 35,000 units were being built and sent up each year in this country and its territories.[160]

---

[157] Curtiss and Astin, J. Aeron. Sci. 3, 35 (1935).

[158] In 1928, with the recent incorporation of the vacuum tube in the Geiger-Muller ion counter (the principle had been established by Rutherford and Geiger in 1908), Dr. Curtiss began a long series of studies on routine quantitative measurements with the counter which led to the later cosmic-ray studies and development of new types of counters. See RP165 (1930), RP191 (1930), RP509 (1932), RP526 (1933), RP1154 (1938), RP1525 (1943).

[159] RP1169, "An improved radio meteorograph on the Olland principle" (Curtiss, Astin, et al., 1938); Curtiss and Astin, "Cosmic ray observations in the stratosphere," Phys. Rev. 53, 23 (1938); RP1254, "Cosmic-ray observations * * *" (Curtiss, Astin, et al., 1939).

[160] NBS Annual Report 1936, p. 65; Annual Report 1937, p. 60; RP1082 "A method for investigation of upper air phenomena * * *" (Diamond, Hinman, and Dunmore, 1937);

The radiosonde, developed for the Navy by the Bureau in 1936, telemeters information on upper air pressure, temperature, and humidity from unmanned balloons. It employs an ultra-high-frequency oscillator and a modulator. The frequency of the latter is controlled by special resistors whose electrical resistance varies with the atmospheric phenomena. At the receiving station on the ground or on shipboard, a graphic frequency recorder, connected in the receiving set output, provides an automatic chart of the variations of the phenomena with altitude.

Subsequent refinements in the radiosonde included improved instruments such as the electric hygrometer,[161] superior electronic components, and more recently, miniaturization. These were also used in the special radiosonde designed for the Navy to operate as an automatic weather station. Installed on isolated islands or in mountainous regions, the radiosonde transmitted data on temperature, pressure, humidity, wind velocity and direction, and rainfall via keyed frequencies picked up and recorded at the nearest Navy base.[162]

The international interest in telemeteorography that led to the radiosonde coincided with a new age of exploration—ionospheric, stratospheric, and terrestrial—marked early in the decade by the Second International Polar Year of 1932–34. Available to that Year were the airplane, radio, and a range of scientific instruments and equipment denied the First Polar Year, held 50 years earlier, in 1882–83. In that initial cooperative assault of science on the icy unknown, meteorologists and astronomers of 11 nations had acted in concert to explore the polar regions and, from 12 bases around the Arctic and in the southern ocean, make observations of polar weather,

RP1329, "An improved radio sonde and its performance" (Diamond, Hinman, et al., 1940); Science, 90, 246 (1939).

Mass production of the radiosonde was turned over to several companies in 1937, including Bendix-Friez of Towson, Md. In the next 26 years, Bendix alone manufactured more than 2 million units. "Baltimore Evening Sun," Sept. 6, 1963, p. B6.

[161] RP1102, "An electric hygrometer * * *" (Dunmore, 1938), and its improvement, RP1265 (1939).

[162] RP1318, "An automatic weather station" (Diamond and Hinman, 1940).

the aurora borealis, and of sun-spot activity and its attendant magnetic storms.[163]

The Second Polar Year, with more countries and more branches of science involved, again centered its studies on meteorology, magnetism, and aurora in the the Arctic, where their effects are strongest and most free from the contamination of civilization. Among prominent new objectives of the Year was the work planned in space phenomena, primarily the study of their effects on radio transmission. Representing the United States were the National Bureau of Standards, the Coast and Geodetic Survey, the Department of Terrestrial Magnetism of the Carnegie Institution, and the Naval Research Laboratory.

The Year unfortunately fell during the worst phase of the worldwide depression. The Bureau had planned to carry out extensive new measurements of the heights and degree of ionization of the ionosphere layers at the station set up at Fairbanks, Alaska. Instead, its participation was limited to the preparation of certain computations for the expedition and construction of some of the automatic recording instruments used by members of the Department of Terrestrial Magnetism.[164] More active participation and extensive research awaited the International Geophysical Year of 1957–59.

The strides of radio and aeronautics in the 1920's made possible the far-ranging exploration that created headlines all through the thirties. Byrd's flight to the North Pole in 1926 was followed by his Antarctic expeditions, sponsored by the National Geographic Society, in 1933 and 1934. Through Dr. Briggs's chairmanship of the special advisory committee and later the research committee of the society, the Bureau took part in the Antarctic studies, as it did in almost every expedition of the society during that decade, actively assisting in the preparation, providing special instrumentation, and in many instances sending staff members along on the expeditions.

With Dr. Briggs, Dr. Tuckerman, and other Bureau members assisting in instrumentation and computations, the National Geographic Society in 1934 and 1935 sponsored two flights into the stratosphere in the largest free balloons constructed up to that time. In the first ascension, the balloon carried more than a ton of scientific instruments arranged by Dr. Briggs, including special meteorographs, electric thermometers, and spectrographs designed or constructed at the Bureau. Manned by two Army Air Corps officers, the huge balloon reached the unprecedented height of 72,395 feet or almost 14 miles. Instruments aboard the gondola recorded data on cosmic radiation, sun and sky spectra, and the ozone layer, collected air samples and information on the functioning of radio equipment at extreme altitudes, and

---

[163] The two Polar Years are compared in J. Tuzo Wilson, I.G.Y.: The Year of the New Moons (New York: Knopf, 1961), pp. 6–8.

[164] Science, 76, 187 (1932); NBS Annual Report 1933, p. 48.

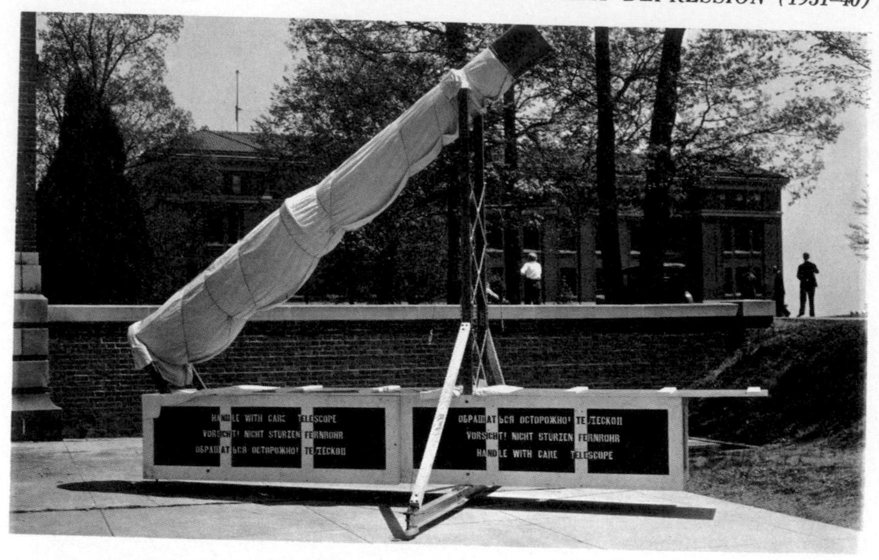

Dr. Gardner's specially designed camera for photographing the solar corona. It was used at Ak Bulak in Asiatic Russia in 1936 and at Canton Island in the South Pacific in 1937. The lens was made at NBS from optical glass poured in the Bureau glass plant.

made comparisons of photographic and instrument measurements at high altitudes.[165]

The next year, in 1936, the National Geographic and the Bureau jointly sponsored an expedition to the Kazak region of Asiatic U.S.S.R., to observe the June solar eclipse. New data on the sun's corona, its prominences, and solar spectra were recorded by the Soviet and Harvard University groups with the expedition. Dr. Irvine C. Gardner of the Bureau brought back the first natural-color photographs ever made of a total eclipse, with a 14-foot eclipse camera and 9-inch astrographic lens wholly designed and constructed at the Bureau.[166] The giant camera went again on the National Geographic-U.S. Navy Eclipse Expedition to Canton Island in the South Pacific the following year.[167]

Another joint National Geographic-Bureau eclipse expedition was made to South America in 1940, and a year later the Bureau itself sponsored the Louise A. Boyd Arctic Expedition, to make new radio, geomagnetic, and auroral measurements for a special study of ionospheric characteristics.[168]

---

[165] Briggs, "Laboratories in the stratosphere," Sci. Mo. 40, 295 (1935), et seq.; Capt. A. W. Stevens, "Man's farthest aloft," Nat. Geo. 69, 59 (1936).
[166] Gardner, "Observing an eclipse in Asiatic Russia," Nat. Geo. 71, 179 (1937).
[167] NBS Annual Report 1937, p. 65.
[168] Sci. Mo., 51, 305 (1940); Science, 93, 420 (1941); Science, 94, 324 (1941).

Dr. Briggs himself led and directed the scientific work of "one of the most extensive efforts ever organized" for spatial and radio research, the 76-man team of scientists, Air Force, Army, and National Geographic members that went to Brazil for the eclipse of 1947.[169]

In light of present knowledge, the First Polar Year of 1882 sought no more than superficial clues to the makeup of the solar system and to spatial influences on weather. The Second Polar Year and the decade of exploration that followed it were not much broader in horizon or more sophisticated in their inquiry, in spite of the progress of radio, aviation, and the new physics. The advances in these three fields of science were not to yield their fruit—foreshadowing command of the atom, human flight in space, and near approach to the planets—for another half a dozen years.

HEAVY WATER

The Bureau studies of cosmic radiations, weather and radio phenomena, of X rays, radium, and their emanations bore only distant relation to far more sophisticated investigations going on elsewhere in the thirties in this country and abroad into the nature of matter and its atomic structure.

Following Roentgen's discovery of X rays in 1895 and Becquerel's demonstration of radioactivity, the new century witnessed a train of discoveries extending illimitably the boundaries of physical knowledge: "the quantum character of light energy (Max Planck and Albert Einstein), the theory of relativity (Einstein), the nuclear structure of the atom (Lord Rutherford and Niels Bohr); interpretation of the light-emitting properties of matter (Prince Louis de Broglie, Erwin Schrödinger, and Max Born), of heavy hydrogen (Harold Urey), of the neutron (Sir James Chadwick), and of means of producing artificial transmutations of the elements (Sir John Cockcroft and Ernest Walton, Frédéric Curie-Joliot, Enrico Fermi, and others)." [170]

The initial concern of the Bureau in the atomic adventure may be said to stem from Becquerel's finding of radioactivity in uranium salts, and was in the chemistry rather than the physics of the atom.

Mapping the group of radioactive elements that had been identified since Becquerel's discovery, the English chemist Frederick Soddy in 1913 found a number of them, because they had identical chemical characteristics,

---

[169] Gilbert Grosvenor, "Earth, sea and sky; twenty years of exploration by the National Geographic Society," Sci. Mo. 78, 296 (1954).

[170] E. U. Condon, "Physics," What Is Science? ed. James R. Newman (New York: Washington Square Press, 1961), p. 110.

occupying the same space in the Periodic Table of Elements even though they possessed different atomic weights. He coined the word "isotope" to describe chemically identical substances with different atomic weights.

The 1920's saw the development of the mass spectroscope, an electromagnetic device that sorted out atoms, both normal and isotopic, according to their masses, and projected them as sharp clear lines in a spectrum. Analysis of the true weights of the atoms of various elements thus became possible, and with this instrument, F. W. Aston of the Cavendish Laboratory at Cambridge showed that not only radioactive elements, but almost all elements, have isotopes.[171]

One element, hydrogen, gave particular trouble. Precise measurement of its atomic weight indicated that it had a heavy isotope, but apparently in so small concentration that Aston could find no trace of it on the spectroscope. At this point the Bureau of Standards became actively associated with this field of atomic research.

In the summer of 1931, Harold C. Urey, associate professor of chemistry at Columbia, then lecturing at the Johns Hopkins University, became convinced that an isotope of hydrogen of mass 2, though unknown, could be found.[172] In conversation with Fred L. Mohler of the atomic physics section of the Bureau, Urey told him that in his studies of the hydrogen spectrum he had found a satellite line next to the hydrogen alpha line that he thought might be heavy hydrogen. Urey sought a way to enrich the suspected isotope, and wondered whether liquid hydrogen might not make better definition possible. Mohler suggested the Bureau's cryogenic laboratory, where Brickwedde was studying ortho- and para-hydrogen. There, successive low-temperature distillations of liquid hydrogen resulted in a concentration whose spectrum left no doubt of the existence of the isotope.[173]

Urey had earlier suggested the possibility of separation of the isotope by electrolysis, but the procedure had been tried and given up as unpromising. Acting on a suggestion of Dr. Washburn, chief of the Bureau chemistry division, Edgar R. Smith on December 9, 1931, began an experiment in the isotopic fractionation of water by repeated hydrolysis of solutions of caustic potash. When 98 percent of the water had been decomposed in this manner, the density of the hydrogen in the residual water proved measurably higher

---

[171] "In the early nineteen-thirties, many atomic masses were very accurately measured and the energy of products of many nuclear reactions became known * * * [making] possible the full quantitative verification of Einstein's 1905 prediction that mass and energy are equivalent." E. U. Condon, "Physics," pp. 145–146.

[172] See Urey, "The natural system of atomic nuclei," J. Am. Cml. Soc. 53, 2872 (1931).

[173] NBS TNB No. 179 (March 1932), p. 23; Urey, Brickwedde, and Murphy, "A hydrogen isotope of mass 2 and its concentration," Phys. Rev. 40, 1 (April 1932); interview with Dr. Mohler, Oct. 1, 1963.

than in normal water, by 164 parts in a million, that is, possessing a specific gravity of 1.000164.[174]

Urey's discovery of the isotope of hydrogen and Washburn's actual separation were revolutionary.[175] The new isotope, winning Urey the Nobel Prize in chemistry in 1934, was given the name "deuterium," with the symbol D (in the form of deuterium oxide or heavy water it is D_2O). Within 2 years it had been prepared in a pure state, its specific gravity 1.015.[176]

Another event in 1932, James Chadwick's discovery of the neutron, was to prove even more important in subsequent events than that of heavy water. In the atom compounded of protons and electrons (its positive- and negative-charged particles), Chadwick in England identified yet another fundamental particle, not electrically charged, which he called the neutron. Its neutral characteristics made it highly penetrating and therefore very effective as an agent in nuclear transmutation. That same year, Cockcroft and Walton, working in Rutherford's laboratory at Cambridge, bombarded a lithium target with high-speed protons. In the experiment, a hydrogen atom reacted with a lithium atom to produce two helium atoms. The first artificial nuclear reaction and true transmutation of elements had occurred.[177]

For a time physicists showed great interest in the deuteron, the nucleus of deuterium or heavy water that Urey had found, because of its "remarkable properties as a projectile for producing transmutation of elements and particularly for the production of neutrons." [178] But while deuterium had a

---

[174] NBS Annual Report 1932, p. 8; Washburn and Urey, "Concentration of the H^2 isotope of hydrogen * * *," Proc. Natl. Acad. Sci. 18, 496 (1932); Washburn, Smith, and Frandsen, "The isotopic fractionation of water," J. Chem. Phys. 1, 288 (1933); RP601, "The isotopic fractionation of water" (Washburn, Smith, and Frandsen, 1933). Urey and Teal summarized deuterium research in Revs. Mod. Phys. 7, 34 (1935).

[175] Dr. Edward W. Washburn came to the Bureau as its chief chemist in 1926, when he was 45. He had recently completed a 4-year project as editor in chief of the monumental International Critical Tables of Numerical Data of Physics, Chemistry, and Technology. He was one of the best scientists ever to work at the Bureau, his research on the fractionation of petroleum, the crystallization of rubber, and on heavy water among his most important achievements in the 8 years there before his untimely death. See Natl. Acad. Sci., Biographical Memoirs, XVII (1935).

[176] NBS Annual Report 1933, p. 54. In Science, 78, 555, (1933), Dr. Washburn urged construction of a plant for quantity production of "deuterium water." The 6 to 10 gallons produced annually would be enough, he believed, for all current needs of physics, chemistry, and biological and medical research. Urey was no more prescient. Many years later he recalled that when he discovered heavy water he never dreamed that it would become a vital ingredient in the making of the atomic bomb. "I thought it might have some practical use in something like neon signs." Time, Feb. 19, 1965, p. 42.

[177] E. U. Condon, "Physics," p. 143.

[178] Sci. Mo., 38, 390 (1934).

part in the final process of nuclear disintegration, the deuteron was not to be the trigger of atomic power as the chemists hoped. This role was reserved for the neutron.

Enrico Fermi, then in England, reasoned that neutrons, lacking charge, should be highly effective in penetrating nuclei, especially those of high atomic number, with consequent release of energy. He selected uranium, at No. 92 the last of the naturally occurring elements, with atomic weight 238. But his bombardment in 1934 of uranium by neutrons slowed down by the use of deuterium proved inconclusive. He obtained only a "confusion" of radioactive substances, two of which, however, proved to have atomic numbers larger than 92. In Germany in late 1938, Otto Hahn and Fritz Strassmann at the Kaiser Wilhelm Institute for Chemistry performed the same experiment and obtained a large variety of radioactive isotopes of chemical elements having half the atomic weight of the original uranium. Announcement of the significance of these two findings was near.

Lise Meitner in Sweden, a refugee physicist from Germany, and her nephew Otto R. Frisch in Denmark, informed of the work of their former colleagues in Berlin and pursuing Fermi's line of investigation, hit on the answer. Meitner and Frisch conjectured that the uranium nucleus, with low stability of form, had divided into two nuclei of roughly equal size, releasing in the process enormous quantities of energy—the "confusion" Fermi had observed. They estimated the total energy resulting from that splitting of the uranium atom as about 200 MeV (200 million electron volts).[179] Their letter explaining the Hahn and Strassmann observations and Frisch's experimental verification, "Disintegration of uranium by neutrons: a new type of nuclear reaction," appeared in Nature magazine on February 11, 1939.[180]

With full knowledge of Frisch's experiments, Niels Bohr arrived in this country the month before the appearance of the paper, and while visiting at Princeton told Einstein, in residence there, and Eugene P. Wigner, Princeton professor of theoretical physics, of its import. He also saw Prof. George B. Pegram at Columbia and Fermi, who had come to work in Pegram's laboratory. He impressed on them the significance of these experiments, told them of the work of Hahn and Strassmann, and something they did not

---

[179] The sum of the mass of the 2 fission fragments, totaling less than the mass of the original uranium nucleus, suggested that the matter that had disappeared had been transformed into energy. Although the matter transformed was small, Einstein's formula $E=mc^2$ indicated the enormity of the energy released, considering that the mass must be multiplied by the square of the speed of light, which is 185,000 miles per second. James P. Baxter, Scientists Against Time (Boston; Little, Brown, 1946), p. 420.

[180] Nature, 143, 239. Niels Bohr's account of the verification, confirmed to him in a telegram from Frisch, appeared in this country in Phys. Rev. 55, 418 (Feb. 15, 1939).

know, that Hitler had placed an embargo on Czechoslovakian uranium, the only source of the ore then known in Europe.[181]

Fermi and Leo Szilard at Columbia, Richard B. Roberts at the Carnegie Institution in Washington and other groups at Johns Hopkins, Princeton, and California independently confirmed the Hahn-Strassmann results.[182] Their success at once raised the fear that other scientists in Germany had done the same, realized the probability of uranium fission, and soon the full resources of German science would be organized in a massive assault on the problem.

Aware that the magnitude of difficulties that had yet to be resolved required Government support, Szilard and Wigner in July 1939 conferred with Einstein in Princeton. In letters addressed to President Roosevelt, Einstein and Szilard explained the significance of the uranium experiments, the probability of achieving a chain reaction, and the urgency of proving out that probability before Nazi Germany did. Alexander Sachs, economist and

---

[181] Testimony of Alexander Sachs, Hearings before the Special Committee on Atomic Energy * * * on S. Res. 179 [McMahon Committee] (Nov. 27, 1945), pt. 1, pp. 2–7.

There seemed reason for alarm, but German research in nuclear physics was thwarted by Nazi ideology. That ideology is illuminated in a note that appeared in Science, 85, 262 (1937):

The Manchester Guardian prints in its issue of February 7 the following: "The Berliner Tageblatt reports a lecture given by Geheimrat (Privy Councillor) Professor Dr. Stark, president of the National Physical and Technical Institution (Physikalisch-Technische Reichsanstalt), on 'Dogmatism and Experience in Atomic Research.' Professor Dr. Stark, according to this report, rejected the theory of the form of the atom the moment it was put forward by Lord Rutherford and Niels Bohr—less on technical (sachlichen) grounds than from fundamental objections to their acceptance of views and dogmas of Jewish physicists. He now wished not only to criticize but to bring forward something better as an alternative. He described his new model of the atom with the aid of a short film. Its main feature is that the electron has not the form of a sphere, assigned to it by the Jewish physicist Abraham, but that of a vortex-ring (Wirbelring). Jewish influence, said Professor Dr. Stark, has gone so far that even non-Jewish scientists like Planck, Bohr, Von Laue, Schrödinger and Heisenberg had become partisans of the false doctrine (Irrlehre), and no young lecturer who gave a thought to his career dared to oppose the dominant theory. Some particularly pushing physicists married Jewish women in order to advance their careers. Now that these monstrous circumstances had been discovered, German and authentic (arteigene) physics would forge ahead. 'Privy Councillor Stark's lecture is to serve,' the report concludes, 'as a new thrust to eliminate from German physics the effects of the Jewish mind.' Unfortunately, Stark said in conclusion, in the two decades no important discovery had been made by physicists of the German alignment."

[182] Szilard and Zinn, "Instantaneous emission of fast neutrons in the interaction of slow neutrons with uranium," Phys. Rev. 55, 799 (1939). Other confirming letters in that issue of Phys. Rev. appeared on pp. 509, 510, 511, 516, 797. That of Bohr and Wheeler, which suggested that fission was more likely in U^{235} than U^{238}, appeared in Phys. Rev. 56, 426 (1939).

director of Lehman Bros., friend of Einstein, and since 1932 an economic adviser to the administration, with direct access to the President, offered to put the letters in the President's hands.

The letters were transmitted on October 11, 1939. After reading them Roosevelt said he must have the advice of Dr. Briggs, his principal counsellor in the official family on scientific matters. With the President's permission, Sachs informed Dr. Briggs the same night of his visit to the White House.[183] That week the President appointed an Advisory Committee on Uranium, with Dr. Briggs as chairman and Col. Keith F. Adamson of Army Ordnance and Commander Gilbert C. Hoover of the Navy Bureau of Ordnance his associates, to look into the question of uranium fission.

The first meeting of the committee on October 21, 1939, attended also by Mohler of the Bureau, Sachs, Szilard, Wigner, and Edward Teller, resulted in a report to the President, dated November 1, saying that a chain reaction, though unproved, was a distinct possibility. In tentative terms it speculated on the potential energy that might be released by splitting of uranium atoms, looking toward the possibility of both a new explosive, in which the military was interested, and a new source of energy, long sought by the Navy to drive its submarines without the need of frequent surfacing. Specifically, the report recommended that 4 tons of pure-grade graphite be obtained at once for research, and later acquisition, if justified, of 50 tons of uranium ore.

Three months after the report, in February 1940, the sum of $6,000 from Army and Navy Ordnance funds was made available to purchase a small quantity of graphite for experiments on its absorption qualities. The war in Europe was then 6 months old. Seven weeks later Hitler invaded Denmark and Norway, preliminary to his attack on the Low Countries and France.

It was an awesome responsibility that had been thrust upon Dr. Briggs. In his 66th year—and seventh as Director of the Bureau—he had gone through a series of investigations of Bureau operations and witnessed a serious reduction in Bureau funds and staff. The depression was still on, and so were many of the constrictions of a planned economy. And no end was in sight. A younger man might have seized on the adventure into the unknown promised by nuclear fission, but Dr. Briggs had learned to be cautious. Nor was he at all certain that this was the kind of research, or direction of

---

[183] Testimony of Alexander Sachs. Roosevelt's choice of Dr. Briggs was also probably dictated by the absence of any other real liaison between Government and science, and the fact that security as well as policy restricted him to official circles. See Richard G. Hewlett and Oscar E. Anderson, Jr., The New World, 1939–1946; A History of the U.S. Atomic Energy Commission (Pennsylvania State University Press, 1962), pp. 19–20.

research, in which the Bureau ought to become involved.[184] He and his committee hesitated.

In April 1940, when the committee met at the Bureau for a second time, with Pegram and Fermi also in attendance, it learned that only the U^{235} isotope of uranium fissioned under bombardment by neutrons of thermal (slow) velocities—a significant discovery, provided U^{235} could be sufficiently concentrated. And it heard that a large section of the Kaiser Wilhelm Institute in Berlin had recently been set aside for research on uranium. Yet on that occasion, and at another meeting in June, the committee adjourned without making any definite recommendation except that funds should be sought to support further investigation of isotope separation and the possibility of a chain reaction with U^{235}.[185]

A month later the committee, with Pegram, Urey, Jesse W. Beams of Virginia, Merle A. Tuve of the Carnegie Institution, Ross Gunn of the Naval Research Laboratory, and Gregory Breit of Wisconsin as new members under Dr. Briggs's chairmanship, became the Uranium (or S–1) Section of the National Defense Research Committee (NDRC), set up by the President under Dr. Vannevar Bush to mobilize science for war.[186] As with other research for national defense turned over to it, NDRC was to contract for S–1 research and thereby accelerate the program.

Responsible for formulation of the S–1 program, Briggs at once urged support for the determination of the fundamental physical constants of uranium and graphite and experimentation in the chain reaction. Fermi began his first uranium and graphite pile at Columbia. Urey, with Briggs's encouragement, continued his study of heavy water as a graphite substitute in a chain reaction.[187]

In June 1941, as the scope of research expanded, NDRC was subordinated to the Office of Scientific Research and Development (OSRD), established to direct the entire research resources of the Nation and close the gap between research and procurement for national defense. The S–1 Section, now directly under Dr. James B. Conant as head of NDRC, but with Dr. Briggs continuing as chairman, was transferred to OSRD. When in September 1941 reports of British progress in nuclear research aroused concern over the lack of results here, Samuel K. Allison of Chicago, Edward U.

---

[184] Continued investigation of heavy water had been the first area of research that the Visiting Committee in 1934 strongly recommended be discontinued at the Bureau. See above, p. 345.

[185] Henry D. Smyth, Atomic Energy for Military Purposes (Princeton University Press, 1945), pp. 48–49; Hewlett and Anderson, pp. 22–23.

[186] A facsimile of the letter from the President to Dr. Bush appears in Robert E. Sherwood, Roosevelt and Hopkins: an Intimate History (New York: Harper, 1948), pp. 155–156.

[187] Hewlett and Anderson, pp. 26–29.

Condon, than associate director of the Westinghouse Research Laboratory, and later Director of the National Bureau of Standards, Lloyd P. Smith of Cornell, and Henry D. Smyth of Princeton, with Henry T. Wensel, a Bureau specialist in temperature measurements, were brought in to strengthen the Uranium Section.[188]

As laboratory research and experimentation evolved processes requiring large-scale plant construction, the final stages of research and production were taken over by the Manhattan District, organized in the Army Corps of Engineers in August 1942 to conceal the making of the bomb in the anonymity of the military establishment. A year later the S–1 Section, though never formally dissolved, became inactive.[189]

Acceleration of research and engineering development of the bomb was achieved under NDRC and OSRD by means of contracts let to universities, industry, and research agencies both in and outside the Government, a number of the research contracts falling within the special province of the Bureau. That part of OSRD and Manhattan District development work in which the Bureau laboratories became actively involved is told in the next chapter.

[188] Ibid., pp. 35–36, 44.
[189] Ibid., 41, 82; Smyth Report, pp. 83–84.

Above, the standard yard and ell bed of Queen Elizabeth I, with inches marked in the yard bed. Below, the ell, with sixteenths of the ell marked.

WORLD WAR II
RESEARCH (1941–45)

CHAPTER VII

"IN THE EVENT OF WAR"

The second worldwide war was foreshadowed in the Japanese invasion of Manchuria in 1931, Mussolini's invasion of Ethiopia in 1935, and Hitler's march into the Rhineland in 1936. Isolated and safeguarded by successive Neutrality Acts passed in 1935, 1936, and 1937, which barred the sale of arms or munitions to any warring nation, America watched the piecemeal fall of small nations, Austria and Czechoslovakia to Hitler, Albania to Mussolini. With the German attack on Poland in September 1939, Britain and France declared war against the dictators and World War II began. The first amendments to the Neutrality Acts were enacted.

By temperament strongly neutral and still in the grip of depression, the Nation had willed belief in Chamberlain's "peace in our time" until shaken by the occupation of Czechoslovakia in the spring of 1939. But certain of war and of America's inevitable involvement was the small band of foreign-born scientists, their spokesman Niels Bohr, who had recently arrived in this country. Shepherding atomic research here, Bohn at once urged restriction in all Allied countries of the publication of further data on the possibility of nuclear fission. Many individual scientists refrained, but control of publication in American scientific journals did not become effective until almost a year later, following Hitler's invasion of Denmark and Norway.

The National Bureau of Standards, convinced by the physicists on its Advisory Committee on Uranium of the certainty of a general war, began to put its affairs in order. On September 1, 1939, the day Germany marched into Poland, and one week before the President declared a state of limited national emergency, Dr. Briggs sent to the Department of Commerce a memorandum of the services the Bureau was prepared to render "in the event of war."

In the event of a European war, the Bureau was ready to test all materials to be purchased under the President's recent Strategic Materials

Act, and to increase the output of its optical glass from the current 9,000 pounds to 75,000 pounds per year. It was prepared to certify U.S. materials sent abroad, especially optical and electrical instruments, master gages, aircraft instruments, textiles, metals, and cement.

Should the United States become involved, the Bureau was prepared to solve technical problems of the military services submitted to it, as it had in the First World War. It would test supplies, particularly high precision instruments such as certain electrical and optical instruments, gages, screw thread standards, rubber, textiles, paper, leather, plastics, metals, and glass. It was also ready to assist in the development of new specifications for war materials.

Attached to the memorandum of readiness was a copy of "The War Work of the Bureau of Standards," covering the activities of the Bureau in 1917–18.[1]

Although the Bureau signified its readiness, the Nation was as unprepared for war as it had been two decades earlier. In 1939 the Army had 500 ancient tanks, 5,000 airplanes, 2 million old rifles, and scarcely enough cartridges for a normal year's training. Even 3 years later trainees were to qualify with the pistol for lack of rifles, and maneuver with simulated guns and tanks.[2] The Navy's newest battleship was 20 years old, and the British fleet was still the first defense of our shores. Across the country, more than 9 million people were unemployed, and industry, despite the production potential it had achieved through the application of science, standardization, and operating efficiency during the depression years, clung to its wait-and-see attitude.

As early as the spring of 1938 the President had promulgated the idea of "educational orders" to assist industry in tooling up for the production of certain war materials. Yet 2 years passed before the first order was actually issued.[3] Other orders, little publicized, followed. The President knew that the majority in the Nation was far from committed to the idea of war. The central issue of the campaign of 1940 appeared in the Democratic Party Platform: "The American people are determined that war, raging in

---

[1] Memo, LJB for John M. Johnson, Assistant to Secretary of Commerce, Sept. 1, 1939 (NBS Box 429, AG).

[2] Reinhardt and Kintner, The Haphazard Years, pp. 165, 188.

[3] The order, promptly accepted by the steering gear division of General Motors, called for 500 .30 caliber Browning machine guns. It was not received until June 1940. In March 1941 the first machine gun ever made by an automobile company was completed. Donald M. Nelson, Arsenal of Democracy; the Story of American War Production (New York: Harcourt, Brace, 1946), pp. 225–226.

Europe, Asia, and Africa, shall not come to America. We will not participate in foreign wars. * * *"[4]

Even as fear rose with the collapse of France and apprehension over the spectacle of beleaguered Britain, the isolationist temper prevailed. Preparations for national defense moved slowly, consistent with plans to supply and support Britain, without upsetting the commitment to the electorate. In June 1940, without fanfare, the President approved the mobilization of science through the creation of the National Defense Research Committee. Over violent protests, Congress enacted the Selective Service Act on September 16, 1940, drafting 1.2 million men for a year of defensive training—an act whose extension just 6 months before Pearl Harbor was to pass by a single vote. The Office of Production Management, set up on December 20, 1940, offered to provide counsel, but little more, for the mobilization of industry.

In the spring of 1941 the President's Office of Price Administration established rationing, to control the rising cost of living. Volunteers manning 5,600 price and rationing boards began measuring out allowances of canned goods, coffee, sugar, meat, butter, cheese, shoes, tires, gasoline, and fuel oil. The nation's undeclared war, marked by Lend-Lease, the President's declaration in May 1941 of an unlimited national emergency, and the arming of our merchant ships, ended with Pearl Harbor.

The reluctance that delayed educational orders to industry for weapons production was reflected in a Bureau letter of February 1940. In reply to an inquiry from Military Intelligence, Dr. Briggs reported that the Bureau was conducting "very few projects * * * for the War Department."[5] In the decade before the war Congress had appropriated every dollar requested by the military for research and development, yet as war neared the Nation remained pathetically unprepared from the standpoint of new weapons. Taking the initiative at the instigation of a few key scientists, the Council of National Defense, with the approval of the President, set up NDRC on June 27,

---

[4] Quoted in Edgar E. Robinson, The Roosevelt Leadership, 1933–1945 (Philadelphia: J. B. Lippincott, 1955), p. 257.

In his annual message in January 1940, Roosevelt requested almost $2 billion for national defense. In May he asked for a program of 50,000 planes a year, and with the fall of France imminent requested an additional $1.28 billion for accelerating the development of military and naval requirements. In July the President approved a bill authorizing a two-ocean navy and construction of 200 warships.

[5] Letter, LJB to Assistant CofS, Military Intelligence Division, WD, Feb. 29, 1940 (NBS Box 442, AG).

1940 under Vannevar Bush, to initiate and speed the development of new and improved instruments of war.[6]

Over the next year NDRC organized four divisions with multiple subunits to propose and direct research, in armor and ordnance; bombs, fuel, gases, and chemical problems; communication and transportation; and detection, controls, and instruments. Wholly manned by physicists, chemists, and engineers from the universities and the laboratories of industry, NDRC was authorized to originate and support military research needs and to utilize as necessary the facilities of the Bureau and other Federal agencies. At the inception of NDRC, the Bureau through Briggs' Uranium Committee had just one specifically assigned project, that of investigating "the possible relationship to national defense of recent discoveries in the field of atomistics, notably the fission of uranium." [7] It was the first of more than a score of NDRC projects assigned to the Bureau.

The mobilization of science and scientists began as the military services sent to NDRC lists of projects in which they were engaged and investigations they believed important but had not started for lack of funds or manpower. To them NDRC added projects of its own, in some cases over the early indifference or even opposition of the services. The projects were apportioned among the NDRC divisions and negotiations opened to assign them by contract to the institutions best qualified to work on them. As 1941 began, a total of 184 contracts had been recommended.[8]

Rounding out the organization of scientific research for national defense, an Executive order of June 28, 1941, established the Office of Scientific Research and Development (OSRD). Vannevar Bush, NDRC chief, moved up to OSRD as James B. Conant assumed direction of NDRC. OSRD extended the range of research beyond weaponry to include medicine. With enlarged authority it was also better enabled to correlate NDRC research and that undertaken by the military services themselves and, with the need to accelerate the atomic bomb program, to bridge the gap between research and procurement of the device.[9]

---

[6] Irvin Stewart, Organizing Scientific Research for War (OSRD, Science in World War II, Boston: Little, Brown, 1948), pp. 3–7. The Council of National Defense, created in 1916 "for the co-operation of industries and resources for the national security and welfare," consisted of the Secretaries of War, Navy, Interior, Agriculture, Commerce, and Labor.

[7] Ibid., p. 19.

[8] Ibid., pp. 18, 20. For the negligible impact on the military of technological advances up to 1940 in weaponry, radio, radar, and aviation, see Reinhardt and Kintner, The Haphazard Years, pp. 131 ff.

[9] As finally reorganized in December 1942, NDRC consisted of 19 divisions, in almost all of which the Bureau had some degree of involvement: Ballistic research; effects of impact and explosion; special projectiles and rocket ordnance; ordnance accessories; new

Largely as a consequence of the assignment of NDRC projects, many of them of a classified nature, the annual report of the Bureau for 1941, for the first time, declared its contents restricted to nonconfidential research. A year later so much of Bureau work was classified that further publication of the report became pointless. Equally valid perhaps was the reason offered by the Department of Commerce, that printing of the reports would cease in order to effect savings of paper, manpower, and printing funds.[10]

The open reports for the years just prior to the war identify the preliminary stages of many of the Bureau's later investigations. The last reference to Bureau work on heavy water, for example, appeared in the report for 1939, describing the preparation in the cryogenic laboratory of pure deuterium (D_2), for measurement of its properties at the Bureau and at Columbia University. The substitution of deuterium oxide (D_2O) for part of the water in standard cells was also noted, the difference of drift between cells with normal and heavy water providing a check on the constancy of the standard cell.[11]

Still unclassified in 1939 was the intensification of work on the paraffin hydrocarbons, in search of an optimum synthetic aviation fuel. (The next annual report, more wary perhaps, emphasized the antiknock characteristics of these hydrocarbons in automotive engines.)

The formation of the Interdepartmental Screw Thread Committee, a joint War, Navy, and Commerce Department board, was reported in 1940, to

---

missiles (of which Hugh L. Dryden was a section chief directing an investigation of jet propulsion and certain guided missile research); subsurface warfare; fire control; explosives; chemistry; absorbents and aerosols; chemical engineering; transportation development; electrical communication (of which J. H. Dellinger headed the radio propagation section); radar; radio coordination; optics; physics; war metallurgy; and miscellaneous weapons. The Bureau was also concerned in three of the five OSRD panels outside the divisions: Applied mathematics, vacuum tube development, and radio propagation. Ibid., pp. 84–97.

Considerable Bureau wartime research was done under NDRC and OSRD auspices, and as a consequence the reports and correspondence relating to that research are to be found principally in the OSRD records now stored in the National Archives. See General Records of OSRD, Transfer of Funds—NBS, in NARG 227, and Master Subject Index, Summary Technical Reports of NDRC. Wartime research for NACA and for the Navy and War Departments was reported directly to these agencies, the reports and records maintained in their files.

[10] A typescript of the annual report for 1943, containing open material only, and with the Commerce note on suspension of publication, is available in NBS Box 482, PRA. An MS annual report for 1944 is in NBS Box 494, PRA. None has been found for 1945 except that portion prepared by the division of weights and measures, in NBS Box 506, PRA.

[11] NBS Annual Report 1939, pp. 51, 53.

make mandatory the interchangeability of parts in industries retooling under educational orders. New research had begun on fire-detection and fire-extinguishing equipment for airplane engines, on better aircraft metals, and on vibration problems that had arisen as airplane engine weights decreased and speeds increased. Optical glass production had gone up sharply, in order to provide an emergency reserve.[12] And "as part of the national defense program," an extensive survey was begun of all standardization, simplification, and code activities of the Nation's technical societies and trade associations, looking to a complete revision of the Bureau's National Directory of Commodity Specifications.

Among the progress reports on the hundreds of projects on which the Bureau had been working during the past decade, the 1940 annual report made special note of the successful preparation of an iron with less than 0.01 percent impurities. This nearly elemental iron was expected to permit better determination of the fundamental properties of the metal than ever before possible.[13] A new investigation was begun that year for the bone char industry in the production of bone char and vegetable carbons. Although the use of bone char for clarifying and decolorizing raw sugar was several centuries old, virtually no fundamental data existed on the functioning of decolorizing media. The exploration of techniques for determining the characteristics of the raw materials, the principles of decolorization of bone char, and bone char revivification continued through the war years and after.[14]

Reported at length that year was the first tabulation of results of an investigation begun in 1936 of truck-weighing scales. As the Bureau had been called on to determine the inequities of commercial weights and measures in 1910, railroad car scales in 1915, and mine scales in 1918, so in the thirties Bureau surveillance of the trucking industry was sought as the juggernauts of the highway began to overtake the railroads in moving pro-

---

[12] The Bureau was awarded a contract by the Procurement Division of the Treasury Department in November 1939 for 11,400 pounds of optical glass as a national reserve, with the request to keep confidential the fact that the glass was for Army aerial camera lenses and Navy binoculars. Monthly Report, LJB to Secretary of Commerce, November 1939 (NBS Box 440, PRM); memo, R. T. Stull for E. C. Crittenden, February 21, 1940 (NBS Box 442, AG). After Pearl Harbor, all optical glass production became a classified project.

[13] RP1226 (Thompson and Cleaves, 1939) and RP1472 (Cleaves and Hiegel, 1942) described the preparation and properties of the iron. By 1949 the Bureau was preparing 5-pound ingots of the iron so pure that detection of aberrations "constituted a major problem" (NBS Annual Report 1949, p. 47).

[14] NBS Annual Report 1940, pp. 71–72; Annual Report 1948, p. 219.

duce and other commodities across the Nation.[15] Testing more than 400 commercial truck-weighing scales in the first year of its inquiry, the Bureau found 80 percent of them with errors exceeding the agreed on allowable tolerance. Moving from State to State with its test vehicle, Bureau inspectors consistently reported three out of four scales with excessive errors, and partly as a result of these errors, a dangerous prevalence of overloaded trucks. The 5-year program was completed in 1941 when all 48 States had been visited and their State and local agencies supplied with the inspection data collected by the Bureau and its specifications for proper test equipment and procedures.[16]

Still not deemed matters of secrecy in 1941 were references to shortages of strategic materials, the acquisition of stores of quartz crystal, and Bureau work in substitute materials.

Among the first metals declared critical were aluminum, zinc, and tin, forcing industry to turn to porcelain-enameled iron for roofing and siding and for kitchen and bakeshop utensils. New technical specifications for Army and Marine Corps canteens, mess plates, and other ware made of enameled iron followed Bureau studies of their weather resistance and impact and torsional resistance.[17] Investigations were also made in the stress-strain properties of stainless steel as a substitute for aluminum alloy in aircraft production and in airplane firewalls and cowlings.[18]

While stainless steel (soon to be in critical supply too) proved in some instances an acceptable substitute for aluminum alloy and enameled iron had its uses, their limitations did much to foster the plastics industry, then in its infancy. In 1936, a year after the establishment of its plastics section, the Bureau prepared a comprehensive survey of the young industry.[19] By 1941 sufficient knowledge was available to set up emergency specifications utilizing plastics in place of scarce metals in many Government purchases. With Navy and NACA funds, research began on the properties and fabrication of these strong lightweight materials, and tests were made of their use as metal substitutes in such aircraft accessories as windshields and transparent enclosures. Utilization of the synthetic resins, as

---

[15] The investigations into weights and measures and railroad car scales are described in chs. II and III. In testing mine scales in 1918, the Bureau did not find a single scale —upon which the wages of coal miners were based—even approximating the reasonable tolerance set by the Bureau, and one scale for weighing loads of less than 2 tons was found out of balance by the extraordinary error of 616 pounds. NBS Annual Report 1918, p. 29.

[16] NBS Annual Report 1937, p. 62; Annual Report 1941, pp. 67–68.

[17] NBS Annual Report 1941, p. 80; Annual Report 1942, p. 120.

[18] NBS Annual Report 1941, p. 74; Annual Report 1942, p. 118.

[19] C411, "Organic plastics" (Kline, 1936); Kline, "History of plastics and their uses * * *," a series of articles in Modern Plastics, vols. 17–18 (1940–41).

well as cellulose derivatives, was also investigated, for their use as protective coverings of aluminum and magnesium alloy aircraft parts.[20]

Two decades of fundamental studies in electrodeposition were available to the Bureau in 1941 when it started adapting its knowledge of plating to production difficulties brought on by metal shortages. At the urgent request of OPM and industry, tableware, guns, cartridge cases, projectiles, surgical instruments, aircraft parts, reflectors, plumbing fixtures, hardware, and other materials with their new plated surfaces or finishes came to the Bureau for study and advice on improving serviceability. The vital importance of plating was amply demonstrated in one instance where iron deposits were satisfactorily substituted for all the nickel and part of the copper normally used in the making of printing plates.[21]

Although the Bureau was conducting little work besides testing for the War Department in the early months of 1940, by July the number of confidential projects for the services, assigned through NACA and NDRC, had so increased that Dr. Briggs felt it necessary to obtain permission to close the laboratories to all but official visitors.[22] The next year, with a special appropriation of $21,000, work started on fencing in the Bureau grounds, guards began their rounds, and plans were made to close off the public thoroughfare, Van Ness Street, that ran through the Bureau site.[23]

By December 1941 fully 90 percent of the Bureau staff was engaged in war research. Not long after, the grounds were declared a "prohibited zone," under patrol by the Military Police.[24] Thus the Bureau was already on a war footing when the attack on Pearl Harbor made the United States a full-fledged belligerent.

Under the first shock of war, apprehension arose that enemy air fleets might attack either of our coasts without warning. Calmer heads doubted the likelihood of 3,000-mile air sorties but encouraged both blackouts and brownouts, knowing that the brightly lit coastal cities provided illumination against which ships well out to sea might be made visible to prowling enemy submarines. The Bureau assisted in the joint Army-Navy program to determine the characteristics of sky glow from artificial sources and the extent to which sky glow and shore lights might aid hostile ships offshore. It also worked with the War Department to establish requirements in blackouts, particularly with respect to street lighting, buildings, and highway movement. Even the blackout of the railroads, in force abroad, was studied, though never resorted to here.

---

[20] NBS Annual Report 1941, pp. 77–78. See below, p. 422.
[21] NBS Annual Report 1941, p. 74; Annual Report 1942, p. 114.
[22] Memo, LJB to Acting Secretary of Commerce, July 10, 1940 (NBS Box 442, AG).
[23] NBS Annual Report 1941, p. 63.
[24] Hearings * * * 1943 (Jan. 12, 1942), p. 208; MS NBS Annual Report 1943, n.p.

A mockup mask devised at the Bureau for cutting the upward glare of sealed beam headlights, one of dozens of such blackout or brownout devices to reduce skyglow over the coastal cities in the first years of the war.

In the spring of 1942 the Office of Civilian Defense instituted dimouts and blackouts in full force. At the request of OCD, the Bureau tested textiles and paper as blackout materials, devised masks to eliminate upward light from automobile headlights, improved Army blackout headlamps, and determined the acoustic properties of suitable air-raid alarms, including sirens, steam and compressed-air whistles, and loudspeakers. A Bureau letter circular went out to city and town authorities on alarm systems they might set up with available materials, and an "Air Raid Protection Code for Federal Buildings" was distributed to Federal offices throughout the country.[25]

The construction of Army camps, bases, and temporary Government office structures that began with passage of the Selective Service Act went into high gear after 1941. The Bureau's building specifications for their fabrication saved much vital material. (Labor costs were something else again.) In the stress of the emergency, glaring deficiencies in building codes that had resisted Bureau efforts at change were rectified by Federal edict,

[25] NBS Annual Report 1942, pp. 110, 115; Lyman J. Briggs, NBS War Research: the National Bureau of Standards in World War II (September 1949), pp. 103–104 (hereafter cited as NBS War Research); LC685, "Devices for air raid warnings" (1942), superseded by LC706 (1942).

accomplishing, the Bureau noted wryly, long overdue "legitimate economies." New knowledge of construction, for example, had made obsolete the use of 2 x 6 beams in roof rafters, where 2 x 4's were more than adequate, and multiplied by tens of thousands of buildings saved forests of precious wood.[26]

Time, labor, and material-saving studies available in the Bureau's building and housing studies had long urged the use of precast concrete flooring, of prefabricated wood and sheet-steel frames, walls, floors, and roofs, of metallic roofing materials, and of fiber and plywood paneling as insulation materials. These as well as the elimination of nonessentials and substitution of less scarce or noncritical materials were to find their way into defense housing projects through new building code requirements.[27]

The greatest inertia in the building world, adding disproportionately to construction costs and most prodigal of labor and materials, was in plumbing. Bureau research since the 1920's on plumbing practices and plumbing hardware had little impact until the war, when a new manual, designed to save "thousands of tons of critical metals," became the basis for emergency plumbing standards made mandatory in all Federal construction.[28]

The shift from educational orders to all-out war production almost immediately quadrupled Bureau testing and certification of measuring instruments and apparatus, particularly of the precision gage blocks that served as master standards in the production and inspection of war materials. Within 6 months Army Ordnance set up 13 district gage laboratories across the country to serve gage manufacturers, and established gage test facilities at all its arsenals turning out guns and shells. The need for enormous quantities of the blocks led to their hasty manufacture by inexperienced firms, forcing the Bureau to reject large numbers of seriously inaccurate or defective sets before its standards were met.[29]

Early wartime tasks with high priority assigned to the Bureau included investigations in the conservation of petroleum, in the production of synthetic rubber, and the testing and stockpiling of quartz crystals. The concern in the twenties over America's dwindling petroleum resources waned with the discovery of new fields in the Americas and the importation of oil from the Caucasus and the Middle East. The flood of oil created a vast new industry and by 1940 propelled more than 32 million automobiles, buses, and trucks over the Nation's roads. But as oil tankers became prime targets of enemy

---

[26] Hearings * * * 1941 (Dec. 9, 1939), pp. 122, 124.

[27] NBS Annual Report 1941, p. 85; Annual Report 1942, pp. 125–127; BMS88, "Recommended building code requirements for * * * war housing" (1942).

[28] Ibid., and BMS66, "Plumbing manual" (1940).

[29] NBS Annual Report 1942, p. 107.

submarines, the supply tightened. Gasoline rationing became severe, however, not so much to save gas as to conserve the rubber in automobile tires.

Convinced by their ration cards that the critical shortage was in gasoline, inventive citizens besieged the Office of the Petroleum Coordinator with gas-saving devices. Almost a hundred of their expedients came to the Bureau for assessment, among them naphthalene fuel dopes, air bleeds or "squirrel cages" in the intake manifold, speed governors in the fuel line, a vacuum gage calibrated to read miles per gallon, and a variety of attachments to the exhaust line—all interesting but not to the purpose.[30]

Far more critical was rubber. Cut off from natural rubber resources by the Japanese conquests in the Pacific, this country began all-out development of synthetic rubber. With precision techniques learned in the 1920's on isoprene when it was a laboratory curiosity, the Bureau was to supply endless measurements of the thermodynamic properties of artificial rubbers and their basic materials, data vital to their manufacture.[31]

As crucial in wartime as petroleum and rubber was a component of radio whose supply was endangered because it had to be imported. That was the wafer-thin quartz crystal, a silicon dioxide formed in the earth under pressure, whose piezoelectric property made it possible to hold radio transmission and reception to a precise frequency. As the heart of all radio apparatus, huge quantities of the crystal were to be needed in the radio communication apparatus of the armed forces in everything from walkie-talkies to radar, as well as in the warborn realm of electronic equipment.

The best quartz crystal was mined almost exclusively in Brazil, and when attempts to produce an artificial crystalline quartz met with only fair success, large-scale importation and stockpiling of the crystal began. Charged with examination and certification of the raw material, a special unit in the optical division of the Bureau by 1942 was testing 75,000 pounds of raw crystal per month, of which approximately a quarter proved suitable for making radio oscillators.[32]

As war approached in 1941, Congress appropriated $100,000 to enlarge the optical glass plant at the Bureau and $230,000 for a permanent radio laboratory at Beltsville, Md., to replace the wooden structure destroyed by fire the previous November. With the acquisition of more powerful radio equipment at the Beltsville laboratory, transmission of standard radio and audio frequencies and other services was extended so that good reception was possible throughout the United States and fair reception over most

---

[30] NBS Annual Report 1942, p. 110.

[31] Ibid., pp. 116–117. The synthetic rubber program is described on pp. 411–412.

[32] NBS Annual Report 1942, p. 111. For more on the crystal program, see pp. 408–410.

of the world.[33] Lost to the Bureau was the expanse of open fields (scarce in the Washington area) on which the radio propagation research laboratory at Meadows, Md., was situated. It was requisitioned in 1942 for the construction of Andrews Air Force Base, and the laboratory moved its recording equipment to new structures at Sterling, Va.

On the 12.5 acres of "Pembroke Park" that the Bureau acquired in 1942, adjacent to the west and north of its Washington site, Congress authorized construction of a new and much needed Materials Testing Laboratory. It was completed in April 1943 at a cost of $600,000. Erection of a 6-foot wind tunnel for bomb and projectile research completed the wartime construction at the Bureau under direct appropriations.[34]

The war saw virtually no change in the organizational structure of the Bureau beyond creation of a special projects section for work on guided missiles and a new division for proximity fuze and other ordnance research. The staff of 950 in 1939 rose to 1,204 by mid-1941. Two years later it totaled 2,263, including over 200 in uniform, and approximately that level was maintained to the end of the war.[35]

More spectacularly, total working funds, direct and transferred, which reached a new high—in excess of $3 million—in fiscal years 1940 and 1941, soared to $7½ million in 1942, and to their peak of $13½ million by 1944. In 1940 transferred funds had been one-sixth of regular appropriations to the Bureau. A year later, with NDRC and service assignments, they were one-half, and by 1944 had grown to almost twice the amount of direct appropriations.[36]

---

[33] Memo, LJB for Acting Secretary of Commerce, July 10, 1940 (NBS Box 442, AG); NBS Annual Report 1941, p. 65; Science, 98, supp. 8 (1943); Science, 101, supp. 10 (1945).

[34] NBS Annual Report 1941, p. 61; Annual Report 1942, p. 103; MS Annual Report 1943, n.p. With the Thom estate, known as "Pembroke Park," the Bureau site comprised 67.8 acres. The estate is described in Hearings * * * 1940 (Apr. 21, 1939), pp. 184–186. The new wind tunnel, authorized in 1943, was completed at a cost of $110,000 2 years later. See G. B. Schubauer, MS "History of the Aerodynamics Section," March 1956 (NBS Historical File). Other construction, under transferred defense funds, included a number of Quonset huts, enlargement of the glass plant, storage and laboratory facilities for the quartz program, and new quarters for the ordnance (proximity fuze) project. Except for the main ordnance building and the addition of a story to the Far West building, all were temporary structures.

[35] MS Annual Report 1943. Of the 2,372 on the Bureau staff in 1944, directors and supervisors numbered 116, research scientists 679, laboratory assistants 576, and clerical, mechanical and other workers 901. Report to the Senate Subcommittee on War Mobilization, Apr. 13, 1944 (NBS Box 489, AGL).

[36] See app. F. The agencies supplying transferred funds in 1942–44, as well as the amounts and in some cases the identity of the projects, are reported in NBS Box 464, AG; Box 477, AG and FP; and Box 489, AGL.

By February 1943, Dr. Briggs reported, the entire staff and facilities of the Bureau were wholly engaged in war work. All conference and lecture rooms had been converted to laboratories, and double and triple shifts were in effect in some sections to make maximum use of space and equipment. The prewar 39-hour week had long since been extended to 44 hours and no overtime pay was permitted.

The rising cost of food, clothing, and rent worked some hardship, but almost everyone at the Bureau subscribed 10 percent of his salary for war bonds. All worried about the 5 percent Victory tax and new income taxes to come, considering their prewar civil service salaries. And because of the pay, the Bureau had had to recruit boys too young for the armed forces as shop assistants and for training as mechanics and instrumentmakers. With few exceptions, they were lost within a year or two to the defense industries.[37]

Within a year after the war began, Dr. Briggs was to recall, "just about everything at the Bureau was classified." The tight security thrown around the work in the laboratories became constricting at times, and on occasion Dr. Briggs felt he had to exercise some discretion. But that discretion did not extend to anything connected with the research on the atomic bomb.[38]

THE BUREAU AND THE ATOMIC BOMB

Under the direction of Dr. Briggs during the first 2 critical years of its inception, the work that led to the atomic bomb grew thereafter beyond the powers of the Uranium Committee to control. It became a technological feat, stretching the capabilities of the greatest concentration of the Nation's scientists and engineers ever assembled. The massive requirements for final production had to be lodged eventually in the vast anonymity of the military establishment.

The Bureau staff was engaged in scores of other fundamental investigations in physics, applied mathematics, chemistry, and engineering for the immediate prosecution of the war and few more than 60 members gave full time to the bomb program. Apart from special assignments at Oak Ridge and at Los Alamos, most of the Bureau participants carried out their work in the Washington laboratories. The Bureau was nevertheless to serve to the end of the war as "a central control laboratory for determining the purity of uranium and other products * * * used," that work, it was said,

[37] Letter, LJB to Department of Commerce, Aug. 11, 1942 (NBS Box 464, AP); letter, LJB to chairman, Senate Commission on Appropriations, Oct. 15, 1942 (ibid., AG); Hearings * * * 1944 (Feb. 26, 1943), p. 77.

[38] Interview with Dr. Briggs, Nov. 1, 1961.

"so closely guarded that the Bureau's participation in the atomic bomb project was not known to the members of the staff not associated with the undertaking."[39]

This, of course, was not entirely so. Even before the close of the photoelectric phase of the proximity fuze project in 1943, when most of that group were sent out to Los Alamos, many at the Bureau suspected or knew generally that some kind of new weapon using uranium was under development. Yet so weighted was the wrap of secrecy that even some directly involved in research on "Tuballoy," the Briticism adopted by the Bureau as the code name for uranium, had no inkling of the real purpose of their research.[40] Wholly engrossed in his determination of the energy states of uranium, one member of the Bureau recalls thinking that the metal might be for a new type of small power plant, possibly for airplanes, to enable them to carry bigger bomb loads, or for submarines, in order to carry a larger store of torpedoes. "The last thing in the world I thought the uranium could be used for was in a bomb," he was to say.[41] The story of that secret research bears retelling.

In the year after verification in this country of the splitting of the uranium atom, Enrico Fermi sought to demonstrate a chain reaction in natural unconcentrated uranium. His colleague at Columbia, John R. Dunning, was investigating the two isotopes of uranium, the rare 235, less than 1 percent of the natural element, and the abundant isotope 238, comprising 99.3 percent of the element. In March 1940, Dunning conclusively demonstrated that U^{235} was the isotope that fissioned with slow neutrons.[42]

That same spring Edwin M. McMillan and Philip H. Abelson at the University of California made an even more spectacular discovery, that neutron absorption by U^{238} resulted in two new elements with atomic numbers 93 and 94. They were named neptunium (Np) and plutonium (Pu). Study of the latter indicated it was probably as fissionable by thermal (slow) neutrons as U^{235}. So nebulous was the "bomb project" at that stage, however, that further investigation of plutonium was delayed while McMillan went off to MIT to work on a more pressing matter, radar.[43]

---

[39] Briggs, NBS War Research, p. 8.

[40] "Tuballoy" came from "Tube Alloys," the meaningless and unintelligible expression used by the British for their uranium bomb program.

[41] Interview with Dr. Carl C. Kiess, May 1, 1964. For Harold Urey's similar reaction concerning his heavy water research, see ch. VI, p. 359n.

[42] Hewlett and Anderson, The New World, 1939–1946: A History of the United States Atomic Energy Commission, pp. 13–14, 22.

[43] Ibid., pp. 33–34; McMillan and Abelson, "Radioactive element 93," Phys. Rev. 57, 1185 (1940). The discovery held out the possibility that element 94 could be produced in a pile and then separated chemically, without the tremendous expense of building isotope separation plants. Moreover, if plutonium was fissionable it would utilize all but a small fraction of the metal in a natural uranium pile.

With attention focused on the work at Columbia, three crucial questions confronted Dr. Briggs and his advisory committee in the early summer of 1940: (1) Were there any circumstances under which a chain reaction could actually be achieved? (2) Could the isotope 235 be separated on a large scale? (3) Could moderators such as graphite or heavy water and other materials be obtained of sufficient purity and in sufficient quantity? [44]

The possibility that deuterium (heavy water) might be a better moderator of a chain reaction than graphite was not overlooked. The British were convinced that a chain reaction would go in relatively small units of uranium and heavy water, and in February 1941 Urey at Columbia began investigating methods for large-scale concentration of deuterium.[45] Although heavy water proved more effective than graphite in slowing down neutrons and showed a smaller neutron absorption, its high efficiency in much smaller quantities than graphite was outweighed by the difficulties of producing useful amounts. Subsequent experiments with a uranium and heavy-water pile demonstrated that such a pile could not be shut down as completely or as rapidly as the graphite pile. Important as heavy water was in later nuclear weapons research, and in scientific, biological, and industrial research, it played little part in the wartime achievement.[46] Procurement, therefore, centered on graphite.

A group at the Bureau under Clement J. Rodden at once started work on methods of analysis for the development of a highly purified graphite. Because of the strong neutron-absorbing characteristics of the boron found in the commercial product, a graphite low in boron was absolutely essential. The work of Rodden in devising a reliable method for boron determination, later successfully applied to boron in uranium as well, enabled carbon manufacturers to produce a much more highly purified graphite. By the middle of 1942 this problem was essentially solved.[47]

Two investigations into the possibility of separating the isotopes of uranium started in the fall of 1940. At Columbia a group under Dunning

---

[44] Smyth, Atomic Energy for Military Purposes (Smyth Report), p. 55.

[45] A fine summary of British encouragement of and contributions to the project appears in Groves, Now It Can Be Told, pp. 406–408. See also report of the Directorate of Tube Alloys, Statements Relating to the Atomic Bomb (London: Her Majesty's Stationery Office, 1945), pp. 13 ff; its summary in Rev. Mod. Phys, 17, 472 (1945); and Margaret Gowing, Britain and Atomic Energy, 1939–1945 (London: Macmillan, 1964).

[46] Smyth Report, pp. 95, 147–149, 153. In July 1942, marking the genesis of the hydrogen bomb, Oppenheimer first disclosed the theoretical calculations of his group at California indicating "that a much more powerful reaction than nuclear fission might be produced by the thermonuclear fusion of deuterium, the heavy hydrogen isotope," and therefore "the possibility of a * * * weapon using a more easily attainable material" than U^{235} or U^{238}. Hewlett and Anderson, p. 104.

[47] Smyth Report, p. 95; NBS War Research, p. 8.

initiated research in a gaseous diffusion method for the separation and concentration of U^{235}. At the Bureau, Philip H. Abelson of the Carnegie Institution attempted separation of the two isotopes by thermal diffusion of uranium hexafluoride, the only gaseous compound of uranium. Although an exceedingly corrosive material, the hexafluoride was workable because it was stable as a liquid at slightly elevated temperatures and moderate pressures. Abelson's work, carried out with Navy funds, was transferred to larger facilities at the Naval Research Laboratory in the summer of 1941.[48]

Efforts made in the Bureau laboratories and at Westinghouse and General Electric to find a method for manufacturing uranium powder or pure ingots progressed slowly and the Columbia group turned to the processed ore, uranium oxide, which was available in small quantities from Canada. It was evident that both Fermi's uranium pile and isotope separation depended upon obtaining uranium in a highly purified metallic form or at least as a highly purified uranium oxide. The problem came to the Bureau, and in the summer of 1941 a group under James I. Hoffman found that ether extraction of uranium oxide after conversion to uranyl nitrate removed virtually all impurities from the oxide.[49]

As a final step in the production of uranium metal, determination and analysis had to be made of the residual boron content of the reconverted oxide. Studies by Bourdon F. Scribner and J. A. Scherrer opened the way to subsequent reduction of the boron content, by reaction with calcium hydride. After months of experimentation, their coworker Clement Rodden distilled an extremely pure calcium making this last step possible. The ether extraction and boron reduction processes, as effective with pitchblende and carnotite ore concentrates as with uranium ores, became standard procedures in the purification of all uranium used in piles.[50]

The winter of 1940–41 was a time of decision. Besides the investigations in gaseous and thermal diffusion methods for isotope separation, Jesse W. Beams at Virginia was working on a centrifuge process and Ernest O. Lawrence at California on electromagnetic methods of separation. While Dr. Briggs felt that quantity separation of isotopes was important from a military standpoint as probably the only way to a chain reaction in a mass small enough for a bomb, separation would be difficult and expensive. Pilot plant construction ought therefore to wait until further studies disclosed the most promising method. Characteristically, his real interest was in power

[48] Both the thermal and gaseous diffusion processes were to be used in the large-scale plants for the production of U^{235} at Oak Ridge, the gaseous method eventually proving the more efficient of the two.

[49] Hewlett and Anderson, pp. 28–29, 86; Smyth Report, p. 93; NBS War Research, pp. 8–9.

[50] Hewlett and Anderson, pp. 66, 87; NBS War Research, p. 9.

production and not a bomb, and therefore in the uranium-graphite experiment and in quantity production of heavy water, which might go better in a pile.[51]

The cautious progress of the bomb project under Dr. Briggs's advisory committee was apparent in the meager funds and the assignment of them proposed in July 1941. The committee recommended grants of $167,000 for a pilot plant to produce heavy water for Fermi's chain-reaction studies, $95,000 for the centrifuge work on elements 93 and 94, $25,000 for gaseous-diffusion experiments, $10,000 for other isotope separation studies, $30,000 for investigation of the chemistry of uranium compounds and studies of separation methods, and just $8,000 for an investigation of element 94, plutonium.[52] The total was $2 billion short of the final cost of the first atomic bomb.

So far as the general public was concerned, the shroud of secrecy that descended after 1940 on what the President called "atomistic research" was almost absolute. The single letter on the subject from an inquiring citizen found in Bureau files was wide of the mark. The reply was more pertinent. In June 1941 a man in Meredith, N.H., wrote to the White House protesting an unnamed scientist's claim that with the smashing of the atom the time would soon come when "every householder would be able to store a thousand years' fuel supply in his cellar." The New Hampshire man saw nothing but disaster in this enormous power confined in his home or, more dangerously in the possession of unfriendly persons, and sought reassurance.

Dr. Briggs's personal reply to the letter, which had been sent on from the White House for an answer, was only vaguely comforting. It also reflected something of his own feeling at the time. There was no need, he wrote, "to feel unduly alarmed about smashing atoms. Up to the present time at least this has been accomplished only by putting into the system as a whole a great deal more energy than can be got out of it." [53]

Although production of Lend-Lease equipment and munitions mounted month by month and such priority projects as radar and rockets, the proximity fuze, and new air, surfacc, and subsurface weapons progressed, no comparable signs of achievement sustained the physicists working on the bomb. British reports in the spring of 1941 that the Germans were producing heavy water in quantity in Norway and were acquiring materials that could only be used in work with uranium prompted demands for greater effort and more results. The fear grew that time was running out.

---

[51] Hewlett and Anderson, pp. 37, 40; James P. Baxter, Scientists Against Time, p. 425.
[52] Hewlett and Anderson, p. 40.
[53] Letter, LJB, June 17, 1941 (NBS Box 455, IPXA). Cf. Leo Szilard's statement in a letter of Jan. 25, 1939, that the possession of atomic energy is not "very exciting * * * if the energy output is only two or three times the energy input." Quoted in Lewis S. Strauss, Men and Decisions (New York: Doubleday, 1962), p. 172.

Partly in order to accelerate the contract research on uranium projects initiated by NDRC and provide better coordinated direction, OSRD was established in June 1941, with direct access to the President. Urgently required was information on the critical mass of a U^{235} bomb, design data on a gaseous diffusion plant for large-scale separation of uranium isotopes, and assessment of a heavy-water pile. Apart from the NDRC assignments of the Advisory Committee (now OSRD's S–1 Section), at the direction of OSRD the problem of large-scale uranium isotope separation was turned over to groups under Lawrence and Urey, and that of production of element 94 (plutonium) to Compton's group at the new and cryptically named "Metallurgical Laboratory" at the University of Chicago.[54]

By the end of 1941 research groups at Columbia, Princeton, Chicago, California and elsewhere had achieved considerable basic knowledge of nuclear properties and of the physical constants of the materials involved. Sufficient mathematical calculations had been made to suggest the probability that the critical size of a bomb either with concentrated U^{235} or the new element plutonium was almost certainly within practical limits.[55] On the other hand, Fermi had constructed an experimental graphite and uranium pile at Columbia but no chain reaction had been achieved principally because of the poisoning effect of the boron in the uranium. No appreciable amount of U^{235} had been separated from U^{238}, only traces of plutonium had been produced, and the production of large quantites of uranium metal, heavy water, and pure graphite still remained largely in the discussion stage.[56]

One week before Pearl Harbor, Dr. Briggs's S–1 Section made the decision recommending a major all-out effort to construct the bomb. Eleven days after Pearl Harbor, at another meeting in Dr. Briggs's office at the Bureau, Arthur H. Compton, as head of a committee of the National Academy of Sciences, outlined the time schedule that the project must strive to meet:

> By July 1, 1942, to determine whether a chain reaction was possible.
>
> By January 1943, to achieve the first chain reaction.

---

[54] Smyth Report, p. 71; Hewlett and Anderson, p. 45.

[55] If plutonium was still an unknown quantity in November 1941, it was known with some certainty that a spectacularly destructive fission bomb would result from bringing quickly together a sufficient mass of U^{235}—somewhere between 2 and 100 kg. (4.4 and 220 pounds)—although nothing like even 2 kg of the material was yet in sight (Hewlett and Anderson, p. 47). On this basis it was conjectured that from 1 to 10 tons of U^{235} would be required to construct the bombs necessary to devastate the major military and industrial objectives in Germany. Tonnage production, either by the gaseous diffusion or centrifuge method, was believed to be 3 or 4 years away (Baxter, pp. 427–428).

[56] Smyth Report, p. 73.

By January 1944, to extract the first element 94 from uranium.
By January 1945, to have a bomb.[57]

Speed became essential. To hasten decisions, the S–1 Section, grown too large for action, was reorganized in June 1942 as the S–1 Executive Committee under James B. Conant of NDRC, with Briggs, Compton, Lawrence, Urey, and Eger V. Murphree (of Standard Oil Development Co.) as members. By then, five possible approaches to bomb production had emerged holding high promise: separation of U^{235} by centrifuge, diffusion, or electromagnetic methods, and production of plutonium in a uranium-graphite or uranium-heavy water pile.[58] All were scheduled to be explored through the pilot plant stage, and all depended to a large degree on what soon became the principal function of the Bureau, the development of analytical procedures for controlling the purity of critical materials in the reactors and in the bomb.

Some of these materials required as many as 20 individual chemical analyses, and spectrographic determinations of as many as 30 elements in their raw state, before methods for refinement could be established.[59] By the end of 1945 nearly 9,000 samples of materials were to come into the Bureau laboratories and almost 30,000 separate analyses completed. Equally extensive investigations in the metallurgy and metallography of uranium were necessary, to determine, for example, the kinds of crucible materials in which uranium could be melted without contamination. Much work was also done at the Bureau toward establishing radioactivity measurements and safety procedures in handling the bomb materials.[60]

The analytical work of the Bureau was accelerated in June 1942 with the approval of funds for three pilot plants for U^{235} production and one for plutonium. The theoretical design of the plants had been accomplished and their construction assigned to the Army Corps of Engineers under the disguise of the "DMS (Development of Substitute Materials) project." In August 1942 the DMS project became the Manhattan District project, its director Brig. Gen. Leslie R. Groves.

---

[57] Hewlett and Anderson, pp. 54–55.
[58] Hewlett and Anderson, p. 71.
[59] The analytic research of the Bureau was reported in the classified Manhattan District Technical Series. The few papers published by the Bureau after the war include a summary account of analysis of the U spectrum, by Kiess, Humphreys, and Laun in RP1729 (1946); the development of a highly sensitive method for spectrographic determination of 33 volatile impure elements in U-base materials, by Scribner and Mullin in RP1753 (1946); and determination of the thermoelectric properties of U, by Dahl and VanDusen in RP1813 (1947). For the work of the Bureau's mathematics group on the atomic bomb and other wartime projects, see OSRD records, NARG 227, file MTP, General Correspondence.
[60] NBS War Research, pp. 9–15; interview with William F. Roeser, Dec. 3, 1963.

If many of the scientists connected with the bomb project under NDRC and OSRD secretly hoped that some principle might emerge proving the inherent impossibility of an atomic bomb, by mid-1942 that hope was past. Theoretical possibility had become high probability, and in December General Groves entered contract negotiations for the design and construction at Oak Ridge, Tenn., of a giant industrial complex beyond anything the original members of the S–1 Committee could possibly have contemplated. The commitment had been made, and with the transfer of all OSRD contracts to the Army in May 1943, the research responsibilities of the S–1 Committee ended.[61]

By the fall of 1942 enough pure graphite, uranium oxide, and uranium metal were arriving at the Metallurgical Laboratory at Chicago from industry to justify building an actual self-sustaining chain reacting pile. Little more than 6 tons of uranium metal were at hand, just barely sufficient for the pile Fermi and his associates erected under the west stands of Stagg Field. There on December 2, 1942, the first nuclear chain reaction was produced in a system using normal uranium.

The immediate objectives of the Metallurgical Laboratory were proved, that a controllable chain reaction could be produced in unseparated uranium, and that separation of fissionable plutonium from the U^{238} in the pile was more feasible than separation of the uranium isotopes. The ultimate objectives of the laboratory still remained, to determine a process for separating the plutonium chemically from the pile, and to obtain theoretical and experimental data on a "fast neutron" reaction, such as would be required in an atomic bomb.[62]

The decision to build a pilot plant for the relatively large-scale extraction and purification of plutonium had been made in January 1942. Construction of the plant known as the Clinton Engineer Works began just above the town of Oak Ridge. The Clinton pile started operating in November 1943, its successful procedures and the data obtained in its performance guiding construction of the large-scale plant going up at Hanford, on the Columbia River, in the State of Washington. The first quantity production of plutonium, from three of the five piles at the Hanford complex, began in September 1944.[63]

On the principle that time was more important than money, and that every probability and process that offered a chance of success must be explored, a number of large-scale separation plants for U^{235} and for deuterium were ordered constructed. At least seven processes for separating uranium

[61] Hewlett and Anderson, p. 115; Smyth Report, p. 224.
[62] Hewlett and Anderson, p. 112; Smyth Report, pp. 98–99; Baxter, p. 432.
[63] Smyth Report, pp. 106–107, 111.

isotopes had become available and two of them, the gaseous and liquid diffusion methods, were successfully pursued to the production stage.

Construction of a steam power plant for the gaseous diffusion process, one of the largest ever built anywhere, based on research at the Naval Research Laboratory, began in June 1943 at the Clinton Works. Before the summer of 1945 it was in operation, furnishing enriched U^{235} for concentration at the nearby electromagnetic plant. The plant for electromagnetic separation of uranium isotopes, based on the research of Lawrence at the Radiation Laboratory in California, had gone up at Clinton beginning in March 1943. By the winter of 1944–45 it was in operation, producing U^{235} of sufficient purity for use in the bomb.[64]

While the basic scientific and engineering research in plutonium and U^{235} had been in progress, in the spring of 1942 Gregory Breit at the Metallurgical Laboratory initiated the experimental planning on a "fast neutron" reaction such as would be required by the bomb. Almost a dozen universities, the Carnegie Institution of Washington, and the Bureau became engaged in basic mechanics and instrumentation for the project. That summer a group at Chicago under J. Robert Oppenheimer of California's Radiation Laboratory began the theoretical work on the physics of the bomb.[65]

Upon transfer of the project to the Manhattan District, search was made for a safe and secret site for the laboratory where the bomb was to be assembled. A remote mesa at Los Alamos, N. Mex., on which a handful of empty structures marked the site of a former boarding school, was found that November. In March 1943, Oppenheimer arrived to direct operations, construction of the laboratory began, apparatus from the laboratories at Harvard, Wisconsin, Illinois, and Princeton arrived, and the first of an extraordinary body of scientists and technicans, including a British group headed by Sir James Chadwick, settled in.

Drawing on research groups from almost a dozen universities, the Metallurgical Laboratory, and the National Bureau of Standards, the Los Alamos staff comprised theoretical and experimental physicists, mathematicians, armament experts, specialists in radium chemistry and in metallurgy, specialists in explosives and in precision measurement, and their technical and housekeeping assistants. Among Bureau members was the group from the proximity fuze program, drafted in the spring of 1943, and Wichers, Schoon-

---

[64] Ibid, pp. 185, 201, 204–205.

[65] Hewlett and Anderson, pp. 43, 104; Smyth Report, p. 103.

A chain reaction in Fermi's uranium pile required neutrons slowed by graphite. In mid-1941 the British predicted that fast neutrons acting on no more than 10 kg of pure U^{235} would produce a chain reaction. A year later Oppenheimer, Teller, and Serber confirmed the theory of the fast-neutron reaction in U^{235} or in plutonium when sufficient quantities were brought together in a critical mass.

THIS DOCUMENT CONTAINS 24 PAGES.
THIS IS COPY 24 OF 36.
SECRET
LIMITED

designated "LIMITED" indicates a report dealing information which is more restricted than the information in the usual secret reports. Persons receiving these reports are not to show them to other members of the project, even of the same laboratory, without specific authorization.

THE LOS ALAMOS PRIMER

The following notes are based on a set of five lectures given by R. Serber during the first two weeks of April 1943, as an "indoctrination course" in connection with the starting of the Los Alamos Project. The notes were written up by E. U. Condon.

1. Object

The object of the project is to produce a practical military weapon in the form of a bomb in which the energy is released by a fast neutron chain reaction in one or more of the materials known to show nuclear fission.

2. Energy of Fission Process

The direct energy release in the fission process is of the order of 170 MEV per atom. This is considerably more than 10^7 times the heat of reaction per atom in ordinary combustion processes.

This is $170\cdot10^6\cdot4.8\cdot10^{-10}/300 = 2.7\cdot10^{-4}$ erg/nucleus. Since the weight of 1 nucleus of 25 is $3.88\cdot10^{-22}$ gram/nucleus the energy release is

$$7\cdot10^{17} \text{ erg/gram}$$

The energy release in TNT is $4\cdot10^{10}$ erg/gram or $3.6\cdot10^{16}$ erg/ton. Hence

$$1 \text{ kg of } 25 \approx 20000 \text{ tons of TNT}$$

3. Fast Neutron Chain Reaction

Release of this energy in a large scale way is a possibility because of the fact that in each fission process, which requires a neutron to produce it, two neutrons are released. Consider a very great mass of active material, so great that no neutrons are lost through the surface and assume the material so pure that no neutrons are lost in other ways than by fission. One neutron released in the mass would become 2 after the first fission, each of these would produce 2 after they each had produced fission so in the nth generation of neutrons there would be 2^n neutrons available.

Since in 1 kg. of 25 there are $5\cdot10^{25}$ nuclei it would require about n 80 generations ($2^{80} \approx 5\cdot10^{25}$) to fish the whole kilogram.

While this is going on the energy release is making the material very hot, developing great pressure and hence tending to cause an exposion.

In an actual finite setup, some neutrons are lost by diffusion out through the surface. There will be therefore a certain size of say a sphere for which the surface losses of neutrons are

... Espionage Act U.S.C. 50: 31 and 32. Its transmission or the revelation of its contents in any manner to an unauthorized person is prohibited by law.

UNCLASSIFIED
SECRET
LIMITED

The first page of "The Los Alamos Primer," reproduced in just 36 copies for key scientists and technicians on the mesa in New Mexico. An air of uncertainty, of speculation concerning the calculations, is found on almost every page of the "Primer."

over, Snow, and Gordon, brought out in January 1944 to take charge of purification of U^{235} scrap so it could be used again, and to prepare especially purified reagents for use in analyses of the uranium and plutonium.[66]

The newcomers were briefed in a series of five lectures given by Robert Serber, Oppenheimer's colleague at the Radiation Laboratory at California. The lectures were set down shortly after their delivery by Dr. Edward U. Condon (to succeed Dr. Briggs as Director of the Bureau 2 years later) in a 26-page pamphlet entitled "The Los Alamos Primer." [67]

"The object of the [Los Alamos] project," the primer began, "is to produce a *practical military weapon* in the form of a bomb in which the energy is released by a fast neutron chain reaction in one or more of the materials known to show nuclear fission." The materials were designated as 25 [U^{235}], 28 [U^{238}], and 49 [plutonium 239]. "Material 49," the primer went on, "is prepared from neutron capture reaction in 28. Only microgram quantities have so far been produced. There is another project going on presently to produce 49 for us in kilogram quantities."

On the basis of current calculations, the primer continued, "the simplest estimate of the minimum size of the bomb is a critical mass of 200 kilograms, in a sphere twice that size." Upon that assumption, "the immediate experimental problem is largely concerned with measuring the neutron properties of various materials and with the ordnance problem * * * to determine the critical size and time scale, working with large but sub-critical amounts of active material."

The hazard of radiation that preoccupied every laboratory experiment and industrial process involving live material and that called on so much engineering effort in the construction of the plants also haunted Los Alamos. But the consuming concern at Los Alamos as the bomb approached realization was predetonation. The primer attempted to estimate the possibility of a premature or incomplete explosion, particularly one that might give the enemy a chance to inspect or recover the materials of the bomb.

Three sources of neutrons were recognized that might provide background giving rise to the danger of predetonation: (1) cosmic rays, (2) spontaneous fission, or (3) nuclear reactions which produce neutrons. Thus, while "there will always be some chance of predetonation," every

[66] Twelve other members of the Bureau, including physicists, chemists, glassblowers, instrumentmakers, and metallurgists, were at other installations of the Manhattan District. Letter, LJB to War Manpower Commission, May 10, 1945 (NBS Box 502, AP).

[67] Thirty-six copies of the primer, classified "Secret—Limited Circulation," were mimeographed for the use of key members of the project. Quotations here are from Dr. Condon's personal copy. The primer was declassified on Feb. 25, 1963. Certain of its information is alluded to in the Smyth Report, pp. 213 ff.

calculation so far made indicated that "in any event the bomb will generate enough energy to completely destroy itself."

The thought of predetonation may have seemed somewhat remote when the lectures were first given, for in a final section of the primer that discussed the mechanics of shooting that would bring the pieces of the bomb together with the right velocity, forming a critical or spontaneously exploding mass, it was admitted that "this is the part of the job about which we know the least at present." Two years after its organization, Los Alamos had the answer.

By early 1944 fear of German success began to recede as the magnitude of the required research and industrial effort in this country became evident. Germany no longer had such resources.[68] By the spring of 1945 Oak Ridge began producing U^{235} in significant amounts and Hanford was shipping increasing quantities of plutonium to Los Alamos. The bomb was a near certainty, though no one yet knew how powerful it would be.

Only the emergency of war could have justified the cost, in excess of $2 billion, of the manmade atomic explosion that occurred on the morning of July 16, 1945. The detonation took place in a remote section of the Alamogordo Air Base, far to the south of Los Alamos. It was 10 weeks after the suicide of Hitler and the war in Europe had ended.

THE RADIO PROXIMITY FUZE (NONROTATING TYPE)

In the shadow of the atomic bomb were two other spectacular developments of World War II, the airburst proximity fuze and radar. Neither idea was new. A fuze that would explode a shell or bomb when directly over its target, rather than on impact, had been sought since World War I. The experimentation leading to radar began in Great Britain in 1919 and in this country, at the Naval Research Laboratory, in 1923.[69] The Bureau was to have little to do with radar, much to do with the proximity fuze.

An artillery or antiaircraft shell, or bomb, rocket, or mortar round with a VT (variable time) proximity fuze has from 5 to 20 times the effective-

[68] As the defeat of Germany neared, a scientific mission somewhat ineptly named ALSOS (the Greek word for "groves"), closely followed the advancing Allied columns and sped through the laboratories and industrial plants of the occupied countries and across the Rhine, to assess the progress the Germans had made in their development of the bomb. Incredible was the discovery that nothing like a real effort had been made anywhere, owing as much perhaps to the death or flight of Germany's first-rank scientists as to Nazi ideology.

[69] In this country Dr. A. Hoyt Taylor, first superintendent of the radio division of the Naval Research Laboratory established after World War I, is credited with discovering the principle of radar by bouncing back a radio beam directed at a ship on the Potomac. Baxter, p. 139.

ness of a round fitted with a contact or pre-set time fuze. In the case of very large bombs whose damage is almost entirely due to blast and airburst almost doubles the area of destruction created by bombs with conventional fuzes.[70]

Bombing runs and antiaircraft fire with ordinary fuzes rarely achieve hits with more than 5 percent of the expenditure. Where foxholes or shallow depressions in the ground offer good protection against anything but a direct hit, even a deep foxhole gives scant protection against a projectile exploding 20 or 30 feet overhead. To get that overhead-burst effect in World War I, artillery counted on tree bursts or attempted to bounce shells off rock walls or hillsides to reach troops below. The potential increase in effectiveness and the estimate that manpower, supply, and other logistical factors were enhanced by five through possession of a proximity fuze, thus warranted almost any degree of expenditure and effort to perfect it.

The radio proximity fuze is essentially a tiny radio sending and receiving station about the size of a 100-watt light bulb. It operates by continuously sending out radio waves. When the waves approach a sizable object—a ship, plane, building or other structure, or open ground—they are reflected back to the receiver in the fuze. As the waves reach a sufficient intensity indicating their effective proximity, they operate an electronic switch that detonates the fuze and the projectile.

The British began intensive efforts to perfect and produce their proximity fuze in 1937. Remembering the zeppelin raids of the First War, they intended to use the fuze primarily as a defense against enemy bombers. Their work became known to scientists in this country in the spring of 1940, and that June NDRC assigned research for a similar fuze to the Department of Terrestrial Magnetism at the Carnegie Institution of Washington, where Dr. Alexander Ellett of the University of Iowa was working on miscellaneous ordnance components.[71] Under a working arrangement with NDRC, Ellett brought the problem to the Bureau, where the team of Diamond, Hinman, and Astin, which had constructed the radiosonde and radiotelemeter, was most familiar with principles that might be adapted to the fuze.

By November 1940 NDRC had determined that two types of radio proximity fuze were needed, one for rotating projectiles, sought by the Navy

[70] Statistical data based on Army and Air Force field tests with radio and conventional fuzes, and agreeing with British findings, indicated these ranges of comparative effectiveness. [Wilbur S. Hinman, Jr.] The Radio Proximity Fuzes for Bombs Rockets, and Mortars (pamphlet of the Ordnance Development Division, NBS, 1945), pp. 5, 31–34 Hereafter cited as Hinman. See also Harry Diamond, "The radio proximity fuze," Natl. Radio News, 11, 16 (1945).

[71] Liaison with the British fuze development groups began in August 1940 and continued to the end of the war. See John S. Rinehart, MS, "Administrative history of Division 4, NDRC" (November 1945), p. 224 (author's copy). Hereafter cited as Rinehart MS.

for the antiaircraft guns protecting their ships; another, nonrotating, for Army and Air Force weapons, specifically for bombs and rockets and, later, for mortars. The radio fuze for rotating projectiles was assigned to a group headed by Merle A. Tuve and Lawrence A. Hafstad in the Department of Terrestrial Magnetism. Its final development was carried out at the Johns Hopkins Applied Physics Laboratory. That for nonrotating projectiles was transferred to the Bureau under Ellett, where Diamond and Hinman's group worked on the nonrotating radio fuze, a group under Dryden investigated an accoustic fuze, and Mohler began studying components of a photoelectric fuze.[72]

By early 1941, through the application of radiotelemetering techniques, Lauriston S. Taylor and Astin had demonstrated that acoustic fuzes were not practicable. They then joined the photoelectric fuze group under Dr. Joseph E. Henderson at the Carnegie Institution, and upon transfer of that group to the Bureau, Astin took over as director. The transfer was effected with the creation of OSRD in June 1941, when Diamond became chief of the radio and photoelectric fuze groups at the Bureau and Ellett the NDRC contracting officer.[73]

The basic principles of the rotating and nonrotating fuze were similar except that the antiaircraft shell fuze had to withstand being fired from a gun. Its stability in flight resulted from its rotation, whereas the bomb and rocket fuze produced at the Bureau had to depend upon fins. And unlike the shell fuze, the bomb fuze had to operate at wide ranges of temperature, including the extreme cold (down to $-40°$ F) encountered at high altitudes.

The group of eight that began work on the fuze on December 28, 1940, was to draw on staff members from many of the other Bureau laboratories and on scientists and technicians from university and industrial laboratories all over the country. In the last 2 years of the war, with the assignment of Army and Navy groups for testing and production, over 400 persons were engaged in the Bureau project alone.[74]

The original assignment of the Bureau was to develop a fuze that would set off a rocket attached to a bomb when the bomb had fallen within several hundred feet of a battleship. By this means, the bomb was expected to attain impact velocities high enough to penetrate and sink the ship. Much too complex and specific for the state of knowledge at the time, this requirement gave way to design of a general purpose proximity fuze.[75]

---

[72] Rinehart MS, pp. 200–204: Baxter, pp. 226–227.

[73] Rinehart MS, p. 15.

[74] Hinman, pp. 41–47, has a roster of all who worked on the NBS fuzes.

[75] Hinman, p. 9. Essentially the same account of NBS fuze research as in Hinman appears in Joseph C. Boyce, ed., New Weapons for Air Warfare (OSRD, Science in World War II, Boston: Little, Brown, 1947), pp. 176–224.

A variety of principles were available for obtaining proximity detonation against a target, including photoelectric and reaction oscillator types under British investigation, a beating oscillator arrangement proposed by the Department of Terrestrial Magnetism, a pressure type based on the radio altimeter, and one on acoustic principles. The most promising for the nonrotating fuze, however, proved to be that utilizing the Doppler effect of reflected radio waves. Hinman and Diamond devised a diode detector arrangement that acted when the amplitude of the reflected signals exceeded a predetermined value, and with that the section began its experiments.[76]

Tests of the first series of crude box models using the radio principle were made between January and April 1941. Despite the fact that only a third of the cumbersome models functioned properly, they proved that a radio proximity fuze was practicable. Turning it into an operational service item was to take almost 2 more years.

Much effort was expended in the early months on the electronic circuits activating the fuze and then on its mechanical switches and safety mechanisms, since a serviceable fuze had to be so safe that anyone could handle and even abuse it without danger.[77] While the circuits and mechanisms proved out on the early models tested at low altitudes, dropping the box fuzes from 10,000 feet and higher produced dismaying results. The higher velocities in the drop set up vibrations that the radio tubes and other components could not withstand.

In the next series of models, instead of the original shock mounting, all components were made so stiff and rugged and mounted so rigidly that they were capable of resisting the severest mechanical vibrations. Circuit elements were either immersed in wax or fixed to a frame and given a heavy protective wax coating. As for the electronic tubes, small hearing aid tubes offered the best solution to difficulties with the large and structurally weak commercial tubes that had been used. Raytheon, Hygrade Sylvania, General Electric and others, already at work on this problem for the shell fuze project, subsequently produced small, high quality, exceedingly rugged tubes for both the shell and bomb fuzes.

A new method of arming the fuze, to improve its exploding time, was introduced in February 1942. It consisted of a special type of circuit that provided a delay in the charging time for producing the current that set off the detonator. Another improvement eliminated use of the bomb body as the antenna of the radio fuze, by building two bars into the fuze itself, providing an antenna separate from the projectile.[78] In May 1942, at

---

[76] Hinman, p. 9; RP1723, "Radio proximity fuze design" (Hinman and Brunetti, 1946).
[77] W. B. McLean and J. Rabinow were the chief designers of the switches and safety mechanisms (NBS War Research, p. 20).
[78] Hinman, pp. 11–13.

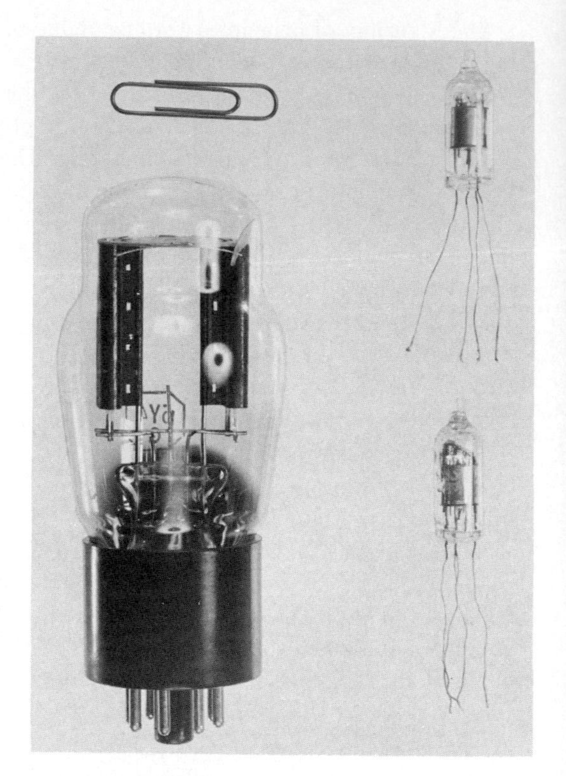

The miniaturization of the electron tube for use in the radio proximity fuze.

this stage in the basic design of the fuze, the Army set up a specific requirement. They wanted a VT fuze for their new 4.5-inch airborne rocket, then on the drawing boards, for use against the German Luftwaffe.

With fuze dimensions agreed upon, its design was completed in 2 days and construction of test models began. Complicated mechanical and plastic parts were fabricated by hand. Temporary switch and safety mechanisms had to be used. The batteries available were still too large for a service fuze but National Carbon and Burgess Battery were working on smaller ones.[79] The final design of the fuze head consisted essentially of a radio transmitter and receiver, a selective amplifier, an electronic switch, a detonator, an electric power supply, and arming and safety devices.[80] Since the 4.5-inch rocket was not ready, the fuze was set in a 3¼-inch substitute rocket. Test operations off the coast near Wilmington, N.C., started a month after receiving the requirement.

---

[79] George W. Vinal's electrochemistry section in July 1941 produced a satisfactory low-temperature wet (perchloric acid) battery for use in the fuze, measuring 2¾ x 2½ inches, later replaced by a commercial dry battery (New Weapons for Air Warfare, p. 184).

[80] C. H. Page and A. V. Astin, "Survey of proximity fuze development," Am. J. Phys. 15, 95, 98 (1947).

Actually, tests of two fuzes were made at that time, the radio fuze developed by Diamond and Hinman's group and the photoelectric fuze by Taylor and Astin. Functionally, the photoelectric fuze was excellent. Equipped with a photoelectric cell and lens and triggered by its sensitivity to changes in light intensity, the fuze detonated its projectile when an object passed between a portion of the lens and the sky. Drawbacks of the fuze were its dependence upon light, making it useless at night, and its tendency to anticipate its target as sunlight moved into and out of the lens. With the help of the Bell Telephone Laboratories, methods for solving both difficulties were found, but the success of the radio fuze finally led to suspension of the photoelectric project in October 1943.[81]

For the tests in June 1942, construction of both radio and photoelectric fuzes for the Army rocket began on small-scale production lines at the Bureau and at Westinghouse. More than a thousand of the two fuzes were made in the Bureau's model shops, "bugs" were ironed out at the proving ground, and late that year, as complete specifications for the fuzes went to industry, full production began. Under procurement for the Signal Corps by agreement with Army Ordnance, almost 400,000 of each type were turned out in 1943 and an additional 400,000 of the radio fuzes before the end of the war.[82]

While the radio fuze for the rocket was primarily designed for use against aircraft in its limited use overseas it functioned equally well from airplanes and from ground rocket launchers against troops and gun emplacements. Its most spectacular use was in multibarreled projects mounted on the General Sherman tank, the 60 VT-fuzed rockets, released in 6 seconds, completely smothering the target area with their concentration of projectile fragments.[83]

Well before the end of 1942 the fuze program had completely outgrown the laboratory in which it began overflowing into a number of temporary structures put up in the open area across Van Ness Street. Upon the assignment of additional fuze types and other ordnance projects to the group that December, the Bureau organized the sprawling units into the ordnance development division, under the direction of Harry Diamond, for better administration of the work.

A month later Army Ordnance renewed its original request for a radio fuze for bombs. The bomb fuze was not, as originally planned, to be used against enemy battleships—the *Bismarck, Scharnhorst, Prinz Eugen,*

[81] Rinehart MS, pp. 111–112; A. V. Astin, ed., "Photoelectric Fuzes and Miscellaneous Projects," vol. 3, Summary Technical Report of Division 4, NDRC (Washington, D.C., 1946), p. 20.

[82] Hinman, pp. 15–17, 31; NBS War Research, p. 21; Baxter, pp. 239–240.

[83] Hinman, p. 17.

An NBS proximity fuze model shop where test models of the fuzes, as well as early production models, were made prior to full-scale production.

and other raiders of the German Fleet had either been sunk or immobilized—but for air-to-air use against enemy bomber formations. Attack planes with these proximity fuze bombs were to climb above enemy air armadas and release their sticks over the formation.

Work on the bomb fuze was well under way before it was realized that such targets had grown scarce, that the Allies, not the enemy, were now sending out bombers in flood formations. The requirement was changed to an air-to-ground bomb fuze, to effect airbursts over troops and other targets of opportunity. When this fuze later arrived overseas it was also fitted into fragmentation bombs. In napalm (gel gas) bombs, the fuze eliminated ground penetration, to which the standard napalm bomb was subject, doubling the area covered by the gel. In these various forms it was used with deadly effect by the 12th Air Force in Italy against both troops and materiel.[84]

Since a bomb is not subject to setback at release, that is, the shock of acceleration upon which the arming of the rocket fuze depends, a different arming mechanism became necessary. The difference in fuze space in the bomb also required some physical redesign. The greatest concern in the bomb fuze, however, was with the dry battery used as a power source. As had been learned with the rocket fuze, it deteriorated rapidly in storage, lasting about a year ordinarily and not more than a month or 2 under tropical conditions. At the subzero temperatures encountered in high-altitude runs, the dry battery wouldn't work at all. Another means for powering the fuze had to be found.[85]

The solution was found by eliminating the batteries and using the arming system of the conventional bomb fuze. In that fuze a small wind-driven vane spinning as the bomb falls actuates the arming mechanism only after a certain number of turns of the vane. By attaching a miniature generator to the vane, sufficient electric power could be obtained for the proximity fuze. The generator assured almost indefinite storage life, performed well over extreme temperature ranges, and increased the safety factor since the fuze could in no way detonate the bomb unless the vane was running at high speed.

The generator designed by Zenith Radio, measuring 3/4 by 2 5/8 inches and built to run at 50,000 r.p.m., went into mass production. With it went a rectifier assembly made by General Electric about half the size of a cigarette, to convert the alternating voltage of the generator to direct current for the fuze. Tests of the new bomb fuze began in May 1943, and by

[84] British tests further disclosed that air-burst chemical bombs filled with a persistent agent such as mustard gas contaminated seven times the area covered by a surface burst. Hinman, pp. 33–34; Baxter, p. 241.

[85] Hinman, p. 18.

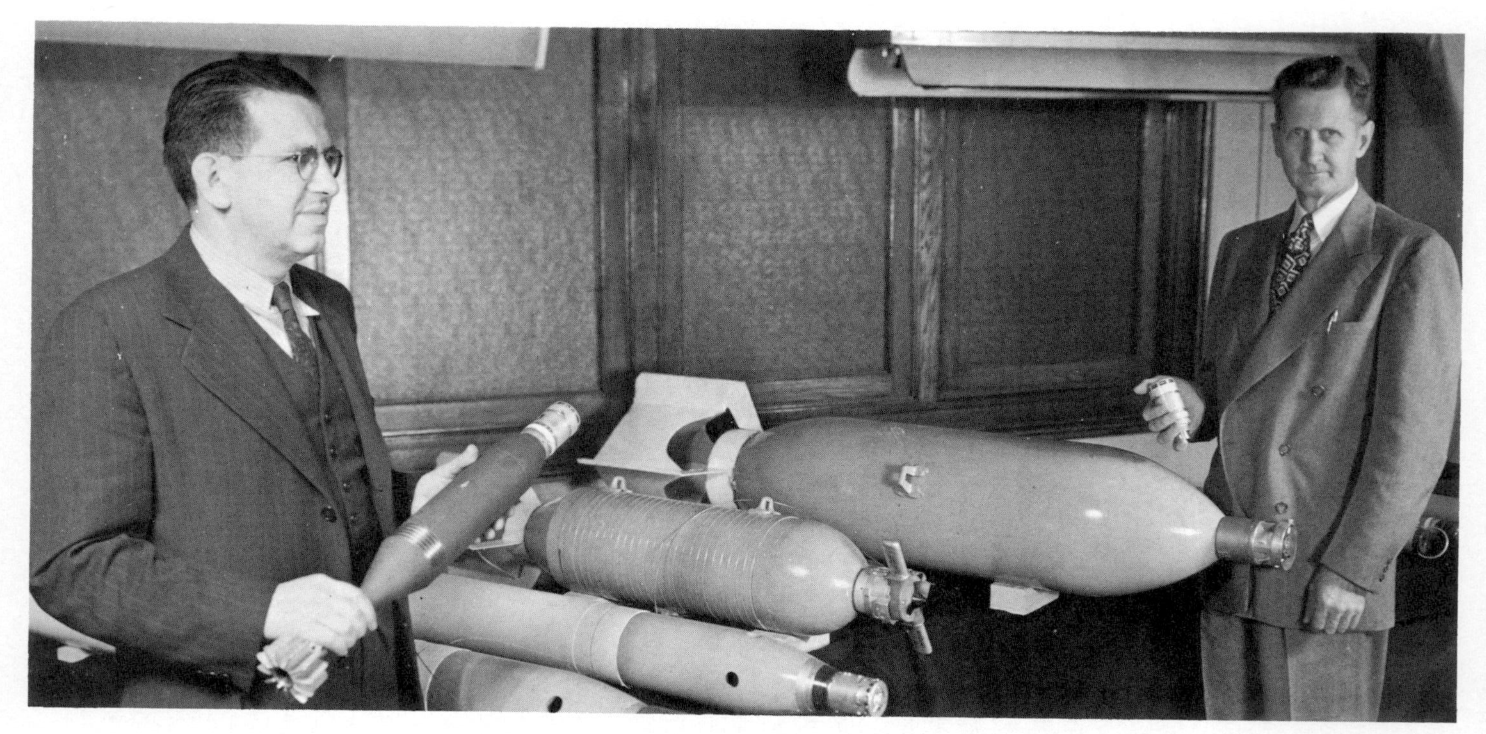

Five types of NBS radio proximity fuzes mounted on the weapons for which they were designed. Mr. Harry Diamond, at left, holds the 81-mm mortar shell with the mortar fuze. Dr. Alexander Ellett, Chief of Division 4, NDRC, holds the mortar fuze unmounted. Left to right on the table are a ring-type bomb fuze adapted for rockets, mounted here on a 5-inch high-velocity rocket; a later developed rocket fuze on the same rocket; a bar-type bomb fuze on a 260-pound fragmentation bomb; and a ring-type fuze on the 500-pound general purpose bomb.

November specifications for quantity production were ready. Army Ordnance called for the fuze on all its bombs between the 100- and 4,000-pound sizes. Approximately 1 million were made by Zenith, Emerson, Philco, and other radio manufacturing companies.[86]

Subsequent modifications made in the bomb fuze included a device designed at the Bureau by Jacob Rabinow to provide delay in arming and permit the fuzed bombs to drop safely through deep formations of bombers, and replacement of the vane mechanism with a miniature turbine, making the whole rotating system in the fuze more compact. Design of special components was initiated by Astin's group to insure optimum heights of burst, and finally a new generator appeared, measuring a mere 1⅛ by 1⅜ inches,[87]

As the sophisticated generator-powered bomb fuze went into production, the Navy through OSRD asked that it be adapted to their 5-inch aircraft rocket. The major modification consisted in changing the arming system from its vane gear back to the use of the acceleration provided by the firing of the rocket. Production of both air-to-ground and air-to-air versions began in December 1944, and both the Army and Navy used them in considerable numbers in the last months of the war.[88]

A late adjunct to employment of the proximity fuze bomb was a special bomb director mechanism, which together with toss bombing, insured bringing the missile close enough to its target for maximum effect. The toss-bombing principle and basic design of the mechanism, the acceleration integrater bomb release, was first suggested by Col. Harold S. Morton of Army Ordnance in January 1943 and developed under Alexander Ellett at the Bureau.[89]

The object of toss bombing is to compensate for the gravity drop of the missile in flight. Instead of depending on an educated guess about the point of bomb release, as fighter pilots did in attacking bomber formations or in dive bombing, the bomb director automatically computed the release point as the pilot commenced pulling out of his dive. The resulting trajectory of the bomb tossed it toward its target, allowing the pilot more time to take evasive action against ground or ship fire.

Some 500 bomb director sets were produced for the Army and Navy toward the end of the war, although only a few more than a hundred, fitted

---

[86] Hinman, pp. 20, 31; Baxter, pp. 239, 241.
[87] Hinman, pp. 21–23; NBS War Research, p. 23.
[88] Hinman, p. 24.
[89] Letter, Acting Assistant Chief of Air Staff-4 to Col. H. S. Morton, Office of Chief of Ordnance, Nov. 8, 1945, and attached correspondence (copy in NBS Historical File); Rinehart MS, p. 158.

in the P–47 fighter plane in the European theater, saw service.[90] They also directed the bombs dropped on Hiroshima and Nagasaki.

The progressive reduction in size of the nonrotating radio fuze was eagerly observed by Army Ordnance, since they wanted it for their trench mortars. The fuzes in production, for all their miniaturization, still weren't small enough when the request came to the Bureau in the late spring of 1944. Besides the necessity of designing a fuze only one-third the size of those in the bomb and rocket, while retaining all their functions, the fuze for the Army's 81-mm mortar shell had to be capable of withstanding a firing shock of 10,000 times the force of gravity or 10 times that of the rocket fuze.

The extreme requirements in size and ruggedness were largely met by what was called a "radical innovation in electric construction" when the subcontractor, Globe-Union, Inc., found a way to produce a considerable part of the electric circuit of the fuze by painting conducting material onto ceramic plates and blocks.[90a] Production of three models of mortar fuzes with these new "so-called printed circuits" started a month after the surrender of Germany. They were initially turned out at the rate of 100,000 a month. In the expectation that the war in the Pacific would last until mid-1946 or early 1947, the rate had just been tripled when the war ended.[91]

The pressure to complete development and hasten production of fuzes both at the Bureau and in industry increased as preparations for the Normandy invasion began. Large quantities of bombs and rockets with the proximity fuze were assembled for use in the preinvasion air assault to soften up the beachhead. Teams headed by OSRD and Bureau members went to England to indoctrinate the U.S. Air Force in the maintenance and use of the fuzes. Then, shortly before D-day, the Air Force announced its decision not to use the fuze. In view of Allied air superiority, it was felt that enemy recovery of one of the fuzes would make the weapon more advantageous to them than to us. The proximity fuze for shells had been used by fighter planes in the Pacific since early 1943, but their use had occurred only over water where they were not recoverable. In Normandy, the fuze

---

[90] Astin, ed., "Bomb, Rocket, and Torpedo Tossing," vol. 2, Summary Technical Report of Division 4, NDRC (Washington, D.C., 1946); Astin, ed., "Photoelectric Fuzes and Miscellaneous Projects," pp. 8–10.

[90a] Although the metalizing art was believed well known, Globe-Union rightly considered its printed circuit technique a trade secret, with great potentialities for the future, making possible economic mass production, saving space and weight, and increasing the reliability of electrical equipment. See Astin, ed., "Radio Proximity Fuzes for Fin-stabilized Missiles," vol. 1, Summary Technical Report of Division 4, NDRC (Washington, D.C., 1946), pp. 241–242, 248, 253–256; C. Brunetti and A. S. Khouri, "Printed electronic circuits," Electronics, April 1946, p. 104.

[91] Hinman, pp. 26–27; Baxter, p. 241; Rinehart MS, p. 182.

might be retrieved from the beach or beachhead. The same negative decision withheld use of the director mechanism for toss bombing.

So great were precautions to keep the proximity fuze out of enemy hands that it was not officially released for general use in the theaters until December 1944, 6 months after D-day. Even then its use was forbidden where enemy observers might identify the nature of the fuze. Among added precautions, the fuzes in rockets for use against aircraft were designed to destroy themselves before striking the ground in case of a miss, and bombs and rockets for air-to-ground strikes had an auxiliary contact fuze that functioned on impact in case of failure of the VT fuze. The single exception to the early restriction was use of the shell fuze in the British defense against the German V–1 robot bomb in the summer of 1944.

Following instruction courses given at the Bureau and at Aberdeen Proving Ground to Navy and Air Force teams, the first major combat use of the bomb fuze, by the 7th Air Force, occurred during the preinvasion bombardment of Iwo Jima in February 1945. In Europe both bomb and rocket fuzes, the latter in the new 4.5-inch rocket carried by fighter planes, were first used against German flak batteries and other ground targets in April.[92]

In 1944, as large-scale production was reached, over 8 million radio proximity fuzes were made, almost a quarter of them bomb, rocket, and mortar fuzes.[93] By then fuze plants were monopolizing 25 percent of the total facilities of the electronic industry and 75 percent of all molding plastics firms. And even more sophisticated fuzes were on the way. As production slackened with the end of the war, research was resumed in a search for better components and more versatile fuzes.[94]

A GUIDED MISSILE CALLED THE BAT

The Bureau borrowed on the wartime radar research carried out elsewhere for its construction of the "Bat," the first fully automatic guided missile ever used successfully in combat.

The guided missile program began late in 1940 when NDRC initiated research on a new weapon it believed might be useful to the services, a

[92] Hinman, pp. 36–40; Baxter, pp. 240–241, 234–235.

[93] Of the 8.3 million fuzes produced, 61 percent went to the U.S. Army, 26.7 percent to the U.S. Navy, and the remaining 12.3 percent to the British armed forces (Baxter, p. 236 n.). It has been estimated that of the fewer than 2 million NBS fuzes made, probably no more than 20,000, primarily bomb fuzes, were used in the European and Pacific theaters (Astin, ed., "Bomb, Rocket, and Torpedo Tossing," p. 8).

[94] Baxter, p. 242; Rinehart MS, p. 260.

winged bomb which would automatically seek out its target and guide itself to hit the target. NDRC was proved right, but its missile was still a year away when in August 1943 German planes, out of range of antiaircraft fire, began to sink Allied shipping in the Bay of Biscay by means of radio-controlled bombs fitted with glider wings.[95]

The aerodynamic characteristics of the prototype weapon that was designed and constructed under RCA contract in 1940–41 presented a number of stubborn difficulties. Early in 1942 NDRC asked the Bureau for help by taking over the aerodynamic and servomechanism (control) development of the weapon. Hugh L. Dryden, chief of the mechanics and sound division of the Bureau and NDRC consultant, whose fundamental work on "Aerodynamics of aircraft bombs" was still basic in that field, was put in charge.[96]

Under the code name "Robin," several full-scale missiles of new design, intended to carry a standard 2,000-pound bomb, were constructed for the Bureau at the Vidal Research Corporation. Tests began in April 1942. The nose of the flying bomb vehicle contained a special RCA television transmitter with pickup tube for viewing the course of the bomb in its flight. A ground operator directed the bomb by manual remote radio control, watching a television receiver in front of him. The test results were not encouraging. Electrical interference and the noise and vibration of the glider seriously affected the television equipment and the servomechanism repeatedly failed under the varying conditions of flight.[97]

Among the observers of the flight tests were Navy Ordnance officers concerned at the time with a radar homing missile under development by the Naval Research Laboratory and the Radiation Laboratory at MIT. While one group at the Bureau continued work on the television-guided "Robin," another, convinced by the Navy of the possible superiority of radar in the Bureau's glider system, began modifying "Robin" to incorporate radar homing principles.

Two basic types of a radar missile were available. One envisioned a glider bomb with a radar receiver tuned to an enemy transmitter that enabled the bomb to home in on the transmitter. The other type contained both transmitter and receiver, in which the transmitter emitted short pulses of high intensity, guiding the missile by the returning echoes from the enemy object. As both types came under study in a new special projects section set up in Dryden's division at the Bureau, the section expanded to more than

[95] Baxter, p. 194.
[96] The 210-page MS report of Feb. 28, 1927, is in NASA Library, File N–7569.
[97] NBS War Research, p. 30.

a hundred members, occupying the whole of the temporarily vacated hydraulics laboratory.[98]

The first radio-operated guided missile ready for testing was the "Pelican," a passive type using a radio receiver only, mounted in the nose of a 450-pound glider bomb. The plane carrying the Pelican illuminated the target with its radio transmitter and the bomb picked up the reflected waves and homed in on them. Foreseeing early use for the weapon, the Navy put the Pelican under highest priority and augmented the staff with a Navy Ordnance Experimental Unit at the Bureau and a Pelican Test Group at Lakehurst, N.J., where the flight tests were to be made.[99]

With receivers provided by Zenith and gliders by Vidal, final assembly was made at the Bureau. The first flight demonstrating homing control took place in December 1942. In the haste to construct test models and get them into production as their design proved satisfactory, minor difficulties with instrumentation were accepted which seriously flawed the production tests. As it turned out, only slight changes in the target selector circuits of the Pelican were necessary to overcome the repeated failures of the missile, but by then the greater promise shown in a concurrent project, the "Bat" missile, a 1,000-pound flying bomb, claimed the major Bureau effort.[100]

As bats emit short pulses of sound and guide themselves by the echo, so the Bat missile, sending out shortwave radiation, was directed by the radar echoes from the target. Unlike the Pelican, the sending and receiving radar set in the Bat made the weapon self-sufficient, since it illuminated its own target. Bell Telephone Laboratories and MIT scientists designed the radar robot pilot of the Bat, while groups under Hunter Boyd and Harold K. Skramstad at the Bureau worked out its aerodynamic and stabilization characteristics.[101]

Flight tests of the Bat, its 10-foot glider wing supporting a dummy bomb, started in May 1944. That autumn, in comparative tests between the Pelican and Bat against a ship hulk anchored 60 miles off shore, both performed well and were accepted. In one respect, as it turned out, the Pelican was somewhat the superior of the two, since its range of 20 miles exceeded

---

[98] NBS War Research, p. 31.

[99] Baxter (p. 195) describes the Pelican as originally an antisubmarine weapon, using a standard depth bomb and a scaled-down air frame steered by its radar receiver from a transmitter in the attacking plane. When the submarine threat receded, "the idea of a glide bomb which would follow a radar beam directly to the target was * * * too good to abandon," and research on the glide missile continued as a weapon against shipping.

[100] NBS War Research, p. 33.

[101] Ibid. A notable report on fundamentals was Dryden's "Some aspects of the design of homing aero-missiles," NBS Report to Division 5, NDRC, October 1945, and attached correspondence (NARG 227, OSRD, Division 5, Box 655).

The "Bat," borne by a Navy torpedo bomber, rides with folded tail fins until, upon release, they open into proper flight position.

The first fully automatic guided missile to be successfully used in combat, the Bat was designed for use against enemy shipping, and particularly against surfaced submarines. The Bat's outstanding features were its self-guidance after release, its long range, high accuracy, low angle of flight, and high pay load.

The "Pelican," developed with the cooperation of the Navy Bureau of Ordnance and the MIT Radiation Laboratory. Here it is rigged with instrumentation for flight tests, the 16 mm gunsight aiming point camera directly beneath the wing pointing at a panel of signal lamps indicating radar controls being applied, and the 16 mm camera, slightly lower and forward, pointing at the ground ahead of the glider.

that of the Bat. But the decision had been made and only the Bat went overseas. In the final months, land-based Navy patrol squadrons in the Pacific made effective use of it against Japanese naval and merchant shipping and against land targets in the forward areas.[102]

Complex and formidable as the Pelican and Bat seemed at the time, they were but pale prototypes of the missiles to come in the postwar years.

RADIO AND RADIO-WEATHER PREDICTING

An important weapon in subduing the German submarine menance was the high-frequency direction finder, called "Huff-Duff," a play on its initials, h–f–d–f. Its progenitor was the radio compass or direction finder designed by Frederick A. Kolster of the Bureau in 1915.[103]

When early in the war the Allies established the convoy system for the Atlantic crossing, the U-boats began stalking the convoys in wolf packs, using their wireless to direct the group operations. The wireless gave away their positions to British and American Huff-Duff stations and allowed radar-equipped planes from land bases or carriers to find them.

Errors in accuracy in existing Navy, Signal Corps, and commercial direction finders sometimes caused the search planes to miss the enemy packs. In April 1941, NDRC requested the Bureau to study the errors in high-frequency finders and determine techniques for measuring these errors. Out of the research came new techniques for assessing a variety of errors possible in the direction finders themselves, and correlation of these errors with the influence of atmospheric disturbances on the finders. The results were set out in two important papers prepared for NDRC, one by Diamond, Lyons, and Post on "High-frequency direction finder apparatus research by the NBS," the other by Kenneth Norton on "The polarization of downcoming ionospheric radio waves." The latter paper NDRC acclaimed as "a thorough development of the physics of ionosphere reflections [that] has become a classic on the subject," and much of the subsequent research on direction finders, both in NDRC and in Allied research centers, was based on the fundamental theories set down in these two reports.[104]

By June 1943 Huff-Duff, together with Asdic, radar, Loran, sonar, and voice and radio communication, had driven the wolf packs from the North

---

[102] NBS War Research, p. 34; Boyce, New Weapons for Air Warfare, pp. 225–235.
[103] See ch. III, p. 142.
[104] See C. G. Suits, G. R. Harrison, and L. Jordan, eds., Applied Physics, Electronics, Optics, Metallury (OSRD, Science in World War II, Boston: Little, Brown, 1948), pp. 135–136, 140.

Atlantic.[105] The Huff-Duff investigation, however, was only a single aspect of a much more extensive project at the Bureau involving the ionosphere and its wide range of effects on radio communications of all kinds. Studies of these effects, as manifestations of radio-weather, had already led to techniques of predicting, with growing accuracy, their influence on communications.

For good reason, then, a month after Pearl Harbor a Bureau letter circular on radio-weather predictions was withdrawn from circulation and all further open publication on the subject ceased. Its data on radio distance ranges had become military secrets and remained so throughout the war.[106]

The influence of the ionized layers of the earth's upper atmosphere, the ionosphere, on radio wave propagation had been recognized ever since the independent experiments of Breit and Tuve and of Appleton in 1925 proved its existence.[107] Through the next decade Norton, Kirby, Gilliland, and Newbern Smith at the Bureau devised a number of techniques for extending the range of ionospheric measurements.[108] Because of the scarcity of ionospheric data and because few realized its importance, use of such data in radio communications before the war was relatively small. The military value of precise knowledge of the usability of various radio frequencies at specific times over specific transmission paths thus gave an enormous impetus to the compilation of sky data during the war.

From the point of view of the services, the extreme crowding of the radio-frequency spectrum made propagation data necessary for the best selection and allocation of available frequencies. Security considerations also dictated that the frequencies used be those least likely to be intercepted by the enemy. Design of new equipment, especially antennas, depended upon knowledge of radio propagation conditions. Finally, not only all radio aids for air navigation over the North Atlantic, but radio direction finding, radiotelephone, radar, telegraphy, and radioteletype required better knowledge of propagation ranges, accuracy, and receivable intensities.

---

[105] Baxter, pp. 38, 45; NBS War Research, pp. 43–44. The Mathematical Tables Project of the Bureau, located in New York, did important work for the Navy on its Loran tables and other computations. Interview, Dr. Franz L. Alt, June 30, 1964.

[106] LC658 (1941). Excepted from classification were the standard frequencies and other broadcasting services provided by the Bureau (see LC591, 1940).

[107] For the work of Breit, Tuve, and Appleton, see RP632, "Studies of the ionosphere and their application to radio transmission" (Kirby, Berkner, and Stuart, 1934).

[108] RP597, "A continuous recorder of radio field intensities" (Norton and Reymer, 1933); RP752, "An analysis of continuous records of field intensities * * *" (Norton, Kirby, and Lester, 1934); RP1001, "Characteristics of the ionosphere * * *" (Gilliland, Kirby, Smith, et al., 1937); RP1167, "Application of graphs of maximum usable frequency * * *" (Smith, Kirby, and Gilliland, 1939).

An aircraft disaster in the European theater, attributed to failure of communications resulting from a magnetic storm, led the British and, soon after, the Australians to establish their propagation services in 1941, in order to furnish radio weather predictions to their Armed Forces.[109] A similar program had its inception in this country when NDRC asked the Bureau to prepare a textbook for the services on basic principles of radio skywave propagation. Assembled by a group under Newbern Smith in Dellinger's radio section, the Radio Transmission Handbook—Frequencies 1000 to 30,000 kc, appeared a year later, in January 1942. In addition to the principles, it gave such computational procedures as were then available, offered preliminary versions of prediction charts, and provided radio predictions for that winter. A supplement in June gave the summer predictions.

So valuable was the information in these handbooks to service radio communication systems that NDRC asked the Bureau to continue the work, and in the summer of 1942, by order of the U.S. Joint Chiefs of Staff, the Interservice Radio Propagation Laboratory (IRPL) was established at the Bureau. It was directed to centralize radio propagation data and furnish the resulting information to the services.[110]

The data were compounded of a number of variables of which little was known. First of all, long-range radio communication depends upon the ionosphere, which acts as an infinite series of tiny radio mirrors to reflect signals back to earth. Communication is imperiled, no matter how good the transmitting or receiving equipment, unless radio waves are propagated with sufficient strength to be receivable. That strength depends upon knowledge of the ever-changing characteristics of the ionosphere, which vary with latitude and longitude, geomagnetic latitude, layer height, ionization density, energy absorption, and radio noise. The latter, radio noise, is both geophysical, caused principally by thunderstorms, and extraterrestrial (stellar and solar), resulting from meteor activity and solar storms.[111]

To predict useful frequencies over skywave paths anywhere in the world, the Bureau had first to obtain adequate ionospheric data on a world-wide basis. With the data, it had to establish methods for calculating maximum usable frequencies over long paths, methods for calculating skywave

[109] Unavoidable because it results from the event, yet similar as a phenomenon, is the total blackout of radio communications experienced by the astronauts in their space flights while reentering the atmosphere. The heat of the falling capsule during reentry ionizes the air around it, sealing off both incoming and outgoing radio signals and stopping registration of the instruments tracking the capsules.

[110] Suits, Harrison, and Jordan, Applied Physics, Electronics, Optics, Metallurgy, pp. 148–9. For the wartime financing of IRPL, first by the Bureau, NDRC, Army, and Navy, and after 1943 wholly by the Army and Navy, see memo, Deputy Secretary, Joint Communications Board, JCS, for Director, NBS, May 24, 1945 (NBS Blue Folder Box 24).

[111] Dellinger, "The ionosphere," Sci. Mo. 65, 115 (1947).

field intensity, determine minimum required field intensities, and methods for forecasting ionospheric storms.

At the time, ionospheric observations were available to IRPL only from the Bureau laboratory in Maryland, two observatories in Australia, and one in New Zealand.[112] Before the end of the war, through the cooperation of the Carnegie Institution of Washington, the U.S. Army and Navy, the Canadian Navy and Air Force, the new British and Australian propagation services, the British Admiralty, the National Physical Laboratory, the British Broadcasting Corp., and the U.S.S.R., 44 stations were regularly reporting ionospheric observations by cable and radio, in cipher, to IRPL.

As a first step, the Bureau evolved a technique for predicting ionosphere characteristics on a worldwide basis, using standard statistical methods and recording the data on comprehensive charts published for the services each month. Next, a simple rapid method was devised for obtaining the maximum usable frequency (m.u.f.) over sky paths in any part of the world for distances up to 2,500 miles. The method made possible preparation of world charts giving predictions of m.u.f. 3 months in advance. The preparation and distribution of these charts, which began in April 1942, was the most important achievement of the Bureau in the field of skywave propagation.[113]

The urgent need to know distance ranges and lowest useful high frequency (l.u.h.f.) necessitated many more calculations of skywave field intensities than were currently available. The Bureau's intensity-recording program, begun early in the previous decade, was expanded by installing recorders at new ionospheric stations set up in the services and elsewhere on the North American continent. Commercial radio companies supplemented these records with their observed worldwide radio traffic log sheets. With the data on skywave field intensity, knowledge of the minimum field densities necessary to overcome atmospheric radio noise was also required. A study began of thunderstorms, the common source of this noise, whose principal generating centers are in the East Indies, Central and South America, and Africa, with secondary centers in the tropical oceans.

A final major problem of IRPL was forecasting ionospheric storms, the great magnetic storms, invisible but of vast energy, triggered by solar flares and eruptions that often blanket the earth and for periods of

---

[112] The Bureau's ionosphere recording equipment and field intensity recorders were located at its field station at Meadows, Md., until 1942 when the Air Force took over the site for Andrews Air Base. The Bureau found another meadowland, an area of 450 acres, at Sterling, Va., near Chantilly, 23 miles northwest of the Bureau. That too was lost when in 1954 it became the site of the Dulles International Airport. By then other field stations of the Bureau, including those at Boulder, Colo., were providing adequate coverage.

[113] NBS War Research, p. 36.

a few hours to several days disrupt all sorts of electrical and electronic equipment.[114] In a magnetic storm, the ionosphere tends to absorb signals instead of reflecting them, often temporarily knocking out long-distance telephone lines and scrambling telegraph transmission and the transatlantic radio circuits upon which overseas flights depend. The military importance of the North Atlantic flight path, which reaches into the auroral zone or zone of maximum disturbance, thus made it imperative to know when communications were likely to be interrupted.

Studies of the behavior of radio direction finder bearings and other ionospheric and cosmic data over the North Atlantic path gathered by monitoring stations in Europe showed that it was possible to predict the advent of a radio disturbance to shortwave communications and issue warnings a few hours to half a day or more in advance. Using these data the Bureau's short-time warning service was inaugurated in 1943.[115]

By the autumn of 1943 adequate solutions to the major difficulties in radio weather predicting had been found and the result was the IRPL Radio Propagation Handbook that appeared in November as an IRPL issue, an Army training manual, and a Navy publication. It described the behavior of the ionosphere and the theory behind maximum and lowest useful frequencies. It discussed the preparation of prediction charts and the techniques for determination of useful frequencies over any path at any time, to the extent that they had become known.[116] The new world of radio explored by the handbook bore only remote resemblance to that described in the handbooks on elementary electricity, radio circuits, and radio measurements that supplied the needs of World War I.

From 1925 to the end of World War II, the radio section of the Bureau was almost wholly engaged in studies of the ionosphere and in radio engineering projects, including its blind landing system, the radiosonde, the proximity fuze, and guided missiles. With a single important exception, radio standards work went into somewhat of an eclipse in that period. The exception was in new precision frequency measurements.

---

[114] For an interesting account of magnetic storms, particularly the great storms of March 1940 and February 1958, see John Brooks, "The subtle storm," The New Yorker, Feb. 7, 1959.

[115] Dellinger and N. Smith, "Developments in radio sky-wave propagation research and applications during the war," Proc. IRE, 36, 258 (1948).

[116] Two months after the IRPL handbook came out, the Bureau began a 2-week training course in the principles of radio weather predicting and methods of problem solution for Army Air Force, Signal Corps, and Navy officers and enlisted men. Some after training went to oversea communications groups and took charge of assignment of radio operating frequencies in the field. Others were sent to training units to organize additional radio weather predicting courses.

As a requirement of the radio wave propagation studies, a group under Harold Lyons undertook in 1944 to establish national primary standards of microwave radio frequencies. Assisted by the military, OSRD, and industrial laboratories, the Bureau set up frequency standards with an accuracy of 1 part in 10 million covering the microwave range continuously up to 30,000 megacycles. All frequencies in the study were derived from a special group of quartz crystal oscillators which constituted the national primary standard of frequency.[117]

At this point some note is appropriate about the multimillion dollar stockpile program in quartz crystals that occupied over a hundred members of the Bureau during the war. It was known that tremendous numbers of quartz crystal oscillator plates would be required by the armed services in their tank, plane, and field radio equipment, in naval communication apparatus, in radar and other detection equipment, and in many electronic precision instruments. In radio the plates not only serve to tune both transmitters and receivers to a desired frequency and to hold the frequency of transmitters within very narrow limits, but also to permit quick changes from one frequency to another merely by changing the crystal in the circuit.

The quartz crystal from which the plates are cut is almost worldwide in distribution but except in Brazil is of inferior quality and available only in insignificant amounts. Just prior to the war, Great Britain, Germany, and Japan, in a scramble to stockpile the crystals, were taking 94 percent of Brazilian output. A mere 4 percent satisfied U.S. requirements.

When in early 1940 quartz crystal was declared critical, it was established that the United States must stockpile at least 100,000 pounds of usable quartz. In March the Procurement Division of the Treasury asked the Bureau to help formulate specifications for crystals of radio grade and to test those to be purchased for the stockpile. Through the first half of 1941 the total amount of raw crystals received came to less than 50,000 pounds.

With our entrance into the war, quartz crystal, still critical, became a strategic material as well, that had to be denied to the enemy at any cost.[118] The Metals Reserve Company of the Reconstruction Finance Corporation, taking over from the Procurement Division, at once contracted for the entire

---

[117] CRPL report, "Radio standards," n.d., p. 8 (NBS Historical File); NBS War Research, p. 39.

[118] Other materials also subject to preemptive or preclusive buying, regardless of cost, by the U.S. Commercial Co. set up under the RFC in March 1942, included wolfram (the source of tungsten used to harden steel), rabbit furs, wool and blankets from Spain, Turkish sausage casings, and all of Portugal's sardines. See Jesse H. Jones, Fifty Billion Dollars: My Thirteen Years with the RFC, 1932–1945 (New York: Macmillan, 1951), pp. 387 ff.

Quartz crystal inspection and testing laboratory, through which more than 6 million pounds of the crystals passed. These are 1-pound raw pieces, from which the small oscillator plates needed in radio and other electronic equipment will be cut.

output of Brazil. So important was it considered to sequester the crystal that almost all that was brought out of Brazil came by air freight, to avoid the possibility of interception by enemy shipping.[119]

As Brazil expanded her mining of quartz to satisfy the insatiable demand for the strategic material, the quality fell off.[120] To handle the volume coming in and salvage and test usable crystal from the raw material, the inspection group under Frederick J. Bates of the polarimetry section at the Bureau rose from the original 3 members assigned to the project to 63 trained inspectors and 13 laborers working in two shifts. By July 1942, with close to 100,000 pounds coming in each month (a year later, five times that amount), three shifts were necessary. The staff finally totaled 166, housed in three temporary structures along Connecticut Avenue, simply to grade and test the incoming quartz.

---

[119] Jones, pp. 448, 575–576. Worldwide exploration in search of the crystal during the war brought the Bureau 73 shipments from 16 foreign countries, but mainly from Mexico, Guatamala, and Colombia. Exploration at home resulted in over 300 shipments from 25 States and Alaska. None of these sources produced significant amounts. NBS War Research, p. 50.

[120] The size of the mined crystal ranged between less than a pound up to 290 pounds and the value between $1 and $30 per pound, depending upon quality.

In 1943 a quartz research laboratory was added to the complex, where technicians under Francis P. Phelps undertook X-ray measurement studies of the crystals, standardization of quartz plates, and fabrication of experimental plates from mother crystal.[121] Before the war, optical perfection of the crystal had been used as the criterion of electrical performance. The quartz laboratory showed that this was not necessary, and as a result new specifications established for the agencies using the crystal made possible regrading of more than 2 million pounds previously rejected by the Bureau.

At the peak of production, 111 firms in this country were drawing on the stockpile at the Bureau to manufacture almost 2 million oscillators each month for the radio equipment of our Armed Forces, for commercial use, and for shipment to our Allies. Shortly before the project closed at the end of April 1946, the Bureau reported it had classified and graded over 6 million pounds of crystalline quartz, or 60 times the original stockpile requirement.[122]

RESEARCH IN CRITICAL MATERIALS

Quartz crystal found a place on every list of critical and strategic materials drawn up on the eve of war. As in 1917, the course of the war in Europe had made our entrance certain before this country began to take stock of its raw material resources and requirements. When it did, it found disquieting lacks not only in quartz crystal but in antimony, chromium, cocoanut char, ferro-grade manganese, magnesium, manila fiber, mercury, mica, quinine, silk, tin, and tungsten. Badly needed too were aluminum, asbestos, cork, graphite, hides, iodine, kapok, optical glass, toluol, vanadium, and wool. It was also evident that enormous quantities of steel and petroleum must be produced, and almost unlimited amounts of copper. But leading all the lists, and most frightening, was the rubber shortage, upon which the wheels of war rolled.[123]

As once before, the Bureau was to make important contributions to research in many of these materials, to the search for substitutes, and to better utilization of available supplies. At the outset, in the emergency, it had an active part in many phases of the establishment of the new synthetic

---

[121] NBS War Research, pp. 45–46.

[122] NBS War Research, pp. 49–50; letter, EUC to Executive Director, Office of Metals Reserve, Jan. 18, 1946 (NBS Blue Folder Box 71).

NOTE.—A memorandum of Apr. 1, 1942, in the building data files of the NBS plant division discloses that at that early stage of the program the value of the quartz stored at the Bureau was $5 million. Assuming a medial value of $10 per pound, the total value of all tested and stockpiled quartz must have come close to $60 million.

[123] Nelson, Arsenal of Democracy, pp. 9–10, 38.

rubber industry—generally acknowledged the outstanding national accomplishment of World War II.

Until the war, synthetic rubber in this country remained a laboratory curiosity.[124] No one, not even Dupont with its experimental Neoprene, believed large-scale production feasible. New technical research and stark necessity were to make it so.

Following a visit by Lawrence A. Wood and Norman P. Bekkedahl of the rubber section to the major German synthetic rubber research laboratory at Leverkusen in 1938, the Bureau prepared a circular based on their observations and on the published literature available.[125] Widely called for after the defeat of France, the circular went through further reprintings as the rubber-producing areas of the British, Dutch, and French in the South Pacific fell before the Japanese advance.

In February 1942 leaders in the petroleum and chemical industries were brought together. They agreed to pool their patents and trade secrets and undertake operation of the synthetic rubber plants that the Government proposed to finance. The initial goal of the plants was set at 400,000 tons a year, a deliberately optimistic figure although it was far below the 900,000 tons of natural rubber consumed in 1941, most of it to make the automobile tires on which the American public had come to depend for locomotion.[126]

Until the war, the raw materials of experimental synthetic rubbers came largely from organic chemicals, manufactured gas, and byproducts of the coking industry. Militating against these rubbers was the production of their components. Neoprene, for example, though it had excellent resistance to oil, required huge quantities of chlorine, and chlorine was in chronic short supply. What made the new industry possible were the synthetics derived from petroleum and, to a lesser degree, the distilling industry's grain alcohols.[127] These synthetics were butyl rubber, well adapted for gas masks, barrage balloons, and inner tubes, and Buna N and Buna S, tougher rubbers suitable for tire casings. After considerable experimenting and testing, ma-

---

[124] For early Bureau interest in the possibilities of synthetic rubber, see letter, GKB to J. M. Morris, MIT, Feb. 4, 1926 (NBS Box 173, ISR).

[125] C427, "Synthetic rubbers: a review of their composition, properties, and uses" (Wood, 1940). Although synthetic rubber cost three to four times as much as natural rubber, by 1940 Germany and Russia, seeking self-sufficiency, had gone over wholly to the synthetic. Experimental in this country but in most cases in production abroad (under other names) were Dupont's Neoprene, a chloroprene polymer; the German Buna rubbers, from butadiene derived from the cracking of petroleum; Thiokol, an organic polysulphide made by the Thiokol Corp. in this country; Vistanex, Standard Oil's isobutane polymer, from petroleum; and Koroseal, Goodrich's vinyl chloride polymer.

[126] Jones, Fifty Billion Dollars, pp. 399, 406.

[127] Butadiene from alcohol cost 40 cents per pound in 1945, from petroleum 10–14 cents. Hearings * * * 1949 (Jan 20, 1948), p. 546.

jor production finally centered on Buna S, the butadiene-styrene composition known as GR–S (Government Rubber—Styrene).[128]

Apart from its studies in 1942 of the polysulphide Thiokol as an interim synthetic for retreading tires, the Bureau rubber section was initially kept busy testing new processes for making rubber that were submitted by public spirited citizens. Rubbers were brought in that had been distilled from the oil of vegetable refuse, from gelatins, glycerine, and tannic acid, and even concocted from rubber itself. None could be wholly ignored. There was always a chance that a new composition or process might be found. But none was, and Donald Nelson, director of the War Production Board, paid a mixed tribute when he said of the hopeful that each with his product was sent "to the Bureau of Standards, on whose hard-working scientists we inflicted all these 'inventors.' "[129]

Bureau participation in the fledgling industry expanded early in 1943 when it was directed to assist the Rubber Research Co. in standardizing the quality of the synthetic rubbers coming into production. More than 50 reports described the test and analytic procedures developed by the Bureau, including methods for determining the styrene content of the GR–S copolymer and the purity of its styrene, butadiene, and other hydrocarbon components, and procedures for determining density, specific heats, and thermodynamic values of GR–S and of the polymerization of styrene.

The studies led to the preparation of a series of standard control polymers making uniform production possible. The controls, specifications, and rapid routine methods of analysis established for the first of the synthetic rubber plants were proved out as each of the other plants came into production. By late 1944, 19 Government-owned plants across the Nation were making synthetic rubber meeting identical specifications, resulting in a product more nearly uniform in quality than natural rubber.[130] The new billion-dollar industry turned out over 700,000 tons of rubber that year, and as the war ended was operating at a rate in excess of a million tons annually. By then 87 percent of the rubber consumed in the United States was synthetic and the industry was producing one-third again as much rubber as the country had actually used before the war.[131]

---

[128] Buna S was essentially a compound of butadiene, from grain alcohol or from petroleum products, and styrene, from ethyl benzene derived from petroleum and coal tar.

[129] Nelson, p. 300; NBS War Research, pp. 117–118.

[130] Frank Freidel, America in the 20th Century (New York: Knopf, 1960), p. 399; Hearings * * * 1946 (Feb. 2, 1945), pp. 261, 270–273; NBS War Research, pp. 115–116.

Feeding the 19 rubber-making plants were 15 others producing butadiene, 5 making styrene, and 9 producing other necessary chemicals (Jones, p. 415).

[131] Jones, pp. 401, 414. Only the Federal Government could afford the construction of whole industries such as aircraft manufacture, nonferrous metals (magnesium and

Dr. Briggs was given a bad moment or two over an incident during the rubber crisis. Early in 1945, the very active Senate Special Committee Investigating the National Defense Program (the Truman Committee) called on him to explain how a study he had made in the bouncing characteristics of golf balls and baseballs could possibly contribute to the war effort. The Committee pointed to a paper he had just published, wonderfully entitled: "Methods for measuring the coefficient of restitution and the spin of a ball." [132]

Dr. Briggs explained and the committee subsided. Prodded to conserve rubber, even in miniscule amounts, the Services of Supply had asked the Bureau about a substitute material being used in the baseballs it was supplying recreation centers at training camps. Extending an investigation he had made of golf balls in an idle hour before the war, Dr. Briggs took on the SOS request himself. The work, he reported to the committee, had been done by a high school boy. He had merely made the analyses, with assistance from Dr. Dryden and Dr. Buckingham on the theoretical considerations.

In baseballs with balata cork centers (made official in the major leagues in 1943), the coefficient of restitution or liveliness of the ball, Dr. Briggs found, was measurably reduced over that of the prewar rubber-cushioned cork center (official in 1938). The coefficient was still lower in baseballs with reclaimed rubber centers. "A hard-hit fly ball with a 1943 center," Dr. Briggs reported, "might be expected to fall about 30 feet shorter than the prewar ball hit under the same conditions." [133] It was an important finding, contributing to the peace of mind not only of the professionals but of the sluggers in the training camps.

The rubber shortage was not solved without considerable anguish to the American motorist, who was first persuaded to turn in any extra tires of natural rubber he might have above the five for his car, and was then severely rationed on gas, to save the rubber he had left. It was a long wait before he got his first synthetic tire.

As the first of the synthetics came out of the molds, the Department of Commerce requested the Bureau to road test them, along with tires made wholly of reclaimed rubber, for possible military service as well as civilian use. The early synthetic tires of Buna S proved satisfactory in all respects but resiliance and adhesiveness, and they ran hot, especially with heavy

---

aluminum), machine tools, synthetic rubber, and shipping required by the war. The RFC financed some 920 new defense plants for the War and Navy Departments at a cost of $6 billion (Jones, pp. 316, 328, 342, 345).

[132] RP1624 (1945).

[133] Letter, James M. Meade, chairman, Special Committee, to LBJ, Mar. 30, 1945 (NBS Box 504, IN).

loads or increasing speeds.[134] Nevetheless, the public had to get along with them since no natural rubber could be spared. Although later synthetic tires were far more satisfactory, tire production was restricted, for much of the new rubber was going into other products. Among materials made of the new rubber and tested by the Bureau for military or domestic use were rubber parts for landmines, cords for barrage balloons, pontoon fabrics, crash pads for tanks, gaskets, soles and heels on shoes, jar rings for home canning, flexible hose, and wire and cable insulation.[135]

While the Bureau, to be sure, could do nothing about the sharp restrictions placed on the use of motor vehicles or the national speed limit, set at 35 miles per hour, it did hurry out a letter circular on how to prepare one's car for dead storage.[136] And it saved many civilian motorists, as well as the military, a devastating headache that threatened when the standard antifreeze compounds, ethylene glycol and ethyl alcohol, were declared critical. The market was soon flooded with substitute compounds with salt or petroleum bases. The War Production Board at once stopped their manufacture or sale when the Bureau demonstrated the dangerously corrosive action of salt compounds, even with inhibitors, and the rapid disintegration of radiator hose caused by even the most highly purified petroleum compound.[137]

Second only to the shortage of rubber was that of steel and steel plate, for the building of ships, war plants, and expansion of steel plants themselves. To feed the blast furnaces, branch rail lines and spurs and abandoned trolley lines all over the country were torn up and buildings and bridges that had fallen into disuse were demolished for their metal.

Equally critical were some of the alloying agents used in steel production, particularly in the making of armorplate and projectiles. The extensive review that was made of specifications of Government buying agencies was not only important but imperative, and the work of the metallurgical experts at the Bureau and in industry to produce "lean-alloy" steels, using less tungsten, less molybdenum, less vanadium, while retaining the essential

---

[134] RP1574, "Measuring the rate of wear of tire treads" (Roth and Holt, 1944).

[135] Hearings * * * 1944 (Feb. 26, 1943), p. 82; M185, "Rubber research and technology at the NBS" (Wood, 1947); RP1554, "Buna-S-Gilsonite for insulation of communication cables" (Selker, Scott, McPherson, 1943); NBS War Research, p. 117.

[136] LC694 (March 1942).

[137] NBS War Research, p. 180; Hearings * * * 1944, p. 81. A number of gasoline additives also came on the market with the usual claims of greatly increased mileage and improved power. Not one except an additive containing iron pentacarbonyl was found useful in the slightest, and while the pentacarbonyl acted like tetraethyl lead to suppress knock, it greatly increased engine wear (Hearings * * * 1944, p. 80).

properties of the steel, became one of the most important jobs done in 1942 and 1943.[138] A significant contribution was the finding made by a Bureau group headed by Thomas G. Digges under NDRC contract, that boron, available in unlimited quantity, might be substituted for a part of the chrome ores commonly used in making hard steel.[139]

The anticipated shortage of chromium-nickel stainless steel launched an investigation under W. H. Mutchler for a substitute for the firewalls between the engine and cockpit of planes. Low-carbon sheet steel with either a thin stainless-steel coating or aluminum coating was found most satisfactory, withstanding high-temperature flames for periods up to 15 minutes without failing. Another acceptable substitute was steel coated with a special heat-resistant vitreous enamel, in place of stainless steel, in the exhaust manifolds on airplane engines and landing craft.[140]

Bureau specialists in metallic erosion and corrosion, in protective coatings, and electroplating were on constant call by industry and the services. Over 5,000 industrial or service items were submitted for solution of coating problems or determination of the effectiveness of metallic or organic (i.e., emulsion or wax) coatings applied against high humidity or salt water. They included food cans, almost all munitions, helmet parts, lifeboat, aircraft navigation, and field equipment, electrical instruments, proximity fuzes, and various firing mechanisms. Even so small an item as the match came to the Bureau for a coating. With the protection devised for their use in the tropics, the matches withstood 5 days' exposure to 95 percent relative humidity or, equally well, immersion in water for 5 hours.[141]

Under William Blum, the electrodeposition section saved tons of precious copper and nickel in the manufacture of printing plates for the Government Printing Office when it showed that these metals could be replaced by iron deposited from suitable plating baths. The section also made improvements in the properties of chromium plating of gun barrels that in the case of machine guns increased the life of the barrel by 30 times over steel barrels. Substitution of steel for brass in cartridge cases, it was found, required coating the cases with electroplated zinc. A baked phenolic varnish also worked well. Other items made serviceable by electroplating with

---

[138] Nelson, p. 351.

[139] Report, NBS to Secretary of Commerce, Mar. 10, 1943 (NBS Box 482, PRM); RP1705, "Spectrographic determination of boron in steel" (Corliss and Scribner, 1946); Suits, Harrison and Jordan, eds., Applied Physics, Electronics, Optics, Metallurgy, pp. 359–360; NBS War Research, pp. 142–144.

[140] MS Annual Report 1943; NBS War Research, p. 149.

[141] Division V report, January 1943 (NBS Box 488, PRM).

substitute metals included tableware, signal mirrors, and lifesaving equipment.[142]

If in the fall of 1941 the Nation's production capacity in steel was tight, the real pinch was in copper and aluminum. Nation-wide scrap drives brought in millions of domestic pots and pans and cleared cellar collections of nickel, tin, aluminum, copper, brass and other metals, but it was still not enough. To get more copper—the metal of communications systems—the Army in the summer of 1942 furloughed 4,000 soldiers who had previously worked in copper mines.[143]

One substitute for copper, when required as an electrical conductor, is silver, which apart from its high cost is as good and in some cases an even better conductor. As an early expedient, half a billion dollars' worth of silver coins and bullion were borrowed from the Treasury and converted into bus bars, transformer windings and the like.[144] Another copper substitution resulted in the "white" pennies that became common from 1943 on. To satisfy the military demand for copper in its cartridge brass, the U.S. Mint was urged to find something else for the 5,000 tons of copper that went into the 1-cent piece annually. Bureau tests of pennies stamped from zinc-plated steel sheets indicated that they would give at least a few years' service, and over a billion went into circulation. When the bronze coin came back again in 1944, the copper content had been reduced from 95 to 90 percent. Wear and tear, it had been determined, would not be affected, and the public was not likely to notice the difference.

The Bureau also presided over some tampering with the 5-cent piece, changing its composition from 75-percent copper and 25-percent nickel to 50-percent copper and 50-percent silver. It made for a more valuable coin, but at the time copper was precious and silver was noncritical. The addition of a trace of manganese and aluminum made it tarnish-resistant and as acceptable as the original in coin-operated devices.[145]

Unlike copper, in the case of aluminum there were few or no mines to be worked. The industry was small to begin with, and limited domestic

---

[142] John E. Burchard, ed., Rockets, Guns and Targets (OSRD; Science in World War II, Boston: Little, Brown, 1948), pp. 357, 396–397; Nelson, pp. 251–252; NBS War Research, pp. 152–156, 170, 179.

Under preliminary development at the Bureau at the end of the war was a unique method of plating by chemical reduction, called "electroless plating," that was to eliminate electrical equipment, deposit coatings of more uniform thickness, and make possible thicker coatings. See Abner Brenner, "Electroless plating comes of age," J. Metal Finishing, 52, 3 (1954).

[143] Nelson, pp. 173–174; Jones, pp. 442–443.

[144] Nelson, p. 355.

[145] Jones, pp. 336–337; NBS War Research, p. 178; interview with Dr. William Blum, Oct. 15, 1963.

supplies of low-silica bauxite, the source of aluminum, meant that 70 percent of all bauxite had to be imported. Urgent investigations were begun under contract at a number of laboratories to develop processes for using some of the less pure bauxite and clays in this country.

At a high-level conference attended by Dr. Briggs and James I. Hoffman in the spring of 1942, it was decided to construct and operate a pilot plant at the Bureau for the extraction of alumina (aluminum oxide) from clays. By autumn both an alkaline and an acid recovery process had been successfully investigated. Pilot plant production started in the alkaline plant under a Bureau team directed by Lansing S. Wells and in the acid plant under Hoffman and Robert T. Leslie.

As the submarine menace waned, increasing supplies of high-grade bauxite ore from the Guianas reduced the need for the new processes. Both, nevertheless, were fully verified in the pilot plant, the alkaline process recovering about 95 percent of the alumina in clay, the acid process resulting in alumina with an average purity of 99.6 percent—almost the equal of that from high-grade bauxite. From May 1943 on, the acid-process plant was in almost continuous operation, finally producing alumina at the rate of 50 pounds a day. In a continuing emergency, large-scale production would have been entirely practicable, but otherwise clay could not compete with the imported ore.[146]

Along with quartz crystal, optical glass appeared on all lists of critical materials. Between the two wars, the Bureau had been the only research organization in the country engaged in both research and production of optical glass, with funds supplied chiefly by the Navy Bureau of Ordnance.[147] Prior to 1940, fewer than 20 people working in the glass plant turned out about 9,000 pounds annually, the entire output going to the Naval Gun Factory for its optical requirements.

With war orders from the Navy, Army Ordnance, Army Engineers, the Treasury's Procurement Division, and OSRD, the optical glass plant expanded. An addition to the kiln building and construction of a second plant with Navy funds more than doubled facilities. The refractories section increased its manufacture of pots from 70 to 2,300 annually, and by working in three shifts production went up from 15,000 pounds of optical glass in 1940 to more than 240,000 pounds in 1942 and in 1943. Even so, the Bureau could not supply more than half the requirements, and Bausch & Lomb, Haywood Optical, and Libbey-Owens Ford furnished the remainder.

---

[146] RP1756, "Development of a hydrochloric process for the production of alumina from clay" (Hoffman, Leslie, et al., 1946) ; NBS War Research, pp. 166–168.

[147] Bausch & Lomb began making optical glass in World War I. It maintained its facilities in the interim years, but admittedly "had no appetite for military business in peacetime." See Fortune, 22, 76, 98 (1940) ; memo, GKB for Bureau of Foreign and Domestic Commerce, Feb. 4, 1926 (NBS Box 152, AG).

An assortment of optical glass specimens made at the Bureau. Center bottom is a coincidence prism used in range finders. One of the most intricate and costly of optical devices, it was made at the Bureau by cementing together a number of small prisms.

Of the services, the Navy was the great consumer. A single big rangefinder for one of its guns contained as many as 160 optical elements.

Altogether, the Bureau furnished close to a million pounds of high-quality optical glass to the Armed Forces. Where the Bureau previously made no more than six types of optical glass, military and research requirements called for 28 types before the war ended. At peak production 400 workers under Alfred N. Finn and Clarence H. Hahner were employed around the clock, not only to produce the glass but to mold it into prisms and lenses for readier use in gunsights, heightfinders, periscopes, rangefinders, and binoculars.[148]

In the optics division (optical glass was a product of the ceramics division), investigations were carried out on improved rangefinders, in methods and instruments for testing airplane cameras and lenses, and in optical measurements and materials for camouflaging ships and shore installations. Assistance was also furnished the Navy Bureau of Aeronautics in the design of special aircraft searchlights for use in night attacks on submarines, and in photoelectric equipment for night photography.

A simple yet new and vitally important device that came out of the optics division was the heliographic signaling mirror or "solar searchlight,"

[148] Hearings * * * 1943 (Jan 12, 1942), p. 208; Hearings * * * 1945 (Jan 11, 1944), p. 189; C469, "Optical glass at the NBS" (Glaze and Hahner, 1948); NBS War Research, pp. 99–101.

as some called it. Early in the war the Joint Chiefs of Staff called for a practical means of aiming reflected flashes at potential rescue craft, both planes and ships, as part of the equipment in liferafts and boats. A member of the Bureau staff at the time, L. L. Young, hit on the rearsight method of aiming mirror flashes, employing reflections from both its front and rear surfaces immediately around a sighting hole in the center of the mirror. Incorporating suggestions made by General Electric, which undertook their manufacture, more than a million of the mirrors, of tempered glass with a surface of vaporized aluminum film, were produced for the air and transport services.[149]

The optics division took part in or carried out alone more than 30 separate investigations, most of them under NDRC auspices. Dr. Briggs's comprehensive report of war research indicates that quite apart from the special groups working for the Manhattan District, on the proximity fuze, on guided missiles, and in radio propagation, each of the other divisions was engaged in as many or more projects as optics. Enumeration of the projects, let alone a description, is beyond the scope of this history. Only a few representative studies can be mentioned.

A laboratory tool of limited interest until the war was a magnetic balance for inspecting certain kinds of steel. Devised by a member of the electrical division in 1932, it was modified by a Bureau chemist 5 years later for gaging the thickness of metal, paint, or enamel coatings on nickel, steel and other metals, making possible nondestructive testing of the coatings. Only a few had been made by the American Instrument Co., under the name Magnegage, until the wartime rash of substitute materials and the necessity of plating made the gages important in many industries, in order to expedite acceptance of military supplies and conserve scarce metals by avoiding the use of unnecessarily thick coatings. Arsenals found the Magnegage invaluable for measuring the thickness of the chromium in the lands and grooves of large caliber guns.[150]

Expansion of Bureau investigations in aviation fuels, lubricants, and motor fuels resulted in greater knowledge of their composition and better control in their production. Many of the war plants making aviation fuels had no previous experience in quality control procedures, and for them the Bureau provided the necessary calibration of primary and reference standard fuels, based on specifications prepared for the American Society for Testing Materials (ASTM), and of "referee" fuels to ensure even quality in production.

---

[149] John A. Miller, Men and Volts at War (New York: McGraw-Hill, 1947), p. 104; NBS War Research, pp. 110–111.

[150] RP532, "A magnetic balance * * *" (Sanford, 1932); RP994, "Magnetic methods for measuring * * * coatings on nonmagnetic base metals" (Brenner, 1937); RP1081, "* * * coatings on iron and steel" (Brenner, 1938); NBS War Research, p. 60.

Of fundamental importance was the wartime work of the petroleum laboratory, originally set up in the summer of 1937 with the support of the Army Air Corps, Navy Bureau of Aeronautics, and NACA to synthesize, if possible, an improved aviation fuel. With the war the investigation turned to study of the paraffin hydrocarbons, found as impurities in primary standard reference aviation fuels, and investigation of those of superior value as components of military aviation gasoline. Working with data and samples provided by the American Petroleum Institute, the Bureau laboratory isolated and synthesized some 78 hydrocarbons and prepared 66 of them in a higher purity than ever before.[151] In the case of 21 of the hydrocarbons, no evidence could be found in the literature to indicate they had ever been made before. An added result of the project was the discovery of a possible method for augmenting the supply of aviation gasoline, using re-formed cracked naphtha. Of considerable interest to NACA and the American Petroleum Institute, it became the subject of continued postwar research.[152]

When the early losses of oil tankers by enemy action imperiled the supply of vehicle fuels to our Allies, the Bureau was asked to find out whether substitute fuels from vegetable matter, which the Allies might produce locally, were possible. Attempts to run cars and trucks on gas substitutes was an old story, but the Bureau looked into it again. The studies of engine performance with alcohol, charcoal, shale oil, naphtha, vegetable products and other known substitutes all pointed to alcohol as most promising. Engine tests using gas produced from charcoal showed that approximately 11 pounds of charcoal produced energy equal to a gallon of gas. But the fact that it took 2 minutes to start up the engine and that the little gas generator required

---

[151] C461, "Selected values of properties of hydrocarbons" (1947); NBS Annual Report 1948, p. 217.

Bureau studies in the chemistry of petroleum oils went back to World War I (see ch. V, pp. 276–277), and cooperative research with the API in the separation of petroleum into its constituent hydrocarbons began in 1928.

The practical problem in the twenties was engine knocking, as compression ratios increased. An octane number scale for expressing the knock rating of motor gasolines was adopted in 1930, with n-heptane for the low and isooctane for the high, and in 1934 the Bureau was asked to set up specifications for these primary standard reference motor fuels. Since that time the Bureau has maintained these national reference standards, on which all octane number measurements throughout the country are based. In 1946 the octane scale was also applied to aviation gasolines.

In the course of its preparation of pure samples, the Bureau found among the aliphatic hydrocarbons several with higher octane numbers than any previously known—the components of later aviation fuels. See RP1027, "Paraffin hydrocarbons isolated from crude synthetic isooctane * * *" (Brooks, Cleaton, and Carter, 1937); RP1160, "Properties of purified normal heptane and isooctane * * *" (Brooks, 1938).

[152] NBS Report 2746, "Hydrocarbon synthesis at the NBS, 1937–1953" (Howard, ed., 1953); NBS War Research, pp. 75–78; interview with Thomas W. Mears, Apr. 14, 1964.

constant servicing were deemed serious drawbacks. Only alcohol seemed a feasible substitute, and it had to be high proof. Made at the request of the Army, studies of low-proof alcohols showed that a vehicle that got 200 miles on a tankful of standard gasoline and 130 miles with absolute alcohol went only 25 miles on a tank of 70-proof alcohol. The waning of the submarine menace ended the unnerving prospect and the project.[153]

A high-precision wear gage, made by Samuel A. McKee of the Bureau in the course of the substitute fuel study, led to an interesting discovery. The gage itself was capable of detecting as little as one hundred-thousandth of an inch of wear in a motor. While making tests with it, the gage demonstrated, surprisingly enough, that most of the substitute fuels, if not as efficient as gasoline, produced significantly less wear and tear on the engine. It was not the sort of measurement many motorists then or later would be concerned about, but the gage fortunately had other uses.[154]

Another kind of detector, devised at the request of the Air Force and NACA, was the Bureau's carbon monoxide indicator. In place of earlier cumbersome apparatus, Martin Shepherd of the chemistry division produced a sensitive calorimetric indicating gel, put up in a small tube, that quickly signaled the presence of small amounts of carbon monoxide fumes. To produce the tubes, for attachment in the cockpits of fighter planes and crew quarters of bombers, a group of 30 took over a section of the gas chemistry laboratory and set up an assembly line. Over half a million units were turned out and distributed before the highly classified project ended.[155]

In an unceasing search, substitutes for metals were found in wood, concrete, and plastics, and involved a host of products from shower stalls and sinks to fuel oil and gasoline storage tanks. No attempt was made as in World War I to build concrete cargo ships, barges, and tankers, but at the time of the steel shortage the Maritime Commission sought new Bureau studies of reenforced steel, with concrete ships in mind. Instead, the research led to the construction of a number of concrete oil storage tanks before steel plate became available again. Lined with liquid-proofing materials recommended by the Bureau, they were used to store a variety of motor fuels, including high-octane gasoline. Contrary to expectations, losses of gasoline by vaporization through the concrete proved of minor significance.[156]

A challenge to the Bureau was the request made by Military Intelligence to find means of sabotaging enemy construction of concrete fortifications and similar military structures. Was there, Intelligence asked, a readily

---

[153] NBS War Research, pp. 79–80.

[154] Ibid.

[155] Shepherd, "Rapid determination of small amounts of carbon monoxide," Anal. Chem. 19, 77 (1947); RP1777 (Shepherd, 1947); NBS Annual Report 1947, p. 206; interview with Mrs. M. Kilday, May 12, 1964.

[156] NBS War Research, p. 95

available material which, when added in small amounts to concrete while it was being mixed, would inhibit its gain in strength? It could not be too effective or act too fast, lest the sabotage become evident to the builders.

The known inhibitors of concrete strength such as inorganic salts, alkalis, and acids, and even organic materials like dextrose and syrups, failed to meet the specifications. After considerable experimenting the answer was found in common sugar. It was highly effective in a matter of weeks when introduced in fractions of as little as 1 percent.[157] As it happend, most of the coastal fortifications of the enemy were completed when the answer came, and if the military had other uses for the knowledge, the Bureau wasn't informed of them.

The growing importance of plastics that led to formation of the Bureau's organic plastics section in 1935 made that section with its experience the ultimate authority when war came. The War Production Board strongly promoted new plastic products and industry turned them out for the armed services, the Maritime Commission, and the Office of Civilian Defense. Among new plastic products sent for testing were helmet liners, resinous coatings used for protection of steel hardware, bayonet handles, Bureau-designed binocular housings, bugles, canteens, clock housings, compass dials, raincoats, food packaging, goggles, insect screening, shaving brushes, and aircraft housings.

The original helmet liner, made of paper pulp covered with fabric, was far from durable, lost its shape after wetting, and had low resistance to impact. A new liner, on which the Bureau worked with the Office of the Quartermaster General, was constructed of cotton-fabric laminated phenolic plastic, its production one of the first large-scale applications of the low-pressure molding technique. The Bureau also made exhaustive tests of Doron, a glass-fabric laminated plastic, as possible body armor. Some of this personal armor was introduced in the Pacific theater late in the war, after it had been shown superior to an equal weight of steel or metal armor in its ability to stop flak and the small arms fire of most Japanese infantry weapons.[158]

Only the extreme range of qualities sought in textiles and fabrics during the war attempted to compete with the proved versatility of plastics. The armed services, so it seemed to one harassed investigator, wanted textiles that were "infinitely strong and infinitely light, that gave perfect protection against heat and cold and finally were digestible in case of emergency."[159] They wanted fabrics that would keep out a driving rain and yet let perspira-

---

[157] NBS War Research, p. 96.
[158] NBS War Research, pp. 119–120.
[159] Ibid., pp. 122–123.

tion through, and they wanted them fireproof, windproof, lightproof, mildew-proof, gasproof, and even bulletproof.

Not only the Army, Navy, and Marine Corps, but the War Production Board, National Research Council, Board of Economic Warfare, and Office of Price Administration, sought the aid of the Bureau's textile section under William Appel in creating these fabrics.[160] Since few military fabrics had to possess more than two or three special characteristics simultaneously, the Bureau was able to help, providing much of the technical data that aided in their production. Too difficult even for modern science were the bullet-proof and edible fabrics allegedly sought, and a solution to their construction was still not in sight as the war ended.

Among the many problems posed Scribner's paper section was a new paper for war maps, requested by the Corps of Engineers. In some of the swift-moving operations in the later stages of the war in Europe, deterioration of much-used maps became as troublesome as running off the edges of the maps at hand. Not long before that, however, the problem had been licked by production of a unique fiber-binding resin paper of great strength, capable of withstanding treatment that quickly disintegrated ordinary map papers. Maps printed on it remained serviceable even when soaked with water or oil and after being trampled in mud and subsequently washed with soap and water or gasoline. All agencies making war maps in this country adopted the new paper as standard and quantities of it were sent to Great Britain under Lend-Lease.[161]

Few were the crises of supply faced in World War I that did not have to be met again in 1940. A conspicuous exception was that of high precision gage blocks, making possible mass production of interchangeable parts. At least 10 manufacturers undertook to turn them out in quantity for industry, and as a result of queries, the Bureau prepared a letter circular for manufacturers and gage users providing criteria for the acceptance or rejection of gage blocks.[162] As early production difficulties were solved, the Bureau thereafter had only the responsibility for calibrating the blocks. Altogether, more than 76,000 gage blocks and accessories, both English and metric, passed through the Bureau's hands for the gage manufacturers, the armed services, war plants, and the Procurement Division. Of more than 24,000 certified in 1944 alone, 50 percent went to the U.S.S.R. by way of Treasury's Lend-Lease.[163]

---

[160] OSRD interest in this Bureau research, particularly in tropic-proofing and light-proofing of textiles, is briefly reported in W. A. Noyes, Jr., ed., Chemistry (OSRD: Science in World War II, 1948), pp. 470–471.

[161] NBS War Research, pp. 126–127; RP1751, "Experimental manufacture of paper for war maps" (Weber and Shaw, 1946).

[162] LC725 (1943).

[163] MS Annual Report 1944, n.p.

Tens of thousands of other types of gages and measuring instruments were calibrated in the Bureau's expanded gage section. A handbook on screw thread standards, originally issued in 1939, was revised in 1942 and again in 1944, to keep up with the improvements in thread standards that evolved during the war.[164] In other sections of the metrology division the certification of standard weights, volumetric glassware, thermometers and other instruments soared as laboratories were set up or expanded in industry and as war plants came into production. Almost 100,000 standard samples of steels, irons, alloys, ores, ceramics, chemicals and hydrocarbons, oils, paint pigments, and other substances were distributed during the period, representing a fourfold increase over the prewar rate.

Little publicized, yet significant in the conservation of critical materials, was the wartime effort of the simplification and commercial standards groups at the Bureau. At the beginning of the defense program in 1940 a number of industry advisory committees were set up as liaison between industry and Government on simplification. Simplified practice recommendations made by these committees were incorporated in regulations issued by the Office of Price Administration and later in the orders of the War Production Board, resulting in important savings in labor, machines, and both critical and noncritical materials.[165]

WPB orders limiting the sizes and weights of tubular radiators, for example, were estimated by that agency to have saved 23,000 tons of cast iron. Builders' hardware was reduced from approximately 27,000 to 3,500 items. Sixty-five percent of all types and sizes of brass and bronze pipe fittings were eliminated and the variety of brass and bronze valves was reduced from 4,079 to 2,504 types, saving thousands of tons of carbon steel, copper, and alloy steel.

Forged axes, hammers, and hatchets were reduced from 636 to 303 types, conserving vital alloy steels, and all use of these steels as well as high-polished finishes were eliminated from rakes, hoes, and forks, while their variety and sizes dropped from 915 to 129 types. Wrenches and pliers were reduced to one style and one grade per manufacturer.

In order to concentrate manufacture on fewer essential types, dental excavating burs were mercifully reduced from 75 to 24 sizes, though all of them, from the point of view of the patient, may still have seemed too large. Other products similarly affected included concrete-reenforcement steel,

---

[164] H25, "Screw-thread standards * * *" (1939, superseded by H28, 1942, and revised in 1944); NBS War Research, pp. 163–164. MS Annual Report 1944 reported that 53,000 copies of H28 were sold.

[165] For industry's reaction to "defrilling" (it approved, but warned its members against voluntary standardization without clearing with a defense agency), see Business Week, Nov. 22, 1941, p. 17, and May 1, 1943, p. 30.

forged hand tools, wood saws, plumbing and heating tanks, refrigerator valves and fittings, shovels and spades, and welded chain.[166]

Among new commercial standards dictated by the war, porcelain-enameled steel utensils replaced the aluminum, stainless steel, and copper pots and pans that were donated to the scrap drives. Extensive use was made for the first time of plywood and fiberboard in the construction of barracks, concrete forms, boats, pontoons and other normally all-wood products. Mineral wool and fiberboard also proved satisfactory and in some cases superior replacements for cork as insulation materials.[167] What with victory gardens, meatless Mondays, and ration books, the war was only months old when it became evident that life on the homefront was to be a matter of substitutes, do-it-yourself, or do without.

Of the hundreds of consumer products merely simplified out of existence by the war, most conspicuous was the automobile. A War Production Board order of January 20, 1942, stopped all production of cars and light trucks. The last passenger car rolled off the assembly line 3 weeks later. Domestic refrigerators came under severe curtailment next, and in a sweeping order in May, the manufacture of more than 400 other civilian products using iron and steel ceased.[168] The great conversion to war production had begun.

An index to the vast potential of production in this country on the eve of war, though it was concealed by the doldrums in which industry continued to languish and by the great pool of the unemployed, appeared in the incredible rapidity with which the Nation became fully armed and supplied for global warfare. By September 1943, hundreds of huge new rubber, steel, petroleum, aluminum, and magnesium plants had arisen and began reaching full-scale operations where fields or forests had ruled before. Tanks, guns, shells, tires, aircraft, and great catalogs of miscellaneous supplies and parts were pouring along assembly lines to waiting freight trains headed for the ports of embarkation. Supplies and equipment that did not cross with troopships filled convoys for the arming of the British, French, and Russians, or for the stockpiles that were being crammed into the English countryside.

November 1943 marked the high point in war production. Thereafter it began to slope downward. The successive targets for production of raw materials and finished products set during the preceding 3 years had been

---

[166] Nelson, p. 240; NBS War Research, pp. 172–173. In some instances sales to industry of the simplified practice recommendations for these products ranged as high as 25–30,000 copies. Many had to be reprinted later to meet the continuing postwar demand. See NBS Annual Report 1946, p. 207.

[167] NBS War Research, pp. 173–174.

[168] Nelson, pp. 224, 283.

met.[169] With the consolidation of the Normandy peninsula, the word "reconversion" was heard for the first time. The supply lines were full and could be maintained with some slacking in production, even though the strategic planning staff foresaw the war against Japan lasting into 1947.

When V–J Day came on August 14, 1945, 3 months and 6 days after victory in Europe, American industry had produced 86,000 tanks, 296,000 planes, 4,800 merchant ships, and 71,000 ships for the Navy. In August and September of 1945 the Army sent out 30,000 telegrams canceling defense contracts and reconversion began.[170] Two months later, in November 1945, the Bureau began its own reconversion—in organization, staff, and program—to research in the postwar world.

[169] Nelson, p. 395. Besides new magnesium and synthetic rubber industries, between 1939 and 1945 aluminum production was tripled, machine tool capacity increased sevenfold, electrical output rose one and a half times its prewar rate, and more iron and steel were produced than in the entire prewar world. The total plant production in the Nation almost doubled. Freidel, America in the 20th Century, p. 400.
[170] Kenney, The Crucial Years, 1940–1945, p. 100.

The standard avoirdupois pound of Queen Elizabeth I, which is believed to have originally weighed about 7,002 troy grains. It was used as a British standard from 1588 to 1825.

THE NEW WORLD OF SCIENCE (1946–51)

CHAPTER VIII

"THE PECULIAR PEACE"

The war ended with a monstrous bang. In "the peculiar peace" that followed, the word "fallout" equally described a metaphorical truth and a new phenomenon loosed on the world. In a decade compounded of inflation, strikes, shortages, Russian intransigence and aggression, and the new presence of the atomic bomb, the Nation was to be ruled by uneasy fears.[1]

By the end of 1946, as price controls went off, living costs were an estimated 39 percent above those of December 1941, and strike after strike hobbled production and pushed prices still higher. Trolley and subway fares went up 2 cents and then a nickel. The 10-cent Sunday paper became 15 cents, then 20. A public with massive war savings fretted over shortages of food, furniture, nylons, electric irons, and clothing. Even razor blades and alarm clocks were hard to find, a new car meant signing up on a multiple of long waiting lists, and housing was either not to be had or the new ones promptly started falling apart. In the summer of 1946 came the meat "famine" as producers refused to send their cattle to market. The black market, a way of life in Europe, came to America.

"Had enough?" the Republicans asked the country, and in 1946 it elected the first Republican Congress since the days of Herbert Hoover. But the worst of the adjustment was already past. Raw materials were again becoming plentiful, the reconversion of industry neared completion, and production began approaching prewar levels.

New sources of tension arose in the United Nations, born in the last year of the war, where Russia, using the veto to shield her expansion in Europe, goaded the assembly, staged stormy walkouts, and sabotaged issue after issue raised, including the most critical of all, international control of atomic energy. Communism's growing threat in Eastern as well as Western Europe slowly impelled America to assume responsibility for restoring their war-wrecked economies.

---

[1] The material of the introductory pages of this section is largely drawn from Eric F. Goldman, The Crucial Decade: America, 1945–1955 (New York: Knopf, 1956).

The Truman Doctrine, announced on March 12, 1947, promised support to free nations resisting pressures from Communism, and a month later the phrase "cold war" was born. The aftermath of World War II was not to be depression but cold war. Out on Connecticut Avenue, Bureau reports echoed the national tension as it prefaced its plans for research with such phrases as "if war comes again," "in the event of any future emergency," "in time of emergency," and described some of its continuing programs as "the difference between obliteration and survival." [2]

A reluctant Nation delayed action on the Truman Doctrine until the fall of Czechoslovakia under Communist domination in February 1948, Russia's menace of Finland, the impasse marked by the Berlin airlift, and the threat of Communist Party takeovers in France and Italy. Russian aggression, aided by hunger, poverty, desperation, and chaos around the globe, could be contained only by long-range economic aid. Under mounting pressure, Congress adopted the Marshall Plan on April 2, 1948, to bolster the economies of Turkey and all the European countries outside the Iron Curtain. It called for an initial expenditure of $17 billion over approximately 4 years.

As the economies of the Western European nations swung upward under the Marshall Plan, containment became policy. The cold war was joined upon the signing of the North Atlantic Treaty Organization (NATO) in March 1949, as 10 nations of northwestern Europe, Canada, and the United States agreed to joint action should any one of them be attacked by Russia. In August of that same year the Marshall Plan received a serious setback when, despite $2 billion in aid, Chiang Kai-shek's nation fell to the Chinese Communist armies.

The cold war took still another turn for the worse. Some American scientists had predicted that Russia would not have an atomic bomb before 1952 or 1953. Others hazarded dates as late as 1956 or even 1960. But Stalin had expressed no surprise when at Potsdam he was first told of the event that had occurred at Alamogordo; Russian scientists may well have begun their study of the bomb as early as 1941, and certainly were at work by 1943, assisted by the knowledge that England and the United States were seriously engaged and, later, by acquisition of engineering designs of the structures raised in Britain and at Oak Ridge, Hanford, and Los Alamos. On September 23, 1949, 6 weeks after the actual event, the President announced the explosion of an atomic device in the U.S.S.R.

The cold war thus became a question of coexistence—a nebulous, uneasy way of life, shaped by the spectre of annihilation and made even more frightening by Truman's decision on January 31, 1950, to resume development of the hydrogen or fusion bomb. The Russians had dupli-

[2] NBS Annual Report 1947, pp. xiv, xv; Annual Report 1949, p. 49.

cated the fission bomb in 4 years; they were almost certainly at work on a fusion bomb, and might not require that much time again.

Stalinism abroad had its fright-counterpart in McCarthyism at home. And the cold war became hot when on June 25, 1950, the American Ambassador to the 2-year-old Republic of Korea cabled that the Chinese-supported armies of North Korea had crossed the 38th parallel. Six days later American planes, ships, and infantrymen put the United States irrevocably into the war. The initial United Nations forces under General MacArthur's command, consisting largely of South Koreans and American troops rushed from Japan, met Soviet-made tanks and fell back. At home the Nation went back on a war footing, back to wage and price controls. Two months after the start of the war a new boom was on as employment passed the 62 million mark.

It was August before the Americans and ROK's ended their retreat and another month before they took the offensive. They had advanced to the Yalu River in late November when 33 Chinese divisions crossed and hit the U.N. line. It fell back slowly to the 38th parallel and there stalemate set in. In June 1951 the Soviet Ambassador to the U.N. hinted that Russia was ready for a cease fire in Korea. The killing continued through 2 years and 17 days of conferences before an armistice was signed on July 27, 1953.

Eight months earlier, on November 1, 1952, this country detonated the first hydrogen bomb. Less than a month after the Korean armistice, on August 12, 1953, the Atomic Energy Commission announced its detection of a similar thermonuclear explosion in the Soviet Union. And both nations were already engaged in the development of intercontinental missiles that would replace planes for the delivery of either the fusion or fission bomb. There appeared to be no alternative to continued research in weaponry; more truly, mankind had no alternative but peace.

If World War II made science for the first time a political, economic, and social force in the Nation, the postwar years, under the pressure of "obliteration," magnified that fact manifold. Yet science could not remain mobilized in the Office of Scientific Research and Development, an emergency agency for military research, and with the end of the war the weapons research projects of OSRD were transferred to the War and Navy Departments for peacetime administration. In 1946 Congress divested the Army Engineer Corps of its Manhattan District and the atomic bomb project was returned to civilian control by creating the Atomic Energy Commission.

Both the military and the AEC were to call on the Bureau for continued technological research on their behalf. In the fall of 1944, Dr. Briggs and Maj. Gen. Levin H. Campbell, Jr., Chief of Army Ordnance, signed an agreement under which the Bureau would continue its research and design of proximity fuze devices. In May 1945 ground was broken for the construction of a half-million-dollar ordnance electronics laboratory on the Bureau grounds. Concurrently, the Navy asked for continuation of the guided missile work, and upon the establishment of the AEC, support was offered for enhanced programs on its behalf. The Bureau was thus committed to a large amount of developmental research in the postwar period.[3]

At the same time, the store of basic research had been seriously depleted by the war and there was growing concern in the Federal Government for its replenishment. It was unlikely that this country could ever again rely on Europe for its basic science, or afford to depend on foreign research for its military strength.[4] This prospect became a major concern of OSRD during the demobilization period; vide Vannevar Bush's Science—The Endless Frontier (1945). The question was raised by the science committee of the Office of War Mobilization and Reconversion and was one of the first orders of business of the AEC. The naval establishment found its answer in the organization of the Office of Naval Research in 1946, to coordinate all research for the Navy and support basic as well as applied research.

With its system of grants and contracts for research in the universities and in public institutions, the Office of Naval Research played a key role in the formation of the National Science Foundation. The establishment of the Foundation in 1950, "to evaluate science research programs undertaken by agencies of the Federal Government," settled the 100-year-old question of a permanent central scientific agency in the Government offering support to basic science.[5]

Even before the establishment of its central agency, the Federal Government had sought to assure itself of a continuing fund of both basic and applied research through the creation of laboratories wholly supported with Federal funds but operated by non-Federal agencies, as were the Los Alamos Laboratory and Radiation Laboratory of the University of California, the Argonne Laboratory at the University of Chicago, the Lincoln Laboratory at MIT, and the Applied Physics Laboratory at the Johns Hopkins University.

---

[3] Memo of agreement, LJB for Chief of Ordnance, Oct. 31, 1944, and attached correspondence (copies in NBS Historical File). In addition to the Navy and AEC research, memo, Joint Chiefs of Staff for Director, NBS, May 24, 1945, requested NBS to assume all obligations of the Interservice Radio Propagation Laboratory (IRPL) as a postwar Bureau function (NBS Blue Folder Box 24, FPE–674c). The magnitude of the defense research commitment by 1950 is described in 20-page memo, Director, NBS for Secretary of Commerce, Nov. 28, 1950 (NBS Historical File).

[4] Don K. Price, Government and Science: Their Dynamic Relation in American Democracy (New York University Press, 1954), pp. 32, 46.

[5] Ibid., p. 60.

Further augmenting its fund of research was the Federal policy of utilizing its own institutions through transferred funds and of entering into contracts with universities and industrial firms to carry out investigations required by its agencies. In the process of formation for many years, the policy was increasingly resorted to during the war and continued at an accelerated rate in the postwar years.[6]

The history of transferred funds at the National Bureau of Standards, for the conduct of research and development on behalf of other Federal agencies, provides an interesting note on the progress of science in the Federal Government. The first such funds formally authorized were transferred to the Bureau in 1921 by the Army, Navy, the National Advisory Committee for Aeronautics, the Coast Guard, the Bureau of Engraving and Printing, and the Department of Agriculture. They totaled slightly more than $60,000.[7] At the height of World War II they approached $9 million, or almost 70 percent of the Bureau's total operating funds. During the Korean war, transferred funds, almost wholly from the Department of Defense and the Atomic Energy Commission, were to exceed $40 million, or 85 percent of operating funds. A decade later they leveled off at approximately $14 million annually, or 40 percent of the Bureau budget. How this imbalance came about merits some discussion.

As early as 1942 the Visiting Committee to the Bureau began urging an end after the war to the Bureau's deep engagement with industry, almost wholly supported by transferred funds. The development of new weapons, new materials, and substitute materials during the emergency made the research for industry necessary, but in peacetime, the Visiting Committee felt, such research belonged in the universities and in the laboratories of industry and not at the Bureau.

> While research and development programs will, in the future, [said the Committee] be even more extensively adopted by American industry, the importance of the Bureau of Standards * * * will undoubtedly increase in respect to its most important function, namely, serving as a court of last resort on those matters of standards which depend upon scientific [determinations] * * *. Direct aid to industry, while very important, should not be allowed to

[6] Dupree, Science in the Federal Government, pp. 371–375.

[7] Exceptions to transferred fund research was the work of the U.S. Naval Radiotelegraphic Laboratory and the Signal Corps Radio Laboratory at the Bureau which from 1908 to 1932 were directly supported by those services (see ch. III, p. 140). The military research and defense funds of 1918–19 were emergency transfers of the President, outside legislative authority.

overshadow the Bureau's position of final arbiter on scientific and technical standards.[8]

Secretary of Commerce Jesse H. Jones was inclined to agree with his Visiting Committee. The Bureau involvement in both commercial and industrial interests seemed excessive. A survey made at his request in 1943 recommended that such purely commercial activities of the Bureau as its simplified practices and trade standards divisions should probably be transferred to Commerce. Industrial standards, not development, was its role, and the survey urged "stronger legislative authorization for contributing [the Bureau's] measurement skills to the anticipated new [industrial] developments." [9] As Under Secretary Wayne C. Taylor wrote:

> The Department of Commerce proposes to ask for funds to enlarge the basic research work of the National Bureau of Standards during the transition period. If our country is to maintain its economic position, research in physics, chemistry, and metallurgy must be sturdily supported to provide the foundation for new industries and greater industrial development.[10]

That burning issue of the thirties, consumer standards, also flared again, and briefly involved the Bureau, in the efforts of Jones and Taylor (and endorsed by Henry A. Wallace when he became Secretary) to expand the Department's interest in the field of standards for commerce, "particularly [in] the development of performance standards for goods sold to the ultimate consumer." [11]

---

[8] Report of the Visiting Committee to Secretary Jesse H. Jones, July 11, 1942, p. 9 (NARG 40, Secretary of Commerce, Box 114, file 67009/5).

[9] Report, Carroll L. Wilson, consultant to Secretary of Commerce, "Standards in Commerce—A Basis for Action," Dec. 8, 1943, revised Sept. 15, 1944, p. 7 (NBS Box 490, IDS–ASA). The report agreed with the view of the Visiting Committee "that the true function of the NBS lay in that domain of standarization that rested upon exact physical measurement, and not on such standardization as involved negotiations, opinion, judgment, and compromise."

[10] Letter, Taylor to Executive Secretary, Committee on Economic Demobilization, OPA, Mar. 10, 1944 (NBS Box 489, AG). The same intention appears in two studies made for Senator Kilgore's Subcommittee on War Mobilization to the Senate Committee on Military Affairs: the 326-page report, "The Government's Wartime Research and Development, 1940–44" (Senate Subcommittee Report No. 5, GPO, 1945), and the 418-page report, "Wartime Technological Developments" (Senate Subcommittee Monograph No. 2, GPO, 1945), the latter prepared as a working basis for the postwar development of new industries and cheaper and improved products. The two studies were represented as sequels to the report, "Research—A National Resource," issued in 1940.

[11] Letter, Acting Secretary of Commerce Taylor to Gano Dunn, Jan. 6, 1944 (NARG 40, Box 114, file 67009/5). For plans proposed by Jones and, later, Wallace to reorganize the Department to make "Washington the home of business," see Bus. Week, Mar. 30, 1945, p. 82, and Feb. 8, 1947, p. 52; also Hearings * * * H.R., 79th Cong., 1st Sess., on first deficiency appropriation bill for 1946, pt. I, Oct. 29, 1945, p. 319.

Dr. Briggs agreed that the Bureau might undertake certain basic research in consumer goods and materials but reserved his enthusiasm for resumption of industrial research. "We need a steady flow of new industries to take up the slack in employment," he wrote in April 1945, with strengthened research facilities at the Bureau to handle its responsibilities for "providing new opportunities for industry." [12] Frail and tired, he had little interest in the new fields of science created by the war. He was content to return to the familiar, to supplying industry and small business with technical information, assisting industry with standardization, continuing basic research in standards. Meanwhile, the Bureau must complete the military projects on hand, and continue to serve other Government agencies and the State governments.

Legislation to strengthen basic research at the Bureau, recommended in the survey for Jesse Jones, also won Wallace's aproval. Explicitly, Wallace proposed amending the organic act of 1901 to include areas of research previously covered by special legislation and, somewhat vaguely, "a limited enlargement of the Bureau's powers in a specified direction with respect to increased freedom in securing high types of personnel." [13]

Vannevar Bush, on the committee, demurred at the apparent implication of the "enlargement." He wanted no fundamental research for science or industry carried out at the Bureau except in the field of metrology. Nevertheless, he made unanimous the Visiting Committee's approval of the proposed legislation:

> I am entirely in sympathy with the Bureau's conducting basic research in the sciences, especially those which involve standards. However, the Bureau of Standards is the only body which has both the responsibility and authority to perform the exceedingly important function of establishing standards of all kinds, and in the future the Bureau is going to be subjected to a heavy and increasing burden in this regard as a result of the rapid progress of science, particularly in the field of atomic energy. The problem of formulating standards in their field alone will be a major challenge to the Bureau.
>
> Hence, while I believe that it [the legislation] is important to the effective organization of the Bureau and to its ability to conduct basic research in science, nevertheless I think it should be unmis-

[12] Memo, LJB for Secretary of Commerce, Apr. 5, 1945 (NBS Box 502, AG).

[13] Discussed in letter, Gano Dunn to Secretary of Commerce Wallace, Nov. 23, 1945 (NARG 40, Box 114, file 67009/5), and Wallace correspondence in Box 112, files 67009/1 and 67009/12.

takably clear that the major emphasis should remain on its unique assignment in the field of standards.[14]

The amendment of the organic act of the Bureau was to be accomplished in 1950. With the cold war growing hot, the question of industrial research and of consumer standards had become academic. Furthermore, the postwar bent of the Bureau had already been determined by its new Director, Dr. Edward U. Condon.

EDWARD UHLER CONDON

On May 7, 1945, 4 months before the end of the war in the Pacific, Dr. Briggs quietly celebrated his 71st birthday. A year beyond the compulsory retirement age, he had served as Director since 1932 under five Secretaries of Commerce, Roy D. Chapin, Daniel C. Roper, Harry L. Hopkins, Jesse H. Jones, and, since the first of the year, under Roosevelt's new Secretary, Henry A. Wallace. Anxious to return to the comfort and quiet of his old laboratory in West building, Dr. Briggs submitted his resignation to Secretary Wallace.[15]

Two members of the Bureau, Dr. Eugene C. Crittenden and Dr. Hugh L. Dryden, came under consideration by the Secretary's Visiting Committee to the Bureau as Dr. Briggs' successor. Dr. Crittenden, at 65, was the senior, with 36 years of service in the Bureau. But he felt his health was not up to the task, and Dr. Briggs urged the candidacy of Dr. Dryden. Secretary Wallace, however, did not have the advice of his Visiting Committee in selecting a successor.[16] Moreover, he was strongly inclined to find someone outside the Bureau for the post. He first met his new Director of the Bureau at a conference of scientists in Chicago.

The successful test of the atomic bomb at Alamogordo in July 1945 had almost at once aroused concern among scientists over the control of the

[14] Letter, V. Bush to Gano Dunn, Nov. 21, 1945, attached to letter, Dunn, Nov. 23.

[15] Dr. Briggs' first years of retirement were spent, at Secretary Wallace's request, compiling the report on NBS War Research (1949). Letter, Wallace to LJB, Oct. 11, 1945 (NARG 40, Box 112, file 67009, pt. 1, 7–12). See also E. U. Condon, "Lyman James Briggs (1874–1963)," Year Book, Am. Phil. Soc., 1963, pp. 117–121.

[16] Interview with Dr. Briggs, Nov. 1, 1961

Dr. Briggs put his request for retirement on the agenda for the meeting of the Visiting Committee on June 22, 1945, just prior to his notification to Secretary Wallace. The chairman of the Visiting Committee subsequently accepted responsibility for the failure of the Visiting Committee to submit promptly its nominations, in response to his request, for the Secretary's consideration. In turn, Secretary Wallace acknowledged that he sent in his own nomination earlier than he had originally contemplated. Reports of the Visiting Committee to the Secretary of Commerce, July 5, 1945, and Oct. 31, 1945 ("Gen Corresp Files of the Director, 1945–1955," Box 6).

weapon and the peacetime development of atomic energy.[17] Ranged against continued military control were most of those who had worked on the bomb at Los Alamos and in the universities. One of the first of the many conferences that were called to discuss the future of atomic energy was that convened by Robert M. Hutchins, Chancellor of the University of Chicago. It met in September 1945 at the opening of the university's new Institute of Nuclear Studies. Lending his support to the conference, Secretary of Commerce Wallace attended and brought with him as special advisor, Dr. Philip M. Hauser, a sociologist on leave from the University of Chicago, then with the Bureau of Census.

Meeting Dr. Condon, associate director of research of the Westinghouse Electric Corp., for the first time at the conference, Dr. Hauser found him "a most amiable and knowledgeable fellow * * * [with] broad interests in the physical sciences." Aware that the Secretary was searching for a replacement for Dr. Briggs, Hauser suggested to Wallace that "this was a man he should meet and consider for the post of Director of the National Bureau of Standards." As Wallace remembers it, he discussed the directorship with several others at the conference, but "Dr. Condon was the only one who was available and really interested." [18]

Dr. Condon's name was submitted by President Truman to the Senate and confirmed without a dissenting vote. On November 7, 1945, he was formally appointed Director.

As Dr. Condon told an Appropriations Subcommittee not long after, he was "born * * * actually in the town where the bomb was tested, but there [was] no connection between those two events." [19] Then in his 43d year, he had indeed been born in Alamogordo, N. Mex., on March 2, 1902, but had spent his early school years largely in California. Taking his doctorate in physics at the University of California at Berkeley in 1926, he went to Germany for a year's study, where the new quantum physics of Heisenberg, Born, Schrödinger, and Dirac was being taught. He returned to lecture in physics at Columbia University and in 1928 went to Princeton as assistant and then associate professor.

---

[17] One result of that concern was the publication of One World Or None (eds. Dexter Masters and Katharine Way, New York: McGraw-Hill, 1946), a report to the public on the meaning of the atomic bomb. Contributors to the report included Einstein, Bohr, Compton, Bethe, Langmuir, Oppenheimer, Szilard, Shapley, Seitz, Urey, Wigner, and Condon.

[18] Communications to the author from Henry A. Wallace, Jan. 7, 1964, and from Dr. Hauser, Jan. 29, 1964 (NBS Historical File). See also Wallace letter in New Republic, 118, 10 (1948). For Wallace's possible prior interest in Dr. Condon, see letter, LJB to H. A. Wallace, Aug. 2, 1945, sub: Standing of certain scientists (NBS Box 504, IG).

[19] Hearings * * * 1947 (Jan. 29, 1946), p. 175.

Dr. Edward U. Condon, fourth Director of the Bureau and the first theoretical physicist to head its operations. Reorganizing the Bureau in the postwar period, he cleared its attics of 50 years of accumulated lumber and began the modernization and systematizing of present Bureau operations.

While at Princeton, he coauthored the Frank-Condon principle in molecular physics; developed the theory of radioactivity decay, with Ronald W. Gurney; a theory of optical rotary power; the theory of proton-proton scattering, with Gregory Breit; and the theory of charge-independence of nuclear forces, with B. Cassen. His definitive treatise on the theory of atomic spectra, with George H. Shortley, established his reputation as an outstanding theoretical physicist.[20]

In 1937, Dr. Condon went to the Westinghouse Electric Corp. at Pittsburgh as associate director of research and there developed a program of nuclear research.[21] Appointed a consultant to the National Defense Research Committee in 1940, he helped organize the Radiation Laboratory at MIT, where America's microwave radar program was started, and wrote a basic textbook on the subject of microwaves for the laboratory. During the war he introduced and directed the microwave radar research program at Westinghouse.

While setting up the radar program, he served on Dr. Briggs's S–1 Committee, meeting monthly at the Bureau. In April 1943 he went to Los Alamos at the request of General Groves as associate director under Dr. Oppenheimer. Later that year he was called to the Radiation Laboratory at the University of California to head the theoretical physics group working on the electromagnetic (mass spectrograph) separation of uranium isotopes. Toward the end of the war he started the nuclear reactor program at Westinghouse which later produced the power plant for the Navy's atomic submarine.

Dr. Condon was no stranger to the Bureau laboratories when he became their Director. Actually, his acquaintanceship dated back to the late 1920's, when as a Princeton professor he attended the annual meetings of the American Physical Society, regularly held for many years at the Bureau. But Dr. Condon had no sooner seated himself in the Director's chair in South building, to learn something of the dimensions of his office, when he was called to Capitol Hill as scientific adviser to the Special Senate Committee on Atomic Energy. The hearings of Senator Brien McMahon's committee on the question of civilian control of atomic energy began on November 27, 1945, and lasted until April 8, 1946.[22]

---

[20] Biographical note, "About Edward U. Condon," What Is Science? ed. James R. Newman (New York: Washington Square Press, 1961), pp. 105–108; interview with Dr. Condon, Oct. 27, 1963. With P. M. Morse, Condon wrote Quantum Mechanics (1929) and with G. H. Shortley, The Theory of Atomic Spectra (1935), both standard works in their fields.

[21] Time, 35, 44 (Feb. 12, 1940), called him "king of the atomic world at Westinghouse," where its new Van de Graaff generator, the only one in industry, was being used to make artificially radioactive substances for studies of nuclear structure.

[22] As a result of the hearings, Congress established the Atomic Energy Commission on Aug. 1, 1946, with complete civilian control over all atomic affairs of the United States,

In the interim, Dr. Crittenden served as Acting Director and Dr. Condon contented himself with brief visits to the Bureau to acquaint himself with its operations and activities. With only his Sundays free, he came with his master key and toured the unpeopled laboratories looking at work in progress, read the reports of current research left on his desk, and studied reports on operational procedures at the Bureau.[23]

Late in January 1946, Dr. Condon appeared for the first time before the House Appropriations Subcommittee for the annual hearing on the budget. Unaware of the deep affection of the committee members for Dr. Briggs and their long-standing interest in the Bureau under his direction, Dr. Condon brought up the subject of Bureau administration. The immediate order of business, Dr. Condon told the committee, was "to modernize and systematize the entire administrative activity of the Bureau, which has just grown up over the years without any special organization unit to coordinate and supervise the work.[24] Dr. Briggs and two division chiefs acting as Assistant Directors had borne the responsibility not only for all research at the Bureau but for the work of the 141 members of the administrative staff.[25] It seemed to Dr. Condon an impossible task.

Dr. Condon asked for funds for three full-time Assistant Directors to administer the professional and scientific functions of the Bureau, and an Executive Director to supervise business management functions. These four, he said, would "do what Dr. Briggs was doing before." As for the Director of the Bureau, he should not have 13 division chiefs and 4 or 5 administrative heads reporting directly to him for decisions and policy determinations. The greater part of his time should be devoted to "main-

---

peaceful and military. All Manhattan District facilities, including the Los Alamos weapons laboratory, the isotope separation plants at Oak Ridge, and the plutonium piles at Hanford, were turned over to the AEC. It became responsible for procuring ores of the fissionable heavy metals, uranium and thorium, for converting them into concentrated pure metal, for manufacturing weapons as well as radioactive isotopes, electric power reactors for ship propulsion, and generators for electricity. The AEC was also charged with conducting all research necessary to keep the United States ahead of the world in atomic development. Finally, the act authorized free international exchange of basic scientific information when an international arrangement and techniques of inspection made that possible. See James R. Newman and Byron S. Miller, The Control of Atomic Energy (New York: McGraw-Hill, 1948).

[23] Interview with Dr. Condon, Oct. 27, 1963.

[24] Hearings * * * 1947 (Jan. 29, 1946), p. 183.

[25] The assistants were Dr. Crittenden, chief of the electricity division, and Dr. McAllister, chief of codes and specifications. The latter retired in the spring of 1945 and had not been replaced when Dr. Condon took over.

taining appropriate relations with the Secretary's Office, other activities of the Department and other Federal agencies, and commercial concerns and educational and scientific societies and institutions with which the Bureau is associated in cooperative or allied work." [26]

Asked by Congressman Louis C. Rabaut, chairman of the subcommittee, if the increased staff would promote greater efficiency at the Bureau, Dr. Condon replied: "That is my hope, and if it does not we will have to do something about that. It is my own feeling * * * that we have a great many overlapping operations and practices there that have just grown up over the years * * *." It was not a diplomatic note and Mr. Rabaut, and many at the Bureau hearing it later, reacted to it.[27] Steeped in an academic rather than industrial or even bureaucratic tradition, the Bureau, with almost a hundred on the staff who had been there since Stratton's time, braced itself for the shock.

---

[26] Hearings * * * 1947, pp. 183–184.

[27] Ibid., p. 184. For Chairman Rabaut's great affection for and delight in Dr. Briggs, see Hearings * * * 1945 (Jan. 11, 1944) and Hearings * * * 1946 (Feb. 2, 1945), passim. For his reactions to Dr. Condon's criticism, see Hearings * * * 1947, passim.

The House subcommittee seems to have resented Dr. Condon's remarks on the state of Bureau facilities and equipment, his observations that there was serious duplication and overlapping in laboratory equipment and in shops, but that "with a complete reorganization of the administrative functions * * * we can introduce many simplified practices"; that the laboratories had become storehouses of obsolete records and equipment, "housing * * * useless items which should be disposed of"; and that despite its famed safety code experts, "the Bureau itself is probably one of the worst violators of its own safety codes" (Hearings * * * 1947, pp. 190–191).

The Congressmen queried Dr. Condon on his choice of speech and efforts at explanation. Despite his acknowledged unfamiliarity with Bureau statistics, they sought from him breakdowns in appropriations, work loads, expenditures and other data that neither Crittenden, Parsons, Thompson, Dellinger, nor other administrative officers at the hearing with Condon could answer offhand.

Three years later the House subcommittee sent up a group of investigators, including inspectors from the Public Buildings Administration, who over a 6-months' period surveyed Bureau grounds and buildings maintenance, the shops and laboratories, efficiency of operations and activities, use of personnel, and administration of research and testing. The questioning of Dr. Condon on the line-by-line details of the resulting House survey report, which everywhere found "the administration of the Bureau * * * weak and timid," occupied almost 75 pages of the hearings for 1951 (Feb. 23, 1950, pp. 2179–2230, 2242–2246, 2249–2260, 2288–2293). Midway in the quizzing, Congressman Daniel J. Flood of Pennsylvania interrupted to ask: "What is the most exciting thing that has happened in the Bureau of Standards in the year outside of this investigation by the

Dr. Condon was not to project a father image as had Stratton, softening the severity of his strictures. He was not to capture cooperation by his appeal for help, as had Burgess, or to inspire devotion by his presence, as had Briggs. Genial, gracious, and the world's best company away from his desk, Dr. Condon brought to an organization largely staffed with experimental physicists the new-broom outlook of the theoretical physicist. Perhaps more than most at the Bureau, he was aware that the war years had revolutionized science and scientific thought and, always a prolific writer, he had for some

---

Appropriations Committee?" Dr. Condon could only deny it had been exciting; it had been rather depressing (p. 2237).

Prior to that questioning, Dr. Condon had talked steadily for over 2 hours (pp. 2158–2181) on the scope of activities of the Bureau, in answer to the repeated queries of the subcommittee: "What does a 'Bureau of Standards' mean?" "Does the Bureau's work embrace all of science and technology?"

At the next year's hearing, in March 1947, Congressman Karl Stefan of Nebraska replaced Rabaut as chairman. Stefan requested that Dr. Condon use layman's language before the committee, and raised again the joke about the scientist and the plumber, alleging that in reply to a New York plumber who had asked the Bureau about the use of hydrochloric acid for clearing drainage stoppages, a Bureau physicist had answered: "The efficacy of hydrochloric acid is indisputable, but the corrosive residue is incompatible with metallic permanence." Assuming that meant it was all right, the plumber wrote thanking the Bureau. The Bureau supposedly replied "We cannot assume responsibility for the production of toxic and noxious residue with hydrochloric acid and suggest you use an alternative procedure." The plumber wrote that he agreed with the Bureau: hydrochloric acid worked fine. Frightened at what might happen to the drainage of New York skycrapers, the Bureau was alleged to have resorted finally to simple speech: "Don't use hydrochloric acid. It eats hell out of the pipes." (Hearings * * * 1948, p. 289). The joke was brought to Dr. Condon's attention in each of the next 2 years. (Hearings * * * 1949, p. 538; Hearings * * * 1950, p. 493).

Representative Walt Horan of the State of Washington quizzed Dr. Condon about the purpose of the Bureau: "The title 'Bureau of Standards' should have some meaning. Otherwise we are going to get lost in a maelstrom of scientific research. What does 'Bureau of Standards' mean?" Continuing the questioning at the next hearing, Congressman Stefan advised Dr. Condon: "Give it to us as Dr. Briggs used to do * * * so that we can understand." At that and subsequent hearings, Dr. Condon was told, "Remember, we are laymen" (Hearings * * * 1948, p. 299; Hearings * * * 1949, p. 526; Hearings * * * 1950, p. 485).

Few men have written more clearly and simply about the complexities of modern physics or are more lucid in general exposition on any subject than Dr. Condon. His sole public rejoinder to his "problem of relations with Congress" occurred in a speech on Sept. 25, 1951, wherein he urged at some length the establishment of a committee of Congress concerned exclusively with science and scientific research in the Government (Physics Today, 5, 6, 1952).

time expounded the new physics in a steady stream of articles in the periodicals.[28]

The Bureau as presently established, Dr. Condon told the Appropriations Subcommittee, is "one of the finest scientific laboratories in the country, and it would be wise to maintain and extend its functions at this time, when there seems to be a disposition to recognize the importance of pure science in the Government's activities more than ever before." [29] As one who had made important contributions to pure science and at Westinghouse brought it to bear on industrial work, he was determined to advance pure science at the Bureau and to move the Bureau rapidly into the postwar world. "Think big!" he repeatedly told the Bureau staff. There was no alternative, and he challenged the staff with his cry, "Are you going to think in terms of peanuts or watermelons?" [30]

Dr. Condon himself thought big. His outstanding characteristic, it proved unnerving to some of the older members of the Bureau, and frightening to congressional appropriation committees. At his second appearance on the Hill, in March 1947, he was to stagger the committee members with a proposed $25 million budget, up from $5 million the previous year.[31] He talked of acquiring not one but three mass spectrometers for the Bureau, not one but two giant betatrons. He requested a fourfold increase in publication

---

[28] See "Making new atoms in the laboratory," Sci. Am. 158, 302 (1938); "Sharpshooting at the atom," Pop. Mech. 74, 1 (1940); "Physics in industry," Science, 96, 172 (1942); "Tracer bullets of science," Pop. Mech. 77, 170 (1942); "Physics gives us nuclear engineering," Westinghouse Eng. 5, 167 (1945); "Science and our future," Science, 103, 415 (1946); "Is war research science?" Sat. Rev. Lit. 29, 6 (1946); "Science and the national welfare," Science, 107, 2 (1948); "60 years of quantum physics," Physics Today, 15, 37 (1962). See also file of his speeches and addresses on electronics, nuclear physics and other fields of Bureau research in NBS Historical File.

[29] Hearings * * * 1947, p. 178.

In the Steelman report to the President in 1947 on the role of the scientific agencies of the Government in the Nation's total scientific effort, the National Bureau of Standards was described as "* * * the principal Federal agency for research in physics, chemistry, and engineering; it acts as custodian of the Nation's standards of measurement, carries on research leading to improved measurement methods, determines physical constants and properties of materials, develops and prescribes specifications for Federal supplies and generally serves the Government and industry as adviser in scientific and technical matters and in testing, research, and development in the physical sciences." (The President's Scientific Research Board, Science and Public Policy, II, The Federal Research Program, Washington, D.C., 1947, p. 151.)

The statement reflected the view of Dr. Condon, who served as an alternate on the President's Scientific Research Board that prepared the report.

[30] Interview with Dr. John D. Hoffman, Apr. 28, 1964.

[31] Only 15 years later the Bureau's operating budget, exclusive of construction appropriations and transferred funds, would rise to $28.5 million.

funds, to expand the regular series of Bureau reports and prepare and publish multivolume tables of atomic energy levels, tables of the thermodynamic properties of chemical compounds, and a new and comprehensive handbook of physics. The Bureau had lately become the central agency in the Federal establishment for radio propagation research and service. Dr. Condon proposed that it also assume direction of all Federal research in synthetic rubber and in mathematical analysis and machine computers.

Was all this, the committee asked, contemplated in the act that created the Bureau? What about the present program? "Are all of your tremendous, gigantic activities out there carried on under a two-page law?" Congressman Stefan asked. Did the Bureau actually intend to "spend about nine or ten million dollars during the next fiscal year on the basis of a two-page law?" [32] The committee began vigorously debating with Dr. Condon on what he thought the phrase "bureau of standards" meant and what such a bureau was really supposed to do. He explained point by point how the new science, enormously stimulated by the war, had changed the Bureau and the Nation.

In many ways Dr. Condon was the very man for the Bureau in the years after the war, sparking new ideas and impulses among his associates and energetically recruiting a new scientific staff.[33] He acknowledged that recent technological developments demanded continuance of the Bureau work on rubber, plastics, textiles, liquid fuels and lubricants, on structural materials, ceramic and electroplated coatings, metallic alloys, electronic devices, and new ranges of radio wave frequencies. But "it would be a serious mistake * * * to let these projects in the fields of applied science interfere with the Bureau's work on fundamental problems of physics and chemistry and on methods of measurement and the standards and instruments which provide the basis for measurements of every kind," as primary responsibilities of the Bureau.[34]

New industries and wholly new technologies were to make unprecedented demands upon the laboratories. Perhaps no one at the Bureau com-

[32] Hearings * * * 1949 (Jan. 20, 1948), p. 526.

[33] As he told the committee, in addition to the prewar cuts in staff, budget, and services, during the war much of the Bureau's basic research had been reduced and its best men put into war work, from which they had not yet been released. The Bureau was therefore very shorthanded in the field of fundamental research, and it was that area he sought to rebuild and expand. He hoped "to be allowed to do for peacetime fundamental research [in the Bureau] something of the sort that [had] recently been announced as part of the Navy's research plans, involving a high degree of collaboration, and intimate cooperation at the working scientists' level with universities throughout the country" (Hearings * * * 1947, pp. 178–179). Dr. Condon referred to the Office of Naval Research, organized later that year.

[34] Hearings * * * 1947, p. 176.

prehended better than the new Director the implications of nuclear technology, just emerging from its pioneer state, or the need for new instruments, materials, and processes spawned by that technology. More than administration and organization, the thought at the Bureau needed redirection, and as the cold war and then the Korean war came and research for defense intensified, Condon's redirection paid off in the years that followed.

New direction required new men, and Dr. Condon's arrival happened to coincide with an almost complete turnover of the top echelon. Age had begun to make its claims and many, like Dr. Briggs, past the retirement age, had waited only for the war to end. The five division chiefs who retired in 1945 had been with the Bureau since World War I or earlier.[35] Submitting requests for retirement with them were two section chiefs and a number of nonadministrative scientists and technicians with long years of service.[36] Still other division chiefs and 14 additional section chiefs reached retirement age over the next 4 years.[37] By 1950 the top echelons of the working force was essentially new, and the average age level at the Bureau had plummeted by some 20 years.[38]

In most instances division chief replacements were found among senior heads of sections. Continuity was further maintained by appointing Bureau-bred members to top administrative positions. The redirection of the Bureau was carried out principally through changes in organization, through new men that came in to head new fields of research, and the special assistants that Dr. Condon brought in from outside.[39]

Appointed Associate Directors early in 1946 were Dr. Crittenden and Dr. Dryden, the latter, upon going to NACA as director of research in 1947, replaced by Dr. Wallace R. Brode, organic chemist and spectroscopist from Ohio State. From the Navy Bureau of Ships that spring came Dr. John H. Curtiss as assistant to the Director, to take charge of mathematical and statistical research and analysis. From Westinghouse came two other assistants, Dmitri I. Vinogradoff, as liaison between the Bureau and foreign scientific and engineering laboratories, and Hugh Odishaw, to oversee sci-

---

[35] They were Bearce of weights and measures, Dickinson of heat and power, Rawdon of metallurgy, P. H. Bates of silicate products, and Fairchild of trade standards.

[36] The section chiefs were Acree in chemistry and Stutz in mechanics.

[37] Retiring section chiefs were Curtis and Dellinger in electricity, Miss Bussey, Wensel, Van Dusen, and Ingberg in heat and power, Bridgeman, Brooks, and Peters in optics, Smither in chemistry, Tuckerman and Whittemore in mechanics, Wormeley in organic materials, and McAdam in metallurgy.

[38] Dr. McPherson of organic materials was to say that in 1943 he was the youngest division chief in point of service; by 1950 he was the oldest. Interview, Dec. 5, 1961.

[39] In a few instances, senior section chiefs were made assistant division chiefs as areas of the Bureau research were phased out or several sections were combined.

entific and technical information and Bureau publications.[40] And in a reorganization of housekeeping elements, budget and management, personnel, plant, and shops became formal divisions.

Changes in Secretary Wallace's Visiting Committee to the Bureau included the appointment in 1945 of Harold C. Urey, research chemist at the University of Chicago and Nobel laureate, and in 1946 of Eugene P. Wigner, physicist at Princeton and director of research at the Oak Ridge laboratories, who was to receive the Nobel Prize in 1963. The appointment of two theoretical physicists resulted in a significant change in the composition of the Visiting Committee, long dominated by representatives of industry. Urey and Wigner joined long-time members Gano Dunn of the J. G. White Engineering Corp., Karl T. Compton, president of MIT, and William D. Coolidge, director of research at General Electric.

In place of the informal notices and occasional memoranda on administrative matters that previous directors had issued were the numbered Bureau Orders, Administration Procedural Memoranda, and Bureau Memoranda introduced in December 1945. They were timely, for the next decade was to see more changes in organization, policies, and staff than in all the previous years put together. For one thing, the wartime influx of workers that raised the staff above the 2,000 level for the first time in Bureau history did not recede with the end of hostilities but increased steadily. Administration grew proportionately more complex.

Between serving on the McMahon committee and familiarizing himself with the Bureau establishment, it was May 1947, a year and a half after assuming the directorship, before Dr. Condon completed his initial reorganization of the Bureau structure.[41] In the new order, divisions were merged to bring related interests or functions together,[42] new divisions and new sections were created,[43] and still other sections were relocated as a matter of logic. Several sections, some of them one- or two-man units, were absorbed

---

[40] A third special assistant, Nicholas E. Golovin, trained in physics but then a management specialist from Naval Ordnance, arrived in the spring of 1949 to take over the analysis and planning of Bureau technical programs.

[41] Announced in NBS BuOrder 47–14, May 19, 1947.

[42] The new electricity and optics division included three sections from optics (photometry and color, optical instruments, and photographic technology) that depended upon electrical standards. Simplified practices and trade standards were combined as the commodity standards division.

[43] The atomic physics division grouped all Bureau facilities and activities relating to atomic and molecular physics and also certain phases of optics and of electronic physics. The Central Radio Propagation Laboratory stemmed from the radio section in electricity. Building technology division took over the fire resistance and heat transfer sections of heat and power, the masonry section (renamed structural engineering) from silicate products division, and the whole of the codes and specifications division. The applied mathematics division had its origin in the New York mathematical tables project.

in larger units elsewhere.[44] Two divisions saw little more than a name change as weights and measures became the metrology division, and clay and silicate products became the mineral products division.[45] And as Dr. Stratton had once headed his own optics division, so Dr. Condon for a time doubled in brass, as chief of his new atomic physics division.

Laboratory space became critical even before the President's decision in 1950 to construct the hydrogen bomb and the onset of the Korean war. Under the shadow of atomic war, talk of dispersal of military installations and defense facilities was translated into policy. The pressure for space and Truman's refusal to permit expansion of facilities in Washington led to the establishment of two Bureau stations far from the Nation's Capital, the Corona Laboratories in California and the Boulder Laboratories in Colorado.

Two major Bureau projects stepped up when the Korean war began were those in nonrotating proximity fuzes for Army Ordnance and guided missiles for the Navy. Additional temporary structures across Van Ness Street were sufficient to accommodate the augmented fuze group, but the missile staff was approaching a hundred members and its development mission had been accelerated by the requirement for an expanded series of production models for possible use in the Pacific. The project needed space quickly and there was no time to build.[46] On June 1, 1951, the project left Washington and moved into surplus Navy hospital structures, idle since the war, at Corona.[47]

Still another cooperative project, for the Atomic Energy Commission, called for large-scale assistance from the Bureau and required facilities for which space was lacking in Washington. The year before, in 1949, a 220-acre tract had been donated by the citizens of Boulder, Colo., at the foothills of the Rockies, on what was then the outskirts of the city, for new radio facilities for the Bureau. On the slope back of the site marked out

---

[44] Underground corrosion went to metallurgy. The huge special projects section (i.e., guided missiles) in mechanics became part of the ordnance development division, and a ballistics group in electricity was transferred to the new division. Transferred to chemistry and no longer separate units were the polarimetry, radiometry, and interferometry sections of optics. Combined with the temperature measurements section of heat and power were the division's thermometry and pyrometry sections. One section in heat and power, aircraft engine research, was discontinued in 1948 when the work was taken over by the NACA laboratory at Cleveland.

[45] Weights and measures administration, for a time a section in metrology, became a separate Office of Weights and Measures in October 1947, and was later joined by an Office of Basic Instrumentation. All of these organization changes are shown in app. J.

[46] Letter, EUC to Secretary of Commerce, Dec. 13, 1949, and letter, EUC to Director, Bureau of the Budget, Sept. 13, 1950 ("General Correspondence Files of the Director, 1945–1955," Boxes 4 and 6).

[47] BuOrd 51–18, June 1, 1951; Hearings * * * 1952 (Apr. 10, 1951), pp. 497–502; interview with Dr. Condon, Oct. 27, 1963.

for the radio laboratories, ground was leveled for the erection of new Bureau cryogenic laboratories.[48]

TECHNOLOGICAL vs. BASIC RESEARCH

In 1944 Harry S. Truman was nominated to the Vice-Presidency, succeeding Henry A. Wallace who had held that office during the previous term. On the day after the inauguration Wallace replaced Jesse Jones as Secretary of Commerce.[49] It was a brief tenure. Truman became President a month later, and in the fall of 1946 Wallace's differences with the President's policy toward the U.S.S.R. led to his resignation.

Jesse Jones, as had his predecessors under Roosevelt, Daniel Roper and Harry Hopkins, found that "The President was never genuinely friendly to business, and there was little the Secretary of Commerce could do for business and industry * * *."[50] Nevertheless, Wallace asked for the Commerce post, in exchange for his loss of place on the ticket.

Wallace had reform in mind, for he was convinced that "not until businessmen were educated could any sort of economic justice be attained in this country."[51] A biographer has said: "As Secretary of Commerce, Wallace * * * settled down into relative obscurity for nearly a year. However, during this period significant changes took place within the ornate walls of the Commerce Building. A strong friend of small business was now in power. Expansion of technical and other assistance for small firms from $300,000 to $4,500,000 per year was initiated."[52] He intended the Bureau to assist in the aid to business.

In a prepared statement before the House Appropriations Subcommittee in January 1946, Wallace outlined his proposed reorganization of the Department. It proved rather a reemphasis of effort than a reorganization,

---

[48] The site was acquired in mid-December 1949 and construction began in the summer of 1951 (Department of Commerce records, NARG 40, file 83583; NBS BuOrd 52–7, Aug. 15, 1951).

[49] For behind the scenes accounts of the juggling of posts and men, see James A. Farley, Jim Farley's Story, pp. 371 ff; Grace Tully, F.D.R.—My Boss, p. 188; Raymond Moley, 27 Masters of Politics, (New York: Funk & Wagnalls, 1949), pp. 84 ff.

[50] Jesse Jones, Fifty Billion Dollars, p. 257. Almost wholly taken up with the operations of the Reconstruction Finance Corporation he also headed, Jones left Department of Commerce details to his Under Secretary, Wayne C. Taylor. Ibid., p. 538.

[51] Russell Lord, The Wallaces of Iowa (Boston: Houghton Miffln, 1947), p. 615.

[52] Karl M. Schmidt, Henry A. Wallace: Quixotic Crusade, 1948 (Syracuse University Press, 1960), p. 7. For the fear that Wallace as Secretary would establish, through the National Bureau of Standards, Federal consumer standards in place of trademarks, see George E. Sokolsky article in "New York Sun," Feb. 27, 1945, copy in NBS Box 503, IDA–ASA.

a new deal designed to promote foreign trade and provide special services to business in the fields of science, technology, management, and marketing. He intended to expand the Department's output of basic statistical information and provide detailed analyses on the economic outlook for the use of business, Government, and the public, and to this end the scientific and technical bureaus of his Department must be strengthened. What he had in mind for the National Bureau of Standards was not spelled out, except that it was to be responsible for "technological research and development on problems of direct and practical interest to industry." [53]

Before the same subcommittee 2 weeks later, Dr. Condon asked for increased funds for intensified activity by the Bureau "from an industrial and economic point of view" in the fields of metallurgy, high polymers, building materials, thermodynamics, rubber, hydraulics, atomic energy, electronics, and radio propagation. Their research was "no more than simple national wisdom." The four fields in which the Bureau planned to concentrate its greatest resources, however, were nuclear physics, building materials and structures, radio propagation, and rubber chemistry. They would require "research in fundamental science of a long-range and basic character" and "a great deal closer cooperation in fundamental research by the universities." [54]

Dr. Condon's remark, that his Assistant Directors would "see that appropriate research work is initiated in new fields * * * [and] that there is not too much effort expended on routine tests [at the expense of basic research]" did not entirely satisfy the subcommittee, the Bureau of the Budget, or senior members of the Bureau who viewed testing—with an appropriation of $1.5 million annually—as a primary and irreducible function of the Bureau.[55]

---

[53] Hearings * * * 1947, p. 5. Considering its importance to the Government, said Wallace, the program and appropriation for the Bureau were modest, no more than "comparable to the scientific program of a single large private corporation" (ibid., p. 8).

[54] Hearings * * * 1947, p. 178; NBS Annual Report 1946, p. 172. Discussed at length at the hearings but unreported elsewhere was an appropriation in the budget of $100,000, to provide specifications for consumer goods. Since the 1930's the Bureau's codes and specifications division had maintained a small section called "consumer contacts." Almost certainly at the prompting of Secretary Wallace, funds were inserted in the 1947 budget to expand the section to 32 members in order to extend the work on Federal specifications and the factfinding tests of products for the Federal Trade Commission to the consuming public. As a beginning, the Bureau was to develop at once methods of testing and test machines for determining consumer standards and specifications in leather goods, to "provide simple means of finding out what we get for our money" (Hearings * * * 1947, pp. 205–206, 217–220). It was a short-lived project. Within months, along with most of the simplified practices and trade standards divisions of the Bureau, it was transferred to another agency of Commerce. Its chief, George N. Thompson, went to the Bureau's new building technology division.

[55] Hearings * * * 1947, p. 191; interview with Dr. McPherson, Dec. 5, 1961.

Amid the general apprehension over the unsettled conditions of the postwar world, Condon anticipated what was later to become a commonplace, that any interruption in the flow of new knowledge, or even a slackening of its pace, posed a potential threat to national security. The war demonstrated the necessity of narrowing the leadtime between the discovery of new knowledge and its application, and the Federal Government had come to recognize its responsibility for securing the basic research that made purposeful application possible.

In a lighter moment early in the hearings in 1946, Congressman Rabaut said to Condon: "With this atomic age on our hands we must treat your Bureau with respect, as we do not want to get in wrong with anybody who has anything to do with it." [56] But neither Congress nor the public was quite ready yet to pay for the basic research of the atomic age. A year later when Dr. Condon presented his research program in greater detail, the mood of the subcommittee was economy.

Dr. Condon's original request to the Department of Commerce for 1948 funds totaled $25 million, almost four times the direct appropriation of the previous year. The new Secretary of Commerce, W. Averell Harriman, had whittled it to $17.1, and the Bureau of the Budget had brought it down further to $10.6 by deleting, "without prejudice," the Bureau's proposed research in synthetic rubber, as well as research auxiliary to the atomic energy program (the latter in the amount of $2.5 million), by reducing initial construction funds for a new radio propagation laboratory in Washington by two-thirds ($1.9 to $0.6 million), and refusing most of the proposed cost of rehabilitating the Bureau plant (including $1.5 million for electrical modernization, $2 million for plumbing). Left more or less intact were the new programs planned in building materials, hydraulics, computers, X-ray research for medicine and industrial radiography, fundamentals of metallurgy, fundamental studies in the properties of chemical compounds, electronics, high polymers, and radio propagation.[57]

The kind of industrial research that the Bureau had long carried on, said Dr. Condon, was no longer necessary, except in building. With industry booming, the civilian economy was running at the highest level in its history, about $200 billion a year, and more than 2,400 industrial laboratories were engaged in keeping that production going. As a consequence, the laboratories were making unprecedented demands on the Bureau

[56] Hearings, ibid.

[57] Hearings * * * 1948 (Mar. 12, 1947), pp. 287–292. Including $1.1 million for equipment and facilities, the final appropriation came to $7.9 million, representing a slight increase over the previous year.

for the fundamental instrumentation they needed and could not do.[58] Some of the new industries, especially those based on electronics, required work on measurements that had never been done before. And the Bureau had to continue to supply basic information to many of the new small businesses that could not afford research laboratories. The funds for this research, on which the Bureau of the Budget had agreed, were approved, but not without a struggle.[59]

Even before final approval, the Bureau began to free itself from considerable industrial-type research, as well as direct research for industry, by abandoning some of its former lines of investigations or shifting to more basic aspects. Research in the rare sugars, for example, turned to wider studies in carbohydrate chemistry and in radioactive carbohydrates. Much of the basic work in plastics, leather, paper, rubber, and other organic materials became centered in the new science of high polymers. In optical glass, production was sharply curtailed and research shifted to the theory and constitution of glass in general. Because of the delay imposed by the Korean war, it was 1957 before all production of optical glass ceased and the plant was dismantled.[60]

Still another Bureau activity, its member participation in the work of the American Standards Association, diminished after 1948 when the association was incorporated under the laws of New York State. As a result, the Department of Commerce and other Federal agencies withdrew from active participation in the administrative affairs of the association, although members of the Bureau continued to serve on the council, boards, and technical committees of the association, as they do to the present day.[61]

---

[58] Hearings * * * 1947, p. 203; Hearings * * * 1948, p. 290; Hearings * * * 1950, p. 483.

[59] In final justification of Bureau funds, Dr. Condon found, at the request of the subcommittee, that the estimate of total appropriations for all Federal research and development in the 1948 budget came to $730 million, of which $10 million, including construction, equipment, and facilities, represented the Bureau's share (Hearings * * * 1948, pp. 299–300).

[60] NBS Annual Report 1948, pp. 218, 230–231; Annual Report 1951, p. 36; NBS Consolidated Report on Projects, fiscal year 1958, Project 0902–40–4408; interview with Clarence H. Hahner, May 6, 1964.

[61] NBS Report 6227, "American Standards Association, Inc." (1958), pp. 11–12 and app. 8. The propriety of NBS membership, on the premise that the Bureau was more consumer-directed than ASA, was first raised in memo, Soliciter, Department of Commerce, for Under Secretary of the Department, June 11, 1943. NBS and Federal withdrawal was also urged in memo, EUC for Secretary of Commerce Harriman, Oct. 16, 1946, based on the doubtful legal grounds of the mixed membership and as misleading to the public (correspondence in NARG 40, Secretary of Commerce, file 75388/18). The formal resignation of the NBS and Department of Commerce from ASA was accepted in letter, Secretary ASA to Secretary of Commerce, July 29, 1948 ("General Correspondence Files of the Director, 1945–1955").

One whole division at the Bureau, commodity standards, a recent consolidation of the trade standards and simplified practices division, was transferred with its staff of 30 out of the Bureau to the Office of Technical Services in the Department of Commerce in July 1950. Essentially nontechnical in nature, and with minor justification under Bureau legislation, the division had little relevance to the postwar mission of the Bureau, to provide standards of physical measurement.[62]

Talk of reducing routine testing, as an impediment to the scientific work of the Bureau, met strenuous objections from both inside and outside the Bureau. Some lines, such as clinical thermometer testing, were subsequently discontinued, and the workload in testing electric lamps, cement and other large-scale Federal purchases was somewhat lightened by resorting to statistical analysis test procedures. But while some routine calibrating and testing decreased, that of materials and equipment and the calibration of instruments increased steadily through the 1950's and 1960's.[63] To share the administrative burden on division and section chiefs, responsibility for all testing was subsequently centered in a new Associate Director for Testing.

Plans to increase fundamental research and reduce technological research foundered on a simple economic fact. The military services and the Atomic Energy Commission had vast sums available for research in the new technologies, and the Bureau had the staff, facilities, and knowledge in these fields. As the principal legacy of World War I had been new fields of industrial research, so that of World War II brought to the Bureau the realms of electronics and nuclear energy. Both offered as much opportunity for pure research as for applied research and technical development. For that reason, the technology could not be refused.

Thus in 1947, with many wartime programs still uncompleted, the Bureau reported military research still "a considerable portion" of the total work of the Bureau. By 1951, in the midst of a new emergency, the greater part of Bureau research was again concerned with national defense projects.[64]

For this research the Bureau acquired a great array of new tools: an electron microscope, the first of its kind ever constructed, using energies up

---

[62] Letter, Secretary of Commerce Sawyer to EUC, May 26, 1950, and attached correspondence ("General Correspondence Files of the Director, 1945–1955," Box 4).

[63] Tests, calibrations, and standard samples in 1946 had an estimated value of $1.2 million. By 1960, test and calibration fees alone amounted to $2.7 million, and by 1963 to $3.4 million (NBS Annual Reports).

[64] NBS Annual Report 1947, p. vii; Annual Report 1951, p. 1. "Three-fourths of the total effort * * * is directed toward meeting vital requirements of the defense program" (NBS BuMemo 52–11, Sept. 17, 1951).

to 1.4 million volts, for research in metallurgy and electron optics; [65] and a magnetic electron spectrometer, for the study of the beta- and gamma-ray spectra of radioactive isotopes and measurement of their disintegration schemes and nuclear energy levels.[66] A mass spectrometer was obtained with the help of the Office of Naval Research, for precise measurement of nuclear masses. It was to be used initially for research in the components of synthetic rubbers.[67] A 50-million-volt betatron was also acquired, for studies in protection and proper shielding against high-energy radiation; [68] and a 1.5-million-volt X-ray tube, for an investigation of the broad X-ray beams used in medical and industrial radiography.[69] Still another new "tool" was the Bureau's ultrasonic laboratory for special studies of the properties of gases and liquids, employing sound waves of extremely high frequency.[70]

In the field of electronics, military and naval ordnance projects predominated, including advanced design work on nonrotating proximity fuzes; development of electronic and servomechanism controls for an advanced guided missile, the Kingfisher series; development of a proximity fuze for guided missiles; and refinement of the toss bombing device, the aircraft bomb director. Important to these projects was the research initiated in the basic elements of electronic computing machines, and the investigation of electronic components in a new electron tube laboratory set up at the Bureau. A secondary purpose of the laboratory was to apply its knowledge of electronic instrumentation and controls to measurement problems in the other divisions of the Bureau.[71]

Apart from the highly classified work on proximity fuzes for guided missiles, the research in electronics centered on electron tubes, printed circuits, and automatic computers. The Bureau designed special equipment

---

[65] NBS Annual Report 1948, pp. xv, 214–215. For the Bureau's new microsectioning procedure involving organic materials, in high polymer studies employing the electron microscope, see RP2020 (Newman, Borysko, and Swerdlow, 1949) and Hearings * * * 1950 (Feb. 23, 1950), p. 2169.

[66] NBS Annual Report 1946, p. 183.

[67] LC791, "The mass spectrometer" (1945) ; NBS Annual Report 1946, p. 193.

[68] NBS Annual Report 1946, p. 184; Hearings * * * 1948, p. 356. With the installation of the first betratron in late 1949, the Bureau ordered a second unit, a 180-million-volt synchrotron (Hearings * * * 1951, p. 217; Science, 105, 230, 1947). Unlike the conventional X-ray machine used in the treatment of most cancer patients, the betatron is used against deepseated cancers, producing high-speed electrons that on striking an internal target produce X rays. Its electron beam can also be used directly to irradiate a tumor. The machines at the Bureau were for studies in basic radiation physics, not medical research or treatment of patients.

[69] NBS Annual Report 1946, p. 184.

[70] NBS Annual Report 1948, p. 221.

[71] NBS Annual Report 1946, pp. 201–203.

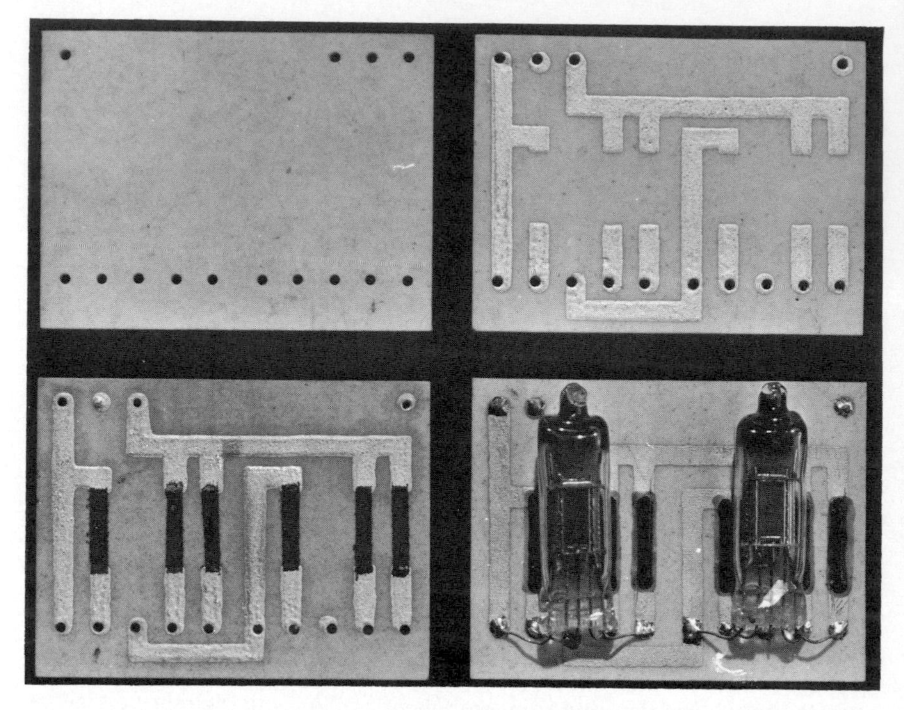

The four stages of an early printed electronic circuit: the plate, the circuit wiring, addition of the resistors, and final assembly with miniature tubes.

for measuring the characteristics of the growing family of electron tubes to determine, among other things, the principles by which their life service might be extended.[72] A new field of research was the semiconductors, crystalline materials of high purity, such as germanium and silicon. With their electrical conductivity between that of a metal and an insulator, and their unique ability to change their resistance characteristics, they opened new vistas in the development of communication equipment.[73] They appeared first in the crystal diode developed during the war for radar, and subsequently in the crystal triode or transistor, as replacements for the vacuum tubes in amplifiers. The ubiquitous pocket transistor radio was less than a decade away.

New advances were made in printed circuits, first devised for the proximity fuze, that substitute printed wiring, resistors, and coils for the conventional rigging in electronic devices. Along with subminiature tubes, semiconductors, and circuit design, the printed circuit established a whole

[72] NBS Annual Report 1948, p. 244; Annual Report 1949, p. 80.
[73] NBS Annual Report 1949, p. 21; Annual Report 1951, p. 4.

new field of electronic miniaturization for which the Bureau was to provide useful engineering data.[74]

Problems submitted to the Bureau by the Navy Bureau of Aeronautics included devising reasonably stable and long-lived electronic components capable of withstanding rapid changes in temperatures, and design of miniaturized amplifiers with printed circuits. Within a year the Bureau produced a radar-type amplifier with the same electrical performance but one-quarter the usual size, and a miniature battery-powered radio transceiver, for use as an air-sea rescue device. A miniature radio range receiver, a navigation aid for the Navy, which fitted into a sealed envelope 6 by 5 by 1¾ inches, had the range and power of a conventional 12-tube unit. These amplifiers and receivers were made possible in part by a Bureau-built rotary printer that applied printed circuits on either flat or cylindrical surfaces.[75] A printed resistor, applied by a silk-screen process (later replaced by an adhesive-tape resistor), and a tiny ceramic capacitor, the latter devised at the request of the Signal Corps, contributed to still more rugged and efficient miniaturization.[76]

Much of the work on electronic tubes, printed circuits, and miniaturization saw its most important application in the automatic electronic computing machine project set up at the Bureau for Army Ordnance early in 1946. Two decades earlier, about 1925, the present era of mechanical computation began when Dr. Vannevar Bush and associates at MIT constructed a large-scale computer run by electric motors. This and an improved model completed in 1942, both requiring hand computations as an adjunct to the machines, were extensively used during the war in the computation of artillery firing tables. The modern electronic computer had its genesis in the work of Dr. John W. Mauchly, physicist at the Moore School of Electrical Engineering, University of Pennsylvania. In 1942, convinced that the mechanical calculation of firing tables could be speeded up by the application of electronics, he began the study of such a machine. Four years later, with J. Presper Eckert, Jr., as designer, the Electronic Numerical Integrater and Automatic Computer (ENIAC) was completed, performing 5,000 additions a second, where mechanical calculators handled 10 a second.[77]

---

[74] C468, "Printed circuit techniques" (Brunetti and Curtis, 1947); M192, "New advances in printed circuits" (1948), a symposium discussing their application to radio, radar, TV, guided missiles, airborne electronic equipment, computers, and industrial control equipment.

[75] NBS Annual Report 1949, pp. 49, 59, 61; Annual Report 1951, pp. 69–70.

[76] NBS Annual Report 1951, pp. 2, 71; C530, "Printed circuit techniques: an adhesive-tape resistor system" (B. L. Davis, 1952).

[77] Eckert, Mauchly, et al., "Description of ENIAC," Applied Mathematics Panel Report 171.2R (NDRC, November 1945); Jeremy Bernstein, The Analytical Engine: Computers—Past, Present and Future (New York: Random House, 1964), pp. 50, 54–55.

Capable of handling large amounts of statistical data with revolutionary speed, thoroughness, and efficiency, the new machines permitted, among other things, the solution of equations hitherto, from the standpoint of time, impossible to solve, and were to take the guesswork out of problems previously undertaken by constructing costly experimental equipment, such as the wind tunnels used in aerodynamic studies.

The computer project at the Bureau was first assigned to the machines development section of the applied mathematics division. An increasing amount of its component research, however, was carried out by another computer section, that under Dr. Chester H. Page and Samuel Alexander in Dr. Astin's electronics division. In the latter division, utilizing its research in specialized electron tubes, high-speed memory organs, transference means, input and output equipment (a system of electric typewriters and magnetic recording devices derived from standard teletype machines), and transcriber and converter elements, the first Bureau computer was built. A crucial breakthrough was the substitution of the new germanium crystal diodes for electron tubes in all switching and computing elements, with tubes used only for power amplification.[77]

In 1947, a year after the Bureau began its research on computer components, the Bureau of the Census and the Office of Naval Research, with assistance from the Air Force, contracted with the Bureau for the construction of two full-scale computers at an estimated cost of $300,000 each. Their design was assigned to the Eckert and Mauchly Computer Corp., the Raytheon Manufacturing Co., Massachusetts Institute of Technology, and Tufts College. One was to be assembled in the electronics division in Washington, the other at the Bureau's Institute for Numerical Analysis, recently organized at the University of California at Los Angeles.[78]

Presiding over the computer project, Dr. Condon saw the Bureau as "the centralized national computer facility" for the Government, the Washington unit serving the eastern half of the Nation, that at Los Angeles the

[77] NBS Annual Report 1946, p. 202; Annual Report 1948, pp. 240, 256; Annual Report 1950, p. 81.

The germanium or silicon crystal as transistor, first developed by Bardeen, Brattain, and Shockley, physicists at the Bell Telephone Laboratories, in 1948, conducts electrical current in much the same way as a vacuum tube. Unlike the tube, which boils off electrons that flow as directed by an electrical field, the transistor operates without heating and there is nothing to burn out (Bernstein, The Analytical Engine, p. 68).

[78] Negotiations began with memo, Director NBS for Director of the Census, Apr. 26, 1946, sub: Design and construction of electronic tabulation equipment ("General Correspondence Files of the Director, 1945–1955"); NBS Annual Report 1947, p. 187; Hearings * * * 1949, p. 523.

The Standards Eastern Automatic Computer (SEAC), its cover doors removed, with the operator's table in the foreground.

From left to right, the nine racks of the computer include the control unit, the arithmetic unit, the time pulse generator, the clock pulse generator, the magnetic wire and magnetic tape input-output unit, controls and power supplies, and electronic circuitry for the punched tape input-output system. The small panels at the bottom of each rack hold "grasshopper" fuses to protect the circuits above them.

western half. Centralizing in the Bureau the solution of complex mathematical problems confronting Federal agencies in aeronautics, atomic and nuclear physics, ballistics, and guided missiles, as well as analysis of massive data problems, would avoid duplicating computer facilities in other agencies and make maximum use of the Bureau facility, as was being done in radio propagation.[79]

The "central facility" idea was short lived. Other agencies wanted their own computers, and at the request of the Army Map Service and the Air Comptroller, the Bureau entered into additional contracts with Eckert and Mauchly.[80]

While awaiting design results, the Bureau began work on a small-scale unit, the NBS Interim Computer, with which to test components, train operators, and handle computational work in its laboratories. The successful operation of the unit led to its expansion, with Air Comptroller support, as a full-scale machine. In the autumn of 1949, 20 months after beginning construction, it emerged as the National Bureau of Standards Eastern Automatic Computer (SEAC).[81]

The fastest general purpose, automatically sequenced electronic computer then in operation, SEAC was dedicated on June 20, 1950. Failure of a single one of its more than 100,000 connections and components, even for a millionth of a second, would result in computer misfunction. Yet operating often on a 24-hour-a-day, 7-day week, SEAC performed for 4,000 hours in its first 9 months without a malfunction. Besides handling a number of classified problems for the military services and the Atomic Energy Commission, it carried out computations on electronic circuit design, optical lens calculations, statistical sorting and tabulating studies for Social Security

---

[79] Hearings * * * 1948, pp. 350–351. The idea persisted, in NBS Annual Report 1950, pp. 71–72, and Annual Report 1951, p. 67.

[80] Discussed in Hearings * * * 1956 (Apr. 18, 1955), p. 29.

[81] NBS Annual Report 1948, p. 239; Annual Report 1949, pp. 64–65; Hearings * * * 1951 (Feb. 23, 1950), p. 2175; Hearings * * * 1952 (Apr. 10, 1951), pp. 502–504; interview with Dr. Edward W. Cannon, July 7, 1964.

In 1950 there were no more than six or eight electronic computers in operation. By 1960 over 10,000 of one type or another had been built. Eckert and Mauchly's Electronic Digital Variable Automatic Computer (EDVAC), for the Ordnance Ballistics Research Laboratory at Aberdeen, was completed in 1950. Between 1951 and 1953 Eckert and Mauchly, at Remington Rand, constructed six Universal Automatic Computers (UNIVAC), the development and assembly of the first of these commercial stored-program computers monitored by NBS for the Bureau of the Census. See Office of Naval Research report, "A survey of automatic digital computers" (Washington, D.C., 1953).

Assembly of the chassis of the Standards Western Automatic Computer (SWAC). SWAC was designed and constructed by the Institute for Numerical Analysis staff to provide a tool for research in numerical analysis. Its relatively high speed resulted from its very rapid cathode-ray-tube type of memory.

and Census, design of supersonic nozzles, and computed data on the crystallography of cement compounds and on the penetration of X rays.[82]

SEAC's high computing speed made it possible to add or subtract pairs of 11-digit numbers 1,100 times a second and multiply or divide them 330 times a second. It completed arithmetical operations of addition or subtraction alone in 50 microseconds, multiplication or division problems in 2,500 microseconds. In a problem of pure mathematics, the machine was directed to compute the factors of any given number up to 100 billion. It rapidly determined that the number 99,999,999,977 has no factors and is therefore a prime number. To do this the machine had to divide 99,999,999,977 by 80,000 different divisors, and solved in 30 minutes a problem that would take a man 2 months working 8 hours a day with a desk calculator.[83]

Dedicated on August 17, 1950, but not fully operative until early in 1952 was the Bureau's second machine, the Western Automatic Computer (SWAC), at the Institute for Numerical Analysis in Los Angeles. It was to handle special problems of the aircraft industry on the west coast for the Navy Department, as well as engineering, physics, and mathematical calculations required by the Bureau institute and by other Federal agencies in the area.[84]

In the course of work on input and output mechanisms for the first Bureau computer, Jacob Rabinow of the electronic division's ordnance development laboratory invented a unique type of electromagnetic clutch. Widely heralded as a new physical principle, the clutch was based on the discovery that frictional forces between solid surfaces and certain types of fluid media (in this case, an oil suspension of iron powder) can be controlled

---

[82] NBS Annual Report 1951, pp. 2, 75–76.

On the use of SEAC to make certain of the calculations for the design of the H-bomb, Edward Teller in "The work of many people," Science, 121, 273 (1955), wrote: "With the help of this facility [a * * * very efficient machine], initial details of the plans were ironed out in a few weeks rather than in tedious months."

[83] NBS Annual Report 1950, pp. 80–81; S. N. Alexander, "The NBSEAC," and Ralph J. Slutz, "Engineering experience with the SEAC," Proc. AIEE–IRE Computer Conference, February 1952, pp. 84, 90.

A second SEAC, DYSEAC, intended for Bureau research alone, was completed in July 1953 but subsequently went to the Signal Corps. See NBS Report 1951, "System specifications for DYSEAC" (Alan L. Leiner, 1952), and C551, "Computer development (SEAC and DYSEAC) at the NBS" (Alexander, Leiner, Slutz, et al., 1955). Other machines based on SEAC were FLAC for the Air Force Missile Test Center at Cocoa, Fla., and MIDAC for the University of Michigan.

[84] NBS Annual Report 1950, pp. 1, 2, 80; Annual Report 1952, p. 2.

SEAC, patterned after EDVAC, employed an acoustic delay line or serial memory. SWAC, patterned after a British computer, had an electrostatic or parallel memory. The two computers were about equally complex, but SEAC had a 512-word memory to SWAC's 256-word memory. Interview with Dr. E. W. Cannon, July 7, 1964.

The principle of the magnetic fluid clutch is based on creating a magnetic field that causes iron particles suspended in oil to become highly viscous and grab together into an almost solid mass.

In the magnetic clutch this oil-and-iron fluid is contained between steel plates. The plates, which operate independently in the absence of electric current, lock together when the current flows into the fluid.

The model car, above, demonstrates the possible use of the principle in automotive vehicles, where two of the magnetic clutches, with suitable gearing, provide the main power transmission.

Dr. Condon of the Bureau and Secretary of the Treasury John F. Snyder, right, demonstrate the NBS electronic currency counter with stacks of worn-out $1 bills.

The assembly on top of the cabinet consists of the turntable and feeding mechanisms and the phototube-light-mirror system. The cabinet houses a binary counter, control circuits, and an air compressor.

by a magnetic field. The principle of Rabinow's magnetic fluid clutch had application not only in computers but, with modifications, in servomechanisms, automatic machines, and possibly even in automobile transmissions.[85] The patent for the clutch, in accordance with Bureau policy, was assigned to "the public interest." So great was that interest that within a year almost 2,000 industrial engineers visited the Bureau to get test data on the invention.[86]

Another device that came out of the electronics division about the same time was the NBS electronic currency counter, a sensing instrument that automatically counted worn paper bills at the rate of 30,000 per hour. The device instantly rejected packets of bills returned by banks to the Treasury for burning that contained more or less than the 100 per packet required by regulations. Since 6 tons of currency are redeemed daily—about $40 million worth, mostly in $1 bills—it was estimated that use of the electronic counter,

[85] NBS Annual Report 1948, pp. vii, 240; Annual Report 1950, p. 78. For the Bureau's high-speed piezoelectric crystal clutch, a nonmagnetic type, also used in computers, see Annual Report 1951, p. 74.

[86] Hearings * * * 1950 (Mar. 9, 1949), p. 490; correspondence with Jacob Rabinow, May 5, 1964.

eliminating hand counting, would save the Government almost a quarter of a million dollars annually.[87]

When planning for the computers first began, the Bureau, with Office of Naval Research and War Department support, established its National Applied Mathematics Laboratories, in order to centralize mathematical research in the Government and begin programming studies for the computers.[88] The laboratories comprised the Institute for Numerical Analysis, at Los Angeles; and in Washington, a computation laboratory, set up with the group brought from the Mathematical Tables Project in New York; a statistical engineering laboratory; and an electronic computing machine development laboratory.

The numerical analysis group, in addition to its preliminary studies for SWAC, undertook solution of linear equations in many unknowns and the representation of complicated functions in terms of simple, easily computable functions. The computation section, besides performing calculations requested by Federal agencies, continued its compilation of highly specialized mathematical tables, particularly those essential to the solution of problems in atomic energy, aerodynamics, radio and radar navigation, and military ordnance.[89]

Allied to the numerical analysis section was the statistical engineering unit, concerned with the application of modern statistical inference to complex engineering experiments, to sampling problems, and analysis of data arising in physical experiments.[90] The computer laboratory sought better

---

[87] NBS Annual Report 1950, pp. 2, 4, 73; Hearings * * * 1952 (Apr. 10, 1951), pp. 462–463.

[88] NBS Annual Report 1948, p. 256. See John H. Curtiss, "The NAML: a Prospectus" (February 1947), intended, as Dr. Condon said in the foreword, as "a strong, easily accessible Federal applied mathematics center."

[89] Described in LC777, "Mathematical tables" (1945), superseded by LC884 (1947); NBS Annual Report 1948, pp. 237–238.

[90] NBS Annual Report 1947, pp. xii, 187–188. Early tasks set the statistical engineering section included the preparation of commercial sampling plans for inclusion in Federal specifications and commodity standards. One, made for the Mail Order Association of America, was a study of data gathered by the Bureau of Home Economics, Department of Agriculture, on body measurements of teenage girls. Hip-and-stature and hip-and-maximum chest girth measurements of 70,000 schoolgirls between the ages of 4 and 17 years were analyzed and diagramed to provide statistically efficient coverage from which garments, patterns, and forms could be sized to assure an accurate fit for a large proportion of the teenage population. A year later the Bureau issued a new commercial standard covering model forms for girls' apparel (NBS Annual Report 1948, pp. 238–239; Annual Report 1950, p. 87).

Studies in the field of probability methods centered on stochastic (random) processes, employing random samples of an odd number of observations and a time element. Applying this statistical technique to sample testing of clinical thermometers permitted techniques for numerical computation and their adaptation to machines, as well as better techniques for training mathematicians in the application of numerical methods.[91]

The new age of mathematics, electronics, nuclear physics, tracer research, radio propagation, and high polymer research challenged the Bureau to provide a host of new fundamental physical standards, physical constants, and standard samples. The Bureau also pursued its work on standards in more familiar areas, some whose adoption had waited only for the end of the war. Thus 1948, the year that saw international adoption of absolute values for the electrical units, new photometric units, and adoption of a revised International Temperature Scale,[92] also witnessed, after 30 years of effort, the first real agreement on unification of the screw thread standards of Great Britain, Canada, and the United States. Despite Lend-Lease and the common border to the north, the screw threads produced in these countries all during the war differed sufficiently to prevent their interchangeability, causing severe inconvenience and great economic loss. After 3 years of study, an accord of unification of the American and British standard systems was signed at the Bureau late in 1948 by representatives of the American Standards Association and their British and Canadian counterparts.[93]

The year 1948 also marked the near realization of an atomic basis for the standard of length. Two decades earlier, the Seventh International Conference on Weights and Measures had agreed to seek a definition of the meter in terms of light waves.[94] Great interest was, therefore, aroused in the increased accuracy recently found possible with a new light wave, that of an isotopic mercury in vapor form. The sharp spectral line of this isotope of mass 198 (Hg^{198}) was first observed in 1942 in the Radiation Laboratory at the University of California. In 1945 Dr. Meggers obtained a small quantity of the mercury isotope, distilled from proof gold exposed to neutrons in a chain-reacting pile, from the atomic pile at Oak Ridge.[95]

In precision, reproducibility, and convenience, Meggers found the wavelength of the green radiation from the mercury isotope far superior to either the standard meter or the wavelength of the red line of cadmium.

---

inspection testing of five times as many units in a given time by the same staff. Cement testing was put on a similar statistical basis (Annual Report 1948, pp. 238, 251; Annual Report 1949, p. 57).

[91] NBS Annual Report 1951, p. 67.

[92] NBS Annual Report 1948, pp. 201–203; Annual Report 1949, p. 14. For the earlier work, see ch. V, p. 246.

[93] NBS Annual Report 1949, p. 10; Annual Report 1951, p. 101; Fortune, 38, 86 (1948).

[94] See ch. VI, pp. 335–336.

[95] No attempt at the reverse process, changing mercury to gold, as the alchemists of the Middle Ages and as a group sponsored by Scientific American in the 1920's tried, was considered. See Sci. Am. 132, 80 (1925), and issues of December 1924 and March 1925.

He announced it the ultimate in a length standard.[96] Three years later the tentative standard was made available to science and industry in the form of the NBS-Meggers Mercury 198 Lamp.

The 13 Meggers lamps initially distributed in 1951 were capable of calibration to a precision of 1 part in 100 million, as opposed to the 1 part in 10 million possible with the standard meter. With further refinement—in particular, the use of an atomic beam of Hg^{198} instead of the vapor, to narrow the line and overcome the slight effect of temperature on the Meggers lamp—the Bureau looked forward to extending that accuracy to one part in a billion.[97]

Funds for a program to try the atomic beam method were not then available and it was 1959 before the work was completed. Meanwhile, the Bureau urged adoption of the mercury 198 lamp as the international standard, considering it a simple and excellent working standard for length measurements. Although the Russian standards laboratories favored the cadmium lamp, the other laboratories abroad settled on the krypton 86 lamp, proposed originally by the Physikalisch-Technische Bundesanstalt (the West

---

[96] Meggers, in J. Opt. Soc. Am. 38, 7 (1948), and Sci. Mo. 68, 3 (1949).

The standard meter, etched on a platinum-iridium bar maintained at the International Bureau, had been the world's standard of length since 1889 (see ch. I, p. 30). The cadmium line, first proposed by Michelson in 1893, had never been adopted. Though widely used, its structure limited the precision attainable. Time, however, and superior radiations witnessed notable improvements in the measurement of light waves.

Wavelengths of light are still measured with a Michelson-type interferometer. By splitting a beam of light, the interferometer permits its speed and wavelength to be measured with extraordinary accuracy. Each normal element or isotope of an atomic element, when made incandescent with high-frequency radio waves, emits a light with a characteristic and unchanging wavelength of its own. The wavelengths are measured in terms of the angstrom, named for A. J. Ångström who introduced the scale of wavelengths in 1868, his unit representing the ten-millionth part of a millimeter or 10^{-10} meter.

The light waves from some elements and isotopes can be measured more accurately than others, among them the red line of cadmium vapor, the orange line of krypton gas, the green light of mercury vapor, and, sharper than these, the green light of the unidirectional mercury atomic beam. Under excitation, the radiation of the atoms of these elements or isotopes is seen as measurable fringes of light between the parallel metallic-coated plates of the interferometer.

In establishing a standard of length, a gage block, meter bar or similar known quantity is measured directly against the wavelength seen in the interferometer, the spectroscopist measuring the half-width of the wave under observation and from that deriving precise values, in terms of angstroms, for the length standard. See NBS M248 (1962), pp. 9–11.

[97] NBS Annual Report 1947, p. 197; RP2091, "Lamps and wavelengths of mercury 198" (Meggers and Westfall, 1950); NBS Annual Report 1951, pp. 6, 29.

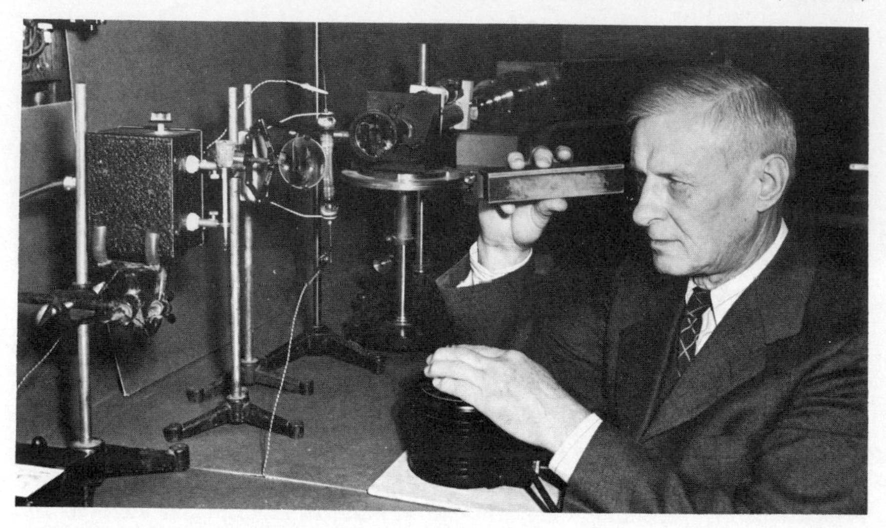

Dr. Meggers observing the spectral line of the mercury isotope of mass 198, a potential basis for an atomic standard of length.

German successor to the PTR), and in October 1960 the krypton lamp was adopted as a new international standard of length.[98]

Other developments in the postwar period, discussed later in the section on nuclear physics, included a standard of time, determined by an atomic clock; a primary neutron standard; and a fundamental nuclear constant, the gyromagnetic ratio of the proton.

Much new work was done in the field of physical constants. The Bureau made available comprehensive data on the infrared absorption spectra of chemical compounds for use in research analysis. It compiled tables of selected values of chemical thermodynamic properties for the simple sulfur compounds and the compounds found in liquefied petroleum gases.

---

[98] R. L. Barger and K. G. Kessler, "Kr^{86} and atomic-beam-emitted Hg^{198} wavelengths," J. Opt. Soc. Am. 51, 827 (1961).

In possible extenuation of the European adoption of the krypton lamp was the fact that at that time only the United States had reactors to supply mercury 198 (interview with Dr. Condon, Oct. 29, 1963).

Objective comparisons made in neutral laboratories reportedly agreed in general that krypton provided the highest precision. Despite the krypton lamp standard, metrology and spectroscopy laboratories both here and abroad use the Meggers lamp for its combination of accuracy and simplicity. Laser sources may yet supersede the atomic beam principle as the ultimate in sharpness in a spectral line standard. Interviews with Dr. Meggers, Mar. 13, 1962, and July 7, 1964; A. G. McNish, "Lasers for length measurement," Science, 146, 177 (1964).

And science and industry also needed the tabulations made by the Bureau of the dielectric constants of liquids, both inorganic and organic.[99]

Equally extensive work was done in standard samples, the array of materials maintained by the Bureau and certified as to their chemical composition or certain physical or chemical properties. Begun in 1905 with the preparation of four types of cast iron, by 1911 the Bureau stock comprised 37 samples of steels, brasses, ores, limestone, and sugars, and 100 standard combustion samples used to standardize calorimeters.[100] In 1951 the Bureau listed more than 500 distinct materials, of which 225 were certified for chemical composition and some 90 of these prepared specifically for spectrographic analysis. Others certified such properties as acidity, viscosity, melting point, density, index of refraction, and heat of combustion. Over 25,000 samples were prepared and distributed that year, for the use of Federal agencies and industry in checking tests, controlling manufacturing operations, and settling disputes between producers and consumers.[101]

Among the newest samples were a tin-bearing steel, a tungsten steel, and two nickel-chromium-molybdenum steels. An additional 32 standard samples of hydrocarbons brought the total of these compounds to 92, and 15 new standards for color or tint made 28 color standards available. Other samples included radioactive iodine and phosphorus for use in tracer micrography, radium gamma-ray standards, radioactive carbon and radon standards, and a series of pH standards.

Work on the pH samples had begun back in 1940 at the urging of the National Canners Association, of dairymen, dry cleaners, textile manufacturers and other groups. The control of acidity was also a problem in manufacturing pharmaceuticals, paper, leather, dyes, sugar refining, and biological materials. Lack of a universally accepted definition of the pH scale, or hydrogen ion concentration, by which the degree of acidity was measured, resulted in frequent confusion and disagreement.[102] After almost 8 years of study and consultation with industry, the Bureau established four standardized substances, representing pH 2, 3.5, 10, and

---

[99] NBS Annual Report 1950, p. 50; Annual Report 1951, p. 42; R. D. Huntoon and A. G. McNish, "Present status of research on the physical constants * * *," Nuovo Cimento (Rome), 6, 146 (1957).

[100] See ch. II, p. 93; NBS Annual Report 1911, p. 80.

[101] Harry A. Bright, "Standard samples program of the NBS," Anal. Chem. 23, 1544 (1951); C398 "Standard samples" (1932) and Supplement (1946); NBS Annual Report 1951, p. 85; C552 "Standard samples" (1954), second ed. (1957); James I. Hoffman, "The evolution of certified reference materials," Anal. Chem. 31, 1934 (1959).

[102] Hearings * * * 1940 (Apr. 21, 1939), pp. 162, 379; Hearings * * * 1946 (Dec. 9, 1939), pp. 136–139; RP1495 "Provisional pH values for certain standard buffer solutions" (R. G. Bates, W. J. Hamer, et al., 1942); LC993, "Standardization of pH measurements" (1950).

11.7, as the basis for a new pH scale. With certified samples of these substances, laboratories were at last provided with means for checking their own scales and maintaining uniformity of procedure.[103]

A series of important postwar projects began shortly after an Army plane, the XS–1, exceeded the speed of sound (760 miles per hour at sea level) for the first time on October 14, 1947. At the request of the National Advisory Committee on Aeronautics and the Navy Department, search was made for engineering and operational data on air turbulence and its effects at supersonic speeds.

The inauguration of supersonic flight also led to new work at the Bureau in high temperature ceramics and the development of a new high temperature ceramic coating, for the turbine blades of jet engines and the liners of rocket motors. Significant studies were conducted on combustion at high altitudes in jet, turbojet, and ramjet engines and thrust augmenters. With special instruments devised for the tests, new measurements were made on rubber and metal reactions at extremely high and low temperatures. But much remained to be done. Jet propulsion and supersonic flight called for almost total revision of data on fuels and the extension of many measurements to higher temperatures, pressures, and velocities.[104]

At the other extreme was a new phase of the Bureau's low temperature work, begun with the acquisition of an improved helium liquefier in 1948 for a program of basic research in superconductivity.[105]

The phenomenon of superconductivity—the disappearance in certain materials of resistance to an electrical current at very low temperatures—seemed a particularly challenging field in low-temperature physics, its spectacular effects giving promise of a basic insight into some of the fundamental properties of matter. Several lines of investigation were started, including studies of the anomalous properties of liquid helium II, an analogue of

---

[103] NBS Annual Report 1948, pp. 219–220: Annual Report 1950, pp. 46–47.

An interesting standard sample was the 15 gallons of very pure isooctane (2,2,4-trimethylpentane) and normal heptane prepared by the Bureau in the late 1940's and put up in ampoules for the American Petroleum Institute as ultimate primary standards for the octane rating of gasolines sold throughout the country. Subsequently the Phillips Petroleum Co. prepared good batches of both isooctane and heptane as working standards, but the Bureau ampoules, known as "the gold-plated standards," are still maintained at the API research laboratory at Carnegie Institute of Technology to settle disputes. Interview with Thomas Mears, Sept. 15, 1964.

[104] NBS Annual Report 1948, pp. 221, 223; Annual Report 1949, pp. 15–16, 18, 49; Annual Report 1950, pp. 8, 58, 64, 66; Annual Report 1951, pp. 24, 43. See also LC832, "Bibliography on gas turbines, jet propulsion, and rocket power plants" (1946); LC872, "Gas turbines and jet propulsion" (1947); C482 (1949), superseded by C509 (1951), on the same subjects.

[105] For earlier note on superconductivity, see ch. V, p. 247.

helium I, its normal liquid form. Liquid helium II, cooled to 2.19 °K or lower, acquires properties so unique that it is often described as a fourth state of matter.[106]

The studies in superconductivity led to the almost simultaneous discovery at the Bureau and at Rutgers University of a new and wholly unexpected relationship, called the isotope effect in superconductivity. A connection was observed between loss of electrical resistance at very low temperatures and the mass of the atomic nucleus. The pure mercury isotope Hg^{198}, it was found, becomes superconducting at a temperature about 0.02 °K higher than natural mercury. From the discovery that heavier mercury isotopes react at lower temperatures than the lighter ones, it was inferred that the nucleus must exert an important effect on the superconducting properties of the metal.[107] The finding appeared to offer a key to a basic understanding of how superconductivity comes about.

Still other lines of research in cryogenics were to be explored after a new laboratory was erected in Boulder, Colo., in 1951.

NUCLEAR PHYSICS AND RADIO PROPAGATION

The postwar research program of the Bureau's atomic physics division ranged widely, from investigations of intense neutron sources and of artificial radioactive isotopes to safety precautions at atomic plants and measurement techniques. The wartime studies in radiation hazards, atomic metallurgy, and atomic energy levels continued when their administration was transferred from the Manhattan District to the Atomic Energy Commission. The AEC also undertook support of a number of studies at the Bureau in atomic and molecular spectra, radiometry, electron optics, mass spectrometry, X rays, radioactivity, and determination of atomic and nuclear constants.[108]

An early achievement was construction of a national primary neutron standard, to serve as a reference unit of neutron intensity for the quantitative measurement of the strength of neutron sources and fluxes. In the absence of the standard, such measurements had previously been possible with an accuracy of only about 20 percent. The new standard, consisting of a beryllium sphere with a radium bromide center, made possible intercomparison of neutron measurements in other laboratories and later proved in-

---

[106] On the Kelvin scale of absolute temperatures, zero is equivalent to —273.15° C or —459.7° F.

[107] E. Maxwell, "Isotopic effect in the superconductivity of mercury," Phys. Rev. 78, 477 (1950); NBS Annual Report 1950, pp. 7–8, 32–33; Annual Report 1951, pp. 16, 26.

[108] NBS Annual Report 1948, p. 216; Annual Report 1951, p. 36.

The NBS standard of neutron intensity, a solid beryllium sphere, 4 centimeters in diameter, enclosing a capsule of platinum-iridium containing a gram of radium bromide compressed to maximum density.

Neutrons are emitted in the sphere by the action of the gamma rays from the radium at a constant rate of 1.1 million per second.

The establishment of a national neutron standard was made imperative by the increasing importance of neutrons as bombarding particles in physical and biological research.

valuable both in the operation of nuclear reactors and in neutron irradiation research.[109]

Accurate determination was first made at the Bureau of a fundamental nuclear constant, the gyromagnetic ratio of the proton, in absolute units, which previously had been made in terms of relative values of other physical constants. An important contribution to the knowledge of nuclear phenomena, it provided a simple and convenient standard for measuring the absolute value of magnetic fields, knowledge necessary in the use of such scientific apparatus as cyclotrons, mass spectrographs, and beta-ray spectrometers, and in such industrial equipment as servomechanisms and electromagnets.[110] Refinement of application of this constant led to a more precise knowledge of such other important atomic constants as the magnetic moment of the

[109] L. F. Curtiss and A. Carson, "Reproducibility of photoneutron standards," Phys. Rev. 76, 1412 (1949); NBS Annual Report 1948, pp. ix, 213. A refinement of the standard, based on a new determination of its emission rate, was reported in NBS Annual Report 1956, p. 36.

[110] NBS Annual Report 1948, pp. ix, 214.

proton, the charge-to-mass ratio of the electron, and the first precise determination of the proton moment in absolute units.[111]

A new instrument, the omegatron, also came out of the atomic physics division. Basically a miniature cyclotron about the size of a pack of cigarettes, the omegatron made possible determination of the values of several important atomic constants with much higher precision than heretofore. In addition, the faraday, previously determined solely by electrochemical measurements, was for the first time evaluated directly by physical methods, the preliminary value obtained representing a slight but significant degree of greater precision over that obtained with either the silver or iodine voltameter. The omegatron also facilitated sharper determination of the magnetic moment of the hydrogen proton.[112]

The formulation within a year or two of three proposed basic standards—length, determined by the green line of mercury 198; the gyromagnetic ratio of the proton, a constant to which the standard of mass might be referred; and time, in the constant natural frequency of the Bureau's atomic clock (see below, pp. 476–477)—led some at the Bureau to hope that "a complete set of primary atomic standards" might not be far off. They saw an increasing number of primary references for physical measurements—the independent and arbitrarily defined units of the last century—replaced by a set of working definitions comprising an atomic meter, atomic second, atomic ampere, atomic newton, atomic coulomb, and atomic kilogram.[113]

The year 1946 saw the inception of Bureau research in tracer micrography, that is, the tracking of the movement of radioactive atoms through organic systems, and later through inorganic systems as well. With radioactive isotopes made available by the Atomic Energy Commission (iodine 131, cobalt 60, phosphorus 32, sodium 22), tracers rapidly became an important tool of research in chemistry, biology, medicine, and industry.

A comparison check made by the Bureau disclosed discrepânices in medical and other research laboratories of several hundred percent in the determinations of amounts of radioactive material in samples of substances being used for medical treatment. The Bureau at once began work on standards for quantitative measurement of each of the tracer elements. Before

---

[111] H. A. Thomas, R. L. Driscoll, and J. A. Hipple, "Measurement of the proton movement in absolute units," Phys. Rev. 75, 902 (1949), and Phys. Rev. 78, 787 (1950); Driscoll, Thomas, and Hipple, "The absolute value of the gyromagnetic ratio of the proton," Phys. Rev. 79, 339 (1950); NBS Annual Report 1949, pp. 19–20; Annual Report 1951, p. 29.

[112] J. A. Hipple, H. Sommer, and H. A. Thomas, "A precise method of determining the faraday by magnetic resonance," Phys. Rev. 76, 1877 (1949); NBS Annual Report 1950, pp. 6, 34.

[113] R. D. Huntoon and U. Fano, "Atomic definition of primary standards," Nature, 166. 167 (1950).

long, standard samples of these isotopic elements were made available, assuring uniformity in the tracers in use.[114]

One of the first tracers produced for industrial research was chromium 51, a quantity of which the Bureau metallurgists acquired for study from the AEC. Preliminary work with this isotope promised to shed new light on the mechanism of electrodeposition, by identifying the type of chromium ions actually reduced to metal.[115] Perhaps the widest publicity on the new tracers, making them generally known to the public, was that given to carbon 14, the radioactive atom found in normal carbon 12.

As a constituent of the atmosphere—about one in a millon carbon atoms is radioactive—C^{14} is present in every living or once living thing. Made only during the life-cycle, production of C^{14} ceases at death and begins its slow but measurable decay, disintegrating at a constant rate. With a "half-life" on the order of 5,700 years, the time required for a given quantity of C^{14} to decay to one-half its original amount, the measurement of the remaining radiocarbon in bone, horn, shells, seeds, wood, charcoal, peat, or any organic matter in history, makes it possible to establish a method of absolute dating. By amplifying the exceedingly faint radioactive pulse or discharge with an ultrasensitive Geiger counter and measuring it against a calibrated scale, the age of the substance, up to 20,000 to 30,000 years, can be determined with considerable precision.[116]

Bureau interest in C^{14} was less in its proficiency as a kind of "atomic clock" than as a tracer in carbohydrate research. The Bureau turned after the war from sugar research to fundamental work in carbohydrates in general, especially in the molcecular structure of sugars and associated compounds. By 1951, under AEC sponsorship, glucose, mannose, galactose, and lactose were prepared for the first time with an atom of C^{14} in their carbon chain for chemical and biological research.

How tracer research proceeded was seen not long after in a Bureau investigation for the Army Surgeon General's Office. Before the medical laboratories of the Surgeon General could determine the possibility of using the commercial sugar compound, Dextran, as a blood plasma extender or even plasma substitute it had to be tagged, in order to track it through its physiological life cycle. The Bureau found a way to label the carbonyl group in the compound and patented the method. The technique of inserting C^{14} in

---

[114] NBS Annual Report 1948, pp. ix, 211; Annual Report 1949, p. 22.

[115] F. Ogburn and A. Brenner, "Experiments in chromium electro-deposition with radioactive chromium," J. Electrochem. Soc. 96, 347 (1949); NBS Annual Report 1949, p. 31.

[116] NBS Annual Report 1949, pp. 22–23; Frederick E. Zeuner, Dating the Past: an Introduction to Geochronology (London: Methuen, 1952), p. 341, reports the pioneer work of Willard F. Libby of the Enrico Fermi Nuclear Institute at Chicago who worked out the theory and technique of radiocarbon dating in 1947. See also L. J. Briggs and K. F. Weaver, "How old is it?" Natl. Geo. 114, 235 (1958).

a sugar compound was subsequently applied also to Inulin, a levulose polysaccharide used in the study of kidney functions.[117]

Elsewhere at the Bureau, after almost 5 years' work, the first volume of "Atomic Energy Levels" was completed in 1949. Designed for the use of workers in nuclear and atomic physics, astrophysics, chemistry, and industry, it was a compendium of all energy states for the first 23 elements, from hydrogen to vanadium, as derived from analyses of their optical spectra. Similar data for the next 19 elements, chromium through niobium (No. 41), comprised the second volume in 1952, and from molybdenum to plutonium (No. 94), a third volume in 1958.[118]

Another compilation made with AEC support was that of the experimental values of nuclear physical constants and properties, greatly needed by nuclear physicists, reactor engineers, and industrial and medical users of radioactive tracer materials. The first edition of "Nuclear Data," containing tables of experimental values found for the half-lives of radioactive materials, radiation energies, relative isotopic abundances, nuclear moments, cross sections, and nuclear decay systems, was issued in September 1950. A supplement appeared in April 1951 and two more late that year and early the next.[119]

Yet another AEC project at the Bureau was the sponsorship of a program of measurement of some previously undetermined properties of hydrogen. Using the helium liquefier acquired for its program in superconductivity, the Bureau made a series of studies over a period of 8 years focused on three isotopic modificiations of hydrogen, the normal hydrogen molecule, (H_2), hydrogen deuteride (HD), and deuterium (D_2), under a wide range of pressures. The report by Woolley, Scott, and Brickwedde on the thermal properties of hydrogen became a classic and established the Bureau as the Federal expert on cryogenic engineering.[120]

[117] NBS Annual Report 1948, p. 218; Isbell in Science, 113, 532 (1951); Hearings * * * 1953 (Jan. 18, 1952), p. 441; Chem. Eng. News 30, 1112 (1952); RP2886, "Carbon-14 carboxy-labeled polysaccharides" (J. D. Moyer and H. S. Isbell, 1958).

[118] NBS Annual Report 1950, p. 44; C467, compiled by Charlotte E. Moore.

[119] NBS Annual Report 1951, pp. 35–36; C499, compiled by Katharine Way, Lilla Fano, et al.

[120] RP1932, "Compilation of thermal properties of hydrogen in its various isotopic and ortho-para modifications" (1948); NBS Annual Report 1948, p. 207. Subsequent research by the cryogenic group made at the request of the AEC early in 1951 included the measurement of the vapor pressures, dew points, and critical constants of hydrogen, deuterium, and hydrogen deuteride (NBS Annual Report 1951, p. 27).

Bureau interest in cryogenics dates back to the turn of the century, when a plant for making and maintaining liquid and solid hydrogen, the invention in 1898 of Prof., later Sir, James Dewar, British physicist, was exhibited at the St. Louis Fair in 1903 and purchased by the Bureau (see ch. II, pp. 83–84). In 1923 Clarence W. Kanolt of the

The Bureau had long since outgrown the facilities for cryogenic research in its small low temperature laboratory in Washington when in April 1951, with the cooperation and financial support of the AEC, ground was broken at Boulder, Colo., for the construction of the world's largest liquid hydrogen plant and cryogenic laboratory. The plant at Boulder was completed that summer and the staff to man the plant and laboratory buildings moved in. The hydrogen liquefiers, the units producing liquid nitrogen to precool the hydrogen, and the purifiers, all in duplicate to insure continuous operation, were designed and their construction supervised by the Bureau. Both the plants and laboratories incorporated elaborate safety and anti-explosion features to minimize the hazards of working with liquid hydrogen in large quantities.[121]

Engineering research and production at Boulder accelerated when in 1956 the Air Force became interested in liquid hydrogen as an aircraft and rocket fuel.[122] Large-scale operations were established after 1957, when the National Aeronautics and Space Administration (NASA) began negotiations for all the liquid hydrogen the Boulder plant could supply, as a missile and satellite fuel. It followed the announcement by the U.S.S.R. in August 1957 of its first successful test of an intercontinental ballistics missile (ICBM). Two months later Russia's 184-pound satellite, Sputnik I, was launched and began orbiting the earth. A new race, to span continents and send men and machines into space, was on.

The cryogenic plant at Boulder shared the 220-acre tract with the Central Radio Propagation Laboratory (CRPL), the new Bureau division evolved from the wartime Interservice Radio Propagation Laboratory (IRPL) that had operated out of the Far West building at the Bureau.[123] Established on May 1, 1946, under Bureau operation and administration, CRPL came under the direction of an executive council representing the Army, Air Force, Navy, Federal Communications Commission, Civil Aeronautics Administration, Coast Guard, the Bureau itself, the Weather Bureau,

---

Bureau devised a standard and precise method of producing liquid and solid hydrogen at a temperature 25° above —459.7° F or absolute zero (Sci. Am. 129, 106, 1923). In 1931, with the same apparatus, Dickinson and Brickwedde, by precooling with solid hydrogen, produced liquified helium for the first time in this country, at a temperature of —456° F. (Science News, 73, 12, 1931; Time, 17, 58, 1931; NBS Annual Report 1931, p. 8).

[121] NBS Annual Report 1952, p. 14.

[122] Russell B. Scott, "Liquid hydrogen for chemical and nuclear rockets," Discovery, 21, 74 (1960).

[123] While the cryogenic plant began operations at Boulder in the fall of 1951, not until completion of CRPL were the Boulder Laboratories formally dedicated, on Sept. 8, 1954.

The NBS Boulder Laboratories in Colorado, housing the radio propagation, radio astronomy, and radio standards laboratories. In the background, on the first rise of the foothills of the Rockies, are the Bureau's cryogenic laboratories.

and commercial radio, as the central agency of the Nation for basic research in the propagation of radio waves.[124]

Besides continuing operation of the worldwide chain of stations—the total number was 58, of which 14 were directly operated or supported by the Bureau—to provide prediction services for long-distance radio, CRPL took over the research functions of the radio section of the Bureau's electrical division. It at once undertook extension of the research in lower frequencies into the ultrahigh frequency and microwave region (3000 megacycles or more) for the new fields of television, of frequency modulation (FM) broadcasting, and military and commercial radar.

Severely limiting the range and minimum usable signals in FM broadcasting, television, and other very-high-frequency services, the Bureau found, was the noise associated with cosmic and solar radio waves reaching earth from outer space. To study these phenomena, the Bureau instituted a program in radio astronomy, setting up at Boulder two solar radiometers with mirrors 25 feet in diameter, operating at different frequencies, to track the sun and observe its outbursts of radio energy.[125]

While outer space phenomena produced measurable limitations on very-high-frequency transmission, the major influences on propagation at microwave frequencies proved to be nearer to earth. Studies in tropospheric meteorology and terrain geometry—that is, the effects of rain and trees and hills—first begun several decades earlier for ordinary radio transmission, were resumed in order to learn the causes of attenuation of very short microwaves, particularly those used in radio relay operations.[126] Both the radio astronomy program and that on the troposphere became long-range projects.

An innovation in the radio services of the Bureau, begun on October 3, 1945, shortly before setting up CRPL, was the shortwave broadcast of standard time signals each 5 minutes around the clock. It augmented the standard radio frequencies, standard time intervals or pulses, standard audio frequen-

[124] Hearings * * * 1948 (Mar. 12, 1947), p. 339. Establishment of CRPL was authorized in letter, Secretary of Commerce Wallace to Secretary of the Treasury, Jan. 9, 1946 (copy in NBS Historical File), and activated as a division of the Bureau by memo, Director, for Division and Section Chiefs, NBS, Apr. 19, 1946 ("General Correspondence Files of the Director, 1945–1955").

[125] NBS Annual Report 1948, p. 247. The new branch of science, radio astronomy, had its beginnings in 1932 when Karl G. Jansky of the Bell Telephone Laboratories described the reception of extraterrestrial radio waves and from their diurnal variation in direction tentatively identified their source in the Milky Way. See Proc. IRE, 20, 1920 (1932); Nature, 132, 66 (1933). Grote Reber, both before and after he came to the Bureau in the 1940's, and the Bureau's chief of radio research, Dellinger, were to extend these observations. See F. T. Haddock, "Introduction to radio astronomy," Proc. IRE, 46, 3 (1958).

[126] NBS Annual Report 1949, p. 71.

cies, and standard musical pitch (middle A at 440 cycles per second), which the Bureau radio station, WWV, had broadcast since 1935.[127] As supplementary to the time signals of the Naval Observatory, the signals are widely used by such industries as mining, shipping, railroads, power, air transport, and communications, among many others.[128]

Within a year after beginning its new time signal service, improved standards resulted in achieving a maximum change of 0.001 second per 24 hours and deviations of as little as 0.009 to a maximum of 0.031 second from corrected Naval Observatory time.[129] Extending reception of the frequency and time signals of WWV, on November 22, 1948, the Bureau established a new experimental broadcast station, WWVH, on the island of Maui in Hawaii. Soon after it began operations, reports confirmed the expected success of the station in reaching with consistency a far greater range of areas in the Arctic and the Pacific than had been possible from Maryland.[130]

CRPL's extension of the primary frequency standard to 40,000 megacycles in 1948 helped to open research in a field of physical science first explored during the war, that of microwave spectroscopy. Of immediate importance to the Bureau work on guided missiles, the new methods devised for measuring electrical quantities at microwave frequencies made possible the use of sharp microwave beams on systems where high resolution was needed, as in short-range target-seeking rockets and missiles.[131]

---

[127] NBS Annual Report 1946, p. 206; NBS TNB 31, 21 (1947); Radio News, 38, 118 (1947).

[128] Long concerned with time as a factor in all measurement, and with clocks, watches, and sundials (on which it issued many Letter Circulars), the Bureau began testing timepieces shortly after its founding. See C51 (1914) and the current C432 (1941) on the testing of timepieces.

The propagation of standard time signals has been by tradition the prerogative of the Naval Observatory at Washington. The Bureau has also had an interest in standard timekeeping, dating back to World War I. Under an act of March 19, 1918, authorizing the establishment of daylight saving time and standard time zones in the United States, Congress appointed the Interstate Commerce Commission to define the limits of each time zone for the Nation. As a matter involving "standards," the ICC requested the Bureau to prepare the map from data that ICC supplied. The map was first published in 1925, in an NBS circular on standard times throughout the world (C280, currently C496, 1950), and a "standard time conversion chart" appeared in 1928 (M84). In 1930, over objections from the Department of Commerce that such a map was no function of the department, the Bureau replied that it was part of its information service to the Nation's commerce. It appeared in a separate publication that year as M111, currently M190, 1948. See Department of Commerce correspondence of August–September 1930 in NARG 40, Box 120, 67009/93.

[129] NBS Annual Report 1947, p. 223.

[130] NBS Annual Report 1949, p. 81.

[131] NBS Annual Report 1948, p. xiv.

Dr. Condon and Dr. Harold Lyons with the first atomic beam clock. It operated with an ammonia-regulated quartz crystal and ran with a constancy of one part in 20 million.

The Bureau atomic clock program sought to provide a spectroscopic standard capable of being used as a new atomic standard of time and frequency to replace the mean solar day and so change the arbitrary units of time to atomic ones. With such a clock, new precise values might be found for the velocity of light; new measurements of the rotation of the earth would provide a new tool for geophysicists; and new measurements of the mean sidereal year might test whether Newtonian and atomic time are the same, yielding important results for the theory of relativity and for cosmology.

The new microwave measurement technique, by overcoming the limitations of conventional optical and infrared equipment, also promised to extend spectroscopic analysis methods to high polymer research, that is, to the investigation of organic substances such as paper, leather, and plastics which are made up of very large molecules.[132] An immediate and dramatic application of the microwave technique, however, was in the Bureau's construction of an atomic clock.

[132] NBS Annual Report 1948, pp. xiv, 249.

Some of the first microwave measurements of the spectrum lines of ammonia gas against the NBS primary frequency standard suggested that they might serve as an invariable secondary frequency standard. A year later, in 1949, the Bureau devised means for utilizing the vibrations of atoms in the ammonia molecule, derived from the microwave region of ammonia gas, to control an oscillator with which to drive a clock.

The result was the first atomic clock ever built. While its magnitude of accuracy was only a little better than that of the 24-hour rotation of the earth, and not as good as time based on the annual rotation of the earth around the sun, a breakthrough had been achieved. With further refinement, using the cesium rather than ammonia atom, and with precise control of the radio frequency, much higher accuracy became possible. A time accuracy of at least 1 part in 10 billion, representing an error of 1 second in 300 years, was thus achieved, without reference to the earth's rotation or the planetary motions.[133] Such timing is not possible with the 2,000-year-old solar time system. And on an earth gradually slowing down, millionths of a second become vital in projecting such feats as timing rocket launches to meet in orbit hundreds of miles above the earth where a space platform might be assembled.

Of special importance to astronomy, both the clock and the method of construction represented new tools of research in technical fields where precise measurement of time and frequency are crucial, from long-range radio navigation systems and tracking of satellites to basic research in microwave spectroscopy and in molecular structures.[134]

HIGH POLYMERS AND BUILDING RESEARCH

In 1944 Dr. Robert Simha, an Austrian chemist teaching at Howard University in Washington, came to the Bureau to give a series of lectures in a new field of science, that of the high polymers. The word "polymers" or "high polymers" was then less than 5 years old, and the study of the molecular

---

[133] H. Lyons, "Microwave spectroscopy frequency and time standards," Elec. Eng. 68, 251 (1949); NBS Annual Report 1951, pp. 13–14; H. Lyons, "Atomic clocks," Sci. Am. 196, 71 (1957). The achievement represented an outgrowth of work started at Westinghouse by Dr. Condon. See William E. Good, "The inversion spectrum of ammonia," Phys. Rev. 69, 539 (1946).

[134] With continued refinement of the cesium atomic beam apparatus, the accuracy of time measurements increased to 1 part in 100 billion, or 200 times greater than that achieved by astronomical means. Subsequent use of atomic hydrogen masers promised to increase the order of accuracy still further. Meanwhile, on Oct. 8, 1964, the 12th General Conference of Weights and Measures, meeting in Paris, authorized a temporary atomic definition of the second, derived from the cesium clock, as the international unit of time. NBS TNB 48, 209 (1964).

properties of these systems little older. The science deals with the chainlike molecules of relatively very high molecular weight that make up substances as different as rubber, textiles, paper, leather, and plastics, all of which owe their strength, elasticity, durability and plasticity to the long chainlike structure of their molecules. Dr. Simha's lecture-seminars led the Bureau to invite him to join the staff, and he remained for 2 years organizing high polymer research at the Bureau.[135]

The growth of the synthetic rubber and plastics industries in this country during the war raised the problem of new standards based on accurate determination of the structures and properties of polymer substances. Awareness of the problem was accentuated by the discovery of German advances made in plastics and textiles, learned from the search of their laboratories in the last months of the war in Europe.[136] Particularly pressing was the need for more basic research in the rubber industry, both in natural rubber, flowing freely once again, and in synthetic rubber, as insurance "in the event of any future emergency." [137]

Apart from the Bureau program, rubber research in industry and in the universities on behalf of the Federal Government was then running over

---

[135] R. Simha, "Preliminary Proposal for a Plan of Research on Molecular Properties of High Polymers," Aug. 1, 1945 (NBS Historical File); Science, 104, 572 (1946).

Important in the history of the Bureau have been the guest lecturers from industry and the universities who have become temporary consultants or staff members in order to initiate new lines of research or even whole new programs at the Bureau. In many instances they have subsequently sent their graduate students or laboratory assistants to join the Bureau staff.

The guest lecturer policy was introduced by Dr. Stratton, who even after leaving the Bureau continued to invite leading scientists, among them Niels Bohr, to lecture there. In 1923 Prof. Arnold Sommerfeld of the Institute of Theoretical Physics in Munich, early pioneer in the quantum theory and quantum interpretation of spectra, spent 2 weeks at the Bureau as consultant and lecturer. The practice continued in the 1930's when, among others, Wojciech Swietoslawski and his pupil Mieczyslaw Wojciechowski of the Polytechnic Institute of Warsaw brought the technique of ebulliometry to the Bureau (ch. VI, see p. 343), and Prof. John D. Ferry of the University of Wisconsin came to lecture on rheology, the science of the flow and deformation of materials.

Dr. Herman F. Mark, who fled Nazi Germany and started polymer science in this country, came as a consultant to the Bureau in 1941–42. Another lecturer on high polymers, Dr. Paul J. Flory of Stanford University, later sent his prize student, Dr. Leo Mandelkern, who did some of the first work in this country on the crystallization of polymers. Similarly, Dr. Herbert P. Broida came to the Bureau in 1949 to work in flame spectroscopy, and stayed to direct a research program on free radicals. The policy continues to the present day. Interviews with Dr. Lawrence A. Wood, June 30, 1964; Dr. Meggers, July 7, 1964; and Dr. Samuel G. Weissberg, Sept. 8, 1964. On the free radicals program, see NBS AdminBul 56–66, Oct. 29, 1956.

[136] NBS Annual Report 1946, pp. 190–192.

[137] NBS Annual Report 1947, p. xv; LC871, "Bibliography of recent research in the field of high polymers" (Simha, 1947); LC922, ibid., 1948; C498, ibid., 1950.

$5 million a year. As Federal activity in this field was in danger of being stopped through termination of the war agency which handled it, Dr. Condon proposed that the Bureau assume direction over the major programs in progress and, "as in the fields of mathematics and radio propagation," become "the centralizing and coordinating agency" in rubber research for the Government.[138] Instead, the whole of the Federal research program was curtailed as operations in its synthetic plants were cut back and a number of the plants were put in standby status. Bureau research in rubber continued as part of the investigation of high polymer substances.

The investigation centered on the constants and properties of the high polymer compounds that are formed chemically in nature by the process known as polymerization. Using X-ray diffraction, infrared spectroscopy, and electron microscopy, along with standard chemical, optical, and thermodynamic techniques, the Bureau sought better knowledge of the fundamental properties of both natural and synthetic polymers. On the basis of early results, the Bureau explored the incorporation of rubber into sole leather to improve wearing qualities, obtained new tire and tube evaluations, standardized fading tests in textiles, and improved leather hides by impregnating them with resins or rubber. Related studies were concerned with the nature of adhesion in polymers, with adhesives among the synthetic resins, and the use of resins in the fabrication of aircraft, housing, and containers.[139]

Research into the molecular dimensions of the polymers provided the standards necessary for the utilization of Dextran as a blood-plasma substitute and the control tests for its manufacture and maintenance in storage.[140] For the Office of Rubber Reserve, important studies were made in the degradation of rubbers and on the rheological (flow and deformation) properties of various rubbers and rubber solutions.[141] And in 1950, with the procedures it had devised for measuring molecular weights by osmotic pressure, viscosity, and light scattering (ultracentrifuge) techniques, the Bureau started its standard sample program of high polymers.[142]

When an examination of the high-polymer characteristics of paper and paper materials offered no immediate solution to a filter problem, the Bureau, with the cooperation of the Naval Research Laboratory, produced from commercial "glass wool" a new kind of paper composed entirely of glass fibers. Originally sought for use in gas mask filters, its excellent in-

---

[138] Hearings * * * 1948 (Mar. 12, 1947), p. 322; NBS Annual Report 1947, p. xv.
[139] NBS Annual Report 1947, p. 209; Annual Report 1948, pp. 224–225.
[140] NBS Report 1713 (Weissberg and Isbell, June 13, 1952). Although the current availability of whole blood from donors reduced the necessity of Dextran except in an emergency, 10 million pints were made and stored against that contingency.
[141] NBS Annual Report 1951, p. 51; Annual Report 1952, p. 34; Annual Report 1953–54, p. 51.
[142] See RP2257 (Weissberg, Simha, and Rothman, 1951).

sulating properties and high resistance to heat readily suggested that glass paper might have extensive use in electronic and other electrical equipment.[143]

An area of research that had become scattered over many divisions at the Bureau was reorganized in 1947 to form a new division, that of building technology. For the first time a unified approach was made to the problems of the construction industry as the Bureau coordinated its investigations of properties of building materials, studies in structural strength, fire resistance, acoustics and sound insulation, heating, ventilation, air conditioning, and building and electrical equipment.[144]

As after every war, the construction industry turned its attention first to conventional housing, of which there was an estimated shortage of 5 million units.[145] The Bureau made home construction its immediate target. With building materials approaching the cost of labor, the Bureau aimed at new structural designs based on engineering principles tested in the wartime construction of ships and planes—something of an innovation itself—and on maximum use of nonconventional building materials that provided structural strength with the minimum of materials and labor. Bureau reports went out to the industry on the properties of materials unknown a decade before, such as some of the new plastics, laminated woods, lightweight concretes, and slag aggregates. New and better masonry paints and asphalts were also reported.[146]

In order to formulate standards of heating, the Bureau built a test bungalow 25 feet square with an 8-foot ceiling. One after another, commercial heating devices including stoves, furnaces, and panel heating were installed and the detailed data gathered on temperature gradients attained inside were correlated with outside temperatures.[147] A long series of fire tests of building structures and materials were carried out in search of better means of reducing the direct annual loss from fire, currently estimated at 8,000 lives and $700 million in property damage.[148]

The next decade witnessed a steady rise in private and public housing, in construction of office buildings and Federal buildings. Aided by the new Swedish-invented hydraulic self-lifting Linden crane, high-rise apartment houses went up as fast, and in some cities, faster than homes. Bureau research figured to some extent in much of the high-rise construction, but could

---

[143] NBS Annual Report 1951, p. 48; M. J. O'Leary, B. W. Scribner, et al., "Manufacture of paper from glass fibers," Tappi, 35, 289 (1952).

[144] NBS Annual Report 1947, pp. xiii–xiv.

[145] Hearings * * * 1947 (Jan. 29, 1946), p. 203.

[146] BMS107, "Building code requirements for new dwelling construction * * *" (Thompson, 1947); BMS109, "Strength of houses: application of engineering principles to structural design" (Whittemore et al., 1948).

[147] NBS Annual Report 1947, pp. 202–203, 208; Hearings * * * 1950, p. 492.

[148] NBS Annual Report 1948, pp. 234–235.

In this test of house wall fire resistance, the fire took 27 minutes to come through the Douglas fir siding as gas flames were applied to the other side. An instrument on the pole measures the bulge of the wall. (Picture by courtesy of the National Geographic Society.)

take no blame for a major flaw in many of the new buildings, their woeful failure in soundproofing. As it only added to the comfort of tenants, acceptance of Bureau studies in the acoustic properties of materials had little appeal. But as they saved time or money or material, Bureau reports on asphalt stabilizers, vapor-barrier materials, thermal conduction, and heat transfer found ready acceptance in the industry.[149]

As a service to new homeowners and old, the Bureau revised and reissued its publication, "Care and repair of the house." On its first appearance in 1931, "Care" went through 12 printings, selling 175,000 copies at 20 cents each.[150] In the 5 years after 1949 that the 209-page revision, Circular 489, was available to the public it sold 253,000 additional copies, at 50 cents each. Undergoing a second revision in 1955, the Bureau's best-

[149] NBS Annual Report 1949, p. 36; Annual Report 1951, p. 61.
[150] See ch. V, pp. 251–253.

seller was suddenly withdrawn from further publication, with the official explanation that it was both an inappropriate publication for a scientific agency of the Government and was competitive with private industry.[151]

Bureau services such as "Care" represented, whether to homeowners or to the public in general, have sometimes been unwelcome to private industry, as well as to the friends of industry on Capitol Hill. One such public effort in the postwar period came close to spelling disaster for the Bureau.

Ever since its founding, the Bureau, alone or in conjunction with the Federal Trade Commission or some other watchdog agency, has from time to time impinged on one aspect or another of rugged individualism or the principle of laissez faire. It was the Bureau that led the first crusade against fraudulent weights and measures in the marketplace, against faulty railroad scales, mine scales, and truck scales. It aroused the ire of the public utilities by pointing out the hazards of electrolysis, of poor gas appliances, and by insisting on electrical safety codes.

It angered the building industry with many of its codes and specifications and some of its assessments of building materials. It repeatedly warned the public against so-called gas-savers on kitchen stoves, against gasoline additives, gasoline "dopes," destructive antifreeze solutions, and useless antileak compounds. It exposed the fraud in proprietary radium and radioactive nostrums. It reported the inferiority of reclaimed rubber for automobile tires. Its research on photographic emulsions was stopped. Attempts were made to suppress a number of its reports, including those on the quality of heating and illuminating gas, on gypsum and certain other building materials, and on chemical glassware. And from time to time the Department of Commerce itself considered it necessary to suppress Bureau releases, as it did one in 1926 describing the quality of dental amalgams.

Every Director of the Bureau has come under fire from business interests or industry, entrepreneurs, or legislators as a result of some Bureau investigation or other. Dr. Condon had been at the Bureau only a matter of months when the "Aquella" incident occurred.

In January 1946 a popular magazine published the story of a fabulous new paint formula for waterproofing masonry, with the claim that it had been tested by the National Bureau of Standards and won an unqualified "Excellent" rating.[152] It was being made at home and sold from door to door by a family of French refugees who had arrived in New York in 1941 with no possessions but the secret formula for their paint. They claimed that their waterproof paint called "Aquella" had been used throughout the Maginot Line.

---

[151] "New York Times," May 15, 1955, p. 68; correspondence with Vincent B. Phelan, March 9–May 27, 1963 (NBS Historical File).

[152] Kurt Steel, "Water, stay away from my wall," Reader's Digest, 48, 45 (1946).

The story with its testimonials drew thousands of inquiries about "Aquella" and hundreds of requests seeking licenses for "Aquella" agencies. On the strength of the mail, the family obtained capital and began selling manufacturing rights to distributors.

The Better Business Bureau of New York asked the Bureau to test the waterproofing paint. The Bureau already had. At the request of the military services it had obtained samples and reported its findings in December 1942. Six months later it had made a second report. The new tests confirmed the earlier ones. Judged "excellent" immediately after application, "Aquella" on the outer face of masonry after 10 months offered no more than "good" protection against water seepage. The inner face rated "poor." "Aquella," at $3 to $4 a quart was judged a fair waterproof paint but no better than a Bureau recipe made with 10 cents' worth of material. The Bureau also learned that "Aquella" had been used in the Maginot Line, but only for decorative purposes, as a blue calcimine.

Newspaper accounts of the Bureau reports, following publication of the magazine story, resulted in almost 20,000 inquiries about the Bureau tests. They were answered with a mimeographed letter summarizing the findings on "Aquella." The mail also brought numerous protests of Government interference with private enterprise, notably the intercession of Gov. Ellis Arnall of Georgia with Secretary Wallace on behalf of prospective "Aquella" distributors in his State. Wallace "recalled and retracted" the Bureau's mimeographed letter.[153]

No such simple détente marked the results of Bureau tests of a battery additive called "Protecto-Charge," later known as AD–X2. Its history went back to the years immediately after World War I when the resurgence of the automobile industry brought on the market a freshet of battery additives, substances whose makers claimed would restore vitality to dying batteries. Through the next three decades the Bureau, at the request of the Federal Trade Commission, the Post Office Department, and various Government agencies with fleets of cars and trucks, tested these additives as they appeared on the market. By the early thirties almost a hundred of the preparations had come to the Bureau, but whether based on epsom salts or other substances, none showed any notable effect on either battery life or performance.[154]

---

[153] "NBS Report of water permeability tests on coating of 'Aquella' paint applied to masonry walls," Dec. 8, 1942; ibid., June 4, 1943; mimeo letter, "Summary of water-permeability tests of 'Aquella' * * *, Aug. 9, 1946; report on "Aquella," Consumers' Res. Bull. 17, 20 (May 1946); letter, H. A. Wallace to President, Prima Products, Inc., New York City, June 3, 1946 ("General Correspondence Files of the Director, 1945–1955"); interview with Dr. E. U. Condon, Oct. 29, 1963.

[154] See ch. V, p. 281. The correspondence on battery additives in the early thirties is in NBS Box 369, TE.

The appearance of new gasoline "dopes," antifreeze compounds, and battery additives continued through the forties. Routine tests to determine the validity of their advertised claims turned up nothing new.[155] Then in the spring of 1948, Jess M. Ritchie, whose firm, Pioneers, Inc., of Oakland, Calif., made the battery additive AD–X2, wrote to the Bureau asking for special tests of his product, on the grounds that it was an exception to the negative findings of the Bureau's Letter Circular 302 on battery additives, published in 1931, but still current and available to the public.[156] Since the Bureau does not make tests for private individuals or firms, it refused.

In January 1949, in connection with a current program of research on the properties of batteries, the Bureau undertook a reinvestigation of battery additives, in preparation for a revision of the 20-year-old LC302. Among the additives tested, but as in all such cases unidentified except by a number, was AD–X2, samples of which had been recently received from the Better Business Bureau of Oakland. Essentially compounded of common epsom and glauber salts (magnesium and sodium sulfates), AD–X2 was found by the Bureau to have no special merits. Where these salts ordinarily sell for about 22 cents a pound, when packaged as a proprietary battery additive, at $3 per packet, they came to almost $20 a pound.

Dr. George W. Vinal of the electrochemistry section, coauthor with Paul L. Howard of the Bureau circular in preparation, reported the test results on AD–X2 to the Better Business Bureau in Oakland in April 1950, identifying AD–X2 by name. This was admittedly a deviation from the usual practice, but was intended as a reply to proponents of AD–X2 that prior statements of the Bureau on battery additives did not apply to that particular product.[157] Four months later the national office made the report public.

Pioneers, Inc., directed its distributors to write to their Congressmen in protest.[158] Before the end of 1951, 28 Senators and 1 Congressman had sent queries to the Bureau on behalf of AD–X2. The issue smoldered for more than a year, arousing public interest for the first time when in December 1952 a national magazine reported that laboratory tests of AD–X2 made at the Massachusetts Institute of Technology were at variance with those of

[155] NBS Annual Report 1947, p. 221; Annual Report 1948, p. 251.

[156] Particularly objectionable to Pioneers, Inc., was the fact that the National Better Business Bureau had reprinted LC302 in its own circular of June 19, 1931, as the authoritative statement on the subject.

[157] [Senate] Hearings before the Select Committee on Small Business * * * on investigation of Battery Additive AD–X2, 83d Cong., 1st sess., March 31–June 26, 1953, p. 220.

[158] The findings on AD–X2, unidentified as such, were also reported in the reissue of LC302 in 1949 and in C504, "Battery additives" (Jan. 10, 1951), the latter including confirming tests of AD–X2 made for the Federal Trade Commission in March 1950. The NBBB letter is reprinted in Senate Hearings, above, p. 549.

the National Bureau of Standards. The issue ignited soon after the Eisenhower administration took office in 1953.

In the controversy over AD–X2 that erupted in the Department of Commerce, the Director of the Bureau was temporarily relieved of his post.[159] Under press attack for an act of dismissal without a hearing, and confronted with the reaction of scientists and scientific organizations, Secretary Weeks rescinded his dismissal order pending a congressional hearing and called upon the National Academy of Sciences to appoint a committee "to evaluate the present functions and operations of the Bureau of Standards

---

[159] In the Eisenhower administration, Sinclair Weeks, a manufacturer from Newton, Mass., became Secretary of Commerce. The new Secretary appointed Craig R. Sheaffer, president of the Sheaffer Pen Co. in Fort Madison, Iowa, his Assistant Secretary for Domestic Affairs.

Both the Secretary and his assistant were concerned over Federal agencies that in their view often hampered the efforts of small business to get ahead. Both seem to have thought the Bureau was one of those agencies. The Federal Trade Commission not long before had forced the Sheaffer company to discontinue advertising its ballpoint pen as a lifetime pen. (Senate Hearings, above, pp. 272, 511). He now found the Bureau, long closely associated with the FTC, under his immediate supervision.

More than a year prior to the Eisenhower election, in August 1951, Dr. Condon, who was Director when Circular 504 on battery additives appeared, resigned from the Bureau to become director of research for the Corning Glass Works. Dr. Allen V. Astin, electronic and ordnance physicist and a guiding hand in the development of the Bureau's proximity fuze, became Acting Director until his appointment as Director was confirmed by the Senate on May 30, 1952 (see Hearings * * * 1954, Jan. 11, 1954, p. 76). During that period, Pioneers, Inc., its distributors, and supporters continued pressure on the Bureau to reverse its findings on AD–X2. At the request of the Post Office Department in September 1951, the Bureau retested AD–X2. Six months later it was again tested for the House and Senate Committees on Small Business, and again, almost a year after, much more extensively, for the House Interstate and Foreign Commerce Committee.

On Feb. 24, 1953, the new Postmaster General, Arthur E. Summerfield, as a consequence of the latest Bureau findings, put AD–X2 on the mail fraud list. Six days later, the fraud order was suspended. Assistant Secretary Sheaffer instructed Dr. Astin to impound all copies of Circular 504 and all other reports, pamphlets, and data on battery additives, including AD–X2.

On Mar. 24, 1953, Secretary Weeks forced the resignation of Dr. Astin "for a number of reasons," none of which was specified, except that "the National Bureau of Standards has not been sufficiently objective because they discount entirely the play of the market place" ("Washington Post," Apr. 1, 1953, p. 1).

The action raised a basic question: whether Government through its regulatory and scientific agencies was to judge the merits of new products offered to the public, or whether this function was to be left to the test of the market place. The integrity of the Government's primary scientific research body had been impugned. The Bureau was being subjected to pressure, and to reorganization in accordance with an outside concept of scientific objectivity. The attack on the Bureau implied a radical reversal in the role of Government as the regulator of commerce.

The Washington, D.C., newspaper cartoonists capture the fervor of the AD–X2 case. (1953 © cartoon by Herblock in the "Washington Post"; other cartoons by courtesy of Berryman and Crocket, "Washington Evening Star.")

in relation to the present national needs." [160] (The report of this committee is considered in the envoi of the present history.) A second committee of the National Academy of Sciences was appointed specifically to appraise the work of the Bureau on AD–X2.

A Department of Commerce press release on August 23, 1953, announced the resumption of his duties by the Director of the Bureau. It also disclosed that on the basis of Senate hearings, the merits of AD–X2 remained controversial but "there [was] insufficient proof of an actual intent * * * to deceive." [161]

On November 13 the committee of 10 scientists named by Dr. Detlev W. Bronk, president of the National Academy of Sciences, to study the claims made for AD–X2, reported that the MIT tests "were not well designed for old batteries differing markedly in the characteristics of the cells." The committee found the Bureau staff fully competent, the quality of its work

---

[160] "Washington Post," Apr. 18, 1953, p. 1. The Director of the Bureau had recommended early in March that the Secretary call upon the Academy and his Visiting Committee to the Bureau to review Bureau operations, including its testing of battery additives. See "Washington Post," Apr. 2, 1953, p. 1.

[161] The Secretary's press release also announced the transfer of direct supervision of NBS from the Assistant Secretary for Domestic Affairs to the Assistant Secretary for Administration. Soon after, Mr. Sheaffer resigned and returned to his business.

The Senate Hearings * * * on * * * Battery Additive AD–X2 comprised 511 pages of testimony and exhibits and 274 pages of appendices.

on storage batteries "excellent * * * without reservations," and supported "the position of the Bureau of Standards that the material is without merit." [162]

GOLDEN ANNIVERSARY

Dr. Condon could have had no inkling of the tempest to be visited upon the Bureau when he approved the letter circular and formal circular on AD–X2. They were routine test reports, as had been that on "Aquella" and hundreds of other commercial products since the founding of the Bureau. Of greater concern to him were the new lines of research he had set going, the reorganization of the Bureau laboratories, the establishment of new facilities at Corona and Boulder, and, not least, the preparation of a new and comprehensive handbook on physics, to be written by the Bureau staff. The handbook, with worldwide distribution, would not only be scientifically important and prestigious but would set a capstone on 50 years of modern physics.

Precedent for the encyclopedic work planned by Dr. Condon was the Dictionary of Applied Physics, the five-volume work edited by Sir Richard T. Glazebrook, first director of the National Physical Laboratory in England and published in 1922–23.[163] The idea of the handbook was preceded in March 1946 by plans for another comprehensive work, a Bureau proposal to the Commerce Science Committee to prepare 50 or more publications designed especially to aid small business. Bureau circulars, letter circulars, and other publications in print were to be revised and new ones prepared by recognized authorities at the Bureau, describing products, methods of manufacture, and processes developed in this country and abroad during the war that might serve as a basis of new enterprises. At the time, the estimated cost of the project, $250,000, was considered by Congress to outweigh the merits of the enterprise.[164]

---

[162] Report of the Committee on Battery Additives of the National Academy of Sciences, Oct. 30, 1953, pp. 1, 31, 33–34 (NBS Historical File); "Washington Post," Nov. 14, 1953, p. 1; Hearings * * * 1955 (Jan. 11, 1954), pp. 105–107.

The AD–X2 affair is presented as a case history in public administration and policy formation, for teaching purposes, in Samuel A. Lawrence's The Battery Additive Controversy, Study No. 68 (University of Alabama Press, 1962).

[163] NBS contributors to the Glazebrook dictionary included Silsbee on superconductivity, McCollum on electrolysis, Coblentz on radiation and radiometry, Gibson on spectrophotometry, and Meggers on the measurement of wavelengths.

[164] The 13-page outline, "Proposed technological services to business, industry, and the public, in collaboration with the Office of Declassification and Technical Services," Mar. 1, 1946, is in NBS Historical File.

The outline for the first project, the "NBS Handbook of Physical Measurements," as it was originally entitled, appeared in a 117-page mimeographed study in December 1946. It called for eight volumes, on metrology, mechanics, heat, electricity, optics, atomic and chemical physics, and physical chemistry, each volume and its chapters and sections assigned to Bureau authorities in the field. In March 1947, Dr. Condon asked the House Appropriations Subcommittee for $30,000 to initiate the project.[165] No demur was made and the work was launched.

Progress on the handbook was slow. Besides their reorganization and some shifting around of laboratories, the divisions were clearing up backlogs of paper work, completing reports on wartime research, and planning new programs of research. Since the handbook was to be a formal Bureau publication, Dr. Condon directed that it might be done on Bureau time. The working day simply wasn't long enough, and the only writing accomplished was that done on nights and weekends, on individual initiative.

Four years later, when Dr. Condon left the Bureau, some 10 or 12 chapters out of the 57 projected had been completed. No longer to be a Bureau enterprise, the handbook was modified in scope and the aid of authorities in industry and the universities was enlisted. A progress report and new outline late in 1952 described a more extensive work. It was to comprise 88 chapters, of which 40 were completed or in the first draft form. The published book, Condon and Odishaw's Handbook of Physics, appeared in 1958. Of the contributors to "what every physicist should know," as the editor described the volume, 13 were members of the Bureau staff.[166] Dr. Condon himself wrote 17 of the final 90 chapters in the 1,459-page handbook.[167]

An accomplishment of importance to the Bureau that Dr. Condon saw achieved in somewhat less time than the handbook was amendment of the Bureau's organic act of 1901. Even before Congressman Stefan raised the question in 1947 of the Bureau's spending millions of dollars "on the basis of a two-page law," Dr. Condon had already initiated final preparation of the draft legislation for submission to Congress in order, as he said, to "remove some of [the] ambiguities and try to state more explicitly and in

[165] Hearings * * * 1948 (Mar. 12, 1947), p. 367.

[166] In addition to their articles and books published under Government imprint, members of the Bureau staff have produced almost a hundred books and textbooks, including two autobiographies. See app. N.

[167] New York: McGraw-Hill Book Co. The progress report of 1952, with instructions for authors and a sample section, is in NBS Historical File.

Some of the material prepared by Bureau members for the handbook subsequently appeared as NBS publications: C476, "Measurements of radioactivity" (Curtiss, 1949); C478, "Colorimetry" (Judd, 1950); C484, "Spectrophotometry" (Gibson, 1949); C544, 'Formulas for computing capacitance and inductance" (Snow, 1954).

more up to date language what the exact functions of the Bureau of Standards are." [168]

The reformulation of functions that the Science Advisory Board recommended in 1934, to cut the depression suit of the Bureau to its cloth, had been filed at the time and all but forgotten.[169] The burst of scientific accomplishment in World War II had since changed the course of Bureau research. Its orientation was to science rather than, as in the original act and in 1934, to industry.

The new statement of Bureau functions, as an amendment to the organic act, became official with the enactment of Public Law 619 in 1950. The restatement included a significant change in direction. In the original act, the basic authority for the functions of the Bureau resided in the Bureau itself. Relieving it of this sometimes onerous responsibility, the amendment transferred the authority to the Secretary of Commerce.[170] The amendment consolidated the broad range of special Bureau activities that had been granted piecemeal in appropriation legislation through the years. Finally, it made specific in the scientific research and testing activities of the Bureau its responsibilities in the new fields of science opened in the past decade.

As in the organic act, the Bureau still had six basic functions, but they included nothing quite like Dr. Stratton's wonderful catchall, "the solution of problems which arise in connection with standards." [171] It was the Secretary of Commerce, rather than the Bureau, that was responsible for:

> The custody, maintenance, and development of the national standards of measurement, and the provision of means and methods for making measurements consistent with those standards, including the comparison of standards used in scientific investigations, engineering, manufacturing, commerce, and educational institutions with the standards adopted or recognized by the Government.

---

[168] Hearings * * * 1948 (Mar. 12, 1947), p. 352; Hearings * * * 1951 (Feb. 23, 1950), p. 2179.

Secretary of Commerce Wallace recommended amendment of the organic act to Congress in 1945, in order to incorporate authority for such Bureau activities as were covered only by supplemental legislation, Executive orders, and customary procedures. The drafting of the amendment was almost entirely the work of Dr. Crittenden. See Report of the Visiting Committee, Oct. 31, 1945, and attached correspondence ("General Correspondence Files of the Director, 1945–1955," Box 6); interview with Dr. Condon, Oct. 28, 1963.

[169] See ch. VI, p. 323n.

[170] For the general reorganization of executive departments, in line with the recommendations of the Hoover Commission, that was the immediate occasion for enactment of the Bureau amendment, see "New York Times," Mar. 14, 1950, p. 1, and May 24, 1950, p. 1.

[171] See ch. I, p. 43.

The determination of physical constants and properties of materials when such data are of great importance to scientific or manufacturing interests and are not to be obtained of sufficient accuracy elsewhere.

The development of methods for testing materials, mechanisms, and structures, and the testing of materials, supplies, and equipment, including items purchased for use of Government departments and independent establishments.

Cooperation with other governmental agencies and with private organizations in the establishment of standard practices, incorporated in codes and specifications.

Advisory service to Government agencies on scientific and technical problems.

Invention and development of devices to serve special needs of the Government.

The first two functions encompassed the original organic act and were virtually identical with the statements of responsibilities. The next two confirmed the responsibilities acquired through the special appropriations that Congress had made to the Bureau over the years. The last two functions represented Bureau responsibilities accrued under transferred funds from other Federal agencies, as established by acts of 1920 and 1932 (see app. C) and, affirming its advisory capacity, gave a firm legal basis to what had become the dominant direction of the Bureau.

Spelled out in the amendment were 19 specific activities of the Bureau which the Secretary of Commerce was authorized to undertake in carrying out these functions.[172]

Public Law 619 was approved on July 22, 1950, 4 months before the Korean incident became a full-fledged conflict and put the Nation on a wartime footing once again. In the national emergency, the Federal Government reopened its synthetic rubber plants that had been on a standby basis, and ordered stepped up production at the Bureau of optical glass for use in large optical elements. Proximity fuze and guided missile development was at once greatly intensified, as were other defense projects at the Bureau, including some scheduled for termination.[173]

Anticipating the acceleration in scientific research, a program of research in basic instrumentation was initiated, in cooperation with the Depart-

[172] The complete amendment appears in app. C. See also "Bureau of Standards Functions," H. Rept. 2349, to accompany S. 2201, 81st Cong., 2d sess. [July 22, 1950]; NBS BuMemo 50-7, Apr. 24, 1950; BuOrd 51-12, Aug. 11, 1950.

[173] NBS Annual Report 1951, pp. 2, 8, 9, 59, 84.

ment of Defense and the Atomic Energy Commission.[174] As the conflict began, the Bureau established its North Pacific Radio Warning Service for the Arctic region, operating 24 hours a day, 7 days a week, to insure reliable radio communications in the war zone. Yet, even with almost half the staff engaged once more in classified defense programs, the Bureau reported a total of 630 unclassified projects going on in its laboratories.[175]

As it braced itself for the national emergency, the Bureau marked the approach of March 3, 1951, the 50th anniversary of its founding. The publications staff prepared a number of designs for a commemorative stamp for the semicentennial but efforts to interest the Post Office were unsuccessful.[176] In celebration of the anniversary, some 30 scientific and technical societies of the country elected to hold their meetings that year in Washington.[177] In addition, the Bureau, with the special cooperation of the Office of Naval Research, sponsored 12 special symposia on subjects of current importance to the Bureau and the Department of Defense.[178]

The symposia were in mid-career when on August 10, 1951, Dr. Condon announced his resignation as Director of the Bureau. For more than 4 years he had been under intermittent attack by a subcommittee of the House Committee on Un-American Activities, headed by Congressman J. Parnell Thomas of New Jersey, as an alleged security risk in high public office.[179]

---

[174] Projected in Condon's "Is there a science of instrumentation?" Science, 110, 339 (1949).

[175] NBS Annual Report 1952, pp. 1, 2

[176] It has been stated that as a rule it is not Post Office policy to so honor Federal bureaus or agencies.

[177] Also marking the semicentennial were companion articles by Dr. Briggs on the early work of the Bureau and by Dr. Condon on its current program, in Sci. Mo. 73, 166 (1951). See also Condon, "NBS: a Semicentennial," Science, 114, suppl. 3 (Aug. 17, 1951).

[178] NBS Annual Report 1951, p. 100, and file, "NBS Semicentennial, 1951," in the Office of Technical Information and Publications, NBS. The subjects of the symposia were low temperature physics (subsequently published as C519, 1952), mechanical properties of metals at low temperatures (C520, 1952), gravity waves (C521, 1952), the solution of systems of linear equations and the determination of eigenvalues (AMS39, 1954), mass spectroscopy in physics research (C522, 1953), energy transfer in hot gases (C523, 1954), electrochemical constants (C524, 1953), polymer degradation mechanisms (C525, 1953), optical image evaluation (C526, 1954), electron physics (C527, 1954), characteristics and applications of resistance strain gages (C528, 1954), and electrodeposition research (C529, 1953).

[179] The trouble began on July 17, 1947, when the press reported that Thomas' Special Subcommittee on National Security was investigating Dr. Condon because his acquaintances included Russian scientists and alleged Communist sympathizers in this country. In the uneasy years after the war, resentment arose against the scientists who worked on the atomic bomb, and over transfer of control of atomic energy from the Army to

Despite the failure of the subcommittee to prove its charges, despite vindication in the press and by the security procedures of the Departments of Commerce and Defense and the Atomic Energy Commission, and the wide support of his fellow scientists, Dr. Condon came to feel that he might best serve Bureau interests by resigning.

Accepting an appointment as director of research at Corning Glass Works, Dr. Condon submitted his resignation to President Truman, effective September 30. The resignation was regretfully accepted.

> You have served [said the President] in a most critical position with continued and loyal attention to your duties as director, and by reason of your standing among scientists and the supervision you have given to the bureau's activities, you have made of it a more important agency than it ever has been before.[180]

After presiding over the semicentennial symposia that month on mass spectroscopy, on electrochemical constants, and on polymer degradation mechanisms, Dr. Condon left the Bureau. Confronting the new Acting Direc-

---

the civilian Atomic Energy Commission. Also, rumor were widespread of domestic Communist activities in connection with the development of the bomb.

Dr. Condon had been at Los Alamos, and was scientific adviser to the McMahon committee that had obtained enactment of the law for civilian control of atomic energy. He now directed, according to Mr. Thomas, "one of the most important national defense research organizations in the United States, the target of espionage agents of numerous foreign powers."

Then in a statement handed to the press on Mar. 1, 1948, the Thomas subcommittee charged that "the Soviet Union and her satellite nations have been desperately attempting to * * * secure our complete atomic knowledge. * * * From the evidence at hand, it appears that Dr. Condon is one of the weakest links in our atomic security." He had, Thomas said, "knowingly or unknowingly, entertained and associated with persons who are alleged Soviet espionage agents."

From the first, Dr. Condon expressed his willingness to appear for a hearing but was ignored. Almost unanimously the press, the world of science, and other members of Congress questioned the charges and the procedure of the House Committee. Although he was cleared by the Loyalty Board of the Department of Commerce and by W. Averell Harriman and Charles Sawyer, the Secretaries under whom he served, the criticism of the Director of the Bureau by this committee of Congress continued.

See Stephen K. Bailey and Howard D. Samuel, Congress at Work (New York: Henry Holt, 1952), pp. 321–336, 487; "Trial by Newspaper," Sci. Am. 180, 16 (1949); and congressional documents and newspaper accounts in NBS Historical File.

[180] "New York Times," Aug. 11, 1951, p. 1.

tor was the trouble, already warming up, over AD–X2. But that too would pass, and with time adjustment to the new world of science would be made.

The standard troy pound of Queen Elizabeth, formed of 8-ounce and 4-ounce nesting weights.

One of the three giant Wurtsburg antennas at the Bureau's Gun Barrel Hill, Colorado, field station. Used in radio propagation research, a dipole at the focal point of the paraboloid reflector receives radio energy from the sun.

THE CRUCIAL DECADE—AN ENVOI

AN AD HOC COMMITTEE REPORTS

In April 1953, in the midst of the impasse raised by the controversy over AD–X2, Secretary of Commerce Weeks asked the National Academy of Sciences to convene an ad hoc committee to evaluate the functions and operations of the National Bureau of Standards in relation to the current national needs. At stake was not only the reputation but the purpose and direction of the Bureau. It was recognized that they were threatened not so much by the controversy over AD–X2 as by the impact on Bureau research of the Korean war.

As in the two World Wars, the staff, facilities, and programs of the Bureau were mobilized for the new conflict across the Pacific. A year after that war began, prolonged negotiations for its end commenced. As in the case of industry, commerce, and science, the Bureau was on a war footing beyond its control. In March 1953, anticipating Secretary Weeks' own request by almost a month, the Director of the Bureau had written him to seek the counsel of the National Academy of Sciences on the current program and operations of the Bureau.

The ad hoc committee appointed by the Academy submitted its initial findings in late July and its formal report on October 15. Under the direction of Dr. Marvin J. Kelly, director of the Bell Telephone Laboratories and a member of the Visiting Committee, the 10 members of the committee thoroughly explored the place of the Bureau in the Federal structure, its organization, programs, technical operations, administration, and funds and financing.

There was no question, the 109-page report declared, of the vital importance of the Bureau to the Nation or of the quality of its professional staff. The heart of the report dealt with certain of the Bureau programs. The years following World War II witnessed an unprecedented growth in the science and technology of the Nation, and the Bureau's basic research programs expanded in aid of them until 1950. Then basic research began to lose ground "at a tragic rate," as the Committee expressed it, to the weaponry development work proffered through transferred funds by the Department of Defense and the Atomic Energy Commission.

The principal recommendation of the ad hoc committee called for the transfer of these weapons programs to the Department of Defense. Except in wartime, such work did not belong in the Bureau. On the other hand, its nonweaponry research, testing and calibration, and evaluation projects for the Department of Defense and the Atomic Energy Commission should continue, as valuable to the basic programs of the Bureau.[1] To redress the imbalance that had occurred, the committee recommended greatly increased direct appropriations for the basic programs of the Bureau and for such fundamental research as the determination of physical constants, properties of materials, standards and standard practices, and testing and evaluation procedures. The committee further recommended that the Bureau decrease many of its remaining repetitive test operations as costly in time, effort, and funds. And it urged the Bureau to seek greater use by other agencies of the Government of its scientific and technical facilities.

The imbalance in the basic programs of the Bureau occasioned by the military demands of the Korean war could be reversed, said the committee, and, with adequate appropriations, the staff and research level of 1950 achieved again within 2 years. Within 4 years "the Bureau should be in a position to perform its authorized functions in balance at the minimum level for the nation's needs." [2]

The Nation was confronted with a permanent industrial revolution, a continuing technological revolution. The objective of the committee study and its recommendations was to restore to the Bureau its "essential services for our industrial society." For the translation of new scientific knowledge into industrial products, the Bureau must maintain balanced programs in those areas of science and technology requiring new measurements and standards. To that end the committee urged that advisory groups from the scientific and technical societies represented on the ad hoc committee be formed to aid the Director in achieving balance in the current program and in instituting new programs.[3]

---

[1] Ad Hoc Committee, NAS, "A Report to the Secretary of Commerce," Oct. 15, 1953, pp. 19–20 (NBS Historical File); NBS Annual Report 1953–54, preface and p. 10.

Only recently had it become true, as the committee said (p. 12), that "the work of the Bureau for the Atomic Energy Commission, which has a dollar value of almost $2,900,000 in 1953, is not of a weapons development nature."

[2] Ibid., pp. 14, 20–21; NBS Annual Report 1953–54, pp. 11, 126. For the procedure by which the Bureau's budget is presented to Congress, and the "need for a new philosophy [in] the appropriation of funds," see pp. 80–81.

[3] Ibid., pp. 18, 95. The 10 technical advisory committees to the Bureau represent the American Institute of Electrical Engineers, Institute of Radio Engineers, American Institute of Physics, NAS Policy Committee for Mathematics, American Institute of Mining

Secretary Weeks accepted the recommendations of the committe in their entirety and promptly began issuing the directives to carry them out. On September 27, 1953, at one stroke, the Bureau lost four of its divisions, comprising the whole of the proximity fuze and guided missile programs. Three of them, the ordnance electronics, electromechanical, and ordnance development divsions, working on fuzes and related materials, centered around the new electronics laboratory erected in 1946 by the Army Engineers on the Bureau grounds across Van Ness Street. This complex became the Harry Diamond Ordnance Laboratories in 1949, honoring the inventive prodigy who came to the Bureau in 1927 and presided over ordnance development from 1940 until his death in 1948. With the staff of almost 1,600 members, the laboratories were transferred to Army Ordnance.[4] At Corona, Calif., the Bureau's missile development division, with a staff of over 400, that same month became the Naval Ordnance Laboratories (Corona).[5]

The transfer of the two major weapons programs involved a loss of over one-third of the Bureau staff and more than half its $50 million budget for the fiscal year 1952–53. A year later the Institute for Numerical Analysis in the applied mathematics division, supported by the Office of Naval Research and the Air Force at the University of California at Los Angeles, was formally transferred to the University. By the end of 1954 the Bureau had been reduced from almost 4,600 to 2,800 members, of which approximately 400 were out at Boulder, Colo.[6]

The curtailment of weapons development was quick. More time was required to implement three other recommendations of the committee: the insuring of quality and incentive in the Bureau staff; adjustment in the testing and calibration program, to reduce the burden of massive routine testing; and the modernization of facilities, with increased space provided for basic programs.

The high quality of the professional staff had become imperiled by the contraction in basic programs in recent years, with consequent reduction in staff as large numbers of the junior staff were siphoned into the Bureau's military programs. The future of the staff was threatened by the challenge of

---

and Metallurgical Engineers, American Chemical Society, American Ceramic Society, American Society of Mechanical Engineers, National Conference on Weights and Measures, and American Society of Civil Engineers (NBS Annual Report 1953–54, p. 127).

[4] NBS BuMemo 49–45 (July 25, 1949). Upon its transfer, the complex was renamed the Diamond Ordnance Fuze Laboratories (DOFL). See AdminBul 53–57 (Sept. 30, 1953). It is now the Harry Diamond Laboratories.

[5] Hearings * * * 1953 (Jan. 11, 1954), pp. 6, 66, 77–82.

[6] NBS Annual Report 1953–54, pp. 12–13.

supply and demand posed by the postwar surge in employment opportunities for young scientists and engineers.[7]

Although not mentioned by the committe, there was also an element of discontent among the staff, particularly in the upper echelons, induced in part by clashing personalities introduced during the previous administration.[8] The postwar reorganization of the Bureau, with its attendant changes in research assignments and work loads, staff changes, and increase in administrative duties and paper work, had been carried out largely by new administrative assistants brought in for that purpose. Some confusion and concern naturally resulted.

In order to hear out the staff, both professional and nonprofessional, and to discover and strengthen the factors making for a good research environment, the Director in November 1953 invited an advisory service, Social Research, Inc., of Chicago, to conduct a survey or inventory of staff attitudes towards the Bureau, Bureau policies, and working relationships. It was an altogether unique experience in the history of the Bureau.[9]

The two reports of Social Research made to all members of the staff 8 months later disclosed that, on the whole, most of the professional staff believed the Bureau compared favorably with the best universities and best industrial laboratories as a place to work, and that it provided many of the amenities of university life with the financial and equipment advantages of industry. Still, a significant group seemed to feel that the Bureau offered less in the way of individual freedom and opportunity to build a scientific reputation than elsewhere, and some apparently considered the pressure to publish or perish a unique requirement for promotion at the Bureau. The morale among the nonprofessional staff was about average, compared with that in similar groups in business and industry—an encouraging finding considering the late highly publicized unpleasantries.

The sheer size of the Bureau and its high degree of specialization, particularly since World War II, had dissipated to some extent the strong sense of community that since its founding had been the special quality of the Bureau. Yet the survey found identification high among the staff, both with their working unit and with the Bureau as a symbol representing a

---

[7] Ad Hoc Committee report, p. 13. Reduction of funds for basic programs resulted in a loss of 328 members of the research, operations, and testing staff between 1949 and 1952, bringing it down from 1,728 to 1,400 members. Report of the Visiting Committee, July 1, 1952 (in the Office of the Director).

[8] As Bernard L. Gladieux, Executive Assistant to the Secretary of Commerce, told the House Appropriations Subcommittee, "There is an underlying problem [of personalities] out there." It was discussed off the record. Hearings * * * 1951 (Feb. 6, 1950), p. 1361.

[9] Announced in NBS AdminBul 53–66, Nov. 25, 1953.

particular way of scientific life. The professional group almost without exception, and most of the nonprofessionals, agreed with the ad hoc committee report on the importance of the basic research programs to the Bureau and with the fact of their recent serious attenuation. The task of the administration, to recover the basic programs and enhance and promote the Bureau symbol, was evident.[10]

The ad hoc committee had urged some modification in the testing program of the Bureau. The program in 1953, comprising calibration, quality control, acceptance, qualification, regulatory, and referee testing, preparation of standard samples, and product testing, had funds amounting to $2.6 million. Both the committee and the Bureau were especially concerned over the relative efforts expended on product or acceptance testing and calibration testing, and the vital need of the latter as the way in which the Bureau disseminated its standards. Yet calibration testing, perhaps the most important end product of the Bureau's basic programs, was to a degree vitiated by the large amounts of repetitive testing, far more than the high level of technology in industry really required. Where such testing could not be dispensed with, said the committee, it should be turned over to commercial laboratories.

While the committee agreed that the Bureau must continue to make evaluation tests on commercial products at the request of other agencies of the Government, such testing was the area that most frequently brought the Bureau to the unfavorable attention of the general public—as had happened with AD–X2. The committee had no solution. The Bureau must make the tests but leave "the policies and activities of a nontechnical nature" connected with such tests to the Secretary of Commerce.[11]

The first postwar Director, Dr. Condon, had for a time resented the effort expended by the Bureau on routine and repetitive testing, but he came to argue more persuasively than any Director for the routine work on Federal purchases, as representing "one of the most fertile fields for Government economy," than any Director ever had before. Contrary to general opinion,

[10] NBS AdminBul 54–49, Aug. 2, 1954; AdminBul 54–68, Sept. 27, 1954.
The "attitude survey" conducted by social scientists has become an accepted adjunct of administration. In 1957 the Bureau joined with eight other Federal agencies and eight private laboratories in a questionnaire designed to find ways "to attract and hold scientists and engineers in the Government." Apart from the predictable responses (low salary scales, Civil Service examining techniques and processes, inadequate incentive, uncertain fringe benefits), the principal finding of the survey was that a permanent group be created in the Civil Service Commission to work with agencies making such attitude surveys (NBS AdminBul 57–39, July 29, 1957; AdminBul 58–1, Jan. 16, 1958).
[11] Ad Hoc Committee report, pp. 15–16.

the Bureau had never been given responsibility for laboratory surveillance over the quality of Government purchases. There never had been any legislation authority for this activity. Such surveillance as existed offered "only a very spotty check," except in the purchase of cement and of electric lamps. Bureau testing controlled the acceptance of some 4 million light bulbs bought for the Government each year, assuring a consistent quality product; the same was true of Government cement purchases.[12]

Not less but much more routine testing was required in other Government purchases, and Dr. Condon pointed to the $100 million spent by Federal agencies for paint each year and the $500 million for labor to apply it. Yet the Bureau in fact tested very little of the paint that the Government bought, although it knew there was abundant reason for more testing. It had neither the funds nor authorization from other agencies to do that testing. The Government spent $12 million annually for automobile tires and $5 million for tires on Air Force planes, without any check on their quality. A preliminary study made at the Bureau on truck tires for the Post Office suggested that $150,000 spent on testing tires offered to the Government might well save between $3 and $4 million annually.[13]

Acting with the support of recommendations of the ad hoc committee, however, the Bureau sought to transfer to nongovernmental organizations a number of its other testing services. Efforts to decrease routine calibration work met with little satisfaction or success. The U.S. Testing Co. of Hoboken, N.J., set up a calibration service for thermometers but met little demand and abandoned it. Urged by the ad hoc committee report, the Bureau approached other commercial testing companies to take over routine calibration not only of thermometers but of volumetric glassware. Following the

---

[12] E. U. Condon, "Developing purchase specifications," Pacific Purchasor, February 1949, p. 13; Hearings * * * 1951 (Feb. 23, 1950), p. 2288; Hearings * * * 1952 (Apr. 10, 1951), p. 473.

[13] Hearings * * * 1951, p. 2288; Hearings * * * 1952, pp. 464–465.

Dr. Stratton was chairman of the committee that drew up the act establishing the Federal Supply Commission (later the Federal Supply Service), responsible for Federal supplies and making purchase contracts. (See Stratton's account of Bureau relations with the Commission, in Hearings * * * 1921, Jan. 2, 1920, pp. 1569–1570.) In 1949 the FSS was transferred from the Treasury Department to a new independent agency, the General Services Administration (GSA). Except for the maintenance of Federal Specifications, the Bureau has been called on to provide little more quality control over Federal purchases under GSA than under the Treasury, despite the interest of GSA and a "memorandum of understanding" between GSA and the Bureau in 1953 (Hearings * * * 1951 Feb. 23, 1950, p. 2288; NBS Annual Report 1953–54, p. 131).

The necessity for the testing is beyond question. In Annual Report 1953–54, p. 99, the Bureau noted that of 280 samples of building materials submitted to the Government in that period and tested by the Bureau, 137 failed to meet specifications.

unfavorable response ("the work does not appear attractive as a commercial venture"), the Bureau began to promote reference standards laboratories [14] in both Government and industry to handle calibrations whose accuracy did not necessitate comparison with the national standards.[15]

Further unburdening itself of routine efforts, in 1953–54 the Bureau turned over three of its service publications requiring periodic revision to the American Society for Testing Materials and the American Standards Association, with considerable success except for necessary price increases.[16] At the same time, commercial firms were given two classes of standard samples to prepare and distribute, the Bureau's short-lived radioisotopes and its viscosity oil standards.[17]

As foreseen, the rapid advances in technology in the decade after the war made relentless demands on the Bureau for more and more testing, calibration, and greater precision measurements. Even with the reduction in repetitive testing and standard samples, restriction of calibration to basic standards, and the institution of statistical engineering procedures and semiautomatic methods of calibration, the number of tests and calibrations continued to rise. With an authorized increase in the charges made for these services, fees rose from $2.9 million in 1953 to more than $5.4 million just a decade later.

Even though increasingly confined to serving the regulatory, purchasing, or functional responsibilities of other Government agencies, the Bureau's testing program and especially its calibration services, grew with the expansion of the Nation's research program. To augment cement testing, for example, a Cement Reference Laboratory was set up at the Bureau under the joint support of NBS, the Bureau of Public Roads, the Army Engineers, and the American Society for Testing Materials. The Bureau also initiated a

---

[14] "Reference standards" are defined in ch. II, p. 76.

[15] Memo, A. T. McPherson, "Experience in turning over activities of NBS to non-governmental organizations," Mar. 19, 1960 (NBS Historical File) ; NBS Annual Report 1953–54, pp. 96–97. For an earlier attempt to shift cement testing to commercial laboratories, without success, see letter, P. H. Bates to N. T. Stadfeld, Dec. 11, 1942 (NBS Blue Folder Box 72).

[16] The publications were M187, "Directory of commercial and college testing laboratories" (1947; issued since 1927); M178, "National directory of commodity specifications" (1945; issued since 1925); and C410, "National petroleum oil tables" (1936; issued since 1916).

[17] Memo, A. T. McPherson, Mar. 19, 1960. Another service discontinued as no longer necessary was the performance testing of dry cells, which began in 1924 and cost $10,000 annually. Memo, Director NBS for Assistant Secretary of Commerce, July 7, 1952 ("General Correspondence Files of the Director, 1945–1955").

mobile laboratory service, to make cement tests where time schedules precluded use of the Bureau's area laboratories.[18]

Calibration and standard samples programs were similarly augmented. In 1955 construction of a new calibration center began at the Boulder Laboratories, initially to calibrate for the Air Force and Navy Bureau of Aeronautics the vast quantity of radio, radar, and other electrical equipment making up more than half the cost of some of their new planes. Representing an investment of $2 million, almost half that sum for interlaboratory standards and special equipment, the center would serve science, industry—particularly the new aerospace industries—as well as the military and other Government agencies.[19]

The new importance of Bureau testing was further recognized when on May 3, 1956, Public Law 940 authorized the Bureau, for the first time since its founding, to retain as working funds its fees charged for the calibration of standards and the sale of standard samples to commerce and industry.[20]

Congress might let the Bureau retain its testing fees, but it could not be immediately persuaded to support the major ad hoc committee recommendation, the restoration of the level of basic research at the Bureau through increased appropriations. The chairman of the committee, appearing before the House Appropriations Subcommittee, informed it that the Bureau was not keeping up with the great growth in U.S. technology and was nowhere "big enough for its normal basic functions." [21] The House members were not moved. Even with the severance of the fuze and missile programs and their funds, the remaining sums transferred to the Bureau by other Federal agencies still exceeded by more than three times the direct appropriations of Congress, and Congress was concerned about those funds beyond its control.

"It is the same old program that we are faced with every year," Congressman Prince H. Preston, Jr., of Georgia told his fellow members on the House subcommittee,

> and that is, lack of control we have over the Bureau of Standards' appropriation by virtue of the fact you have so much transferred

[18] NBS Annual Report 1957, p. 98.

The new facilities, and better test methods, resulted in more testing of cement but reduced the volume handled by the Bureau. By the 1960's, just two of the NBS cement laboratories were in operation, at Seattle and Denver, and those at Houston, Kansas City, San Francisco, Allentown, Pa., and Riverside and Permanente in California were closed down. Conversation with Martin R. Defore, Dec. 22, 1964.

[19] NBS Annual Report 1955, p. 123. Wider dissemination of high precision laboratory standards, calibrations, and procedures was the objective of the first meeting of the National Conference of Standards Laboratories held in 1962, attended by over 600 representatives of 200 industrial laboratories and other organizations and reported in NBS M248 (1962).

[20] NBS Annual Report 1956, pp. 108, 140.

[21] Hearings * * * 1955 (Jan. 11, 1954), p. 81.

> money or reimbursable projects. * * * I do not know what the answer * * * is as long as [the Bureau] can get more money from other agencies than we appropriate * * *. As a matter of fact, if we were to try some economies * * * a 20 percent cut [for example] * * * there would be nothing in the world to prevent the Bureau of Standards from doing a little staff negotiation with the Navy, or somebody [and get more transferred funds. Thus the Bureau doesn't] have to put into effect any reduction by virtue of the appropriations we make. [It] would just be going to some other source to get the money we denied.[22]

Apart from the presumed ease with which the Bureau obtained transferred funds was the fact that, while they supported research valuable to basic programs of the Bureau, little fundamental research was ever authorized by those funds. For that research, and for expansion, the Bureau looked to Congress. The predicament was to be resolved 3 years later, with the coming of the space age.

GAITHERSBURG

Second only to the importance of restoring the basic programs at the Bureau to their former high level was the ad hoc committee's recommendation for modernization of its facilities and increased space for those basic programs. Attention had been called to the condition of the Bureau plant a year after the war when a new plant division chief arrived. His initial survey disclosed that Bureau facilities were "in a sordid mess." The main buildings were 30 to 40 years old and looked it, since funds had never been made available for their periodical rehabilitation. Deterioration had accelerated with their great use, abuse, and meager care during the war. Just as alarming was "the almost total lack of basic records on what had been built at the Bureau, where power, steam, water, electrical and other lines ran, and what the ramifications of the facilities really were." [23]

The Public Buildings Administration, responsible for the design, construction, and protection of all Federal buildings, was called to reconstruct

---

[22] Ibid., pp. 90–91, and Hearings * * * 1957 (Mar. 20, 1956), p. 102.

The counterpart of this observation had been voiced three decades earlier in industry's complaint that the special appropriations of Congress to the Bureau expanded its sphere of operations, without controls and contrary to the intention of the organic act of the Bureau. See ch. V, p. 231n.

[23] Interview with William I. Ellenberger, Aug. 12, 1964. The condition of the buildings and the so-called excessive expenditures for their maintenance were particular targets of the House Appropriations Subcommittee survey made at the Bureau in 1949. See Hearings * * * 1951 (Feb. 23, 1950), pp. 2179 ff.

the records and survey the Bureau plant.[24] Its restoration of records, recommendations for rehabilitation of utilities, and for destruction of some of the temporary structures beyond repair were salutary. The modernization of electrical, plumbing, and heating facilities, accomplished in 1949–53 as a result of the survey, still left the Bureau plant a maze of over a hundred buildings, annexes, and minor structures. Most were antiquated and far short of modern laboratory standards, and all were so crowded that no expansion of activities was possible in them.[25]

As a solution to the maze, the visiting PBA architects drew up splendid plans for a completely remodeled Bureau on its present site, reconstructing the entire interiors of the major buildings and replacing the scores of lesser buildings with a dozen new and architecturally satisfying modern structures.[26] The plans were subsequently described as "purely objective * * * on the presumption of unlimited resources," a condition to which Congress was not likely to agree.[27]

Less than a decade later, convinced of the need of new Bureau facilities and their importance to the national welfare, Congress approved relocation.[28] In May 1956 the Director selected a 550–acre plot of high-level ground near Gaithersburg, Md., approximately 19 air miles (45 minutes by

---

[24] The PBA reconstruction is the basis for the Bureau's plant data given in app. O.

[25] The request to the PBA, to survey the plant and determine the repairs and alterations necessary to put it in satisfactory condition, was made in January 1946. The report was made on May 21, 1947. The survey is discussed in Hearings * * * 1948 (Mar. 12, 1947), pp. 295, 308; Hearings * * * 1949 (Jan. 20, 1948), p. 537; Hearings * * * 1951 (Feb. 23, 1950), p. 2274; and NAS–NRC Report, "The role of the Department of Commerce in science and technology," Mar. 2, 1960, p. 92.

[26] In a three-stage "redesign of the entire plant," the prospectus called for retention and thorough modernization of 26 of the original buildings, demolition of 68, and erection of 12 new structures. "Redevelopment Program Survey, NBS," Oct. 1, 1948 (PBA, Federal Works Agency, Project 49–118, in NBS Historical File). The estimated cost of the PBA modernization was subsequently reported as approximately $40 million. [Senate] Hearings * * * 1958 (Apr. 11, 1957), p. 137.

[27] Interview with W. I. Ellenberger, Aug. 12, 1964.

[28] As late as the fall of 1957 the Visiting Committee to the Bureau wrote to Secretary Weeks that the immediate needs of the Bureau were so great that the committee would prefer modernization, new buildings, and expansion at the present site rather than reconstruction at a new site. Letter, M. J. Kelly, Chairman, Visiting Committee, to Secretary Weeks, Oct. 17, 1957 (Visiting Committee files in Office of the Director).

A year later the Visiting Committee approved the decision to build on a new site, but in the interest of haste recommended retention of the Washington site and construction only of new types of research facilities at Gaithersburg (Minutes of meeting of the Visiting Committee, June 19, 1958).

Ultimately, complete reconstruction was agreed on. A new plant could be more efficiently managed and, as had dictated the choice of the original Bureau site, relocation would remove the Bureau from a variety of mechanical, electric, and atmospheric disturbances to precise scientific measurement that now surrounded the Bureau in the city.

car) from downtown Washington, and available for an estimated $750,000.[29] Four years later Congress appropriated approximately $23.5 million as the first installment on a building program estimated to cost in the neighborhood of $70 million for buildings and $45 million for special facilities and equipment.

On June 14, 1961, ground was broken. The first contracts had been let for construction of the central boiler plant, to serve the complex planned, and for an engineering mechanics laboratory. That fall additional contracts were negotiated for a radiation physics laboratory, administration building, supply and plant structures, the shops, and a service building. The third phase called for construction of seven general purpose laboratories, each occupying an area larger than a football field. The fourth and final phase was to include several small special purpose laboratories and a reactor building. When completed the new Bureau complex would comprise over 20 structures.

The ad hoc committee report of 1953, laying down fresh guidelines for the work of the Bureau, gave it a direction it had almost lost in the turbulence of the postwar decade. The approval of plans to construct a great Bureau plant at Gaithersburg bespoke new national needs and a confidence in the future. It also reflected the phenomenal involvement of the Federal Government in postwar science.

Before World War II, Federal participation in research in the physical sciences was negligible. Striving to close the gap in the technology of war, the Federal research budget between 1940 and 1944 rose from $74 to $1,377 million. Two decades later, in continuing escalation, Federal research and development exceeded $15 billion annually or close to 15 percent of the national budget. Almost 60 percent of all research scientists and engineers in the Nation worked wholly or in part on programs financed by the Government. Approximately 68 percent of the $15 billion went into development research, 22 percent to applied research, and 10 percent to basic research, encompassing every field of physical, biological, and social science. The Department of Defense and the National Aeronautic and Space Administration alone accounted for nearly 80 percent of the total funds, supporting development research in hardware immediately pertinent to the national defense, as well as basic and applied research in meteorology, oceanography, astronomy, high temperature physics, and low temperature physics.[30]

---

[29] NBS Budget and Management Division, Summary of Files on Gaithersburg (Office of the Director). Early estimates of the cost of the Gaithersburg plant appear in Senate Hearings * * * 1958 (Apr. 11, 1957), p. 138.

[30] National Science Foundation, "Federal Funds for Research, Development, and other Scientific Activities" (Washington, D.C., 1964), p. 2 and appendix, table C-32; NSF, "Reviews of Data on Research and Development" (Washington, D.C., 1963), p. 1.

Gaithersburg, showing the high-rise administration building, surrounded by and interconnecting with the general purpose laboratories, as these principal units neared completion in 1965.

It was this fact, the mobilization of national science as a permanent peacetime responsibility of the Government, that made anomalous the Bureau's topheavy role in development research. As a consequence, the Bureau was unable to produce new methods of measurement and standards at the rate required by the Federal science program. The result was a growing measurement pinch in the physical sciences.

An event in 1957, the lofting of Russia's Sputnik I into space, marked the advent of the space age and made glaring the gap in measurement.[31] Three years before, both the ad hoc committee and the Bureau had expressed concern about the unpredictable advances that were being made in science, about the shortening lead time between basic discoveries and their application. Forty years had separated Maxwell's publication of the laws of the electromagnetic field and the first radio experiments; 10 years the discovery of the neutron and the first nuclear reaction; and 6 years the invention of the transitor and its appearance in an amplifier on the market. Although space science was moving in this country, its slow pace was suddenly mocked by the Russian achievement.

The Nation's missile and space programs lagged badly for want, among other things, of high temperature measurements in the combustion of high-energy missile fuels; accurate thrust measurements in the million-pound range, instead of the hundred-thousand-pound range available; and high and low temperature, corrosion, and radiation damage measurements of metals, alloys, ceramics, and other materials. Measurements were needed on the effects of sudden and violent changes of temperature and pressure on the thousands of components in a missile system, on the materials and mechanisms of their rocket engines, airframes, electronic devices, and guidance systems.[32]

Science, industry, and the military establishment looked to the Bureau for new precision measurements that only the most basic research in chemistry, physics, and mathematics could provide. But reflecting public opinion during and after the Korean war, budget cuts over the 5 years after 1950 reduced the basic research capabilities of the Bureau by almost 30 percent.[33]

---

[31] The significance of the event, and of Russia's support of five standards laboratories and 129 calibration centers, was discussed at Hearings * * * 1959 (Apr. 23, 1958), pp. 421–22.

[32] See Beverly Smith, Jr., "The measurement pinch," Sat. Eve. Post., Sept. 10, 1960; "Measurement standards report," ISA J., February 1961, pp. 1–40.

[33] Operations and research funds fell from $5.5 million in 1951 to $3.9 million in 1955. By 1957 small congressional increases over the previous 3 years brought the staff up to 75 percent of the 1950 level. Transferred funds still accounted for 63 percent of total Bureau funds, even though half of the transferred fund programs were reported as

Famed for its lead time in measurement to meet the requirements of industry, the Bureau for almost the first time in its history found itself caught in a measurement pinch, by the surging demands of the space age.

As public opinion veered, the budget cuts were reversed. New planning began in order to restaff the Bureau and provide new facilities and programs. Waiting for the Bureau to acquire more physicists, chemists, and mathematicians and space research results, the Army, Navy, and Air Force resorted to long and costly series of empirical trials and test firings. Waiting for the Bureau, the services worked to improve their measurement procedures, training engineers and technicians in metrology and calibration and setting up calibration centers and mobile measurement laboratories.

Even before ground was broken at Gaithersburg, better thrust measurements were in sight, temperature calibrations rose from 2,800° C beyond the 15,000° mark, and intensified research in high-purity materials had begun. Highest priorities were assigned to the construction at Gaithersburg of the mechanical engineering laboratory, to undertake thrust measurements for new missiles; the radiation laboratory, with its linear accelerator in the 100 million-electron-volt range, for safety studies of radiation exposure; and housing for the Bureau's new research reactor, for programs on neutron and fission physics measurements, radiation damage, and radioisotope applications—all of which were impractical or impossible in the Washington laboratories.[34] As appropriation of research funds rose, the Bureau came on course.

To meet the challenge of space research, to affirm the purpose, focus, and urgency of Bureau operations, and give meaning to the individual effort of each Bureau staff member, the Director prepared for the staff a formal statement of the Bureau's central, continuing mission. The emergence of science and technology as the paramount concern of the Nation in the 20th century, he declared, demanded the highest order of measurement competence, in order to provide the standards and measurement techniques on which maintenance of scientific progress depended. The paramount mission of the Bureau henceforth, because of its unique responsibility for leadership

---

close enough to Bureau statutory responsibilities to be put under direct appropriations. Minutes of meeting of the Visiting Committee, Apr. 25, 1957 (Office of the Director).

A special advisory committee of the National Academy of Sciences, chaired by Dr. M. J. Kelly who had headed the ad hoc committee in 1953, was appointed in 1958 at the request of Secretary Weeks to evaluate the operations of all elements of the Department of Commerce. The focus of the restudy of Bureau operations was on the progress of implementation of the 1953 recommendations. The principal finding was that the Nation's need for measurements and standards was not being met by the Bureau, "only because of inadequate funds." NAS–NRC Report, "The role of the Department of Commerce in science and technology," Mar. 2, 1960, pp. 81, 94.

[34] Minutes of meeting of the Visiting Committee, June 29, 1959 (Office of the Director).

in physical measurement, must be: (1) Provision of the central basis within the United States of a complete and consistent system of physical measurement, and coordination of that system with the measurement systems of other nations; (2) provision of essential services leading to accurate and uniform physical measurements throughout the Nation's science, industry, and commerce, and consonant with their advancing requirements; (3) provision of data on the properties of matter and materials which are of importance to science, industry, and commerce, and which are not available of sufficient accuracy elsewhere.[35]

The mission statement by no means encompassed all of the Bureau's future activities. The Bureau had, and would continue to assume, other important tasks within its special competence, as its organic act and amendments provided. But physical measurement, and those specialized services of a supporting nature, such as applied mathematics and instrumentation, were to be the essential focus of future Bureau activities.

RETROSPECT AND PROSPECT

In creating a National Bureau of Standards in the Federal structure at the turn of the century, Congress sought to redress a long-standing need, to provide standards of measurement for commerce and industry, the public, and the Government. Inevitably, the focus was on industry. The United States had only recently become a trading nation, manufacturing for the first time more than it could consume and moving into foreign markets. Recognition of the need for higher standards of measurement, of better quality of product and performance, had prompted manufacturing interests to become the moving force in the founding of the Bureau.

In its first two decades the Bureau won an international reputation for its outstanding achievements in physical measurement, development of standards, and test methods. Through its new standards of measurement, instrumentation, and performance it sought to raise the scientific level of industry. Industry accepted the measurements it so desperately needed but tended to resist the introduction of scientific methods for the achievement of better products and service. In seeking to goad into action those elements of industry reluctant to improve the quality of their product or service, the Bureau championed consumer causes, and in testing commodities purchased for the Government found a lever to move industry.

The latter effort fell short of its goal because the lever could not be fully applied. At the end of World War I the Bureau reluctantly admitted

[35] Minutes of meeting of the Visiting Committee, June 29, 1959; NBS AdminBul 60–40, Sept. 9, 1960; NBS Annual Report 1960, p. 150.

that Federal agencies, representing the largest single consumer of products in the Nation, were still far from united on the need for quality or standardization in their purchases, and tended to neglect or ignore test results made by the Bureau on their behalf.

The techniques of mass production introduced during the war nevertheless gave an enormous impetus to standardization of methods and materials, and the wartime impact of science on industry raised Bureau hopes that it might find readier acceptance of its efforts. Determined to foster the new industries born of the war, the Bureau sought to become the national research laboratory for all industry. By the early 1920's a few industries had begun to exploit the new industrial revolution, most successfully in radio and the automobile, but in general industry and commerce resumed their wasteful habits.

Under the Hoover administration, the Bureau continued its efforts to raise the scientific level of industry and saw itself firmly tied to the service of commerce. In Hoover's crusade to eliminate waste in industry, conserve materials and resources, and standardize products and procedures, almost every element of the Bureau participated. The Bureau made notable advances in both scientific and industrial research in the period, but as a result of its almost total identification with industry, shared the obloquy heaped on commerce and industry when the depression came.

Industrial research funds dried up and industrial projects were curtailed or eliminated during the great disenchantment. With greatly reduced appropriations and staff, but its top echelon almost intact, the Bureau turned increasingly to fundamental research during the depression. The fund of basic knowledge acquired in those years served the Nation well in the Second World War, and with the mobilization of science in the Nation vastly extended the limits of technological attainment. Few could have foreseen the wartime developments in nuclear physics, atomic energy, electronics, mathematics, in aviation, and in missile research, requiring the extension of ranges of all former measurements and determination of an array of new measurements never contemplated before.

Unlike the experience after World War I, the impetus given science and technology did not recede but accelerated enormously in the succeeding years. The import of science for the national welfare became so imperative that the Federal Government dared not relinquish its direction of science, and its costs had become so great that only Government could support it. The Bureau found itself in the forefront of the scientific revolution that had overtaken the Nation.

In the stream of the new revolution were the basic programs introduced or built up at the Bureau in nuclear and atomic physics, electronics, mathematics, computer research, and polymer research, as well as in the instrumentation, standards, and measurement research required by the pace of science and industry. In this period of rapid reorientation some of the long established programs at the Bureau suffered, and for a time the measurement requirements in new fields of science appeared to flourish at the expense of traditional metrology. The onrush of space science put all metrology at hazard. Resolution of that hazard became the aim and continuing achievement of the present decade.

In that same decade, as the Bureau prepared to move to its new laboratories at Gaithersburg, its organization and functions underwent a new realinement of focus and purpose. Believing the Bureau soundly grounded in its role as adjunct of the new science, the Department of Commerce called for reorientation of its services to increase its effectiveness as "a principal focal point in the Federal Government for assuring maximum application of the physical and engineering sciences to the advancement of technology in industry and commerce." [36]

Early in 1964 the programs of the Bureau were regrouped into four institutes. The Institute for Basic Standards comprised its long-standing programs in the field of basic measurement standards and its recently established National Standard Reference Data Program. The Institute for Applied Technology brought together the industry-oriented programs of the Bureau and the Department's program in textile technology and its Office of Technical Services, for the promotion of technological innovation and use of the results of science and technology in industry. The Institute for Materials Research combined the Bureau programs in chemistry and metallurgy, with a view to augmenting their measurements of the properties of materials, strengthening and extending the standard samples program, and improving the efficiency of production processes in industrial technology.

A year and a half later the Bureau's Central Radio Propagation Laboratory at Boulder, originally intended as a fourth institute, became scheduled for transfer from the Bureau to a new agency within the Department of Commerce, the Environmental Science Services Administration (ESSA). With inclusion of the U.S. Weather Bureau and the Coast and Geodetic Survey, the new environmental agency of the Commerce Department was planned to provide broader based research and better service to the public, to business, and to industry.[37]

---

[36] Department of Commerce, Department Order No. 90 (revised), "National Bureau of Standards" (Jan. 30, 1964).

[37] Memo, Director NBS for all employees, May 13, 1965. Exempted from the transfer to ESSA was the radio standards work carried on at Boulder, which was to remain a function of NBS.

The Visiting Committee of Commerce to the Bureau in 1957. Left to right, Dr. Clyde E. Williams, Dr. Crawford H. Greenewalt, Dr. Mervin J. Kelly, Dr. Detlev Bronk, Prof. Frederick Seitz, and the Bureau's fifth Director, Dr. Allen V. Astin.

The spin-off of CRPL, the new realinement of functions and purposes, are endemic in the history of the Bureau. Its history over more than half a century discloses a highly viable form, a living organism of the Federal Government, responsive to national needs as they arose. Established to do no more than provide the Nation with its necessary yardsticks of measurement and performance, a seemingly mechanical destiny, the Bureau from the beginning reached out to the whole life, the whole welfare of the Nation.

The present history has tried to show this life force that is the Bureau, acting as individuals and as agency, and the part it has played in the scientific, industrial, and business life of the Nation. As crusader and arbiter, creator and counselor of standards, it works for the future, as it has in the past, for the good society, and by its learning and good will makes itself felt throughout the Nation and the world.

The Exchequer standard corn gallon of Henry VII

APPENDIX A

FERDINAND RUDOLPH HASSLER

First Superintendent of the Coast Survey and of Weights and Measures

When Professor Stratton arrived at the Office of Weights and Measures on B Street in Washington in the spring of 1898 to survey its equipment and operations, he found there in the person of Louis A. Fischer, the adjuster, a link with Ferdinand Rudolph Hassler, the first Superintendent of Weights and Measures in the Federal Government. It was in the atmosphere of the office over which Hassler had presided, Stratton said,

> with its sacred traditions concerning standards, its unsurpassed instrument shop, its world-known experts in the construction and comparison of standards, and especially in the most precise measurement of length and mass, that the boy Fischer, scarcely over 16, found himself when he entered the employ of Government in a minor capacity [about the year 1880]. * * * Scarcely 40 years had passed since the end of Hassler's services and the beginning of Fischer's. His first instructors were the direct disciples of Hassler and he knew and talked with those who had come in personal contact with the first superintendent.[1]

Fischer's reminiscences concerning the early history of the Weights and Measures office, gathered from his association with the successors of Hassler, were never recorded, to Stratton's regret, and the only biography of Hassler, by Florian Cajori, professor of mathematics at the University of California, centers on his career in the Coast Survey gathered from his association with the successors of Hassler, were never recorded, to in the history of science in the Federal Government, is the principal source of the present sketch.[2]

---

[1] Stratton, "Address Memorializing Louis Albert Fischer, 1864–1921," 15th Annual Conference on Weights and Measures, May 23–26, 1922, NBS M51 (1922), p. 3.

[2] Cajori, The Chequered Career of Ferdinand Rudolph Hassler, First Superintendent of the United States Coast Survey: A Chapter in the History of Science in America (Boston: Christopher Publishing House, 1929).

The biography is a sound summary of the known facts about Hassler. It is based on the numerous published reports Hassler made of his work for the Government; on the Hassler correspondence in the Ford Collection of the New York Public Library; Rosalie L. H. Norris's unpublished "Recollections" (written in Paris, 1856) in the Simon Newcomb Papers, Manuscript Division, Library of Congress; and the papers in the Archives of the American Philosophical Society. Considerable use is also made of the 558-page work, Emil Zschokke's Memoirs of Ferdinand Rudolph Hassler, published in Aarau, Switzerland, 1877, with supplementary documents published in 1882, and translated by Rosalie L. H. Norris (Nice: V.-Eng. Gauthier & Co., 1882). Zschokke's actual memoirs occupy pp. 11–31, and a "Sketch of His Life" by Hassler himself, appears on pp. 35–40. The bulk of the Memoirs, an omnium-gatherum, comprises reports, newspaper accounts, letters and other correspondence by or relating to Hassler.

Hassler, a man highly trained in mathematics and of great practical ability as a scientist, had scant talent in the art of living and even less in the management of everyday affairs. Proud, improvident, singleminded in his pursuit of precision, and intolerant of expediency, he was destined by events to a life of unending storm and stress. Had not revolution in Europe brought him to America, he might have found his place in the scientific community abroad. The political and economic climate of the New World had room for the practical, the philosophical scientist, but little for the often impractical but wholly dedicated man of science such as Hassler.[3]

He was born in the town of Aarau, in the northern or German part of Switzerland, on October 7, 1770, his father a member of a distinguished family, a prosperous watch manufacturer, and high local official. At 16, Hassler entered the institute that was later to be the University of Berne and there came under the influence of Johann Georg Tralles, a young professor of mathematics and physics, who turned Hassler from the study of law to mathematics, astronomy, and geodesy.

[3] The scientific climate Hassler found in America is well depicted in Brooke Hindle's The Pursuit of Science in Revolutionary America, 1735–1789 (University of North Carolina Press, 1956), especially pp. 79, 84, 255–256, 327.

Ferdinand R. Hassler

An engraving of young Hassler, probably made sometime in the 1790's. From the scenery and the spyglass in Hassler's hand, it may be inferred that he and his friend Tralles were at that time mapping the area around Berne, Switzerland. Less than a decade later, Hassler left for America.

Geodetics became their hobby, and in 1791, with apparatus and funds supplied by Hassler, the two began mapping the area around Berne. Since even tolerable maps of any part of the canton did not exist then, the town fathers encouraged the project, seeing that it would promote better land utilization and development. Among the difficulties that confronted Tralles and Hassler was the lack of precise instruments and measurement standards, and so began young Hassler's lifelong preoccupation with instrumentation. Between field expeditions, Hassler traveled to Paris and the university towns of Germany to attend courses, collect books for his growing library, and acquire better instruments and standards for the survey work. His friend Tralles in that same period, as deputy of the Helvetic Republic, was to participate in the establishment of the metric system in France.

The French Revolution of 1798 brought rebellion and French military occupation to Switzerland. That same year Hassler, now 28 and a prominent local official, married Marianne Gaillard, daughter of a schoolteacher. Of a cheerful disposition and great social ambitions, Marianne was not of a very domestic turn and is said to have concerned herself little with the seven sons and two daughters she subsequently bore Hassler.

Under some harassment from the new political regime, and his association with Tralles severed when the latter left to become a member of the Academy of Science in Berlin, Hassler in 1804 joined with a chance acquaintance to organize a stock company for the purchase of large tracts of land in South Carolina, or possibly Louisiana, and there found a Swiss colony. On May 15, 1805, Hassler left his native land with his wife, four children, servants, and 96 trunks and bales for the trip down the Rhine. He had also engaged 120 laborers, artisans, and craftsmen, with their families, to establish the colony, defraying all their expenses. At Amsterdam he chartered the 350-ton ship *Liberty*, out of Philadelphia, and on October 18 after a 6-week voyage the company arrived at that port.

His partner, who had sailed earlier, had in the meantime speculated with the funds entrusted to him and lost them. To maintain his family while waiting for remittances from his father, Hassler sold many of the works of art he had brought with him. He assisted his company of colonists to find new places and, determined not to return home, applied for American citizenship.

Shortly after his arrival in Philadelphia, the seat of Government at that time, he met and was cordially welcomed by his compatriot Albert Gallatin, Secretary of the Treasury, and introduced to President Jefferson. Through them he became a member of the American Philosophical Society in 1807. To the Society he later sold some of his instruments and standards in order to maintain his family, and to the Library of Congress part of his scientific library of about 3,000 volumes.

Hassler came to America intending to lead a rural life as steward of the colony he planned to establish somewhere in the South. His mathematical books and instruments were to be his recreation, and his youthful interest in triangulation and astronomy only recollections of former employments. Instead, a year after his arrival, his possessions much reduced, he settled on a small farm on the banks of the Schuylkill, north of Philadelphia, and began looking for an occupation. He was now 35, possessed of a hardy constitution, considerable learning, but with few immediate prospects. Like many of the well-educated of his time he knew Latin and spoke several languages, in his case German, French, Italian, and English, the latter clear but heavily accented and unidiomatic. Besides his training and experience in political science and jurisprudence, he had an extensive knowledge of mathematics and a good knowledge of chemistry, mineralogy, and all the other branches of natural philosophy. And he was versed in astronomy and practical geodetics.

When he made known his need of an income, his new friends in the Philosophical Society wrote to President Jefferson recommending Hassler's employment in a geodetic survey of the coast then under consideration. On February 10, 1807, Congress appropriated $50,000 for—

> a survey to be taken of the coasts of the United States, in which shall be designated the islands and shoals, with the roads or places of anchorage, within twenty leagues of any part of the shores of the United States; and also the respective courses and distances between the principal capes, or head lands, together with such other matters as [the President] may deem proper for completing an accurate chart of every part of the coasts within the extent aforesaid.[4]

Of a number of plans solicited for conducting the survey, Hassler's proved most satisfactory. It provided for the determination of true geographic positions by astronomical means at key points near the coast, networks of precise triangulation between these points, a topographical survey of the coast, and a hydrographic survey of coastal waters controlled by triangulation.[5]

The President recommended that Hassler be appointed to carry out the work, but the solicitations and more pressing affairs of state delayed action on the survey for 4 years.

While awaiting acceptance of his plans for the coast survey, Hassler secured a place as acting professor of mathematics and natural philosophy at West Point, resigning in February 1810 to teach natural science at Union College at Schenectady. He left a year later when Secretary of the Treasury Gallatin commissioned him to go to London to obtain the instruments he would need for the survey. Hassler had stipulated in seeking the post that "good instruments are never to be obtained by buying in shops, where only instruments of inferior quality are put up to sell; they must be made on command and by the best mechanicians." He embarked with his family for Europe on August 29, 1811, to seek out those mechanicians and direct the construction of his instruments.

Hassler's eighth child and sixth son was born to his wife during the 4-year stay in London and named Edward Troughton, after his next door neighbor and the chief instrumentmaker supplying the equipment for the survey. Besides Hassler's reluctance to hurry the construction of his instruments, delays arose when shortly after his arrival war broke out between England and his country, and for a time he was detained in London as an alien. Two years later while his family was living in Paris, England and her allies invaded France, Napoleon escaped from Elba and, collecting troops as he went, marched to his final battle. Hassler went to France to extricate his family.

Not all the instruments that Hassler ordered abroad were for the coast survey. Some were for two astronomical observatories, as "a permanent national institution," that Hassler planned, one in Washington or somewhere in the Southern States, the other in the North. Not until his return were the President or Congress to learn of, and defer, Hassler's "institution."

---

[4] Quoted in Annual Report of the Board of Regents of the Smithsonian Institution. Report of the U.S. National Museum, part II, A Memorial of George Brown Goode * * * " [including his] history of science in America (Washington, D.C. 1901), p. 293. Jefferson, anticipating war with Great Britain and aware that the only charts of the coast were those of the early Dutch, English, and French colonists, proposed the survey to Congress in 1806.

[5] A. Joseph Wraight and Elliott B. Roberts, "The Coast and Geodetic Survey, 1807–1957" (Washington, D.C., 1957), p. 5.

When not tending the construction of his instruments and apparatus, the great 24-inch theodolite for measuring the angles of the survey, and the telescopes, transit instruments, astronomical clocks, chronometers, barometers, thermometers, micrometers, and balances he had ordered, Hassler met and discoursed with the astronomers and geodecists in London and Paris on the state and progress in these fields in Europe. He procured new copies of both French and English standard weights and measures, for their like was not known in America and they were needed for the survey, and made comparisons of the meter bars and other measures with Troughton's own scales.

In the spring of 1815, upon the death of his father, he went to Switzerland to settle the estate, returning with his inheritance of some 1,100 pounds sterling. Besides more instruments he bought lavishly of the best and most recent books on astronomy and geodesy, some for the instruction of the young officers who would be employed in the survey, the rest for his own use and instruction.

The value of the equipment ordered by Hassler in London and Paris came to $37,550. With his salary of $4,500 and traveling expenses, his accounts came to a grand total of $55,634, well above the congressional appropriation. He had to come home at his own expense. In the first week of August 1815 he and his family left London, to arrive in Philadelphia 9 weeks later. He had, as Gallatin pointed out, outrun his time and his funds, but the instruments he had procured were excellent.

In the spring of 1816, without waiting for formal approval, Hassler set to work. On August 3, 3 months after Congress appropriated funds to initiate the survey itself, Hassler was notified of his appointment as Superintendent of the Survey of the Coast, with a salary of $3,000 and $2,000 for expenses. He had discussed with the Secretary of the Treasury the operation of the survey and the amount of freedom he should have in the work. In a confirming letter that rang like a personal declaration of independence he said in part:

> My task would be fully large enough, to make all the combinations, operations, and principal observations; to bring up the young officers given to me to the capability required for their employment, (as it will in fact be a practical school that I shall have to keep, besides the work), and to direct, inspect, and verify, the detailed surveys, and their uniting in proper charts, etc. To load me with any of the mechanical, or economical parts, would be impeding the work, * * * and place me in a situation not to be supported.

At 46, Hassler's character was fully formed. He was a scientist of unlimited enthusiasm and devotion to his work. He was honest, a proud spirit, and knew his worth. He also habitually planned things on a large scale, without giving much thought to the practical realities or limitations of his projects. The Swiss colony project had been characteristic, and his mentors should have been warned by the apparatus he had purchased for his two unauthorized observatories. And, his biographer notes, as "the head of a large family, the husband of a woman fond of society and unqualified to struggle along devotedly on small means, a scholar who in youth was accustomed to almost unrestricted expenditures for books, scientific instruments, and travel, he was to find himself in maturer years in sharp conflict with economic conditions." But he had on his side warm supporters in the American Philosophical Society, and more valuable, the Presidency. As Jefferson first befriended him, so succeeding Presidents Madison, Monroe, Adams, and Jackson were to come to his defense and to extricate him from his repeated difficulties with accountants and Congress.

A letter from the Treasury in February 1817, 6 months after his appointment, asked Hassler to state the probable time required to complete the survey. He couldn't say, for he had not yet begun. Owing to the severity of the winter, he had not even found

Hassler sets up camp in the field, a drawing based on a reproduction of a time-darkened painting.

Visible under tents are his 24-inch theodolite for measuring angles and his wonderful Jersey wagon, with its wine chamber, disappearing dining and work table, and array of compact instrument and provision chests.

a satisfactory location for a baseline. On the other hand, he had started to train the first of the lieutenants of artillery sent him from West Point as assistants, and there was under construction a remarkable carriage for transporting the theodolite and other delicate instruments to be used.[6] Not until April did he determine on the location for his first baseline, near the Hackensack River in New Jersey, and begin establishing triangulation points.

A year after beginning the survey, Hassler was asked again when it would be completed and was warned of Congress's dissatisfaction with his meager progress. On April 14, 1818, Congress acted, modifying the law authorizing the survey in order to put Army and Navy officers in charge of the work, thereby excluding Hassler from further direction or participation. His biographer is doubtless right in declaring that

---

[6] As completed a year later, the barouche-like vehicle he designed to convey his instruments, some weighing a hundred pounds or more, was based on a Jersey wagon mounted on strong braces and huge springs, to be drawn by two or four horses. Ruggedly constructed to maneuver on rough roads and hilly terrain, it had numerous compartments in a double bottom for storing smaller instruments, tools, stationery and books, and a music box to keep him company as he worked late into the night. In a locker under the seat were his traveling clothes and "a little spirit-room," containing his supply of Swiss wines and the crackers and cheese he lived on in the field. A tent covering secured the carriage in bad weather. With its suspended table, the vehicle served as Hassler's office by day and, with the table secured, as a sleeping chamber at night.

"Hassler wanted his survey to be not only practically useful, but also a contribution to the science of geodesy * * * on a par with European contributions * * *. Congress had not the least idea of the coast survey as a science; to them it was an enterprise no different from the survey of the Northwest Territory"—a simple matter of using compass and chain and turning out maps and charts with regularity. After a year's work Hassler had no maps to offer.[7]

The next decade was as bleak a period for Hassler as it was for the progress of the survey. A week after militarization of the coast survey, President Monroe appointed Hassler as one of the astronomers in the party sent to fix the boundary line with Canada in upper New York State, as provided in the treaty ending the War of 1812. A year later Hassler, in conflict with the U.S. Commissioner over his progress and his expenses, resigned. He sought a professorship at Jefferson's University of Virginia, still under construction. He considered returning to Europe, but his wife would not consent. He decided to farm and teach, and in 1820, despite the known severity of climate and his complete lack of experience as a farmer, he purchased a tract of land at Cape Vincent in New York State, overlooking the Thousand Islands in the St. Lawrence. There he planned, with characteristic enthusiasm, to establish a normal school and agricultural college.

With high expectations, he sold at a sacrifice most of the furniture and all of the pictures, statuary, and Sèvres porcelain in the house the family was then occupying on the Commons in Newark, N.J., and almost all that was left of his original collection of books. The remaining furniture was packed in two large Jersey wagons, and with Hassler's wonderful instrument carriage, which he purchased when it was sold at auction in 1819, the family set out on the 400-mile journey to Cape Vincent.

The house he had bought sight unseen in New York State for $1,000 proved to be two 1-room log cabins. Gathering together the carpenters and masons in the neighborhood, he began construction of a great 16-room house, destined to be completed but never occupied. Some farming was begun, but the plan for a college was soon abandoned. In the spring of 1823, while Hassler was on one of his frequent absences from home, perhaps attending a meeting of the Philosophical Society in Philadelphia, and his children were in the fields, his wife gathered her personal belongings and left him, never to return.

Leaving his eldest son in charge of the farm, Hassler soon after took a teaching position at Union Hall Academy at Jamaica, Long Island, and brought the other children to New York. When the Academy failed in 1827, he taught at another in Richmond, Va., and continued to seek a university position. But his marked foreign accent, his rather erratic temperament, and his age, then 55, were against him. Always a tireless talker, he had also been a tireless writer, about his projects, his progress in the survey work, his construction of instruments, his scientific observations delivered before the Philosophical Society. Now he turned to writing textbooks, and with some success found publishers for his "Elements of Analytical Trigonometry" (1826), "Elements of Arithmetik, Theoretical and Practical" (1826), "Elements of Geometry of Planes and Solids" (1828), "A Popular Exposition of the System of the Universe with Plates and Tables" (1830), and "Logarithmic and Trigonometric Tables" (1830). the latter with introductions published in five languages.

---

[7] Hassler's undertaking, "which Congress supposed would be finished in a few years, has now taken 150 years, and no end is in sight." Elliott B. Roberts, "United States Coast and Geodetic Survey, 1807–1957," Ann. Rep., Smithsonian Institution, 1957, p. 222.

A new employment came in the autumn of 1829 when, impelled by want, Hassler accepted an appointment as gager in the New York Custom House. Then his fortunes began to look up. For some time Congress had been discussing the establishment of standards of weights and measures for the United States. There was much talk about the jeopardy to this country's international trade arising from the different concepts of pounds and bushels entertained by the various collectors of customs. On May 29, 1830, the Senate adopted a resolution directing a comparison of the weights and measures used at the principal customhouses. Five months later, on November 2, President Jackson placed Hassler in charge of the study, at $3,000 per year, to make an inspection and review of the measures used in the customhouses.

After 3 months, Secretary of the Treasury Ingham reported Hassler's inspection "far advanced; and it has exhibited such a remarkable disparity in the weights and measures used at the different customhouses, as to demonstrate the urgent necessity of providing standards for their regulation." Called in from the customhouses,

> the standards, where any such existed, were transmitted to Washington, and it soon appeared that they were of so irregular character, and so unworthy of confidence, that the comparison of them, indefatigably pursued by Mr. Hassler, was a task entirely beneath his attention. The measure which proved the nearest to the standard was a *folding* yard stick from Philadelphia, the length of which is stated at 36.0002465 standard inches.[8]

With no authority but the approval of Secretary Ingham and the President, Hassler determined to adopt standards for the United States and produce and distribute them to the customhouses. From among the standards that he and Gallatin had secured abroad many years earlier for the survey of the coast, Hassler selected the units to be used for the construction and comparison of suitable weights and measures, and out of his knowledge and skill began construction of the balances and other apparatus for their verification. The fundamental units of length, mass (weight), and capacity recommended by Hassler were adopted by the Treasury Department in 1832, and Fdward Troughton Hassler, his 23-year-old son, was taken on to assist in the construction of standards based on those units.[9]

Apprised by Treasury reports of Hassler's progress, Congress in a joint resolution of June 14, 1836, gave its formal approval and directed the Treasury to fabricate for the customhouses the standards of weights and measures that had been established—that is, established by Hassler. By reason of the joint resolution of 1836, the Office of Weights and Measures in the Coast Survey, as the immediate antecedent of the present National Bureau of Standards, is considered formally established as of that date.

Meanwhile, on July 10, 1832, 2 years after calling for the inquiry into the customhouses, Congress reestablished the Coast Survey on the basis of the original act of 1807. Upon President Jackson's recommendation, Hassler again became its Superintendent, at

---

[8] Report of Alexander D. Bache in J. Franklin Inst. 13, 238 (1834). Cited in Cajori, p. 156, and available on L/C microfilm reel 283, series 01104.

H. Doc. 229, 22d Cong., 1st sess., 1832 (L/C: J66), is Hassler's report on his examination in 1831 of the weights and measures used in the principal customhouses, and includes his description of the collection of instruments available to him for constructing weights and measures.

[9] The start of the work is described in Hassler's Documents Related to the Construction of Standards of Weights and Measures for the Custom-Houses from March to November 1835 (New York: William van Norden, 1835). L/C: QC1000U58.

a salary of $3,000 and $1,500 for expenses, and was to continue his superintendency over the work in Weights and Measures, without additional compensation..

The survey of the coast that had been carried out after 1818 largely under naval auspices produced a vast body of partial maps and charts at vast expense, Secretary of the Navy Southard reported in 1828. The maps and charts were based on nautical and chronometric surveys, not triangulation, and so far as their use for commercial and naval interests and means for national defense was concerned, Southard declared them "unsafe, and in many instances, useless and pernicious." Hassler resumed the survey on his original plan.

Once again in charge, he borrowed the mathematical books he had sold to West Point more than a decade before, refurbished his traveling carriage brought down from Cape Vincent, and ordered from Troughton of London a new and improved theodolite made to his specifications, as well as a dividing engine, new telescopes and microscopes of his devising, and other instruments. While his son Edward continued the work on weights and measures, Hassler himself began measuring a new baseline at Fire Island, off the south shore of Long Island, "the longest baseline," it was later reported, "ever run in the history of geodetic surveys." At the peak of activities in 1841, Hassler, with the Army topographic engineers and Navy officers detailed to the Survey, had under his superintendence in the two offices a staff of 93 officers and civilians.

The years between 1832 and 1843 were filled with skirmishes with the Secretaries of the Treasury, with accountants and auditors, and with Congress over the financial procedure in operating the offices, over congressional demands that would have meant a less accurate, less scientific, and cheaper survey, and threats to form committees to supervise Hassler's expenditures and progress. In March 1834, possibly to insure more professional administration, the Coast Survey was transferred from the Treasury to the Navy Department, and Hassler at once asked to be relieved from the Survey work. President Jackson intervened, kept the accounting of Survey funds in the Treasury, and Hassler accepted Navy administration.

At the time of the transfer, Hassler insisted that he keep his salary of $3,000 for superintending Weights and Measures alone. Secretary of the Treasury Levi Woodbury replied that the Office need not require much time and attention, and $1,200 or $1,500 was enough for the work. Hassler answered that he had large plans for Weights and Measures. As he wrote to the Secretary, he intended "to form an establishment which has never even been attempted in this country," for which much heavier expenditures would be necessary. He may have had in mind somthing like the bureau established almost 70 years later, but what he intended is not known. Before the plans were committed to paper, President Jackson in March 1836 restored the Coast Survey to the Treasury and to Hassler.

It is said that on the occasion of the restoration a dispute arose about more compensation for Hassler's two superintendencies, and Hassler carried his case to the White House.

> "So, Mr. Hassler, it appears the Secretary and you cannot agree about this matter," remarked Jackson, when Hassler had stated his case in his usual emphatic style. "No, Sir, ve can't." "Well, how much do you really think you ought to have?" "Six thousand dollars, Sir." "Why, Mr. Hassler, that is as much as Mr. Woodbury, my Secretary of the Treasury, himself, receives." "Mr. Voodbury!" declared Hassler, rising from his chair, "There are plenty of Voodburys, plenty of Everybodys who can be made the Secretary of the Treasury. But," said he, pointing his forefinger toward himself, "there is only one, *one* Hassler for the head of the Coast Survey." President Jackson, sympa-

thizing with a character having some traits in common with his own, granted Hassler's demand.[10]

Then in his middle sixties and going strong, Hassler wore flannel both summer and winter, believing it kept off the heat as well as kept out the cold. He never used glasses for reading or writing, but kept his vest pockets filled with snuff, which he was convinced excited the optic nerves and was the only help his eyes needed. Working at night at the Coast Survey office, first on 13th Street and later in adjoining row houses on Capitol Hill, he had for light at his desk six or eight large wax candles, remolded from commercial candles to about 2 inches in diameter with double or triple plaited wicks.[11] His daughter Rosalie in her "Recollections" of her father was to say that he never went to bed before 2 or 3, and finally lost the sight of one eye shortly before his death "by the over fatigue in adjusting the yard and liquid measures." To the last his heavy accent sometimes made it difficult to understand him, "but his singularities of manner," recalled a zealous friend in the House, Joseph L. Tillinghast of Rhode Island, "did not touch his intelligence and eminent capacity in his vocation."

Between 1832 and 1841 Congress appropriated a total of $620,000 for the Coast Survey offices. At Hassler's death in 1843 Survey funds had paid for the triangulation of an area of 9,000 square miles, furnishing determinations of nearly 1,200 geodetic stations for the delineation of 1,600 miles of shoreline. One hundred and sixty-eight topographical maps had been surveyed and 142 hydrographic charts, although only 5 large charts were engraved and ready for publication.[12]

In the Weights and Measures Office, Hassler saw complete sets of weights with their multiples and submultiples finished and delivered to the customhouses and to the States. Half of the capacity measures and a third of the measures of length were constructed, but 13 years would pass before the last of them, and the necessary balances, were delivered.

The summer and fall of 1843 found Hassler, now 73, in the field, surveying in New Jersey and Delaware. In a rain and sleet storm that October he fell and injured himself on a rock while trying to save the tent protecting one of his instruments. As a result of the injury and exposure he developed a fever and inflammation of the lungs that forced him to go home to Philadelphia for medical help, where Rosalie could look after him.

During his last weeks he wrote out his annual report to the Secretary of the Treasury. The comprehensive plan for the continuation and expansion of the work that he outlined in the report had already been approved by the President. Its execution was begun by his successor, Alexander Dallas Bache, and the plan remained the basis for survey operations until the enabling act of 1947 established a new, but not greatly

---

[10] Reported by T. C. Mendenhall in 1916 and by Cajori in 1929, at least two versions of this anecdote existed prior to 1900, in E. Zschokke's Memoirs, pp. 529–530, and in Harper's, 58, 508 (1878–79). It was therefore very much alive in 1900 when Secretary of the Treasury Lyman Gage retold it as his own story, with reference to Dr. Stratton's proposed salary. See ch. I, p. 45.

[11] Admiral Richard Wainwright, who came to the Survey just after Hassler's death, said he "knew the old office building thoroughly, from the weights and measures in the basement to the computers' rooms in the attic." Centennial Celebration of the U.S. Coast and Geodetic Survey (Washington, D.C., 1916), p. 91.

[12] For an account of Hassler's search for high grade copper plates in this country, Austria, and France, and his importation of two highly trained engravers from Hamburg, see Cajori, p. 216.

According to Dr. Lewis V. Judson, who came to the weights and measures division of the Bureau in 1917, this plaque or nameplate in gold with Hassler's name in black letters was brought from the Office of Weights and Measures on New Jersey Avenue to Connecticut Avenue by Mr. Fischer.

altered statement of functions. Hassler continued to work, writing in his journal, until shortly before his death on November 20, 1843.

He left behind his daughter Rosalie Lätitia Norris; his eldest son John James Scipio, a topographical assistant in the Coast Survey; Edward Troughton, in the Weights and Measures Office; Charles August, a surgeon in the Navy; Ferdinand Eugene, consul at Panama; and his second daughter, Caroline, a childlike woman of 43, in the care of Rosalie. His three other sons had died under age or in infancy. His wife Marianne, whom he saw just once briefly a few years after she left home, lived with friends for a number of years, then with her eldest son in Pennsylvania, later with Rosalie in New Brunswick, and finally with friends on Long Island, where her death occurred in 1858 at the age of 86. Hassler left no debts at this death, nor did he leave any money either. The farm at Cape Vincent was all that his surviving children inherited.

Tribute to Ferdinand Rudolph Hassler as the first scientist of rank in the employ of the Federal Government has increased with the years. His genius lay in the design of instruments for his geodetic work and in his tireless efforts to contrive the best possible standards of weights and measures with the best possible materials. He was dogmatic and uncompromising, qualities destructive in his personal life, perhaps, but true to the spirit of inquiry. As his biographer, Cajori, says, he "stands out greatest in perceiving what was best in the practical geodesy of his time, in making improvements upon what he found, and then clinging [without compromise to what] he had initiated as being the best that the science of his day had brought forth."

At the centennial celebration of the Coast and Geodetic Survey in 1916, with its many tributes to Hassler, it was said:

> To him belongs the credit that to-day the operations of the Survey are bound together by a trigonometric survey with long lines and executed by the most accurate instruments and the most refined methods.

Dr. Stratton on that occasion called him—

> not only the first and foremost man in the scientific work of our country at that time but one of the leading * * * metrologists of his day. I doubt if there were more than half a dozen people in the world at that time who

> possessed the scientific knowledge and the deftness of the artisan necessary to undertake his work.

More recently it has been said:

> His greatest gift to America was not the surveys he accomplished—it was his reverence for sound thinking, integrity, and accuracy, which have endured as basic elements of Survey philosophy * * *. He may have been as consecrated a public servant as ever lived.[13]

---

[13] Annual Report, Smithsonian Institution, 1957, pp. 223, 225.

APPENDIX B

THE METRIC SYSTEM IN THE UNITED STATES

THE FRENCH ORIGIN OF THE METRIC SYSTEM

The genesis of the modern metric system was a decimal system, based on the length of an arc of 1 minute of a great circle of the earth, first proposed by Gabriel Mouton, a vicar of Lyons, France, in the late 17th century. The proposal confronted a plethora of arbitrary systems of weights and measures current in France, as in the rest of Europe, their lineage going back to medieval measures based on the size of barley corns and the length of human feet. Mouton's plan was discussed for almost a hundred years before the progress of commerce and science called for more rational measures than the weights and measures in common use.

The beginning of order took place in 1790 when Tallyrand proposed to the French National Assembly the desirability of a system of weights and measures that would not only bring uniformity to France but would also be international in application. It must, therefore, he reasoned, be based on some invariable unit of nature that could not only be readily reproduced but would be capable of being measured with a high degree of precision.

A decree of the National Assembly on May 8, 1790, sanctioned by Louis XVI on August 22, called upon the Academy of Sciences, in concert with the Royal Society of London, "to deduce an invariable standard for all the measures and all the weights."[1] When English interest in a French undertaking could not be obtained, a committee of philosophers of the Academy, composed of Borda, Lagrange, Laplace, Monge, and Condorcet, began deliberations, reporting its conclusions in March 1791. The choice of a fundamental unit as the basis of a rational system of measures was between the length or fraction of the length of a pendulum, vibrating in intervals of 1 second or some chosen unit of time; the quadrant of a great circle of the equator; and the quadrant of a great circle of the earth's meridian. Since the pendulum introduced a new and unlike element, the second, and depended on the varying intensity of the gravitational force on the earth's surface, the committee preferred a terrestrial arc.

---

[1] William Hallock and Herbert T. Wade, The Evolution of Weights and Measures and the Metric System (New York: Macmillan, 1906), p. 47. Hallock and Wade and the article by Henrie Moreau, "The Genesis of the Metric System and the Work of the International Bureau of Weights and Measures," J. Chem. Educ. 30, 3 (1953), provide the basis for this account of the metric system. Other sources that have been consulted but not cited here include NBS S17, "History of the standard weights and measures of the United States" (Fischer, 1905), reprinted as M64 (1925); M122, "Weights and measures in Congress" (S. A. Jones, 1936); C570, "Units and systems of weights and measures" (Judson, 1956); C593, "The Federal basis for weights and measures" (R. W. Smith, 1958); TNB 43, 1–3 (1959); and M247, "Weights and measures of the United States" (Judson, 1963). The most complete history of the metric system is that of Guillaume Bigourdan, Le Système Métrique des Poids et Mesures (Paris, 1901).

As the more practicable of the two earth circles, the committee proposed to measure an arc of meridian between Dunkirk, on the northern coast of France, and Barcelona, on the Mediterranean Sea. From the distance determined, computation would be made of the length of the entire quadrantal arc from the pole to the equator, allowing for the deviation of the earth's form from a true sphere. The ten-millionth part of the total computed length was then to be taken as the base or fundamental unit of length and accurately marked off on a suitable number of specially constructed metal bars, copies of which would provide working standards for science and commerce.

The plan was adopted and the Academy of Sciences assigned the term mètre (meter) from the Greek metron, a measure, to the one ten-millionth part of the quadrant, fixing the new unit provisionally at 3 pieds 11.44 lignes, based on calculations made of a meridian in France by Lacaille in 1740.[2] This unit was roughly similar to the Dutch ell, the English yard, the Italian braccio, and other standard lengths in the nations of Europe.

From the concept of this single length standard, all other weights and measures were to be derived. Decimal multiples and submultiples of the meter were to express its macro and micro versions. A new, single unit of weight or mass, the gram, with similar decimal multiples and submultiples, was to replace existing weights, the new standard corresponding to the mass of 1 cubic centimeter (that is, a cube one-hundredth of a meter on a side) of pure water. The unit of capacity, the liter, would be a volume of pure water equal to 1 cubic decimeter. The measure of volume, especially for cord wood, the stere, was to be a meter cubed. And the unit of land area, the are, was to be a square 10 meters on a side or 100 square meters.

The concept had and still has merit and profundity. But as we shall see, the theoretical perfection of the metric system could not be realized.

Working with the greatest precision attainable with the instruments and knowledge available, members of the Academy measured by triangulation the meridional distance through Paris of the arc from Dunkirk to Barcelona, a strip of country made up of mountainous and inaccessible districts. The work was not only arduous but hazardous, since it was carried out during the Reign of Terror and was subject to repeated harassment.

In April 1795, even before a definitive meter was derived from the astronomical and geodetic measurements along the Dunkirk-Barcelona meridian, the revolutionary government instituted the metric system in France, using the provisional meter as standard and fixing the nomenclature of the new units of measure.

In June 1798, 6 years after beginning the fieldwork, the observations of the parties of geodecists under Méchain and Delambre were completed and at the invitation of the government a committee of delegates from the republics of Europe studied the assembled computations. While one section of the committee examined the measurements of the arc of meridian and the actual length of the meter, another, which included Johann Georg Tralles, deputy of the Helvetic Republic,[3] undertook determination of the unit of mass, the gram. When so small a mass could not be realized with sufficient accuracy, its multiple, the kilogram, was selected for construction of the standard of mass.

---

[2] Interestingly, the provisional meter in brass, constructed by Lenoir of Paris in 1795, proved to differ from the meter finally determined by only about 0.33 millimeter.

Before the establishment of the metric system, the principal units in use in France were the pied du Roi (0.325 meter) for lengths and the livre poids de marc (489.5 grams) for weights. The pied du Roi was divided into 144 lignes, and 6 pieds du Roi made a toise (1.949 meters), the common unit of length.

[3] See Hassler appendix for note on Tralles.

The results of the computations gave the distance from the pole to the equator as 5,130,740 toises, with the length of the meter 3 pieds 11.296 lignes. The weight of a cubic decimeter of distilled water at maximum density gave the value 18,827.15 grains (a submultiple of the livre poids de marc), which was adopted as the weight of the kilogram.[4]

THE METER AND KILOGRAM OF THE ARCHIVES

Construction in platinum of the prototype meter and kilogram was completed in June 1799, for deposit in the Archives of the Republic. Iron copies of these standards were then made and distributed among the committee delegates as models for the construction of their new weights and measures. On December 10 the provisional meter was abolished and the new standards adopted by statute as the definitive standards of the measures of length and of weight throughout the Republic.[5] The grand plan of unifying weights and measures was completed.

One of the iron copies of the Meter of the Archives, the gift of Tralles to his friend Hassler, and destined to be known in the United States as the "Committee Meter," was brought to this country by Hassler in 1805. He also brought a copy of the kilogram, another gift of Tralles, and 3 toises, the rival of the meter in France until late in the 19th century.

In financial distress, Hassler in 1806 sold these standards to a member of the American Philosophical Society. They were loaned to him when he became Superintendent of Weights and Measures in the Coast Survey, his Committee Meter serving as the standard of length in the Coast Survey until 1890. With other standards secured by Hassler abroad, it is now preserved in the vault of the National Bureau of Standards.[6]

The advantages of the metric system then as now resided in its simplicity, uniformity, and convenience. It is entirely decimal, like our system of counting.[7] The measures of area, capacity, and volume are obtained by squaring and cubing measures of length. Weights are directly related to the measures of volume. And the names of their multiples and submultiples are obtained by the simple addition of prefixes to the principal unit, for example, kilo (k) = 1,000; hecto (h) = 100; deka (dk) = 10; deci (d) = 0.1; centi (c) = 0.01; milli (m) = 0.001. Thus a kilometer is 1,000 meters, and a milligram is a thousandth (0.001) of a gram.[8]

But the metric system was not beyond cavil. Lukewarm to pronounced opposition under the succeeding imperial government confronted the standards established by the

---

[4] Hallock and Wade, p. 62.

[5] Ibid., p. 63.

[6] The metric and English weights and measures acquired by or available to Hassler for his survey of the coast are described in his report to Congress, H. Doc. 299, 22d Cong., 1st Sess., 1832.

[7] The metric system is a decimal system, but the terms "metric" and "decimal" are not synonymous. The decimal system, of oriental origin, refers to a numbers system progressing by tens, based on the biological fact that man has that many articulate fingers. Equally arbitrary and useful numbers systems have been based on 2, 5, 6, 8, and the duodecimal system of 12.

[8] In 1962 the International Committee on Weights and Measures added two new metric prefixes (atto, the submultiple 10^{-18} and femto, 10^{-15}) to the scale already ranging from tera, 10^{12} to pico, 10^{-12}. See NBS TNB 48, 61–62 (1964).

republican regime, as witnessed by the failure of the State to construct and distribute the necessary secondary standards. The new standards were especially threatened by a decree of Napoleon in 1812 that, yielding to prejudice, permitted for a decade a system of *mesures usuelles* using odd multiples and fractions of the metric system to harmonize with the very measures the metric system was intended to replace, those long established in commerce and common usage. In 1837 the State repealed the edict and allowed 3 years for full compliance with the new measures. After January 1, 1840, under pain of severe penalties for the use of any other weights and measures, the metric system was made universal and compulsory throughout France.

The instability of 19th-century Europe, with its profusion of petty kingdoms and principalities and its wars and revolutions acted to retard acceptance of the metric system. Upon Tralles' return from Paris he urged introduction of metric weights and measures into Switzerland and in 1801 saw a law passed adopting them. But the metric system was not made compulsory in that country until 1856.

Some of the Italian provinces adopted it in the early 19th century, in 1816 the metric system was declared obligatory in the Low Countries, and Spain accepted it in 1849. After 1860 adoptions increased rapidly, the entering wedge in most instances the necessity of uniform weights and measures in international trade.

The metric system crossed the Atlantic when by law it came into effect in Mexico in 1862, and before the end of the century it had become the legal system in most South and Central American countries. Italy made the metric system obligatory in 1863. In Great Britain, an act of July 29, 1864, authorized the use of the metric system concurrently with the imperial system. Two years later, with passage of the Metric Act on July 28, 1866, Congress also made use of the metric system legal throughout the United States.[9] By this act, the meter was declared to be 39.37 inches, the kilogram 2.2046 pounds, based on the best metric standards available in this country, Hassler's Committee Meter and the platinum Arago kilogram obtained in 1821 by Secretary of State Gallatin.

The agreement among the federated states of Germany in 1868 to adopt the metric system became obligatory under the empire in 1872, the same year it was officially adopted in Portugal. Austria made its use compulsory in 1876, and Norway in 1882.

THE METRIC CONVENTION

It was not commercial application of the metric system but its growing use in scientific work in Europe that made the accuracy of its fundamental units of increasing concern, especially to mathematicians, geodecists, and physicists. The more accurate measurements of arcs of meridians reported by British and Russian geodecists at the International Geodetic Conference held at Berlin in 1867 resulted in new computations of the shape of the earth and hence the length of the quadrant. The changes in this last quantity therefore affected the length of the meter and raised serious questions about it as a natural and absolute standard.[10]

---

[9] An act of Congress on July 27, 1866, authorizing the Secretary of the Treasury to furnish the States with sets of metric weights and measures, actually preceded passage of the Metric Act by 1 day. Hallock and Wade, pp. 128–129.

[10] Hallock and Wade, p. 69. The actual difference in the Meter of the Archives, as in the International Meter that replaced it, is minute but significant in metrology. It is about 0.2 millimeter shorter than its definition, the ten-millionth part of the quadrant of the earth's meridian. Similarly, the International Kilogram exceeds by 0.028 gram

In response, the French Government in 1872 held an international conference, attended by scientific representatives from 26 countries, including the United States, that resolved on the preparation of new prototypes. They would be arbitrary prototypes—as arbitrary, in a sense, as the weights and measures that the metric system supplanted—but practical, and if adopted internationally would place metric standards on a permanent basis for the service of science and commerce.

The conference agreed to the construction of a number of prototype meters and prototype kilograms, their values copied exactly from those of the units in the Archives in Paris, made 75 years before. Upon examination, the meter and kilogram of the Archives were found perfectly preserved, and comparison of the meter with two others constructed at the same time demonstrated it had not appreciably altered in length. The Archives units were therefore to be reproduced in a new metal, a more stable shape, with greater refinement of line, and other precision factors. One each of the new meters and kilograms was to be chosen as the international standard of length and weight, respectively, and to be deposited in an international repository. It was agreed that the repository and its laboratory be located at Paris, its site neutral ground, acccessible to all the participating countries, and under their common care. After selection of the international prototypes, the remaining prototypes were to be distributed by lot to the contracting governments as their national metric standards.

An international treaty, the Metric Convention (Convention du Mètre), concluded in Paris on May 20, 1875, and signed by 18 countries including the United States and Russia, with Great Britain and Holland abstaining, put the recommendations into effect. The Pavilion de Breteuil, orginally a small royal palace, on the bank of the Seine near Sèvres, off the Paris-Versailles Road, was offered by the French Government as the repository and designated the International Bureau of Weights and Measures (Bureau International des Poids et Mésures).

After construction and verification of the new standards, the permanent functions of the Bureau were to include custody of the international metric prototypes, official comparison with national standards, comparison of other units with the metric standards, the standardization of geodetic instruments and other standards and scales of precision, and such other scientific work as international metrology might require.

As organized in 1875 and continuing today, the authority governing the Bureau, its Director, and his staff emanates from the General Conference of Weights and Measures which meets every 6 years, made up of delegates from all the countries belonging to the Metric Convention, presently 40 in number, whose contributions support the expenses of the Bureau. The decisions of the General Conference are put into effect by a permanent International Committee of Weights and Measures, at present numbering 18 scientists or technologists, each from a different member nation that has adopted the metric system, and this committee meets every 2 years at the Bureau at Sèvres.[11]

The new standards constructed in the laboratories of the International Bureau were composed of an alloy of 90 percent platinum and 10 percent iridium. The international prototype meter was defined as the distance between two fine lines on a particular platinum-iridium bar, at 0° C., the temperature of melting ice. The kilogram was determined with reference to its weight in a vacuum, using a new balance of extreme precision, especially constructed for that weighing. The actual work of construction began in 1877.

---

its original definition, the mass of a cubic decimeter of pure water at maximum density. See Moreau, p. 13.

[11] The U.S. representatives on the International Committee have been J. E. Hilgard (1875–97), B. A. Gould (1887–96), A. A. Michelson (1897–1905), S. W. Stratton (1905–31), A. E. Kennelly (1933–39), E. C. Crittenden (1946–54), and A. V. Astin (1954–).

The preparation of the standards, the tracing of the defining lines, and comparison with the standards of the Archives were carried out by the French section of the International Bureau. In 1889, at the First General Conference of Weights and Measures, the prototype units were selected and deposited in a multiple-locked subterranean vault located between the pavilion and observatory of Sèvres. Distribution of the remaining identical meters and kilograms began, the national copies of the meter said to agree with the international unit within one-hundredth of a millimeter and with a probable error not exceeding two ten-thousandths of a millimeter. The copies of the kilogram agreed within 1 milligram, with a probable error not exceeding five-thousandths of a milligram. Two thermometers reading to one-hundredth of a degree Centegradc accompanied each pair of national standards.

The initial copies of the international prototype meter and kilogram allotted to the United States, meter No. 27 and kilogram No. 20, arrived in Washington in January 1890 and with appropriate ceremonies were deposited in a fireproof room at the Office of Weights and Measures in the Coast Survey building. The following July, meter No. 2 and kilogram No. 4 were received and deposited with those accepted as the national standards.

The new U.S. standards, meter No. 27 and kilogram No. 20, were formally recognized by an order of the Secretary of the Treasury on April 5, 1893, as the basis for deriving the customary units, the yard and pound, and for constructing and standardizing secondary metric standards. Over the next decade, efforts to legislate adoption of metric weights and measures as the universal standards in this country came closer to realization than at any time in the history of the Nation. Such legislation, seeking uniformity in weights, measures, and coinage, had been under consideration since the Colonies joined in the Articles of Confederation.

THE AMERICAN ATTITUDE TOWARD THE METRIC SYSTEM

The Colonies were in the midst of their war for independence when the question of uniform coinage was raised by Thomas Jefferson. The decimal system he urged was finally adopted by Congress on July 6, 1785, and a law of 1828 established a brass weight obtained by the Minister of the United States at London as the standard troy pound of the U.S. Mint for the control and stabilization of the currency.

From the first, President after President and the successive Secretaries of the Treasury appealed to Congress for uniformity in the weights and measures, as well as the currency, "a subject of great importance," as Washington declared in 1789, "and will, I am persuaded, be duly attended to."

Shortly after adoption of decimal coinage, Jefferson, disapproving of a unit derived from an arc of meridian determined on European soil, proposed instead decimal weights and measures based on a foot derived by taking one-fifth of the length of a rod forming the seconds pendulum.[12] A Senate committee in 1792 reported favorably on its adoption but Congress took no legislative action. Nor was Congress moved by the President's report in 1795 announcing adoption in France of the metric system and urging its adoption also in America.

The Coast Survey was the first Federal agency to require a definite length standard. Its Superintendent, Hassler, chose the iron-bar standard copied by Lenoir of Paris in 1799 from the Meter of the Archives (the U.S. Committee Meter), given

[12] Hallock and Wade, p. 112.

him by Tralles. Thus from the outset Coast Survey operations in the United States were based on a metric standard, and all base measurements of the Survey continued to be referred to this meter until receipt of the national prototype in 1890.

Although arguments for uniformity were raised at almost every session of Congress, the slow progress of the metric system in France did not encourage its introduction in this country. Secretary of State John Quincy Adams in his classic report of 1821, prepared at the request of Congress, wrote that the French system "approaches to the ideal perfection of uniformity applied to weights and measures * * *. The meter will surround the globe in use as well as multiplied extension, and one language of weights and measures will be spoken from the equator to the poles."[13] Nevertheless, Adams did not think its introduction practicable at that time, nor did Congress.

A degree of order in the weights and measures in common use was achieved by Hassler when in 1838 his Office of Weights and Measures began delivering to the States and a year later to the customhouses sets of standard weights, measures of length, capacity measures, and balances, derived from yard and pound standards he had secured in England. In 1893 the incumbent Superintendent of Weights and Measures, T. C. Mendenhall, fixed their values by relating them to the international meter and kilogram. To this day the United States has no legal material standard yard or pound.

USE OF THE METRIC SYSTEM MADE LEGAL

Not until after the Civil War did serious consideration of the metric system arise again, when on July 28, 1866, upon the advice of the National Academy of Sciences, Congress authorized permissive and legal use of the metric system thoughout the Nation. Another act directed the Secretary of the Treasury to furnish a set of standard metric weights and measures to each of the States, and a third act that year authorized use of metric measures by the Post Office Department.[14]

As increasing numbers of scientists and professional men went to Europe in that period for their education and returned trained in the metric system, interest in it spread. About 1870 metric tables began to appear in American college textbooks, particularly in chemistry and physics, and a decade later in high school textbooks.[15] Such active reform groups as the American Metrological Society, established in New York in 1873 (ceased publication in 1888), and the American Metric Bureau, founded in Boston in 1876, sought nationwide acceptance and use of the metric system in place of yards and pounds.[16]

When in 1869 France first proposed to construct new metric standards, the strong interest in this country led the Government to send delegates to Paris to participate in the deliberations. Prof. Joseph Henry, the preeminent physicist in America at that time, and Prof. Julius E. Hilgard, in charge of weights and measures in the Coast Survey,

---

[13] Hallock and Wade, p. 117.

[14] For a contemporary account of the provision of metric measures to the States, see Prof. J. E. Hilgard's report to Congress in H. Misc. Doc. 61, 45th Cong., 2d sess., May 18, 1878.

[15] Hallock and Wade, p. 125 n.

[16] At the height of the movement, the first "society for opposing introduction of the French Metric System in this country" was also formed, with the establishment in Boston in 1879 of the International Institute for Preserving and Perfecting Weights and Measures. See Edward F. Cox, "The International Institute: First Organized Opposition to the Metric System," Ohio Hist. Q. 68, 3 (1959).

and later Superintendent of the Survey, were sent to join the committee that assembled in 1872 to oversee the work of construction. On May 20, 1875, when the American Minister to France, Elihu B. Washburn, signed the Metric Convention that established the International Bureau of Weights and Measures, commitment of the United States to the principle of international metric measures was formalized.[17]

The arrival of the national prototype meter and kilogram in 1890 again stirred interest in reform. Early in 1894 the Army Surgeon General's Office, following the Marine Hospital Service and the Navy Bureau of Medicine and Surgery, directed use of the metric system in all transactions pertaining to medical supplies, and Congress moved a step closer when its act of July 12, 1894, defined the national units of electrical measurements in the new international metric terms.[18] In another affirmation, continuation of the metric system, in everyday use in both Puerto Rico and the Philippines when they became a protectorate and possession, respectively, of the United States in 1898, was confirmed. And a known champion of the metric system was raised to bureau status in the Federal Establishment when the Office of Weights and Measures became the National Bureau of Standards in 1901.

Besides acquiring new standards for promulgation in American science and industry, the Bureau was also concerned with reverifying its existing standards. In 1904 Louis A. Fischer took meter No. 27 to Paris for comparison with the standards at the International Bureau and redetermined its value in terms of the International Prototype. The minute difference that Fischer reported, in the first scientific paper published by the Bureau, had little significance at that time; and since the relation of No. 27 to No. 21, the other national prototype, was accurately known, the Bureau considered its standards quite sufficient to guarantee the accuracy and permanency of the measures in the United States.[19]

LEGISLATION FOR THE METRIC SYSTEM

Legislation around the turn of the century for replacement of customary measures with the metric system appeared increasingly imminent and each bill won stronger support than the last. In 1896 a bill to make mandatory the metric system received unanimous recommendation for adoption by the House Committee on Coinage, Weights, and Measures, only to fail of passage in its third reading. Another bill in 1901 was received too late to be considered by the Congress then in session. Hearings were held on similar bills again in 1902 and 1903, and although none proposed compulsory acceptance but only gradual extension of the metric system into universal use, they succumbed in committee. So did a new bill in 1905 that sought establishment of the metric system in all transactions and activities of the Federal Government, whence, it was thought, its use would filter down to industry and eventually to the general public.

A notable impetus towards wider acceptance of the metric system loomed in 1914–15 when American industries supplying the French with war materiel necessarily converted their plants to the metric system. The conversion in industry became widespread in 1917–18 when the American armies in France adopted the metric system not only in ordnance and instrumentation but in all operational computations. But the armies did not bring the metric system home with them, and American industry reverted to its former habits when the war production lines stopped.

[17] Hallock and Wade, pp. 129–130.
[18] Ibid., pp. 195–196, 208–210.
[19] NBS S1, "Recomparison of the United States Prototype Meter" (1904).

By the 1930's metric measures had become sufficiently important in American industry to call for a simple factor for converting inch measurements to metric measurements, and in 1933 the American Standards Association approved an American standard inch-millimeter conversion for industrial use in which the inch was defined as 25.4 millimeters.

As a result of difficulties in interchanging precision parts and products manufactured during World War II, legislation was again sponsored between 1945 and 1947 to define the relation as a standard, this time as 2.54 centimeters. Although passage again failed, the obvious usefulness of the centimeter-inch ratio led to its adoption in 1952 by the National Advisory Committee for Aeronautics.

When the Director of the National Bureau of Standards realized that legislation was not necessary if agreement could be reached with the other national standards laboratories to use the conversion factor, it was proposed to them. Apart from the Coast and Geodetic Survey, which, with its amassed calculations fixed, would be excepted, the proposal won agreement. On July 1, 1959, the directors of the national standards laboratories of Australia, Canada, South Africa, the United Kingdom, and the United States adopted the equivalents, 1 yard=0.9144 meter (whence 1 inch=25.4 millimeters) and 1 avoirdupois pound=0.453 592 37 kilogram. Without national legislation, the differences between the United States inch and pound and the British inch and pound, so important to industry and trade, were reconciled and uniformity was established in the science and technology of the English-speaking nations.

WAVELENGTH DEFINITION OF THE METER

When the National Bureau of Standards was established in 1901, the principal units of weights and measures were the yard and pound as defined by Mendenhall ($\frac{3,600}{3,937}$ meter and 0.453 592 427 7 kilogram, respectively) and the gallon and bushel as defined by Hassler (a volume of 231 cubic inches and of 2,150.42 cubic inches, respectively).[20] These definitions remained unchanged for 58 years, and the last two are still the official values.

Failure of the metric legislation in the United States has not, however, deterred American contributions to continuing refinement of the value of the meter upon which our units depend. When the original basis of the metric system on a terrestrial dimension proved untenable, and a more serviceable and secure basis was found in an internationally accepted definition of the meter, world metrologists continued to seek some other natural, physical standard that would make for higher precision and more universal reproducibility. Such a physical standard became available in 1892–93 when Prof. Albert A. Michelson, on leave from the physics department of the University of Chicago for a year's work at the International Bureau at Sèvres, showed that the standard of length could be replaced by reference to a specific wavelength of light, one of those in the cadmium spectrum.

The line of research stimulated by Michelson's work was not to change the magnitude of the meter unit but to define it as a specified number of wavelengths. More than a quarter of a century later, in 1927, the Seventh General Conference of Weights and Measures provisionally adopted as a supplementary standard of length the equation, 1 meter=1 553 164.13 wavelengths, with an accuracy within 1 part in 10 million, as the relation between the meter and Michelson's red cadmium light wave.

---

[20] See ch. I, pp. 26–27, 30.

The small palace that is the International Bureau of Weights and Measures near Sèvres, France.

After another three decades of research, which saw light wave measurements pass from those of the elements to their isotopes, the 11th General Congress on October 14, 1960, adopted as a new definition of the meter, 1 650 763.73 wavelengths of the orange-red radiation of the isotope of krypton with mass 86.

Adoption by the National Bureau of Standards of the new definition does not invalidate the fact that the International Prototype Meter is still the major source and support of the common measures of the United States, even though it is no longer necessary to take the U.S. prototype meter to the International Bureau for comparison. And, periodically, legislation will continue to be proposed for conversion in one degree or another to the metric system. Its completeness, uniformity, simplicity, and widespread use elsewhere in the civilized world make its use obligatory in almost all scientific measurements and computations. Besides our coinage, it is found in general use in library catalog cards, in book, pamphlet, postage, and film measurements, in describing the properties of photographic lenses, in track and field events in athletics, in electrical units of measurement, and in exact mechanical work. The thickness of metals, paper, and glass is commonly measured in metric terms, as is the diameter of wire, tubing, and similar products.

The metric system is used in microscopy and spectroscopy, in geodesy and engineering, in the scientific measurement of mass and volume and capacity, and in much of international commerce. No voice disputes the complexity of the system in daily use that still necessitates, as do our "English" measures, weighing copper by one standard, silver by another, medicine by a third, diamonds and other precious stones by a fourth, and chemicals by a fifth, all noninterchangeable.

The varieties of units universally used in trade in the English-speaking countries have their source in a conglomeration of discordant series with no simple relation either between the different sets of units or between units of different size in a given series. The uniformity in measures that the founding fathers sought has yet to be duly attended to.

APPENDIX C

BASIC LEGISLATION

Relating to Standards of Weights and Measures and to the Organization, Functions, and Activities of the National Bureau of Standards*

9 July **1778** ARTICLES OF CONFEDERATION, Art. 9, § 4:

The United States, in Congress assembled, shall also have the sole and exclusive right and power of regulating the alloy and value of coin struck by their own authority, or by that of the respective States; fixing the standard of weights and measures throughout the United States. . . .

CONSTITUTION of the UNITED STATES, Article 1, § 8.

The Congress shall have power . . . To coin money, regulate the value thereof, and of foreign coin, and fix the standard of weights and measures. . . .

Act of 19 May **1828** (4 Stat. 278)—[Adoption of a brass troy pound weight copied by Captain Henry Kater from the British troy pound of 1758 as the standard for coinage. An Act of 12 Feb 1873 (17 Stat. 424, 432) reenacted the provisions of 1828 concerning the troy pound weight.]

An Act . . . for the purpose of securing a due conformity in weight of the coins of the United States. . . . The brass troy pound weight procured by the minister of the United States at London, in the year 1827, for the use of the mint . . . shall be the standard troy pound of the mint of the United States, conformably to which the coinage thereof shall be regulated.

Joint Resolution of 14 June **1836** (5 Stat. 133)—A Resolution Providing for the [construction and] distribution of weights and measures [as modified by Acts of 14 February 1903 and 4 March 1913 transferring the responsibility to the Secretary of Commerce].

That the Secretary of the Treasury be, and he hereby is directed to cause a complete set of all the weights and measures adopted as standards, and now either made or in the progress of manufacture for the use of the several custom-houses, and for other purposes, to be delivered to the Governor of each State in the Union, or such person as he may appoint, for the use of the States respectively, to the end that an uniform standard of weights and measures may be established throughout the United States.

*In most instances only the pertinent parts have been reproduced here.

Joint Resolution of 27 July **1866** (14 Stat. 369)—Joint Resolution to enable the Secretary of the Treasury to furnish to each State one Set of the Standard Weights and Measures of the Metric System [as modified by Acts of 14 February 1903 and 4 March 1913 transferring the responsibility to the Secretary of Commerce].

Be it resolved . . ., That the Secretary of the Treasury be, and he is hereby, authorized and directed to furnish to each State, to be delivered to the governor thereof, one set of the standard weights and measures of the metric system for the use of the States respectively.

Act of 28 July **1866** (14 Stat. 339)—An Act to authorize the Use of the Metric System of Weights and Measures.

Be it enacted . . ., That from and after the passage of this act it shall be lawful throughout the United States of America to employ the weights and measures of the metric system; and no contract or dealing, or pleading in any court, shall be deemed invalid or liable to objection because the weights or measures expressed or referred to therein are weights or measures of the metric system.

SEC. 2. *And be it further enacted*, That the tables in the schedule hereto annexed [omitted here] shall be recognized in the construction of contracts, and in all legal proceedings, as establishing, in terms of the weights and measures now in use in the United States, the equivalents of the weights and measures expressed therein in terms of the metric system; and said tables may be lawfully used for computing, determining, and expressing in customary weights and measures the weights and measures of the metric system. . . .

Joint Resolution of 3 March **1881** (21 Stat. 521)—Joint resolution authorizing the Secretary of the Treasury to furnish States, for the use of agricultural colleges, one set of standard weights and measures and for other purposes [as modified by Acts of 14 February 1903 and 4 March 1913 transferring the responsibility to the Secretary of Commerce].

Resolved . . ., That the Secretary of the Treasury be, and he is hereby, directed to cause a complete set of all the weights and measures adopted as standards to be delivered to the governor of each State in the Union, for the use of agricultural colleges in the States, respectively, which have received a grant of lands from the United States, and also one set of the same for the use of the Smithsonian Institution: *Provided*

That the cost of each set shall not exceed two hundred dollars, and a sum sufficient to carry out the provisions of this resolution is hereby appropriated out of any money in the Treasury not otherwise appropriated.

Act of 11 July **1890** (26 Stat. 242)—An Act Making appropriations . . . for the fiscal year ending June 30, 1891. . . . [to the] Office of Construction of Standard Weights and Measures [as modified by Acts of 14 February 1903 and 4 March 1913 transferring responsibility to the Secretary of Commerce], making sums available:

For construction and verification of standard weights and measures, including metric standards, for the custom-houses, and other offices of the United States, and for the several States. . . .

For the purchase of materials and apparatus . . .: *Provided,* That hereafter such necessary repairs and adjustments shall be made to the standards furnished to the several States and Territories as may be requested by the governors thereof, and also to standard weights and measures that have been, or may hereafter be, supplied to United States custom-houses and other offices of the United States, under act of Congress, when requested by the Secretary of the Treasury.

For the construction of standard gallons and their subdivisions for the use of States and Territories which have not received the same. . . .

For purchase of a balance of precision and its mounting. . . .

[Subsequently, the Sundry Civil Appropriation Act of 18 August 1894 (28 Stat. 383) directed the Secretary of the Treasury to furnish precise copies of standard weights and measures when lost or destroyed, upon defrayment of the expense of their construction.]

Joint Resolution of 12 April **1892** (27 Stat. 395)—Joint resolution to encourage the establishment and endowment of institutions of learning at the National Capital by defining the policy of the Government with reference to the use of its literary and scientific collections by students. [Basis for the admission of Research Associates to the use of the research facilities of the National Bureau of Standards and for providing educational courses for undergraduate members of the staff towards higher degrees.]

Whereas, large collections illustrative of the various arts and sciences and facilitating literary and scientific research have been accumulated by the action of Congress through a series of years at the National Capital; and

Whereas it was the original purpose of the Government thereby to promote research and the diffusion of knowledge, and is now the settled policy and present practice of those charged with the care of these collections specially to encourage students who devote their time to the investigation and study of any branch of knowledge by allowing to them all proper use thereof; and

Whereas it is represented that the enumeration of these facilities and the formal statement of this policy will encourage the establishment and endowment of institutions of learning at the seat of Government, and promote the work of education of attracting students to avail themselves of the advantages aforesaid under the direction of competent instructors: Therefore,

Resolved: That the facilities for research and illustration in the following and any other Governmental collections now existing or hereafter to be established in the city of Washington for the promotion of knowledge shall be accessible, under such rules and restrictions as the officers in charge of each collection may prescribe, subject to such authority as is now or may hereafter be permitted by law, to the scientific investigators and to students of any institution of higher education now incorporated or hereafter to be incorporated under the laws of Congress or of the District of Columbia, to wit: 1. Of the Library of Congress. 2. Of the National Museum. 3. Of the Patent Office. 4. Of the Bureau of Education. 5. Of the Bureau of Ethnology. 6. Of the Army Medical Museum. 7. Of the Department of Agriculture. 8. Of the Fish Commission.

9. Of the Botanic Gardens. 10. Of the Coast and Geodetic Survey. 11. Of the Geological Survey. 12. Of the Naval Observatory.

Also

Deficiency Appropriation Act of 3 March **1901** (31 Stat. 1039):

. . . That facilities for study and research in the Government Departments, the Library of Congress, the National Museum, the Zoological Park, the Bureau of Ethnology, the Fish Commission, the Botanic Gardens, and similar institutions hereafter established shall be afforded to scientific investigators and to duly qualified individuals, students, and graduates of institutions of learning in the several States and Territories, as well as in the District of Columbia, under such rules and restrictions as the heads of the Departments and Bureaus mentioned may prescribc.

Act of 12 July **1894** (28 Stat. 101)—An Act To define and establish the units of electrical measure.

Be it enacted . . ., That from and after the passage of this Act the legal units of electrical measure in the United States shall be as follows:

First. The unit of resistance shall be what is known as the international ohm, which is substantially equal to one thousand million units of resistance of the centimeter-gram-second system of electro-magnetic units, and is represented by the resistance offered to an unvarying electric current by a column of mercury at the temperature of melting ice fourteen and four thousand five hundred and twenty-one ten-thousandths grams in mass, of a constant cross-sectional area, and of the length of one hundred and six and three-tenths centimeters.

Second. The unit of current shall be what is known as the international ampere, which is one-tenth of the unit of current of the centimeter-gram-second system of electro-magnetic units, and is the practical equivalent of the unvarying current, which, when passed through a solution of nitrate of silver in water in accordance with standard specifications, deposits silver at the rate of one thousand one hundred and eighteen millionth of a gram per second.

Third. The unit of electro-motive force shall be what is known as the international volt, which is the electro-magnetic force that, steadily applied to a conductor whose resistance is one international ohm, will produce a current of an international ampere, and is practically equivalent to one thousand fourteen hundred and thirty-fourths of the electromotive force between the poles or electrodes of the voltaic cell known as Clark's cell, at a temperature of fifteen degrees centigrade, and prepared in the manner described in the standard specifications.

Fourth. The unit of quantity shall be what is known as the international coulomb, which is the quantity of electricity transferred by a current of one international ampere in one second.

Fifth. The unit of capacity shall be what is known as the international farad, which is the capacity of a condenser charged to a potential of one international volt by one international coulomb of electricity.

Sixth. The unit of work shall be the Joule, which is equal to ten million units of work in the centimeter-gram-second system, and which is practically equivalent to the energy expanded in one second by an international ampere in an international ohm.

Seventh. The unit of power shall be the Watt, which is equal to ten million units of power in the centimeter-gram-second system, and which is practically equivalent to the work done at the rate of one joule per second.

Eighth. The unit of induction shall be the Henry, which is the induction in a circuit when the electro-motive force induced in this circuit is one international volt while the inducing current varies at the rate of one Ampere per second.

SEC. 2. That it shall be the duty of the National Academy of Sciences to prescribe and publish, as soon as possible after the passage of this Act, such specifications of details as shall be necessary for the practical application of the definitions of the ampere and volt hereinbefore given, and such specifications shall be the standard specifications herein mentioned.

Act of 3 March 1901, 31 Stat. 1449 (Public Law 177—56 Congress)—An Act To establish the National Bureau of Standards

Be it enacted by the Senate and House of Representatives of the United States of America in Congress assembled, That the Office of Standard Weights and Measures shall hereafter be known as the National Bureau of Standards.

SEC. 2. That the functions of the bureau shall consist in the custody of the standards; the comparison of the standards used in scientific investigations, engineering, manufacturing, commerce, and educational institutions with the standards adopted or recognized by the Government; the construction, when necessary, of standards, their multiples and subdivisions; the testing and calibration of standard measuring apparatus; the solution of problems which arise in connection with standards; the determination of physical constants and the properties of materials, when such data are of great importance to scientific or manufacturing interests and are not to be obtained of sufficient accuracy elsewhere.

SEC. 3. That the bureau shall exercise its functions for the Government of the United States; for any State or municipal government within the United States; or for any scientific society, educational institution, firm, corporaion, or individual within the United States engaged in manufacturing or other pursuits requiring the use of standards or standard measuring instruments. All requests for the services of the bureau shall be made in accordance with the rules and regulations herein established.

SEC. 4. That the officers and employees of the bureau shall consist of a director, at an annual salary of $5,000; one physicist, at an annual salary of $3,500; one chemist, at an annual salary of $3,500; two assistant physicists or chemists, each at an annual salary of $2,200; one laboratory assistant, at an annual salary of $1,400; one laboratory assistant, at an annual salary of $1,200; one secretary, at an annual salary of $2,000; one clerk, at an annual salary of $1,200; one messenger, at an annual salary of $720; one engineer, at an annual salary of $1,500; one mechanician, at an annual salary of $1,400; one watchman, at an annual salary of $720; and one laborer, at an annual salary of $600.

SEC. 5. That the director shall be appointed by the President, by and with the advice and consent of the Senate. He shall have the general supervision of the bureau, its equipment, and the exercise of its functions. He shall make an annual report to the Secretary of the Treasury, including an abstract of the work done during the year and a financial statement. He may issue, when necessary, bulletins for public distribution, containing such information as may be of value to the public or facilitate the bureau in the exercise of its functions.

SEC. 6. That the officers and employees provided for by this Act, except the director, shall be appointed by the Secretary of the Treasury, at such time as their respective services may become necessary.

SEC. 7. That the following sums of money are hereby appropriated: For the payment of salaries provided for by this Act, the sum of $27,140, or so much thereof as may be necessary; toward the erection of a suitable laboratory, of fireproof construction, for the use and occupation of said bureau, including all permanent fixtures, such as plumbing, piping, wiring, heating, lighting, and ventilation, the entire cost of which shall not exceed the sum of $250,000, $100,000; for equipment of said laboratory, the sum of $10,000; for a site for said laboratory, to be approved by the visiting committee hereinafter provided for and purchased by the Secretary of the Treasury, the sum of $25,000, or so much thereof as may be necessary; for the payment of the general expenses of said bureau, including books and periodicals, furniture, office expenses, stationery and printing, heating and lighting, expenses of the visiting committee, and contingencies of all kinds, the sum of $5,000, or so much thereof as may be necessary, to be expended under the supervision of the Secretary of the Treasury.

SEC. 8. That for all comparisons, calibrations, tests, or investigations, except those performed for the Government of the United States or State governments within the United States, a reasonable fee shall be charged, according to a schedule submitted by the director and approved by the Secretary of the Treasury.

SEC. 9. That the Secretary of the Treasury shall, from time to time, make regulations regarding the payment of fees, the limits of tolerance to be attained in standards submitted for verification, the sealing of standards, the disbursement and receipt of moneys, and such other matters as he may deem necessary for carrying this Act into effect.

SEC. 10. That there shall be a visiting committee of five members, to be appointed by the Secretary of the Treasury, to consist of men prominent in the various interests involved, and not in the employ of the Government. This committee shall visit the bureau at least once a year, and report to the Secretary of the Treasury upon the efficiency of its scientific work and the condition of its equipment. The members of this committee shall serve without compensation, but shall be paid the actual expenses incurred in attending its meetings. The period of service of the members of the original committee shall be so arranged that one member shall retire each year, and the appointments thereafter to be for a period of five years. Appointments made to fill vacancies occurring other than in the regular manner are to be made for the remainder of the period in which the vacancy exists.

Approved, March 3, 1901.

31 Stat. Ch. 872, p. 1449

Act of 14 February **1903** (32 Stat. 825)—An Act to establish the Department of Commerce and Labor [as modified by Act of 4 March 1913].

Be it enacted . . ., That there shall be at the seat of government an executive department to be known as the Department of Commerce and Labor, and a Secretary of Commerce and Labor, who shall be the head thereof. . . .

SEC. 4. That the following named . . . bureaus . . . of the public service, now and heretofore under the jurisdiction of the Department of the Treasury, and all that pertains to the same, known as . . . the National Bureau of Standards . . ., be, and the same hereby are, transferred from the Department of the Treasury to the Department of Commerce and Labor, and the same shall hereafter remain under the jurisdiction and supervision of the last-named Department. . . .

Act of 4 March **1909** (35 Stat. 904)—An Act making appropriations for the legislative, executive, and judicial expenses of the Government for the fiscal year ending June 30, 1910, and for other purposes. [Beginning of special appropriations to the Bureau.]

. . . .

Bureau of Standards:

. . . .

For the investigation of the Pentane, Hefner, and other flame standards used in the measurement of the illuminating power of gas, and determining the accuracy practically obtainable in such measurements; also for the determination of the heat of combustion of certain gases which occur in illuminating gas, which are used as a basis for computing the heat value of the gas, and for the determination of the heat combustion of materials employed by engineers in the standardization of industrial calorimeters. . . .

To enable the bureau to collect information relative to the weights and measures used in trade and to aid State sealers and other officers in adopting standard practice as to the establishment of tolerances, methods of inspection and sealing, and other technical details necessary to insure correct weights and measures in commerce and trade. . . .

Sundry Civil Appropriations Act of 25 June **1910** (36 Stat. 743)—[Repealed Act of 16 May 1910 (36 Stat. 369), which transferred the work of investigating structural materials for the use of the United States from the Geological Survey to the Bureau of Mines. The work was transferred, instead, in the regular appropriations act, to the Bureau of Standards, with the sum of $50,000 to continue the investigation.]

Act of 4 March **1911** (36 Stat. 1354)—An Act To amend sections thirty-five hundred and forty-eight and thirty-five hundred and forty-nine of the Revised Statutes of the United States, relative to the standards for coinage.

Be it enacted . . ., That section thirty-five hundred and forty-eight of the Revised Statutes of the United States be, and the same is hereby, amended so as to read as follows:

"SEC. 3548. For the purpose of securing a due conformity in weight of the coins of the United States to the provisions of the laws relating to coinage, the standard troy pound of the Bureau of Standards of the United States shall be the standard troy pound of the Mint of the United States conformably to which the coinage therof shall be regulated."

SEC. 2. That section thirty-five hundred and forty-nine of the Revised Statutes of the United States be, and the same is hereby, amended so as to read as follows:

"SEC. 3549. It shall be the duty of the Director of the Mint to procure for each mint and assay office, to be kept safely thereat, a series of standard weights corresponding to the standard troy pound of the Bureau of Standards of the United States, consisting of a one-pound weight and the requisite subdivisions and multiples thereof, from the hundredths part of a grain to twenty-five pounds. The troy weight ordinarily employed in the transactions of such mints and assay offices shall be regulated according to the above standards at least once in every year, under the inspection of the superintendent and assayer; and the accuracy of those used at the Mint at Philadelphia shall be tested annually, in the presence of the assay commissioner, at the time of the annual examination and test of coins."

Act of 4 March **1913** (37 Stat. 736)—An Act To create a Department of Labor.

Be it enacted . . ., That . . . the Department of Commerce and Labor shall hereafter be called the Department of Commerce, and the Secretary thereof shall be called the Secretary of Commerce, and the Act creating the said Department of Commerce and Labor is hereby amended accordingly.

Act of 4 March **1913** (37 Stat. 945)—An Act Making appropriations to provide for the expenses of the government of the District of Columbia for the fiscal year ending June 30, 1914, and for other purposes. [This act, by inference, recognized the testing of materials for the Federal Government, not specified in the Organic Act of the Bureau or elsewhere, as a function of the Bureau.]

. . . Hereafter materials for fireproof buildings, other structural materials, and all materials, other than materials for paving and for fuel, purchased for and to be used by the government of the District of Columbia, when necessary in the judgment of the commissioners to be tested, shall be tested by the Bureau of Standards under the same conditions as similar testing is required to be done for the United States Government.

Act of 29 July **1914,** 38 Stat. 573 (Public Law 155, 63 Congress)—[Transfer of miscellaneous testing laboratory in Bureau of Chemistry, Department of Agriculture, to NBS]

The salaries of employees of the Department of Agriculture transferred to the Department of Commerce for the purpose of testing miscellaneous materials, including the supplies for the Government departments and independent establishments, may be paid from July first, nineteen hundred and fourteen, from the appropriation of $20,000 in the legislative, executive, and judicial appropriation Act for the fiscal year nineteen hundred and fifteen, made for testing miscellaneous materials under the Bureau of Standards.

Act of 3 March **1915,** 38 Stat. 930 (Public Law 271, 63 Congress)—An Act Making appropriations for the naval service. . . .

[NBS representation on National Advisory Committee for Aeronautics]

An Advisory Committee for Aeronautics is hereby established, and the President is authorized to appoint not to exceed twelve members, to consist of two members from the War Department, from the office in charge of military aeronautics; two members from the Navy Department, from the office in charge of naval aeronautics, a representative each of the Smithsonian Institution, of the United States Weather Bureau, and of the United States Bureau of Standards; together with not more than five additional persons who shall be acquainted with the needs of aeronautical science, either civil or military, or skilled in aeronautical engineering or its allied sciences:

Provided, That the members of the Advisory Committee for Aeronautics, as such, shall serve without compensation:

Provided further, That it shall be the duty of the Advisory Committee for Aeronautics to supervise and direct the scientific study of the problems of flight, with a view to their practical solution, and to determine the problems which should be experimentally attacked, and to discuss their solution and their application to practical questions. In the event of a laboratory or laboratories, either in whole or in part, being placed under the direction of the committee, the committee may direct and conduct research and experiment in such laboratory or laboratories:

And provided further, That rules and regulations for the conduct of the work of the committee shall be formulated by the committee and approved by the President.

That the sum of $5,000 a year, or so much thereof as may be necessary, for five years is hereby appropriated, out of any money in the Treasury not otherwise appropriated, to be immediately available, for experimental work and investigations undertaken by the committee, clerical expenses and supplies, and necessary expenses of members of the committee in going to, returning from, and while attending meetings of the committee:

Provided, That an annual report to the Congress shall be submitted through the President, including an itemized statement of expenditures.

Urgent Deficiency Act of 15 June **1917** (40 Stat. 216)—[Beginning of NBS military research during World War I]

. . . To enable the Bureau of Standards to cooperate with the War and Navy Departments by providing the scientific assistance necessary in the development of instruments, devices, and materials, and the standardization and testing of supplies . . ., $250,000.

. . . To provide by cooperation of the Bureau of Standards the War Department, the Navy Department, and the Council of National Defense, for the standardization and testing of the standard gauges, screw threads, and standards required in manufacturing throughout the United States, and to calibrate and test such standard gauges, screw threads, and standards . . ., $150,000. . . .

Act of 18 July **1918** (40 Stat. 912)—An Act To provide for the appointment of a commission to standardize screw threads [as amended by Act of 3 Mar 1919 (40 Stat. 1291)].

Be it enacted . . ., That a commission is hereby created, to be known as the Commission for the Standardization of Screw Threads, hereinafter referred to as the commission, which shall be composed of nine commissioners, one of whom shall be the Director of the Bureau of Standards, who shall be chairman of the commission; two commissioned officers of the Army, to be appointed by the Secretary of War; two commissioned officers of the Navy, to be appointed by the Secretary of the Navy; and four to be appointed by the Secretary of Commerce, two of whom shall be chosen from nominations made by the American Society of Mechanical Engineers and two from nominations made by the Society of Automotive Engineers.

SEC. 2. That it shall be the duty of said commission to ascertain and establish standards for screw threads, which shall be submitted to the Secretary of War, the Secretary of the Navy, and the Secretary of Commerce for their acceptance and approval. Such standards, when thus accepted and approved, shall be adopted and used in the several manufacturing plants under the control of the War and Navy Departments, and, so far as practicable, in all specifications for screw threads in proposals for manufactured articles, parts, or materials to be used under the direction of these departments.

SEC. 3. That the Secretary of Commerce shall promulgate such standards for use by the public and cause the same to be published as a public document.

SEC. 4. That the commission shall service without compensation but nothing herein shall be held to affect the pay of the commissioners appointed from the Army and Navy or of the Director of the Bureau of Standards.

SEC. 5. That the commission may adopt rules and regulations in regard to its procedure and the conduct of its business.

SEC. 6. That the commission shall cease and terminate at the end of one year and six months from the date of its original appointment.

[The term of the National Screw Thread Commission was extended for two years from 21 Mar 1920 by Joint Resolution of 23 Mar 1920 (41 Stat. 536), and for five years from 21 Mar 1922 by Joint Resolution of 21 Mar 1922 (42 Stat. 469).]

Appropriation Act of 20 May **1920** (41 Stat. 683)—[Beginning of transferred funds to NBS]

. . . .

Department of Commerce

. . . .

Bureau of Standards

. . . .

During the fiscal year 1921, the head of any department or independent establishment of the Government having funds available for scientific investigations and requiring cooperative work by the Bureau of Standards on scientific investigations within the scope of the functions of that Bureau, and which it is unable to perform within the limits of its appropriations, may, with the approval of the Secretary of Commerce, transfer to the Bureau of Standards such sums as may be necessary to carry on such investigations. The Secretary of the Treasury shall transfer on the books of the Treasury Department any sums which may be authorized hereunder and such amounts shall be placed to the credit of the Bureau of Standards for the performance of work for the department or establishment from which the transfer is made.

Act of 27 February **1925** (43 Stat. 1019)—An Act Making appropriations for the Departments of State and Justice and for the Judiciary, and for the Departments of Commerce and Labor, for the fiscal year ending June 30, 1926, and for other purposes.

. . . .

International Obligations.

. . . .

International Bureau of Weights and Measures.

For contribution to the maintenance of the International Bureau of Weights and Measures, in conformity with the terms of the convention of May 20, 1875, the same to be paid, under the direction of the Secretary of State, to said bureau on its certificate of apportionment, $3,000.

Economy Act of 30 June **1932** (47 Stat. 410)—[Amendment to Section 8 of the Act establishing the National Bureau of Standards, authorizing payment of fees, except for other Federal agencies, for NBS tests and calibrations]

. . . .

SEC. 312. Section 8 of the Act entitled "An Act to establish the National Bureau of Standards," approved March 3, 1901, as amended and supplemented [U.S.C., title 15, sec. 276], is amended to read as follows:

"SEC. 8. For all comparisons, calibrations, tests, or investigations, performed by the National Bureau of Standards under the provisions of this Act, as amended and supplemented, except those performed for the Government of the United States or State governments within the United States, a fee sufficient in each case to compensate the National Bureau of Standards for the entire cost of the services rendered shall be charged, according to a schedule prepared by the Director of the National Bureau of Standards and approved by the Secretary of Commerce. All moneys received from such sources shall be paid into the Treasury to the credit of miscellaneous receipts."

Act of 30 June **1932,** 47 Stat. 417 (Public Law 212, 72 Congress)—[Restatement of policy of transferring funds, making the policy general throughout the Federal Government]

. . . .

Title VI—Interdepartmental Work.

SEC. 601. Section 7 of the Act entitled "An Act making appropriations for fortifications and other works of defense, for the armament thereof, and for the procurement of heavy ordnance for trial and service, for the fiscal year ending June 30, 1921, and for other purposes," approved May 21, 1920 [U.S.C., title 31, sec. 686], is amended to read as follows:

"SEC. 7(a). Any executive department or independent establishment of the Government, or any bureau or office thereof, if funds are available therefor and if it is determined by the head of such executive department, establishment, bureau, or office to be in the interest of the Government so to do, may place orders with any other such department, establishment, bureau, or office for materials, supplies, equipment, work, or services of any kind that such requisitioned Federal agency may be in a position to supply or equipped to render, and shall pay promptly by check to such Federal agency as may be requisitioned, upon its written request, either in advance or upon the furnishing or performance thereof, all or part of the estimated or actual cost thereof, as determined by such department, establishment, bureau, or office as may be requisitioned. . . .:

Provided, however, That if such work or services can be as conveniently or more cheaply performed by private agencies such work shall be let by competitive bids to such private agencies. . . .

Executive Order 10096, 23 January **1950**—Providing for a uniform patent policy for the Government with respect to inventions made by Government employees and for the administration of such policy.

Whereas inventive advances in scientific and technological fields frequently result from governmental activities carried on by Government employees; and

Whereas the Government of the United States is expending large sums of money annually for the conduct of these activities; and

Whereas these advances constitute a vast national resource; and

Whereas it is fitting and proper that the inventive product of functions of the Government, carried out by Government employees, should be available to the Government; and

Whereas the rights of Government employees in their inventions should be recognized in appropriate instances; and

Whereas the carrying out of the policy of this order requires appropriate administrative arrangements:

NOW, THEREFORE, by virtue of the authority vested in me by the Constitution and statutes, and as President of the United States and Commander in Chief of the Armed Forces of the United States, in the interest of the establishment and operation of a uniform patent policy for the Government with respect to inventions made by Government employees, it is hereby ordered as follows:

1. The following basic policy is established for all Government agencies with respect to inventions hereafter made by any Government employee:

(a) The Government shall obtain the entire right, title and interest in and to all inventions made by any Government employee (1) during working hours, or (2) with a contribution by the Government of facilities, equipment, materials, funds, or information, or of time or services of other Government employees on official duty, or (3) which bears a direct relation to or are made in consequence of the official duties of the inventor.

(b) In any case where the contribution of the Government, as measured by any one or more of the criteria set forth in paragraph (a) last above, to the invention is insufficient equitably to justify a requirement of assignment to the Government of the entire right, title and interest to such invention, or in any case where the Government has insufficient interest in an invention to obtain entire right, title and interest therein (although the Government could obtain same under paragraph (a), above), the Government agency concerned, subject to the approval of the Chairman of the Government Patents Board . . . shall leave title to such invention in the employee, subject, however, to the reservation to the Government of a non-exclusive, irrevocable, royalty-free license in the invention with power to grant licenses for all governmental purposes, such reservation, in the terms thereof, to appear, where practicable, in any patent, domestic or foreign, which may issue on such invention. . . .

Act of 29 June **1950,** 64 Stat. 279 (Public Law 583, 81 Congress)—An Act Making appropriations to supply deficiencies in certain appropriations for the fiscal year ending June 30, 1950, and for other purposes.

. . . .

Chapter III

. . . .

Department of Commerce

. . . . . .

National Bureau of Standards

Working Capital Fund

For the establishment of a working capital fund, to be available without fiscal year limitation, for expenses necessary for the maintenance and operation of the National Bureau of Standards, including the furnishing of facilities and services to other Government agencies, not to exceed $3,000,000. Said funds shall be established as a special deposit account and shall be reimbursed from applicable appropriations of said Bureau for the work of said Bureau, and from funds of other Government agencies for facilities and services furnished to such agencies pursuant to law. Reimbursements so made shall include handling and related charges; reserves for depreciation of equipment and accrued leave; and building construction and alterations directly related to the work for which reimbursement is made.

Act of 21 July **1950,** 64 Stat. 369 (Public Law 617, 81 Congress)—An Act To redefine the units and establish the standards of electrical and photometric measurements.

Be it enacted by the Senate and House of Representatives of the United States of America in Congress assembled, That from and after the date this Act is approved, the legal units of electrical and photometric measurements in the United States of America shall be those defined and established as provided in the following sections.

SEC. 2. The unit of electrical resistance shall be the ohm, which is equal to one thousand million units of resistance of the centimeter-gram-second system of electromagnetic units.

SEC. 3. The unit of electric current shall be the ampere, which is one-tenth of the unit of current of the centimeter-gram-second system of electromagnetic units.

SEC. 4. The unit of electromotive force and of electric potential shall be the volt, which is the electromotive force that, steadily applied to a conductor whose resistance is one ohm, will produce a current of one ampere.

SEC. 5. The unit of electric quantity shall be the coulomb, which is the quantity of electricity transferred by a current of one ampere in one second.

SEC. 6. The unit of electrical capacitance shall be the farad, which is the capacitance of a capacitor that is charged to a potential of one volt by one coulomb of electricity.

SEC. 7. The unit of electrical inductance shall be the henry, which is the inductance in a circuit such that an electromotive force of one volt is induced in the circuit by variation of an inducing current at the rate of one ampere per second.

SEC. 8. The unit of power shall be the watt, which is equal to ten million units of power in the centimeter-gram-second system, and which is the power required to cause an unvarying current of one ampere to flow between points differing in potential by one volt.

SEC. 9. The units of energy shall be (a) the joule, which is equivalent to the energy supplied by a power of one watt operating for one second, and (b) the kilowatt-hour, which is equivalent to the energy supplied by a power of one thousand watts operating for one hour.

SEC. 10. The unit of intensity of light shall be the candle, which is one-sixtieth of the intensity of one square centimeter of a perfect radiator, known as a "black body," when operated at the temperature of freezing platinum.

SEC. 11. The unit of flux light shall be the lumen, which is the flux in a unit of solid angle from a source of which the intensity is one candle.

SEC. 12. It shall be the duty of the Secretary of Commerce to establish the values of the primary electric and photometric units in absolute measure, and the legal values for these units shall be those represented by, or derived from, national reference standards maintained by the Department of Commerce.

SEC. 13. The Act of July 12, 1894 (Public Law 105, Fifty-third Congress), entitled "An Act to define and establish the units of electrical measure," is hereby repealed.

Act of 21 July **1950,** 64 Stat. 370 (Public Law 618, 81 Congress)—An Act To provide authority for certain functions and activities in the Department of Commerce, and for other purposes. [Authorization for the initial planning leading to the move of the Bureau from Washington, D.C. to Gaithersburg, Md.]

Be it enacted by the Senate and House of Representatives of the United States of America in Congress assembled, That . . . .

SEC. 2. Within the limits of funds which may be appropriated therefor, the Secretary of Commerce is authorized to make improvements to existing buildings, grounds, and other plant facilities, including construction of minor buildings and other facilities of the National Bureau of Standards in the District of Columbia and in the field to house special apparatus or material which must be isolated from other activities: *Provided,* That no improvement shall be made nor shall any building be constructed under this authority at a cost in excess of $25,000, unless specific provision is made therefor in the appropriation concerned.

Act of 22 July **1950,** 64 Stat. 371 (Public Law 619, 81 Congress)—An Act To amend section 2 of the Act of March 3, 1901 (31 Stat. 1449), to provide basic authority for the performance of certain functions and activities of the Department of Commerce, and for other purposes. [First complete restatement of Bureau functions since 1901]

Be it enacted by the Senate and House of Representatives of the United States of America in Congress assembled, That section 2 of the Act of March 3, 1901 (31 Stat. 1449), as amended, be, and the same hereby is, furthter amended so as to read in full as follows:

SEC. 2. The Secretary of Commerce (hereinafter referred to as the "Secretary") is authorized to undertake the following functions:

(a) The custody, maintenance, and development of the national standards of measurement, and the provision of means and methods for making measurement consistent with those standards, including the comparison of standards used in scientific investigations, engineering, manufacturing, commerce, and educational institutions with the standards adopted or recognized by the Government.

(b) The determination of physical constants and properties of materials when such data are of great importance to scientific or manufacturing interests and are not to be obtained of sufficient accuracy elsewhere.

(c) The development of methods for testing materials, mechanisms, and structures, and the testing of materials, supplies, and equipment, including items purchased for use of Government departments and independent establishments.

(d) Cooperation with other Government agencies and with private organizations in the establishment of standard practices, incorporated in codes and specifications.

(e) Advisory service to Government agencies on scientific and technical problems.

(f) Invention and development of devices to serve special needs of the Government.

In carrying out the functions enumerated in this section, the Secretary is authorized to undertake the following activities and similar ones for which need may arise in the operations of Government agencies, scientific institutions, and industrial enterprises:

(1) the construction of physical standards;

(2) the testing, calibration, and certification of standards and standard measuring apparatus;

(3) the study and improvement of instruments and methods of measurements;

(4) the investigation and testing of railroad track scales, elevator scales, and other scales used in weighing commodities for interstate shipment;

(5) cooperation with the States in securing uniformity in weights and measures laws and methods of inspection;

(6) the preparation and distribution of standard samples such as those used in checking chemical analyses, temperature, color, viscosity, heat of combustion, and other basic properties of materials; also the preparation and sale or other distribution of standard instruments, apparatus and materials for calibration of measuring equipment;

(7) the development of methods of chemical analysis and synthesis of materials, and the investigation of the properties of rare substances;

(8) the study of methods of producing and of measuring high and low temperatures; and the behavior of materials at high and at low temperatures;

(9) the investigation of radiation, radioactive substances, and x-rays, their uses, and means of protection of persons from their harmful effects;

(10) the study of the atomic and molecular structure of the chemical elements, with particular reference to the characteristics of the spectra emitted, the use of spectral observations in determining chemical composition of materials, and the relation of molecular structure to the practical usefulness of materials;

(11) the broadcasting of radio signals of standard frequency;

(12) the investigation of the conditions which affect the transmission of radio waves from their source to a receiver;

(13) the compilation and distribution of information on such transmission of radio waves as a basis for choice of frequencies to be used in radio operations;

(14) the study of new technical processes and methods of fabrication of materials in which the Government has a special interest; also the study of methods of measurement and technical processes used in the manufacture of optical glass and pottery, brick, tile, terra cotta, and other clay products;

(15) the determination of properties of building materials and structural elements, and encouragement of their standardization and most effective use, including investigation of fire-resisting properties of building materials and conditions under which they may be most efficiently used, and the standarization of types of appliances for fire prevention;

(16) metallurgical research, including study of alloy steels and light metal alloys; investigation of foundry practice, casting, rolling, and forging; prevention of corrosion of metals and alloys; behavior of bearing metals; and development of standards for metals and sands;

(17) the operation of a laboratory of applied mathematics;

(18) the prosecution of such research in engineering, mathematics, and the physical sciences as may be necessary to obtain basic data pertinent to the functions specified herein; and

(19) the compilation and publication of general scientific and technical data resulting from the performance of the function specified herein or from other sources when such data are of importance to scientific or manufacturing interests or to the general public, and are not available elsewhere, including demonstration of the results of the Bureau's work by exhibits or otherwise as may be deemed most effective.

SEC. 3. The Bureau shall exercise its functions for the Government of the United States; for any State or municipal government within the United States; or for any scientific society, educational institution, firm, corporation, or individual within the United States engaged in manufacturing or other pursuits requiring the use of standards or standard measuring instruments. All requests for the services of the Bureau shall be made in accordance with the rules and regulations herein established.

SEC. 4. (Salaries of officers and employees. This section superseded by Classification Act.)

SEC. 5. The Director shall be appointed by the President, by and with the advice and consent of the Senate. He shall have the general supervision of the Bureau, its equipment, and the exercise of its functions. He shall make an annual report to the Secretary of Commerce, including an abstract of the work done during the year and a financial statement. He may issue, when necessary, bulletins for public distribution, containing such information as may be of value to the public or facilitate the Bureau in the exercise of its functions.

SEC. 6. The officers and employees of the Bureau, except the Director, shall be appointed by the Secretary of Commerce at such time as their respective services may become necessary.

SEC. 7. The Secretary shall charge for services performed under the authority of Section 3 of this Act, except in cases where he determines that the interest of the Government would be best served by waiving the charge. Such charges may be based upon fixed prices or cost. The appropriation or fund bearing the cost of the services may be reimbursed, or the Secretary may require advance payment subject to such adjustment on completion of the work as may be agreed upon.

SEC. 8. In the absence of specific agreement to the contrary, additional facilities, including equipment, purchased pursuant to the performance of services authorized by Section 3 of this Act shall become the property of the Department of Commerce.

SEC. 9. The Secretary of Commerce shall, from time to time, make regulations regarding the payment of fees, the limits of tolerance to be attained in standards submitted for verification, the sealing of standards, the disbursement and receipt of moneys, and such other matters as he may deem necessary for carrying this Act into effect.

SEC. 10. There shall be a visiting committee of five members to be appointed by the Secretary of Commerce, to consist of men prominent in the various interests involved, and not in the employ of the Government. This committee shall visit the Bureau at least once a year, and report to the Secretary of Commerce upon the efficiency of its scientific work and the condition of its equipment. The members of this committee shall serve without compensation, but shall be paid the actual expenses incurred in attending its meetings. The period of service of the members of the committee shall be so arranged that one member shall retire each year, and the appointments to be for a period of five years. Appointments made to fill vacancies occurring other than in the regular manner are to be made for the remainder of the period in which the vacancy exists.

SEC. 11. (a) The Secretary of Commerce is authorized to accept and utilize gifts or bequests of real or personal property for the purpose of aiding and facilitating the work authorized therein.

(b) For the purpose of Federal income, estate, and gift taxes, gifts and bequests accepted by the Secretary of Commerce under the authority of this Act shall be deemed to be gifts and bequests to or for the use of the United States.

SEC. 12. (a) The National Bureau of Standards is authorized to utilize in the performance of its functions the Working Capital Fund established by the Act of June 29, 1950 (64 Stat. 275), and additional amounts as from time to time may be required for the purposes of said Fund are hereby authorized to be appropriated.

(b) The working capital of the Fund shall be available for obligation and payment for any activities authorized by the Act of March 3, 1901 (31 Stat. 1449), as amended, and for any activities for which provision is made in the appropriations which reimburse the Fund.

(c) In the performance of authorized activities, the Working Capital Fund shall be available and may be reimbursed for expenses of hire of automobile, hire of consultants, and travel to meetings, to the extent that such expenses are authorized for the appropriations of the Department of Commerce.

(d) The Fund may be credited with advances and reimbursements, including receipts from non-federal sources, for services performed under the authority of Section 3 of this Act.

(e) As used in this Act the term cost shall be construed to include directly related expenses and appropriate charges for indirect and administrative expenses.

(f) The amount of any earned net income resulting from the operation of the Fund at the close of each fiscal year shall be paid into the general fund of the Treasury; provided, that such earned net income may be applied first to restore any prior impairment of the Fund.

SEC. 13. To the extent that funds are specifically appropriated therefore, the Secretary of Commerce is authorized to acquire land for such field sites as are necessary for the proper and efficient conduct of the activities authorized herein.

SEC. 14. Within the limits of funds which are appropriated for the National Bureau of Standards, the Secretary of Commerce is authorized to undertake such construction of buildings and other facilities and to make such improvements to existing buildings, grounds, and other facilities occupied or used by the National Bureau of Standards as are necessary for the proper and efficient conduct of the activities authorized herein: PROVIDED, That no improvement shall be made nor shall any building be constructed under this authority at a cost in excess of $40,000 unless specific provision is made therefor in the appropriation concerned.

SEC. 15. In the performance of the functions of the National Bureau of Standards the Secretary of Commerce is authorized to undertake the following activities: (a) The purchase, repair, and cleaning of uniforms for guards; (b) the repair and alteration of buildings and other plant facilities; (c) the rental of field sites and laboratory, office, and warehouse space; (d) the purchase of reprints from technical journals or other periodicals and the payment of page charges for the publication of research papers and reports in such journals; (e) the furnishing of food and shelter without repayment therefor to employees of the Government at Arctic and Antarctic stations; (f) for the conduct of observations on radio propagation phenomena in the Arctic or Antarctic regions, the appointment of employees at base rates established by the Secretary of Commerce which shall not exceed such *Maximum rates as may be* specified from time to time in the appropriation concerned, and without regard to the civil service and classification laws and titles II and III of the Federal Employees Pay Act of 1945; and (g) the erection on leased property of specialized facilities and working and living quarters when the Secretary of Commerce determines that this will best serve the interests of the Government.

Act of 20 June **1956,** 70 Stat. 321 (Public Law 604)—An Act Making appropriations for the Department of Commerce and related agencies for the fiscal year ending June 30, 1957, and for other purposes. [Formal approval for the construction of a new Bureau plant at Gaithersburg.]

Be it enacted . . . That the following sums are appropriated . . . for the Department of Commerce . . . namely:

Title I—Department of Commerce

. . . .

National Bureau of Standards

. . . .

Construction of facilities: For acquisition of necessary land and to initiate the design of the facilities to be constructed thereon for the National Bureau of Standards outside of the District of Columbia to remain available until expended, $930,000, to be transferred to the General Services Administration.

APPENDIX D

THE NATIONAL BUREAU OF STANDARDS IN THE FEDERAL ADMINISTRATION

UNITED STATES PRESIDENTS	DEPARTMENT SECRETARIES	NBS DIRECTORS
William McKinley 1897-1901 Theodore Roosevelt 1901-9 William Howard Taft 1909-13 Woodrow Wilson 1913-21	Lyman J. Gage Secretary of Treasury 1897-1901 Leslie M. Shaw 1901 George B. Cortelyou Secretary of Commerce and Labor, 1903-4 Victor H. Metcalf 1904-6 Oscar S. Straus 1906-9 Charles Nagel 1909-13 William C. Redfield Secretary of Commerce 1913-19 Joshua W. Alexander 1919-21	Samuel W. Stratton 1901-22
Warren G. Harding 1921-23 Calvin Coolidge 1923-29 Herbert C. Hoover 1929-33	Herbert C. Hoover 1921-28 William F. Whiting 1928-29 Robert P. Lamont 1929-32	George K. Burgess 1922-32
Franklin D. Roosevelt 1933-45 Harry S. Truman 1945-53	Roy D. Chapin 1932-33 Daniel C. Roper 1933-39 Harry L. Hopkins 1939-40 Jesse Jones 1940-45 Henry A. Wallace 1945-46 W. Averell Harriman 1947-48 Charles W. Sawyer 1948-52	Lyman J. Briggs 1932-46 Edward U. Condon 1946-51
Dwight D. Eisenhower 1953-61 John F. Kennedy 1961-63 Lyndon B. Johnson 1963-	Sinclair Weeks 1952-58 Lewis L. Strauss 1958-59 Frederick H. Mueller 1959-61 Luther H. Hodges 1961-65 John T. Connor 1965-	Allen V. Astin 1951-

APPENDIX E

MEMBERS OF THE VISITING COMMITTEE of the Secretary of Commerce to the National Bureau of Standards[1]

	Term
ALBERT LADD COLBY Consulting engineer in metallurgy, South Bethlehem, Pa., and secretary, Association of American Steel Manufacturers.	1901–07
DR. ELIHU THOMSON Electrical engineer, General Electric Co., Lynn, Mass.	1901–18
DR. IRA REMSEN Director of Chemical Laboratory and president, Johns Hopkins University.	1901–09
DR. HENRY S. PRITCHETT President, Massachusetts Institute of Technology; later president, Carnegie Foundation for the Advancement of Teaching.	1901–10
PROF. EDWARD L. NICHOLS Professor of physics, Cornell University.	1901–11
DR. ROBERT S. WOODWARD President, Carnegie Institution of Washington.	1908–12
PROF. HENRY M. HOWE Professor of metallurgy, Columbia University.	1909–14
PROF. ARTHUR G. WEBSTER Director, Physics Laboratory, Clark University.	1910–15
PROF. JOHN F. HAYFORD Director, College of Engineering, Northwestern University.	1912–21
PROF. ARTHUR E. KENNELLY Professor of electrical engineering, Harvard University.	1912–17
JOHN R. FREEMAN Consulting engineer, Providence, R.I.	1915–24, 1926–31
PROF. WILLIAM A. NOYES Director, Chemical Laboratory, University of Illinois.	1915–20
PROF. JOSEPH S. AMES Director, Physical Laboratory, Johns Hopkins University.	1917–22
PROF. FRED W. McNAIR President, Michigan College of Mines, Houghton, Mich.	1921–23
PROF. WILDER D. BANCROFT Professor of physical chemistry, Cornell University.	1920–25
DR. AMBROSE SWASEY Chairman of the Board, Warner & Swasey Co., Cleveland, Ohio.	1921–26
DR. SAMUEL W. STRATTON President, Massachusetts Institute of Technology.	1923–31

[1] Sources: NARG 167, NBS Box 296; NARG 40, files of Secretary of Commerce, 67009/5; current files, Office of the Director, NBS.

	Term
GANO DUNN	1923–48
President, J. G. White Engineering Corp., New York.	
PROF. WILLIAM F. DURAND	1924–29
Professor of mechanical engineering, Leland Stanford University.	
DR. WILLIS R. WHITNEY	1925–30
Director, General Electric Research Laboratory, Schenectady, N.Y.	
DR. CHARLES F. KETTERING	1929–34, 1947–52
Director of research and vice president, General Motors Corp.	
DR. CHARLES L. REESE	1930–35
Consulting chemist to E. I. du Pont de Nemours & Co.	
MORRIS E. LEEDS	1931–41
President, Leeds & Northrup Co., Philadelphia, Pa.	
DR. KARL T. COMPTON	1931–47
President, Massachusetts Institute of Technology.	
DR. WILLIAM D. COOLIDGE	1935–49
Vice president and director of research, General Electric Co.	
DR. FRANK B. JEWETT	1935–45
Vice president in charge of research and development, American Telephone & Telegraph Co.; president, National Academy of Sciences.	
DR. VANNEVAR BUSH	1942–46
President, Carnegie Institution of Washington; director, Office of Scientific Research and Development.	
DR. HAROLD C. UREY	1945–50
Research professor of chemistry, University of Chicago.	
DR. EUGENE P. WIGNER	1946–51
Metallurgical Laboratory, University of Chicago; director of research, Clinton Laboratories, Oak Ridge, Tenn.	
DR. ROBERT F. MEHL	1948–53
Director, Metals Research Laboratory, Carnegie Institute of Technology.	
DR. DONALD H. MENZEL	1949–54
Chairman, Department of Astronomy, Harvard University; associate director, Harvard Observatory.	
DR. DETLEV W. BRONK	1950–60
President, Johns Hopkins University.	
PROF. JOHN H. VAN VLECK	1951–56
Dean, Division of Applied Science, Harvard University.	
DR. MERVIN J. KELLY	1952–62
President, Bell Telephone Laboratories.	
DR. CLYDE E. WILLIAMS	1953–58
Director, Battelle Memorial Institute, Columbus, Ohio.	
DR. CRAWFORD H. GREENEWALT	1954–64
President, E. I. du Pont de Nemours & Co.	
PROF. FREDERICK SEITZ	1956–61
Chairman, Department of Physics, University of Illinois.	
DR. LLOYD V. BERKNER	1957–62
Scientific research administrator; chairman, Space Science Board, National Academy of Sciences.	
PROF. CHARLES H. TOWNES	1960–65
Department of Physics, Columbia University, consultant, Brookhaven National Laboratories.	

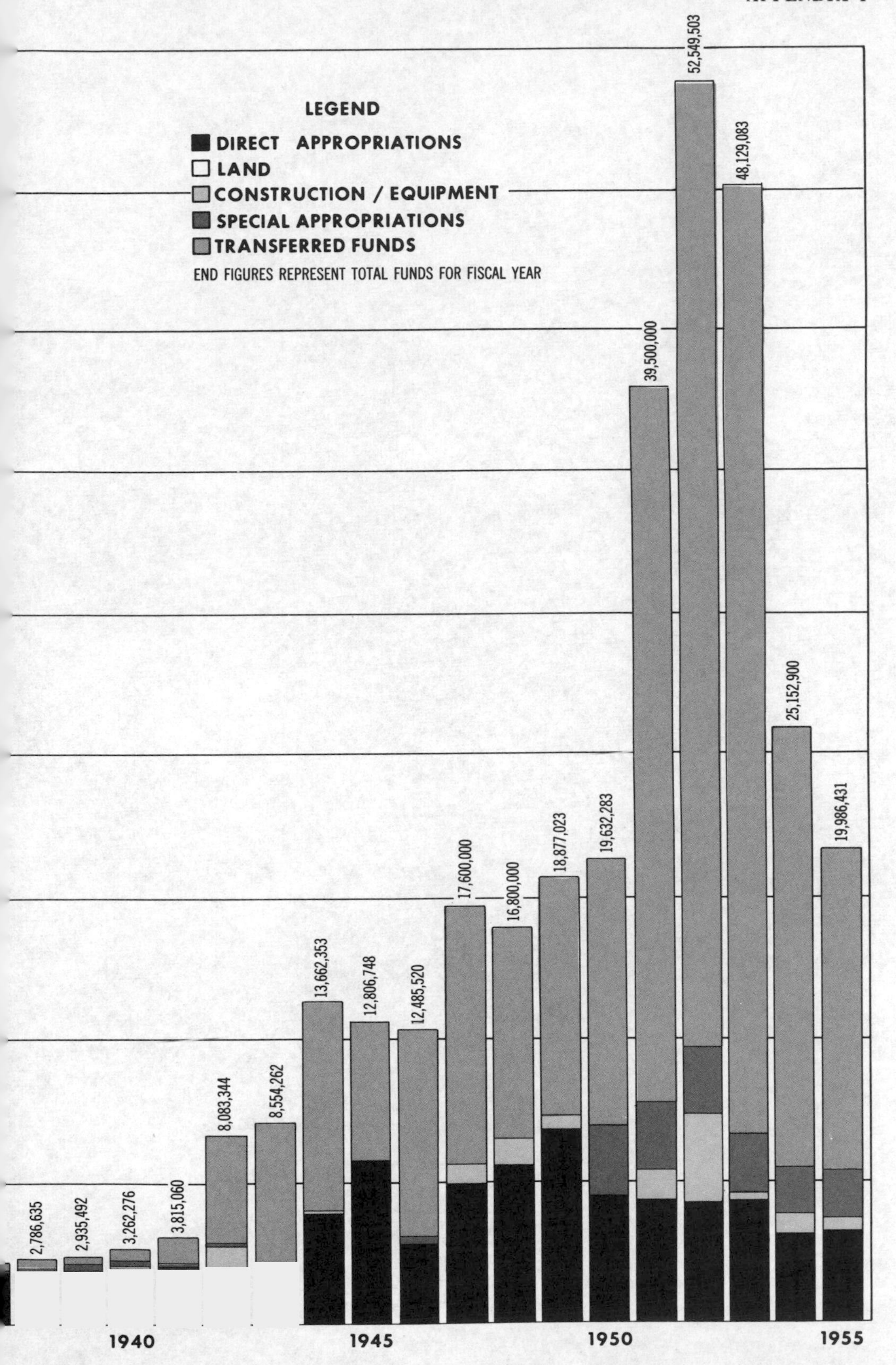

ANNUAL REPORTS 1902-1942, 1946-1948, 1954-1955. Data for fiscal years 1943-1945, 1949-1953 supplied by NBS BUDGET and MANAGEMENT DIVISION

NBS SPECIAL APPROPRIATIONS, 1910-1935

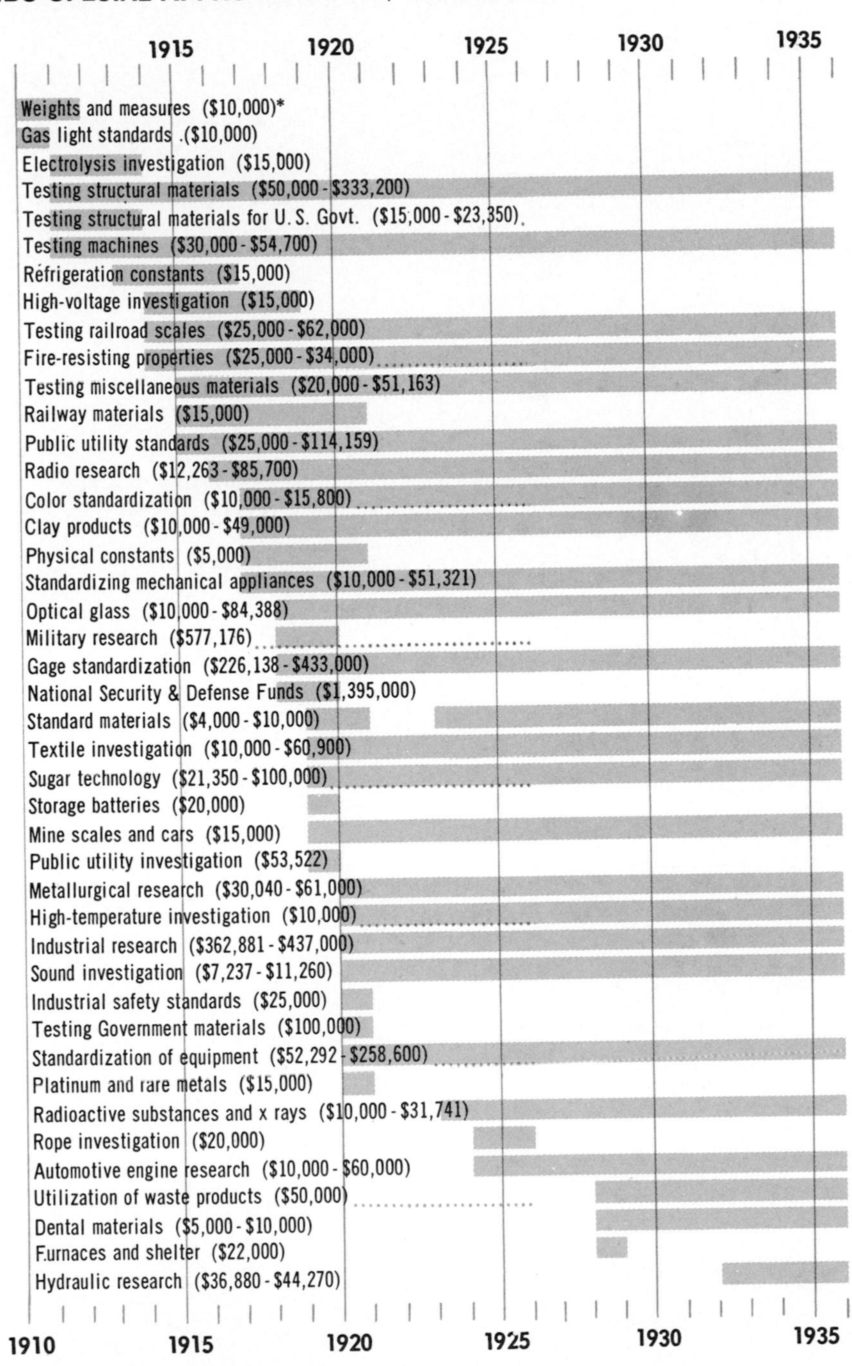

*Figures represent initial and maximum appropriations.

Note: Special appropriations continued after 1935 in special annual appropriations for Standards for commerce (1936-1946), Investigation of building materials (1938-1942), and Radio propagation and standards (1950-1955).

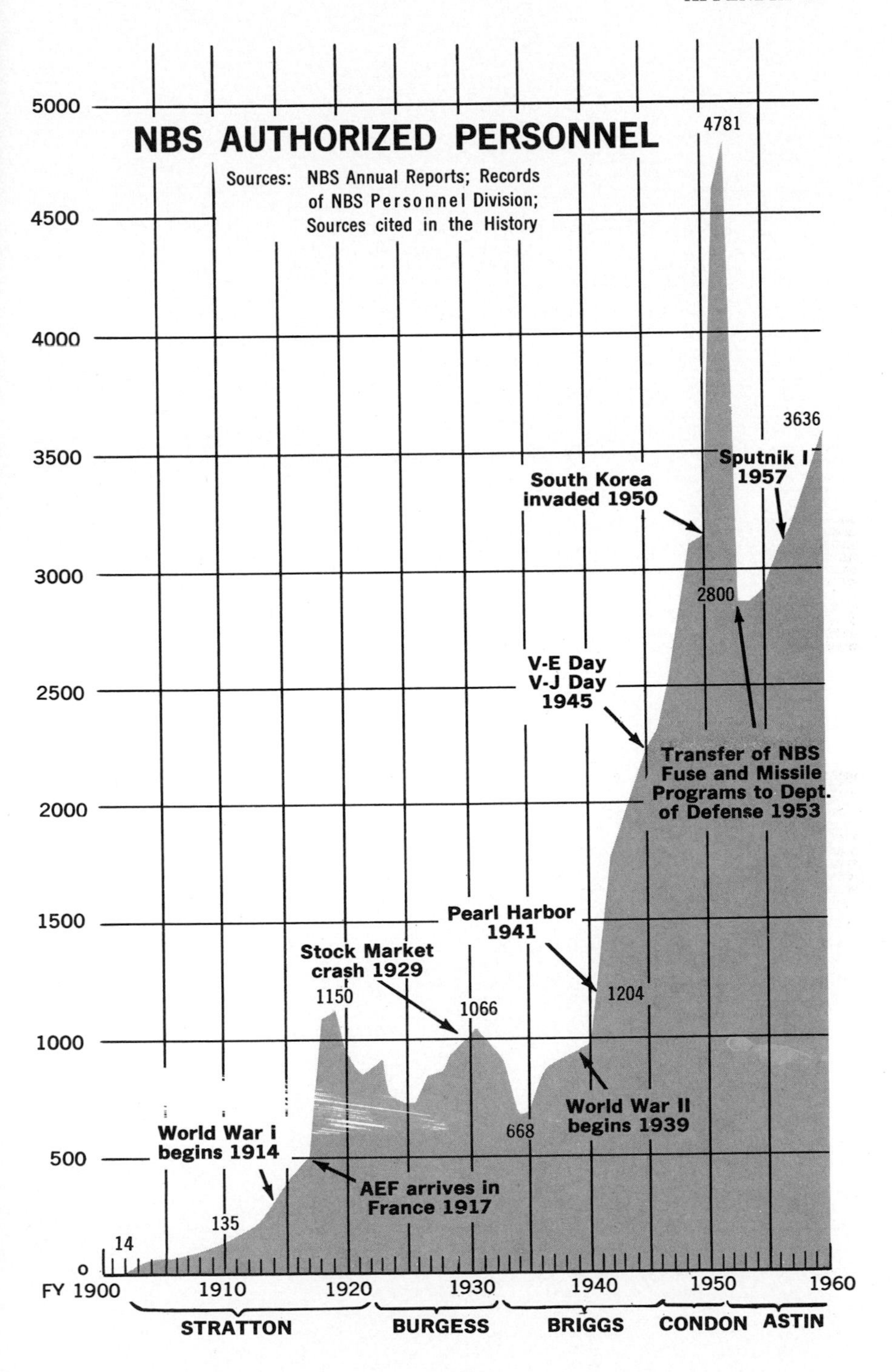
NBS AUTHORIZED PERSONNEL
Sources: NBS Annual Reports; Records of NBS Personnel Division; Sources cited in the History
5000
4500
4000
3500
3000
2500
2000
1500
1000
500
0
FY 1900
1910
1920
1930
1940
1950
1960
14
135
1150
1066
668
1204
4781
2800
3636
World War i begins 1914
AEF arrives in France 1917
Stock Market crash 1929
Pearl Harbor 1941
World War II begins 1939
V-E Day V-J Day 1945
South Korea invaded 1950
Transfer of NBS Fuse and Missile Programs to Dept. of Defense 1953
Sputnik I 1957
STRATTON
BURGESS
BRIGGS
CONDON
ASTIN

APPENDIX I

PUBLICATIONS

OF THE NATIONAL BUREAU OF STANDARDS

NOTES

The Annual Reports of the Bureau, 1901–1960, are the source for the basic data of this publications chart.

Dash lines on the chart span years when the Annual Report omitted publication data. In some instances of omission the number of publications was determined by actual count in NBS C460, which lists all formal Bureau publications issued by the Government Printing Office from 1901 to 1947, and in Supplements to C460 for publications since 1947.

Not represented on the chart are revisions, reprints, and new editions of Bureau publications (as many as 50 to 90 annually by 1915) ; publicity releases and general articles in the periodical literature on the work of the Bureau; nor calibration and test reports prepared by the staff.

NBS RESEARCH PUBLICATIONS include the early Scientific Papers (1904–1928) and Technologic Papers (1910–1928), combined in 1928 in a single Journal of Research as Research Papers until the reorganization of NBS publications in 1959, noted below.

MISCELLANEOUS NBS PUBLICATIONS in the chart comprise:

Circulars, the compilations of information related to NBS scientific, technologic, and engineering activities, published from 1903 to 1959. They include the extensive NBS and U.S. Government Specifications series in the years 1912–1937.

Miscellaneous Publications (1905 to date), which include the NBS Annual Reports, Weights and Measures Conference Reports, the Standards Yearbook from 1927 through 1933, and charts, directories, and administrative reports.

Handbooks (1921 to date).

Building and Housing Publications (1922–1932).

Simplified Practice Recommendations (1923 to date).

Technical News Bulletin, published monthly (1924 to date).

Letter Circulars, in mimeograph form (1924 to date).

Commercial Standards (1929 to date).

Building Materials and Structures Reports (1930–1939).

Mathematical Tables (1941–1945).

Applied Mathematics Series (1948 to date).

Basic Radio Propagation Predictions, published monthly (1952–1959) ; Central Radio Propagation Laboratory Ionospheric Predictions (1960 to date).

NON-NBS PUBLICATIONS, first recorded in 1925, comprise articles by members of the staff appearing in the journals of professional and scientific societies.

NBS REPORTS, on research conducted under transferred funds and formalized in 1951 (estimated in 1952 as more than a thousand reports), actually began before World War II as nonpublished reports to NACA on special research for that agency, and later as reports to NDRC, OSRD and other wartime agencies. They continue to comprise classified and unclassified reports to other Government agencies on projects supported by transferred funds.

Reorganization of NBS Publications: In 1959 the Journal of Research was reorganized into four separately published sections: A. Physics and Chemistry; B. Mathematics and Mathematical Physics; C. Engineering and Instrumentation; D. Radio Propagation.

Two nonperiodicals, Monographs (papers too long for the Journal) and Technical Notes (scientific data of limited or transient interest) were established that same year.

Continuing nonperiodicals included the Applied Mathematics Series, Handbooks, and Miscellaneous Publications. Commercial Standards and Simplified Practice Recommendations, discontinued as NBS publications from 1951 to 1963, were resumed as Bureau publications.

Continuing monthly periodicals included the Technical News Bulletin and CRPL Ionospheric Predictions (former Basic Radio Propagation Predictions).

APPENDIX J

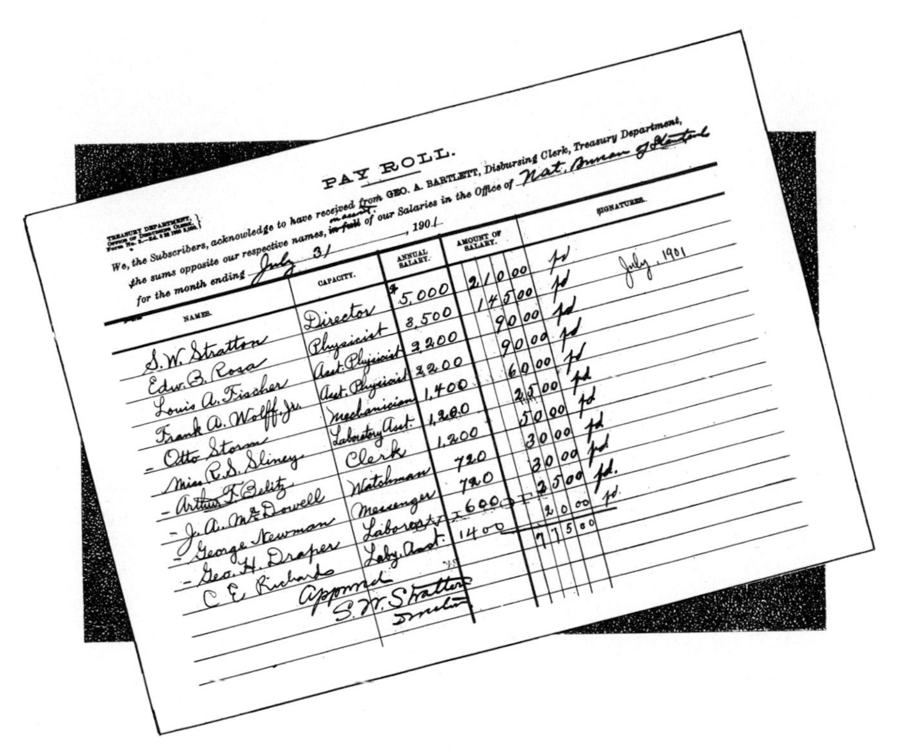

TREASURY DEPARTMENT, ...

PAY ROLL.

We, the Subscribers, acknowledge to have received from GEO. A. BARTLETT, Disbursing Clerk, Treasury Department, the sums opposite our respective names, ~~in full~~ on account of our Salaries in the Office of Nat. Bureau of Standards for the month ending July 31, 1901.

NAMES.	CAPACITY.	ANNUAL SALARY.	AMOUNT OF SALARY.	SIGNATURES.
S. W. Stratton	Director	$5,000	210 00	pd July, 1901
Edw. B. Rosa	Physicist	3,500	145 00	pd
Louis A. Fischer	Asst. Physicist	2,200	90 00	pd
Frank A. Wolff, Jr.	Asst. Physicist	2,200	90 00	pd
- Otto Storm	Mechanician	1,400	60 00	pd
- Miss R. S. Sliney	Laboratory Asst.	1,200	25 00	pd
- Arthur F. Beltz	Clerk	1,200	50 00	pd
- J. A. McDowell	Watchman	720	30 00	pd
- George Newman	Messenger	720	30 00	pd
- Geo. H. Draper	Laborer	600	25 00	pd.
C. E. Richards	Laby. Asst.	1400	20 00	pd.
			775 00	

Approved
S. W. Stratton
Director

Almost certainly the first official NBS payroll and roster, these half-monthly payments, according to the paybook cover, were made on July 15.

The appearance of Miss Sliney's name on the roll cannot be explained. She may have been a temporary appointment before Dr. Stratton took over. Her name does not appear on subsequent payrolls or on staff rosters.

APPENDIX J

DIVISION AND SECTION CHIEFS OF THE SCIENTIFIC AND TECHNICAL STAFF NATIONAL BUREAU OF STANDARDS

as of July 1, 1905*

DIRECTOR	**Stratton, Dr Samuel W.**	**1901–22**
WEIGHTS AND MEASURES	Fischer, Louis A.	1901–21
Comparison of Capacities	Ferner, Roy Y.	1903–18
Weights and Measures Assistant	Pienkowsky, Arthur T.	1905–44
HEAT AND THERMOMETRY	Waidner, Dr Charles W.	1901–22
Low Temperature Investigations	Waidner, Dr Charles W.	
High Temperature Investigations	Burgess, Dr George K.	1903–32
Comparison of Thermometers	Dickinson, Dr Hobart C.	1903–45
Heat and Thermometry Assistant	Mueller, Eugene F.	1905–44
LIGHT AND OPTICAL INSTRUMENTS	Stratton, Dr Samuel W.	
Spectroscopy	Nutting, Dr Perley G.	1903–12
Magneto-optics	Bates, Frederick J.	1903–47
Computer	Coblentz, Dr William W.	1905–44
ENGINEERING INSTRUMENTS AND MATERIALS	*Sponsler, Charles F.	1902–13
Engineering Instruments and Materials Assistants	*Merrill, Albert S.	1903–06
	*Lange, Oscar G.	1902–37
ELECTRICITY	Rosa, Dr Edward B.	1901–21
Inductance and Capacity	Rosa, Dr Edward B.	
	*Grover, Dr Frederick W.	1903–11

*This 1905 roster is based on information in MS, N. Ernest Dorsey, "Some memories of the early days of the NBS," Oct. 28, 1943 (NBS Historical File).

The names preceded by an asterisk are staff members who left the Bureau before the next roster. Their subsequent employment or other reason for separation is noted below.

The dates on the right both mark the first appearance of a staff member in these rosters and his inclusive dates of association with the Bureau.

*Sponsler, resigned Mar. 22, 1913.

*Merrill, resigned May 3, 1906; returned briefly Mar.–July 1920.

*Lange, retired Nov. 30, 1937.

*Grover, to Colby College, 1911–20; to Department of Electrical Engineering, Union College, Schenectady, N.Y., 1920.

ELECTRICITY—Continued		
Magnetism and Absolute Measurement of Current	*Guthe, Dr Karl E.	1903–06
Electrical Measuring Instruments	Brooks, Herbert B.	1903–39, 1942–45
	*Lloyd, Dr Morton G.	1902–10, 1917–41
	Reid, Clarence E.	1903–05
Photometry	*Hyde, Dr Edward P.	1903–08
Electrical Resistance and Electromotive Force	Wolff, Dr Frank A.	1901–41
	*Middlekauff, Dr George W.	1903–17
Electricity Assistants	*Cady, Francis E.	1903–20
	Durston, Franklin S.	1903–17
	*Dorsey, Dr N. Ernest	1903–20, 1928–43
	*Shoemaker, Maynard P.	1905–36
Naval Radio Research Laboratory	*Austin, Dr Louis W.	
Army Signal Service Radio Laboratory	*Cramm, E. R.	
CHEMISTRY	*Noyes, Dr William A.	1903–08
Chemistry Assistants	*Stokes, Dr Henry N.	1903–09
	Cain, Dr John R.	1905–21, 1936–45
	Waters, Campbell E.	1904–42

*Guthe, to State University of Iowa as chairman, Physics Department, 1906.
*Lloyd, to "Electrical Review and Western Electrician," Chicago, as technical editor, 1910–17.
*Hyde, to NELA Research Laboratory, General Electric, 1908.
*Middlekauff, resigned 1917.
*Cady, to National Lamp Works, Nela Park, 1920.
*Dorsey, private consultant and consultant in physics to NBS, 1920–28; independent research worker at NBS, 1928–43; died July 6, 1959.
*Shoemaker, retired 1936.
*Austin, died June 27, 1932.
*Cramm, no data available.
*Noyes, to Department of Chemistry, University of Illinois, as chairman, 1908.
*Stokes, to "Library Critic," as editor, 1909.

CHIEFS OF THE SCIENTIFIC AND TECHNICAL STAFF

as of September 1, 1910*

DIRECTOR	**Stratton, Dr Samuel W.**	
I. ELECTRICITY	Rosa, Dr Edward B.	
Inductance and Capacity	Curtis, Dr Harvey L.	1907–46
Precision Resistance Measurement	Wenner, Dr Frank	1907–43
Electrical Measuring Instruments	Brooks, Herbert B.	
Magnetism	Burrows, Dr Charles W.	1906–18
Electrical Testing	Vinal, Dr George W.	1904–50
Photometry	Crittenden, Dr. Eugene C.	1909–50
Electrolysis	McCollum, Burton	1909–26
Electromotive Force and Resistance	Wolff, Dr Frank A.	
Electricity Assistants	*Agnew, Dr Paul G.	1906–20
	Taylor, Dr A. Hadley	1909–21
	McBride, Russell S.	1909–20
	Grover, Dr. Frederick W.	
II. WEIGHTS AND MEASURES	Fischer, Louis A.	
Length and Expansion Measurements	Gray, Dr. Arthur W.	1909–16
Capacity Measurements	Ferner, Roy Y.	
Mass	Pienkowsky, Arthur T.	
Density	(Vacant)	
Time	Ferner, Roy Y.	
Trade Weights and Measures	Holbrook, Fay S.	1909–40
Weights and Measures Assistant	Bearce, Henry W.	1908–45
III. THERMOMETRY, PYROMETRY AND HEAT MEASUREMENT	Waidner, Dr Charles W.	
Thermometry	Dickinson, Dr Hobart C.	
Calorimetry	Mueller, Dr Eugene F.	
Pyrometry	Burgess, Dr George K.	
Low Temperature Investigations	Kanolt, Clarence W.	1909–25

*This and subsequent rosters are based on NBS personnel records, NBS telephone directories, archival materials, and interviews with present and past staff members. In some instances available records were incomplete; in others, the Federal Records Center at St. Louis, Mo., reported "no records found."

*Agnew, to American Engineering Standards Committee as executive secretary, 1920.

III. THERMOMETRY, PYROMETRY AND HEAT MEASUREMENT—Continued		
Thermometry, Pyrometry and Heat Assistant	Buckingham, Dr Edgar	1906–37
IV. OPTICS	Stratton, Dr Samuel W.	
Radiometry	Coblentz, Dr William W.	
Polarimetry	Bates, Frederick J.	
Spectroscopy and Applied Optics	Priest, Irwin G.	1907–32
Interferometry	*Nutting, Dr Perley G.	
V. CHEMISTRY	Hillebrand, Dr William F.	1908–25
Electrochemistry	Blum, Dr William	1909–52
Oils, Rubber, Paper, Textiles	Waters, Campbell E.	
Metals, Cement, Bituminous Materials	Voorhees, Samuel S.	1910–21
ENGINEERING INSTRUMENTS	Hersey, Dr Mayo D.	1910–20, 1927–31
STRUCTURAL, ENGINEERING AND MISCELLANEOUS MATERIALS	Wormeley, Philip L.	1910–47
Structural Materials	*Howard, James E.	1910–14
Cement	Pearson, Joseph C.	1910–24
Lime	(Not known)	
Metals	(Not known)	
Protective Coatings	(Not known)	
Paper and Textiles	*Clark, Dr Frederick C.	1910–19
PITTSBURGH LABORATORY	Bleininger, Dr Albert V.	1910–23
	Emley, Warren E.	1910–43
	Bates, Phaon H.	1910–45
NORTHAMPTON LABORATORY	*Humphrey, Richard L.	1910–10
ATLANTIC CITY LABORATORY	Wig, Rudolph J.	1910–14

*Nutting, to research laboratory of Eastman Kodak Co., Rochester, N.Y., 1912; to Westinghouse Electric Co. as research director, 1916.

*Howard, transferred to Interstate Commerce Commission, 1914.

*Clark, to American Writing Paper Co., Holyoke, Mass., 1919.

*Humphrey, NBS member Aug. 5–10, 1910; no further record.

CHIEFS OF THE SCIENTIFIC AND TECHNICAL STAFF

as of July 1, 1915

DIRECTOR — **Stratton, Dr Samuel W.**

Division / Section	Chief	Years
I. ELECTRICITY	Rosa, Dr Edward B.	
Inductance and Capacity	Curtis, Dr Harvey L.	
Precision Resistance Measurement	Wenner, Dr Frank	
Electrical Measuring Instruments	Brooks, Dr Herbert B.	
Magnetic Measurements	Burrows, Dr Charles W.	
Electrochemistry	Vinal, Dr George W.	
Photometry	Crittenden, Dr Eugene C.	
Electrolysis	McCollum, Burton	
Radio Measurements	Dellinger, Dr J. Howard	1907–48
Radio Engineering	Kolster, Frederick A.	1911–21
Electromotive Force and Resistance	Wolff, Dr Frank A.	
Electrical Service Standards	Meyer, Dr J. Franklin	1913–41
Electricity Assistants	Agnew, Dr. Paul G.	
	Silsbee, Dr Francis B.	1911–59
II. WEIGHTS AND MEASURES	Fischer, Louis A.	
Mass	Pienkowsky, Dr Arthur T.	
Density and Capacity	Peffer, Elmer L.	1913–48
Trade Weights and Measures Investigations	Holbrook, Fay S.	
Time and Length	*Ferner, Roy Y.	
III. THERMOMETRY, PYROMETRY, AND HEAT MEASUREMENT	Waidner, Dr Charles W.	
Thermometry	Dickinson, Dr Hobart C.	
Pyrometry	Foote, Dr Paul D	1911–27
Calorimetry	Mueller, Eugene F.	
Low Temperature Investigations	Kanolt, Clarence W.	
Fire Resistance	Ingberg, Simon H.	1914–47
IV. OPTICS	Stratton, Dr Samuel W.	
Radiometry	Coblentz, Dr William W.	
Polarimetry	Bates, Frederick J.	
Spectroscopy	Meggers, Dr. William F.	1914–58
Colorimetry	Priest, Irwin G.	
Interferometry	Peters, Chauncey G.	1913–49
Dispersoids	Wells, Dr Philip V.	1913–23

*Ferner, to go into private business, 1918.

Division / Section	Chief	Years
V. CHEMISTRY	Hillebrand, Dr William F.	
Electrochemistry	Blum, Dr William	
Metals, Cement, Bituminous Materials	Voorhees, Samuel S.	
Gas Chemistry	Weaver, Elmer R.	1912–57
Reagents and Apparatus	Smither, Frederick W.	1914–46
Paint, Varnish, Soap, etc.	Walker, Dr Percy H.	1914–37
VI. ENGINEERING RESEARCH AND TESTING	Stratton, Dr Samuel W.	
Engineering Instruments and Mechanical Appliances	Stutz, Walter F.	1912–47
Aviation Instruments	Hersey, Dr Mayo D.	
VII. METALLURGY	Burgess, Dr George K.	
Foundry and Mechanical Plant	Karr, Carydon P.	1913–25
Microscopy of Metals	Rawdon, Dr Henry S.	1912–45
Working of Metals	*Woodward, Dr Raymond W.	1914–21
	*Merica, Dr Paul D.	1914–19
VIII. STRUCTURAL, ENGINEERING AND MISCELLANEOUS MATERIALS	Bates, Phaon H.	
Clay	Bates, Phaon H.	
Lubricating Oils	Herschel, Dr Winslow H.	1913–43
Cement, Sand, Stone	Pearson, Joseph C.	
Rubber, Leather, Textiles	Wormeley, Philip L.	
PITTSBURGH LABORATORY	Bleininger, Dr Albert V.	
Optical Glass	Bleininger, Dr Albert V.	
Lime, Gypsum, Sand, Brick	Emley, Warren E.	

*Woodward, to Whitney Manufacturing Co., Hartford, Conn., as chief metallurgist, 1921.

*Merica, to International Nickel Co., Bayonne, N.J., 1919.

WARTIME PROJECTS OF THE SCIENTIFIC AND TECHNICAL STAFF

as of September 1918*

DIRECTOR	**Stratton, Dr Samuel W.**	
Technical Assistant to the Director	*Schlink, Frederick J.	1913–19
ELECTRICAL DIVISION	Rosa, Dr Edward B.	
Technical Assistants	Agnew, Dr Paul G.	
	Crittenden, Dr Eugene C.	
Standards of Resistance		
Airplane gun control and other problems	Wenner, Dr Frank	
	Macaulay, D. L.	
High frequency sound waves in water	*Wright, Winthrop R.	1917–19
Centrifugal gun and other problems	*Purington, Ellison S.	1915–19
Inductance and Capacity		
Ballistics of large caliber guns	Curtis, Dr Harvey L.	
Exterior ballistics of large caliber guns	*Duncan, Robert C.	1917–21
	Richards, Horace C.	
	*Moore, Harry H.	1915–23
Interior ballistics of large caliber guns	Kester, Frederick E.	
Subterranean sound investigations	Hufford, Mason E.	
	Wood, Capt. H. O.	
	Crane, 1st Lt. E. C.	
Machine gun synchronization	*Morgan, Raymond	1917–42
Jump and whip of gun at time of firing	Mertz, Pierre	
Electrical Measuring Instruments		
Fire-control apparatus	Brooks, Dr Herbert B.	
	*Stannard, Winfield H.	1909–19
Ignition	Silsbee, Dr Francis B.	
	*Dempsey, James B.	1916–39
	*Gorton, William S.	1917–19
Electric trucks and tractors	Farmer, T. O.	

*Source: Letter, Director NBS to Technical Information Section, Bureau of Aircraft Production, WD, for the General Staff, Sept. 20, 1918 (NBS Box 10, IG).
*Schlink, to instrument control department, Firestone Tire and Rubber Co., 1919; assistant secretary, AESC, 1922; technical director and president, Consumers' Research, Inc., 1929.
*Wright, returned to teaching, 1919.
*Purington, to Hammond Radio Laboratory, Gloucester, Mass., 1919.
*Duncan, to Bureau of Ordnance, Navy Department, 1921.
*Moore, to Navy Department, 1923.
*Morgan, to Department of Physics, University of Maryland, 1942.
*Stannard, to Central Scientific Co., Chicago, 1919.
*Dempsey, retired, May 11, 1939.
*Gorton, to Western Electric Co., New York, 1919.

Magnetic Measurement

Supervision of section; magnetic mines	Sanford, Raymond L.	
Magnetic testing of metals for rifle barrels	*Kouwenhoven, Prof. William B.	
Magnetic testing of airplane tie wires	*Fisher, Melvin F.	1913–43
Airplane and marine compasses	Dawson, Leo H.	
Magnetic testing of welded ship plates	Becker, James A.	

Photometry and Illuminating Engineering

Special illuminating equipment	Taylor, Dr A. Hadley	
	*Commery, Eugene W.	1917–19
Properties of incandescent lamps	*Skogland, James F.	1908–31
Methods of photometric measurement	*Morse, Marie L. T.	1918–31
Field searchlights	Karrer, Enoch	
	*Willis, Benjamin S.	1917–24
	Zahn, E. T.	

Radio Communications Section

Vacuum tube measurements	Beltz, H. H.	
Radio measurements	Grover, Dr Frederick W.	
	*Freeman, Herbert M.	1917–19
	*Breit, Gregory	1918–19
	Harmon, H. W.	
	Merriman, A. G.	
	Montgomery, N.	
	Snow, H. A.	
	Werden, E. T.	
Radio design	Buckley, J. P.	
Radio development	Dellinger, Dr J. Howard	
	*Dunmore, Francis W.	1918–49
	*Hull, Lewis M.	
	Hillebrand, L. E.	
	Kolster, Frederick A.	
	*Lowell, Percival D.	1913–24, 1941–62
	*McDowell, Louise S.	
	*Miller, John M.	1907–19
	Ould, Richard S.	1918–23
	*Preston, J. L.	

---

*Kouwenhoven, returned to Johns Hopkins University staff.
*Fisher, died Dec. 23, 1943.
*Commery, to National Lamp Works, Nela Park, Cleveland, Ohio.
*Skogland, died Feb. 10, 1931.
*Morse, resigned, illness 1931.
*Willis, to Iowa State College, 1919.
*Freeman, to Westinghouse Electric and Manufacturing Co., Pittsburgh, Pa., 1919.
*Breit, to University of Leiden, Holland, on National Research Fellowship, 1919, and then to Carnegie Institution, Washington, D.C.
*Dunmore, retired, 1949.
*Hull, L. M. to Radio Frequency Laboratory, Boonton, N.J.
*Lowell, retired, 1962 (now consultant).
*McDowell, to Wellesley College, Mass.
*Miller, to Atwater Kent Radio Corp., 1919.
*Preston, to Bureau of Lighthouses.

Radio Communications Section—Continued		
Radio development—Continued		
	*Southworth, George C.	1917–18
	*Whittemore, Laurens E.	1917–24
	Wade, W. G.	
	*Willoughby, John A.	1916–22
Electrolysis Prevention		
Sound ranging	McCollum, Burton	
	Eckhardt, Dr Englehardt A.	
	*Weibel, Dr Ernest E.	
	*Karcher, Dr J. C.	
	*Peters, Orville S.	1910–29
	*Fisher, J. Carl	
	Melton, E. R.	
	Goren, David	
	*Snyder, Carl F.	1909–60
Electrolysis mitigation	*Shepard, Edgar R.	1914–33
Standards of electric railway service	Logan, Kirk H.	
	Baller, M. J.	
	Monroe, W. P.	
Electrical Safety Engineering		
Public utility standards	Lloyd, Dr Morton G.	
Industrial safety standards	*Oakes, Charles E.	1917–21
Electrical safety standards	Sahm, Paul A. B.	1916–NRF
	*Waldschmidt, Albert	
	Congdon, W. E.	
Wind pressure on wires	Dahm, P. E.	
Gas Engineering		
Coke ovens, toluol, gas standards	McBride, Russell S.	
	*Reinecker, Charles E.	1916–23
	Lausley, J. W.	
Hydrogen gas plant operation	*Berry, Walter M.	1916–23

*Southworth, to Yale University, 1918; American Telephone & Telegraph Co., New York, 1923.
*Whittemore, to Bureau of Navigation, Department of Commerce, 1920; to American Telephone & Telegraph Co., New York, 1925.
*Willoughby, to the Naval Research Laboratory, 1922.
*Weibel, killed in France, August 1918.
*Karcher, to Western Electric, Chicago, 1923; later to Amerada Oil Co.
*Peters, resigned to become consultant engineer, 1929.
*Fisher, to Consolidated Gas and Electric Co., Baltimore, Md.
*Snyder, retired 1960.
*Shepard, to Department of Agriculture, 1933.
*Oakes, to Pennsylvania Power and Light Co., Allentown, Pa.
*Waldschmidt, to Patent Office, Department of Commerce, 1920.
*Reinecker, to United Gas Improvement Co., Philadelphia, Pa.
*Berry, to California Gas Research Council, Los Angeles, Calif.

Gas Engineering—Continued

Natural gas, economic problems, standards	Morgan, C. S.	
	Frankel, M. J.	
Assistants in gas engineering	Gray, G. A.	
	*Eiseman, John H.	1916–57

Electrical Service Standards

Electric light and power service	Meyer, J. Franklin	
Jurisdiction of state public service commissions	Crawford, J. P.	

Telephone Service Standards

Supervision of telephone investigations	Wolff, Dr Frank A.	
Telephone traffic investigations	Macomber, G. S.	
Telephone equipment investigations	Brown, W. E.	
Methods of measurement	*Taylor, Dr Hawley O.	
Assistant to Dr Taylor	Pike, C. E.	
Standard cell and microphone investigations	*Shoemaker, Maynard P.	1905–36
The audion and its applications	Beltz, H. H.	
Transmission investigations	*Sasuly, Max	1913–24
Microphone investigations	Godfrey, C. M.	

Electrochemistry

Battery research and testing	Vinal, Dr George W.	
Chemistry of primary and storage batteries	*Holler, Dr H. D.	
	Sefton, Miss L. B.	
Development of galvanic piles	Schott, R. C.	
Dry cell and small storage batteries	Koller, L. R.	
Storage batteries	Cole, T. S.	

Radioactivity and X–Ray Measurements

Properties, use, and measure of luminous materials	Dorsey, Dr N. Ernest	
X-ray apparatus and materials	Huff, Dr W. B.	
Self-luminous materials	*Brown, Prof. T. B.	
	Richmond, J. E.	
	Taylor, M. D.	
Assistant observer in investigations	McCrea, W. D.	
Application of self-luminous materials	Yung-Kwai, Elizabeth	
X-ray protective materials	Alderton, Nina M.	

---

*Eiseman, retired Dec. 31, 1957.
*Taylor, H. O., to the Franklin Union, Boston, Mass., as director of the electrical department, 1921.
*Shoemaker, to the Treasury Department, 1936.
*Sasuly, reduction in force, 1924.
*Holler, to Geology Department, Vassar College.
*Brown, to George Washington University.

WEIGHTS AND MEASURES	Fischer, Louis A.	
Length, Time, and Capacity Section		
Calibration of scales, haemacytometers	Judson, Dr Lewis V.	
	Maslin, M.	
Stop watches (Ordnance), clocks (Shipping Board)	Beal, Arthur F.	
Gas measuring devices, aviation instruments	Stillman, Marcus H.	
Packaging of materials for oversea shipment	Roeser, Harry W.	1914–34
Laws, Weights, and Measures		
Density and thermal expansion of liquids	Peffer, Elmer L.	
Dilution pipettes (haemacytometers)	Hill, E. E.	
Gas Measuring Instruments		
Aircraft inclinometers, telephone transmitters, gas measuring, photography	Stillman, Marcus H.	
Thermal Expansivity		
Thermal expansion of airplane alloys, spark plug insulators, etc., silicon	Souder, Dr Wilmer	
	Hidnert, Dr Peter	
	Eisinger, J. O.	
Mil scale study for Signal and Navy; rulings for Ordnance	Souder, Dr Wilmer	
Gage Research		
Supervision of gage research	*Van Keuren, Harold L.	1914–19
Miscellaneous gages; weighing	*Briggs, Clarence A.	1910–24
	Gordon, E. D.	
	Fullmer, Irwin H.	
	*Haigh, Joseph A.	1917–44
	Bean, Howard S.	
HEAT AND THERMOMETRY	Waidner, Dr Charles W.	
Thermometry		
Thermometer testing; airplane thermometry	Wilhelm, Robert M.	1908–20
	Martin, Frank W.	
Thermal properties of methane	Finkelstein, Joseph L.	
Pyrometry		
Chief of high temperature investigations	Foote, Dr Paul D.	
Optical and radiation pyrometry	Fairchild, Charles O.	
Optical glass	Tool, A. Q.	
	Valasek, Joseph	

*Van Keuren, to Wilton Tool Co., 1919.
*Briggs, to Department of Agriculture, 1924.
*Haigh, retired, Aug. 17, 1944 (disability).

Project	Staff member	Years
Pyrometry—Continued		
Gas explosions; spark plugs for airplanes	Mohler, Dr Fred L.	
Optical pyrometry and ionization	Rognley, O.	
Thermocouple testing; specific heats	*Harrison, Thomas R.	1915–20
Melting points of refractories	Dana, Leo I.	
Coke ovens and optical glass (Signal Corps)	Christie, Pvt. J. L.	
Heat Measurements		
Heat measurement problems	Mueller, Eugene F.	
Thermal conductivity; balloon problems	VanDusen, Dr Milton S.	
Thermal properties of methane at low temperatures	*Osborne, Nathan S.	1903–39
	Stimson, Dr Harold F.	1916–60
	*Sligh, Thomas S. Jr.	1916–26
	Cragoe, Carl S.	1918–50
	Jessup, Ralph S.	
Torpedo investigations	Meyers, Cyril H.	
	DuPriest, J. R.	
Thermodynamics		
Technical thermodynamics	Buckingham, Dr Edgar	
Low Temperature		
Operation of liquid air plant	Ford, Thomas B.	
Low temperature testing	Cook, J. Williamson	
Fire Resistance		
Fire tests of building columns	Ingberg, Simon H.	
	*Griffin, Harry K.	1908–21
Fire tests of reinforced concrete columns	*Hull, W. A.	
	Fulton, W. C.	
Fire resistance of structural materials; methane	Kanolt, Clarence W.	
Fire resistance and aspects of city building codes	*Glading, Frank W.	1914–19
Airplane Power Plant		
Supervisor of airplane engine research	Dickinson, Dr Hobart C.	
Assistant to supervisor	*James, William S.	1911–24
Aeronautic engine performance	Anderson, G. V.	
	Boreman, R. W.	
	Brinkerhoff, V. W.	
	Lapp, Sgt. C. J.	
	Lee, T. E.	

*Harrison, resigned, 1920.
*Osborne, retired 1939.
*Sligh, to Studebaker Corp., 1926.
*Griffin, to Barnett Co., 1921.
*Hull, to Terra Cotta Service, Chicago, Ill., 1924.
*Glading, to Baldwin Locomotive Works as industrial engineer.
*James resigned, 1924.

Airplane Power Plant—Continued		
Aeronautic engine performance—Continued	Long, A. R.	
	McKenzie, D.	
	Sparrow, Stanwood W.	
	Stern, A. G.	
	Scholz, W. P.	
	Thomson, Malcolm	
	Walden, C. O.	
	Wetherill, Frederic V.	
Spark plugs	Arnold, S. B.	
	Bradshaw, G. R.	
	Fonseca, Edward L.	
	Honaman, R. Karl	
	Johnson, G. M.	
	Sawyer, L. G.	
Lubrication	Bingham, F. C.	
	Grosklaus, O.	
	Markle, F. H.	
	Menzies, W. C.	
	Schulze, J. E.	
	Willey, B.	
Carburetion	Blackwell	
	Brewer, R. E.	
	Stanton, W. F.	
	Tice, P. S.	
Physical properties of carburetor air	*Hoxton, Dr Llewelyn G.	1901–04, 1917–18
Radiators	Brown, William B.	
	Castleman, Robert A. Jr.	
	*Harper, Dr D. Roberts Jr.	1909–25
	Harvey, A. R.	
	Haydoch, E.	
	Kleinschmidt, Robert V.	
	Parsons, S. R.	
	Van de Water, Jean	
	Voorhees, L. E.	
Indicators	Newell, F. B.	
LIGHT AND OPTICAL INSTRUMENTS		
Spectroscopy		
Infra-red spectroscopy and photography	Meggers, Dr William F.	
	*Burns, Dr Keivin	1913–19
	Kiess, Carl C.	1917–
Color sensitive photographic emulsions	*Merrill, Dr Paul W.	1916–19
	Ellis, J. H.	
	*Walters, Francis M.	

---

*Hoxton, returned to Physics Department, University of Virginia.
*Harper, to engineering laboratory of General Electric Co., Schenectady, N.Y., Sept. 30, 1925.
*Burns, to Allegheny Observatory, Pittsburgh, Pa.
*Merrill, to Mt. Wilson Observatory.
*Walters, to Carnegie Institute of Technology.

Spectroscopy—Continued		
Photographic lens design	*Mellor, Lewis L.	
Glass weathering, spectroscopic analysis	*Burka, Samuel M.	
Polarimetry		
Magneto optics; sugar technology	Bates, Frederick J.	
Physical chemistry of carbohydrates	*Jackson, Dr Richard F.	1907–43
Physics relating to sugar testing	Phelps, Francis P.	
Interferometry and Colorimetry		
Color standards; spectrophotometry; chromatic camouflage	Priest, Irwin G.	
	Gibson, Dr Kasson S.	
	*Tyndall, E. P. T.	
	McNicholas, Harry J.	
Dyes	Mathewson, Capt. W. E.	
Lens Testing		
Effect of striae on optical glass	*Bennett, A. H.	
	Smith, Thomas T.	
Glass for goggles	Wensel, Dr Henry T.	
Camera designing for the Navy	Curtis, Dr Heber D.	
Optical designing for the Navy	*Michelson, Albert A.	
Lens design	Eckel, Arthur F.	
	Schultz, Harry I.	1913–NRF
	White, H. S.	
Radiometry		
Radiometers; photoelectric signaling	Coblentz, Dr William W.	
Assistant	Kahler, H.	
Sound		
Transmission of sound in airplane ranging	Jones, A. T.	
CHEMISTRY	Hillebrand, Dr William F.	
Physical Chemistry		
Physical constants and purification of methane; standard samples	*McKelvy, Ernest C.	1907–19
	Taylor, Dr Cyril S.	
	*Isaacs, Aaron	1913–34
Analysis of gasolines	*Yurow, Louis	1913–19
	Simpson, D. H.	
	Ruderman, A.	

---

*Mellor, to Bell & Howell.
*Burka, to Optical Division, Patterson Airfield, Dayton, Ohio.
*Jackson, died June 1, 1943.
*Tyndall, to Iowa State University.
*Bennett, to American Optical Co.
*Michelson, returned to Physics Department, University of Chicago.
*McKelvy, accidental death, Nov. 29, 1919.
*Isaacs, resigned, 1934.
*Yurow, resigned, 1919.

Field	Name	Years
Electrochemistry		
Electrodeposition	Blum, Dr William	
Commercial electroplating	Hogaboom, G. B.	
	Liscomb, F. J.	
	Slattery, T. J.	
Analytical methods for plating	Jencks, E. Z.	
	Ritchie, LeMarr	
	Ham, L. B.	
Physical-chemical methods for plating	Bell, A. D.	
Special plating problems	Madsen, C. P.	
Gas Chemistry		
Balloon fabrics: life tests, permeability	*Edwards, Junius D.	1913–19
	Moore, Irwin L.	
	Pickering, S. F.	
	Schoch, H. K.	
	Saper, P. G.	
Automatic gas analysis: nitrate plant; submarines	*Franklin, Dr E. C.	
	Frantz, H. W.	
	Gordon, B. D.	
	Mackenzie, J. D.	
	Palmer, P. E.	
	Crump, C. C.	
	Weaver, Elmer R.	
	Young, S. W.	
	*Bliss, Dr W. J. A.	
Balloon gases	Ledig, P. G.	
Balloon temperatures	Long, Maurice B.	
Gas engine exhaust analysis	MacPherson, Dr Archibald T.	1918–
Reagents and Apparatus		
Chemistry of the platinum metals	Smither, Frederick W.	
	Wichers, Dr Edward	1917–63
	Gilchrist, Dr Raleigh A.	1918–62
Methods of testing chemical reagents	Sive, Benjamin E.	
Analytical Methods and Standard Samples		
Tungsten, molybdenum, zirconium analysis	Lundell, Dr Gustave E. F.	1917–48
Methods of iron and steel analysis	*Witmer, Luther F.	1909–20
	Hoffman, James I.	1918–62
	Silwinski, A. A.	
Determination of zirconium in ores	*Knowles, Howard B.	1913–50
Determination of tungsten in ores	Rennie, W. E.	

*Edwards, resigned, 1919.
*Franklin, returned to Chemistry Department, Stanford University.
*Bliss, returned to Chemistry Department, Johns Hopkins University.
*Witmer, resigned, 1920.
*Knowles, retired, June 29, 1950.

Oils, Rubber, Paper, Textiles, Ink, Glue

Subject	Name	Years
Lubricants	Waters, Campbell E.	
Airplane dopes and related subjects	Smith, W. Harold	1910–57
	Jacobson, I. M.	
Leather	Whitmore, Lester M.	
Dyestuffs	Mathewson, W. E.	
	Clark, Edgar R.	
Textile dyeing	Sleeper, R. R.	
Rubber analysis	Epstein, Samuel W.	
Printing inks	Basseches, J. L.	

Metals, Cement, and Bituminous Materials

Subject	Name	Years
Cement, alloys, and bituminous materials	Voorhees, Samuel S.	
	Bright, Harry A.	1913–60
	*Fitch, Roy O.	1913–18
	*Scherrer, John A.	1910–40
	Burger, E. N.	
Corrosion of metals	Finn, Alfred N.	1911–42
Toluol benzol	Washburn, Frederic McL.	

Paint, Varnish, and Soap

Subject	Name	Years
Paint, varnish, detergents	Walker, Dr Percy H.	1918–37
	*Bower, John H.	1914–48
	McNeil, Hiram C.	
	*Schmidt, George C.	1914–22
	*Lewis, A. J.	1914–20
	Demovsky, A.	
	Cooke, Sgt. G. W.	
Varnish, drying oils, enamels	*Wertz, Franklin A.	1913–18
Preservative materials	Prince, Lt. K. P.	

ENGINEERING INSTRUMENTS

Mechanical Appliances and Engineering Instruments

Subject	Name	Years
Mechanical applicances	Wormeley, Philip L.	
Theory and design of measuring instruments	Schlink, Frederick J.	
Engineering instruments	Stutz, Walter F.	
	Hodge, Orlando J.	
	Baster, F. S.	

Aviation Instruments

Subject	Name	Years
Altimeters, elasticity, viscosity	Hersey, Dr Mayo D.	
Ground speed indicators	Hunt, Dr Franklin L.	1917–24
Gyroscopic stabilizers and bomb sights	Franklin, Dr W. S.	
Vibrations in airplanes	*Nusbaum, Dr Christian	

*Fitch, died Oct. 13, 1918.
*Scherrer, retired, Dec. 31, 1940.
*Bower, retired, June 30, 1948.
*Schmidt, resigned 1922.
*Lewis, to H. H. Franklin Manufacturing Co., Syracuse, 1920.
*Wertz, resigned, 1918.
*Nusbaum, returned to Case School of Applied Science, Cleveland, Ohio.

Aviation Instruments—Continued		
Tachometers	Washburn, George E.	
	Sylvander, Roy C.	
	Rawlins, C. H.	
Elastic properties of diaphragms	Nelms, W. S.	
Rate of climb indicators	Mears, Atherton H.	
Oxygen control apparatus	Hoffman, Leslie A.	
	Smith, B. A.	
	Keat, W. G.	
Air speed indicators	Stearns, Howard O.	
Inclinometers	Stillman, Marcus H.	
Bimetallic strips	Peterson, J. B.	
Aviation Physics		
Aerodynamical laboratory investigations	Briggs, Dr Lyman J.	
Wind tunnel investigations	Heald, Roy H.	
	Upton, Frederick E.	
	McMurdie, Alex M.	
	Cook, Robert	
Scientific instrument design	Simpson, W. S.	
	Blackwood, W. J.	
Construction of research apparatus	Dolmar, M.	
	Oser, O.	
ENGINEERING, STRUCTURAL, AND MISCELLANEOUS MATERIALS	Voorhees, Dr Samuel S.	
Metals		
Metal airplane construction	Whittemore, Dr. Herbert L.	
	Johnston, R. S.	
Airplane instruments	*McNair, Dr F. W.	
	Templin, Richard L.	
Calibration testing machines	Moore, H. F.	
Strength of welded ship plates	Hoffman, Charles P.	
	Curts, H. L.	
Strength of reinforced concretes	Larson, L. J.	
Impact strength of steel	Cushing, B. L.	
Impact strength of wood	Robbins, L. L.	
Causes of failure in steel rails	Anderson, H. A.	
Strength of full-length airplane beams	Sorey, T. L.	
Strength of military construction materials	Wise, F. J.	
	Rynders, G. W.	
Cement, Concrete, Stone, Gravel, Sand		
Reversal of stress on concrete beams	*Smith, George A.	1916–26
Concrete investigations	Kessler, Daniel W.	

*McNair, to presidency of Michigan School of Mines.
*Smith, resigned, 1926.

Cement, Concrete, Stone, Gravel, Sand—Continued		
Concrete ship construction problems	Maconi, G. V.	
	Davis, Watson	
Design of reinforced concrete	Slater, W. A.	
Effect of alkali and sea water on concrete	*Williams, Guy M.	1911–23
Volume change in concrete	Laubly, Charles S.	
Miscellaneous Materials		
Section chief	Worméley, Philip L.	
Lubricants	Herschel Dr Winslow H.	
Leather	Hart, Reeves W.	
	Cheney, Walter L.	
	Bowker, Roy C.	
	Wallin, F. W.	
Rubber	*Patrick, Erwin C.	1912–20
	Collier, S.	
	Morgan, W. F.	
	Linscott, R. F.	
	Bond, E. R.	
Textiles		
Airplane fabrics	*Walen, Ernest D.	1914–19
	Fisher, Russell T.	
Cotton fabrics	Dickson, E. E.	
	Bauldry, C. E.	
	Perkins, J. H.	
Wool fabrics and felt	Webster, P.	
	Spicer, E.	
	McGavan, F. R.	
General military fabrics	Duman, R. W.	
	Philpot, I.	
	Wackman, C. F.	
Textile microscopy	Basche, H.	
Ceramics (Pittsburgh Laboratory)		
Chemistry of cements, clay, glass	Stecker, H. C.	
	Royal, H. F.	
	Maag, O. L.	
Structural Materials (Pittsburgh Laboratory)		
Physical properties of portland and sorel cements	*Parsons, Walter E.	1916–20
	Greenwald, A. H.	
Properties of cements and concretes	Bates, Phaon H.	
Fire Resisting Materials (Pittsburgh Laboratory)		
Fire-resisting qualities of structural materials.	*Hull, Walter A.	1914–23
	Fulton, W. C.	
	Gunning, R. T.	

---

*Williams, resigned, 1923.
*Patrick, to Mason Tire and Rubber Co., Kent, Ohio, as chief chemist and engineer, 1920.
*Walen, to manager, Textile Research Co., Boston, 1919.
*Parsons, reduction in force, 1920.
*Hull, W. A., to Northwestern Terra Cotta Co., Chicago, Ill., 1923.

Steel, Concrete, Cement (Pittsburgh Laboratory)

Steel columns, building tile	*Hathcock, Bernard D.	1916–NRF
	*Griffith, John H.	1911–NRF
Earth resistance of cement and concrete	Virgin, W. H.	
Cement, concrete, wire rope, manila rope	*Newell, Palmer F.	1913–NRF

Paper

Section chief	Clark, Dr Frederick C.	
Wall board, adhesives, test methods	*Conley, Albert D.	1916–NRF
Paper for gas masks and airplane fabrics	Durgin, Albert G.	
	Harding, R. H.	
Operation of paper machine for gas masks	Houston, P. L.	
	Bicking, G. W.	
Microphotography of balloon fabrics	Loftan, R. E.	
Optical methods for testing gas mask paper	Curtis, Cpl. Frederick A.	
Paper samples from military agencies	Mendel, Pvt. J. P.	

METALLURGY DIVISION — Burgess, Dr George K.

Microscopy of Metals

Microscopy studies; corrosion of nonferrous alloys	Rawdon, Dr Henry S.	
Microstructure of ordnance steels, brass	Nauss, George M.	

Heat Treatment and Thermal Analysis

Heat treatment of steels; rust proofing	Grossmann, Marcus A.	
Heat treatment of metallic alloys	Freeman, John R. Jr.	
	*Scott, Howard	1912–25

Physical Properties and Miscellaneous

Light aluminum alloys; electric welding	Merica, Dr Paul D.	
	*Waltenberg, Romaine G.	1912–21
	France, R.	
	Oesterle, Pvt. J. F.	
Bearing metals; tin conservation	*Woodward, Dr Raymond W.	1914–21
Tin conservation; solders	Gurevich, Louis J.	
Electric welding	Hurvitz, B.	

---

*Hathcock, resigned, 1919.
*Griffith, resigned, 1919.
*Newell, resigned, 1919.
*Conley, resigned, 1919.
*Scott, resigned, 1925.
*Waltenburg, resigned, 1921.
*Woodward, to Whitney Manufacturing Co., Hartford, Conn., as chief metallurgist, 1921.

Chemical Metallurgy		
Preparation of alloys	Jordan, Louis Owens, A. W.	
Methods for determining gases in steel, iron	Wetmore, A. S.	
General metallurgical research	Cain, Dr John R.	
Foundry and Mechanical Plant		
Aluminum alloys for airplane work	Karr, Carydon P.	
Foundry work in aluminum alloy research	Flegel, A.	
Molding sands; vitreous enamels for metals	Staley, Prof. Homer F.	
CLAY PRODUCTS	Bleininger, Dr Albert V.	
Ceramics		
Special spark plugs, optical glass, light clay aggregates for concrete ships, graphite crucibles, porcelain studies	Bleininger, Dr Albert V. Riddle, F. H. Wright, Joseph W. Fuller, D. E. McDaniel, W. W. *Cutler, Charles H.	 1914–31
Spark plugs for airplanes	Geiger, C. F.	
Containers for firing airplane spark plugs	Hornung, M. R.	
Optical Glass		
Optical glass research	Gregory, M. C. Rand, C. C. Payne, A. R. Dodd, L. E. Roberts, George C. McKee, A. P. Zimmer, Casper Williams, W. S. Noyes, M. P.	
Lime		
Lime and gypsum products	Kirkpatrick, Frank A. Orange, William B. Householder, F. F.	

*Cutler, retired, Nov. 30, 1931.

CHIEFS
OF THE SCIENTIFIC AND TECHNICAL STAFF

as of January 1, 1920

DIRECTOR	***Stratton, Dr Samuel W.**	
Technical Assistant to the Director	Brown, Dr Fay C.	1919–27
I. ELECTRICAL	*Rosa, Dr Edward B.	
1. Standards of Resistance	Wenner, Dr Frank	
2. Inductance and Capacity	Curtis, Dr Harvey L.	
3. Electrical Measurings Instruments	Brooks, Dr Herbert B.	
4. Magnetic Measurements	Sanford, Raymond L.	1910–54
5. Photometry and Illuminating Engineering	*Taylor, Dr A. Hadley	
6a. Radio Research and Testing	Dellinger, Dr J. Howard	
6b. Radio Development	*Kolster, Frederick A.	
7. Electrolysis Prevention	McCollum, Burton	
8. Safety Engineering	Lloyd, Dr Morton G.	
9. Gas Engineering	*McBride, Russell S.	
10. Electrical Service Standards	Meyer, Dr J. Franklin	
11. Telephone Service Standards	Wolff, Dr Frank A.	
12. Electrochemistry	Vinal, Dr George W.	
13. Radioactivity and X-ray Measurements	Dorsey, Dr N. Ernest	
II. WEIGHTS AND MEASURES	*Fischer, Louis A.	
1. Length	Judson, Dr Lewis V.	1917–65
2. Mass	Pienkowsky, Dr Arthur T.	
3. Time	*Beal, Arthur F.	1917–23
4. Capacity and Density	Peffer, Elmer L.	
5. Gas Measuring Instruments	*Stillman, Marcus H.	1910–20
6. Thermal Expansivity	Souder, Dr Wilmer	1910–13, 1917–54

*Stratton, to M.I.T. as president, Jan. 1, 1923; died Oct. 18, 1931.
*Rosa, died May 17, 1921.
*Taylor, A. Hadley, to Nela Park, Cleveland, 1921.
*Kolster, resigned to join Federal Telegraph Co., 1921.
*McBride, to McGraw-Hill, 1920, later private consulting chemical engineer.
*Fischer, died July 25, 1921.
*Beal, to Census Bureau, 1923.
*Stillman, to Fairbanks Scale Co., 1920.

Division / Section	Chief	Years
II. WEIGHTS AND MEASURES—Continued		
7. Weights and Measures Laws and Administration	Holbrook, Fay S.	
8. Investigation, Testing of Scales	Holbrook, Fay S.	
9. Gages	Bearce, Henry W.	1908–45
III. HEAT AND THERMOMETRY	*Waidner, Dr Charles W.	
1. Thermometry	*Wilhelm, Robert M.	
2. Pyrometry	Foote, Dr Paul D.	
3. Heat Measurements	Mueller, Eugene F.	
4. Thermodynamics	*Buckingham, Dr Edgar	
5. Cryogenic Laboratory	Kanolt, Clarence W.	
6. Fire Resistance	Ingberg, Simon H.	
7. Airplane and Automotive Power Plant	Dickinson, Dr Hobart C.	
IV. LIGHT AND OPTICAL INSTRUMENTS	Skinner, Dr Clarence A.	1919–41
1. Spectroscopy	Meggers, Dr William F.	
2. Polarimetry	Bates, Frederick J.	
3. Colorimetry	Priest, Irwin G.	
4. Refractometry and Optical Instruments	*Schultz, Harry I.	1913–20
5. Radiometry	Coblentz, Dr William W.	
6. Dispersoids	*Wells, Dr Philip V.	
7. Photographic Technology	(Planned)	
8. Interferometry	Peters, Chauncey G.	
9. Searchlight Investigations	*Karrer, Enoch	1918–22
V. CHEMISTRY	Hillebrand, Dr William F.	
1. Physical Chemistry	*Taylor, Dr Cyril S.	1913–20
2. Electrochemistry	Blum, Dr William	
3. Metallurgical Chemistry	*Cain, Dr John R.	
4. Gas Chemistry	Weaver, Elmer R.	
5. Reagents and Apparatus	Smither, Frederick W.	
6. Analytical Methods, Standard Samples	Lundell, Dr Gustave E. F.	
7. Oils, Rubber, Paper, etc.	Waters, Campbell E.	
8. Metals, Cement, Bituminous Materials	*Voorhees, Samuel S.	
9. Paint, Varnish, Soap	Walker, Dr Percy H.	

*Waidner, died Mar. 11, 1922.
*Wilhelm, to C. J. Tagliabue Manufacturing Co., Aug. 31, 1920.
*Buckingham, consultant to engineering physics division, NBS, 1923–37; retired 1937; died Apr. 29, 1940.
*Schultz, resigned to set up private business, 1920.
*Wells, to E. I. duPont (Redpath Laboratories), Parlin, N.J., 1923.
*Karrer, to General Electric, 1922.
*Taylor, to Aluminum Company of America, in research laboratory, 1920.
*Cain, NBS Research Associate, 1921–36; member of NBS, 1936 until retirement May 31, 1945.
*Voorhees, died Sept. 21, 1921.

Division / Section	Chief	Years
VI. ENGINEERING PHYSICS	Stratton, Dr Samuel W.	
1. Mechanical Appliances	Wormeley, Philip L.	
2. Engineering Instruments	Stutz, Walter F.	
3. Aviation Instruments	*Hersey, Dr Mayo D.	
4. Aviation Physics	Briggs, Dr Lyman J.	1917–46
5. Special Investigations (Sound)	*Hayford, John F.	1917–21
VII. ENGINEERING, STRUCTURAL, AND MISCELLANEOUS MATERIALS	Stratton, Dr Samuel W.	
1. Metal Structures	Whittemore, Herbert L.	1917–46
2. Cement, Sand, Stone, etc.	*Pearson, Joseph C.	
3. Rubber, Leather, etc.	Wormeley, Philip L.	
4. Textiles	*McGowan, Frank R.	1918–25
5. Paper	*Curtis, Frederick A.	1918–24
6. Lubricating Oils	*Herschel, Dr Winslow H.	
7. Lime, Gypsum, Sand, Brick	Emley, Warren E.	
VIII. METALLURGY	Burgess, Dr George K.	
1. Microscopy of Metals	Rawdon, Dr Henry S.	
2. Heat Treatment and Thermal Analysis	French, Herbert J.	1919–29
3. Physical Properties of Metals	Burgess, Dr George K.	
4. Chemical Metallurgy	Cain, Dr John R.	
5. Foundry and Mechanical Plant	*Karr, Carydon P.	
IX. CERAMICS	*Bleininger, Dr Albert V.	
1. Clay Products	Bleininger, Dr Albert V.	
2. Optical Glass	*Taylor, William H.	1918–25
3. Refractories	*Staley, Homer F.	1918–20
4. Enameled Metal Products	Staley, Homer F.	
MISCELLANEOUS		
Sound	Eckhardt, Dr Englehardt A.	1917–25

*Hersey, NBS consultant, 1921–22; in physics laboratory of U.S. Bureau of Mines, 1922–26; returned to Bureau 1926.

*Hayford, completed investigation, June 30, 1921.

*Pearson, to Lehigh Portland Cement Co., Allentown, Pa., 1924.

*McGowan, to Cotton Textile Institute, New York, as director, Jan. 30, 1925; continued as consultant to NBS.

*Curtis, to American Writing Paper Co., Holyoke, Mass., 1924.

*Herschel, section discontinued; continued research until retirement, Aug. 31, 1943.

*Karr, died June 10, 1925.

*Bleininger, to Homer Laughlin China Co., West Virginia, 1923.

*Taylor, W. Hadley, to Pittsburgh Plate Glass Co., 1925.

*Staley, former professor in department of ceramic engineering, Iowa State College; resigned to enter commercial work, Dec. 31, 1920.

CHIEFS OF THE SCIENTIFIC AND TECHNICAL STAFF

as of February 1, 1925

DIRECTOR	**Burgess, Dr George K.**	
Assistant to the Director	*Brown, Dr Fay C.	
I. ELECTRICAL	Crittenden, Dr Eugene C.	
1. Resistance Measurements	Wenner, Dr Frank	
2. Inductance and Capacitance	Curtis, Dr Harvey L.	
3. Electrical Measuring Instruments	Brooks, Dr Herbert B.	
4. Magnetic Measurements	Sanford, Raymond L.	
5. Photometry and Illuminating Engineering	Meyer, Dr J. Franklin	
6. Radio Communication	Dellinger, Dr J. Howard	
7. Electrolysis Prevention	*McCollum, Burton	
8. Safety Engineering	Lloyd, Dr Morton G.	
9. Electrochemistry	Vinal, Dr George W.	
10. Telephone Standards	Wolff, Dr Frank A.	
II. WEIGHTS AND MEASURES	Holbrook, Fay S., and Bearce, Henry W.	
1. Length	Judson, Dr Lewis V.	
2. Mass	Pienkowsky, Dr Arthur T.	
3. Time	Gould, Ralph E.	1918–50
4. Capacity and Density	Peffer, Elmer L.	
5. Gas Measuring Instruments	Bean, Howard S.	1917–58
6. Thermal Expansivity	Souder, Dr Wilmer	
7. Weights and Measures Laws Administration	Smith, Ralph W.	1920–50
8. Investigation and Testing of Scales	*Roeser, Harry W.	
9. Gages	Miller, David R.	1908–52
III. HEAT AND POWER	Dickinson, Dr Hobart C.	
1. Thermometry	Mueller, Eugene F.	
2. Pyrometry	*Fairchild, Charles O.	1915–26

*Brown, to Museum of the Peace Arts (later renamed New York Museum of Science and Industry) as director, 1927.

*McCollum, to McCollum Geological Exploration Inc., as technical director, 1926.

*Roeser, separated in reduction in force, June 30, 1934; contract employee from 1944 to death in 1950.

*Fairchild, to Tagliabue Manufacturing Co., Brooklyn, N.Y., 1926.

Division / Section	Chief	Years
III. HEAT AND POWER—Continued		
3. Heat Measurements	Mueller, Eugene F.	
4. Heat Transfer	(Vacant)	
5. Cryogenic Laboratory	*Kanolt, Clarence W.	
6. Fire Resistance	Ingberg, Simon H.	
7. Automotive Power Plant	*Sparrow, Stanwood W.	1918–26
IV. OPTICS	Skinner, Dr Clarence A.	
1. Spectroscopy	Meggers, Dr William F.	
2. Polarimetry	Bates, Frederick J.	
3. Colorimetry	Priest, Irwin G.	
4. Optical Instruments	Gardner, Dr Irvine C.	1921–59
5. Radiometry	Coblentz, Dr William W.	
6. Atomic Physics, Radium, X-Ray	*Foote, Dr Paul D.	
7. Photographic Technology	Davis, Raymond	1911–58
8. Interferometry	Peters, Chauncey G.	
V. CHEMISTRY	*Hillebrand, Dr William F.	
1. Paints, Varnishes, Bituminous Materials	Walker, Dr Percy H.	
2. Detergents, Cement, Corrosion	Smither, Frederick W.	
3. Rubber, Lubricants, Textiles, Inks	Waters, Campbell E.	
4. Metal and Ore Analysis and Standard Samples	Lundell, Dr Gustave E. F.	
5. Reagents	Wichers, Dr Edward	
6. Electrochemistry	Blum, Dr William	
7. Gas Chemistry	Weaver, Elmer R.	
VI. MECHANICS AND SOUND	Briggs, Dr Lyman J.	
1. Engineering Instruments and Mechanical Appliances	Stutz, Walter F.	
2. Sound	*Eckhardt, Dr Englehardt A.	
3. Aeronautic Instruments	Eaton, Herbert A.	1918–53
4. Aerodynamical Physics	Dryden, Dr Hugh L.	1918–47
5. Engineering Mechanics	Whittemore, Herbert L.	
VII. STRUCTURAL ENGINEERING AND MISCELLANEOUS MATERIALS	Bates, Phaon H.	
1. Structural and Engineering Materials	(Vacant)	

*Kanolt, to Cryogenic Laboratory, Bureau of Mines, 1925; later to Farrand Optical Co., N.Y.

*Sparrow, to Studebaker Corp. as director of research, 1926.

*Foote, to Gulf Research and Development Co., Pittsburgh, as director of research, Aug. 1, 1927; returned through National Academy of Sciences in 1960 as Executive Secretary of NAS–NRC Technical Advisory Panels to NBS

*Hillebrand, died Feb. 7, 1925.

*Eckhardt, to Gulf Research and Development Co. as geophysicist, 1925; to Marlan Refining Co., Oklahoma, as assistant chief of research, 1927.

VII. STRUCTURAL ENGINEERING AND MISCELLANEOUS MATERIALS—Continued		
2. Cement, Sand, Stone	*Hitchcock, Frank A.	1918–26
3. Rubber, Leather, etc.	Wormeley, Philip L.	
4. Textiles	(Vacant)	
5. Paper	Scribner, Bourdon W.	1923–52
6. Lime, Gypsum, etc.	*Porter, John M.	1921–28
VIII. METALLURGY	*Gillett, Dr Horace W.	1924–29
1. Optical Metallurgy	Rawdon, Dr Henry S.	
2. Thermal Metallurgy	*French, Herbert J.	
3. Mechanical Metallurgy	*Freeman, John R. Jr.	1918–29
4. Chemical Metallurgy	Jordan, Louis	1917–36
5. Experimental Foundry	Saeger, Charles M. Jr.	1918–45
IX. CERAMICS	Bates, Phaon H.	
1. Pottery	*Wadleigh, Walter H.	1918–34
2. Optical Glass	Finn, Alfred N.	1911–42
3. Refractories	Geller, Roman F.	1918–55
4. Enameled Metals	*Wolfram, Harold G.	1923–26
BUILDING AND HOUSING	*Gries, Dr John M.	1921–28
SIMPLIFIED PRACTICE	*Hudson, Ray M.	1922–29
STANDARDIZATION OF SPECIFICATIONS	Burgess, Dr George K. (Chairman, Federal Specifications Board)	
Federal Specifications	*Harriman, Norman F.	1921–33
Industrial Specifications	McAllister, Dr Addams S.	1923–45

---

*Hitchcock, to George Washington University, 1926.
*Porter, to American Cyanamid Co., 1928.
*Gillett, to Battelle Memorial Institute, Columbus, Ohio, as director, 1929.
*French, to research laboratory, International Nickel Co. of New Jersey, 1929 (died 1955).
*Freeman, to American Brass Co., Waterbury, Conn., 1929.
*Wadleigh, reduction in force, June 30, 1934.
*Wolfram, to Porcelain Enamel Manufacturing Co., Baltimore, Md., 1926.
*Gries, to Division of Public Construction, Department of Commerce, 1928.
*Hudson, to New England Council, Boston, as technical advisor, 1929.
*Harriman, to Treasury Department, 1933.

ADMINISTRATIVE, SCIENTIFIC, AND TECHNICAL STAFF CHIEFS

as of April 1, 1930

DIRECTOR	***Burgess, Dr George K.**	
Assistant Director for Research and Testing	Briggs, Dr Lyman J.	
Assistant Director for Commercial Standardization	McAllister, Dr Addams S.	
I. ELECTRICAL	Crittenden, Dr Eugene C.	
1. Resistance Measurements	Wenner, Dr Frank	
2. Inductance and Capacitance	Curtis, Dr Harvey L.	
3. Electrical Instruments	Brooks, Dr Herbert B.	
4. Magnetic Measurements	Sanford, Raymond L.	
5. Photometry	Meyer, Dr J. Franklin	
6. Radio	Dellinger, Dr J. Howard	
7. Underground Corrosion	Logan, Kirk H.	1911–44
8. Safety Standards	Lloyd, Dr Morton G.	
9. Electrochemistry	Vinal, Dr George W.	
10. Telephone Standards	Wolff, Dr Frank A.	
II. WEIGHTS AND MEASURES	Holbrook, Fay S., and Bearce, Henry W.	
1. Length	Judson, Dr Lewis V.	
2. Mass	Pienkowsky, Dr Arthur T.	
3. Time	Gould, Ralph E.	
4. Capacity and Density	Peffer, Elmer L.	
5. Gas Measuring Instruments	Bean, Howard S.	
6. Thermal Expansivity	Souder, Dr Wilmer	
7. Weights and Measures Laws and Administration	Smith, Ralph W.	
8. Railroad Scales and Test Cars	Holbrook, Fay S.	
9. Gages	Miller, David R.	
III. HEAT AND POWER	Dickinson, Dr Hobart C.	
1. Thermometry	Busse, Miss Johanna	1918–49
2. Pyrometry	Wensel, Dr Henry T.	1917–46
3. Heat Measurements	Mueller, Eugene F.	
4. Heat Transfer	VanDusen, Dr Milton S.	1913–46
5. Cryogenic Laboratory	Brickwedde, Dr Ferdinand G.	1925–57
6. Fire Resistance	Ingberg, Simon H.	

*Burgess, died July 2, 1932.

Division / Section	Chief	Years
III. HEAT AND POWER—Continued		
7. Automotive Power Plant	Cummings, Herbert K.	1922–53
8. Friction and Lubrication	*Hersey, Dr Mayo D.	
IV. OPTICS	Skinner, Dr Clarence A.	
1. Spectroscopy	Meggers, Dr William F.	
2. Polarimetry	Bates, Frederick J.	
3. Colorimetry	*Priest, Irwin G.	
4. Optical Instruments	Gardner, Dr Irvine C.	
5. Radiometry	Coblentz, Dr William W.	
6. Atomic Physics, Radium, X-rays	Mohler, Dr Fred L.	1917–60
7. Photographic Technology	Davis, Raymond	
8. Interferometry	Peters, Chauncey G.	
V. CHEMISTRY	*Washburn, Dr Edward W.	1926–34
1. Physico-chemical Research	Washburn, Dr Edward W.	
2. Paints, Varnish, Bituminous Materials	Walker, Dr Percy H.	
3. Detergents, Cement, Corrosion	Smither, Frederick W.	
4. Rubber, Lubricants, Textiles	Waters, Campbell E.	
5. Metal and Ore Analysis, Standard Samples	Lundell, Dr Gustave E. F.	
6. Reagents and Platinum Metals	Wichers, Dr Edward	
7. Electrochemistry	Blum, Dr William	
8. Gas Chemistry	Weaver, Elmer R.	
VI. MECHANICS AND SOUND	Briggs, Dr Lyman J.	
1. Engineering Instruments and Mechanical Appliances	Stutz, Walter F.	
2. Sound	Heyl, Dr Paul R.	1920–42
3. Aeronautic Instruments	Brombacher, Dr William G.	1927–54
4. Aerodynamical Physics	Dryden, Dr Hugh L.	
5. Engineering Mechanics	Whittemore, Herbert L.	
6. Hydraulic Laboratory	Eaton, Herbert N.	
VII. ORGANIC AND FIBROUS MATERIALS	Emley, Warren E.	
1. Rubber	Wormeley, Philip L.	
2. Textiles	Appel, William D.	1922–59
3. Paper	Scribner, Bourdon W.	
4. Leather	Bowker, Roy C.	1918–43
VIII. METALLURGY	Rawdon, Dr Henry S.	
1. Optical Metallurgy	Rawdon, Dr Henry S.	
2. Thermal Metallurgy	*Dowdell, Dr Ralph L.	1928–30
3. Mechanical Metallurgy	Swanger, William H.	1921–42
4. Chemical Metallurgy	Jordan, Louis	
5. Experimental Foundry	Saeger, Charles M. Jr.	

*Hersey, senior physicist, 1928–31; to Vacuum Oil Co., New Jersey, 1931.
*Priest, died July 19, 1932.
*Washburn, died Feb. 6, 1934.
*Dowdell, to University of Minnesota, as Chairman, Department of Metallurgy, 1930.

Division / Section	Chief	Years
IX. CLAY AND SILICATE PRODUCTS	Bates, Phaon H.	
1. Whiteware	Geller, Roman F.	
2. Glass	Finn, Alfred N.	
3. Refractories	Heindl, Raymond A.	1923–55
4. Enamels	Harrison, William N.	1922–63
5. Heavy Clay Products	Stull, Ray T.	1927–44
6. Cement and Concrete Materials	Tucker, John Jr.	1916–17, 1926–49
7. Masonry Construction	Parsons, Douglas E.	1923–63
8. Lime and Gypsum	*Murray, James A.	1926–30
9. Stone	Kessler, Daniel W.	1914–52
X. SIMPLIFIED PRACTICE	Ely, Edwin W.	1923–47
1. Stone, Clay and Glass	*Colwell, Herbert R.	1921–31
2. Wood, Textiles and Paper	Schuster, George	
3. Metal Products and Construction Materials	*Dunn, Peter H. H.	1927–33
4. Containers	Braithwaite, William E.	
5. Promotion and Adherence	*Galt, Alexander B.	1924–33
XI. BUILDING AND HOUSING	*Taylor, James S.	1921–34
1. Building Codes	Thompson, George N.	1923–55
2. Building Practice and Homebuilders' Problems	Phelan, Vincent B.	1927–50
3. City Planning and Zoning	Taylor, James S.	
4. Construction Economics	*Riggleman, Dr John R.	1929–33
5. Mechanics Liens	*Wheeler, Daniel H.	1923–33
XII. SPECIFICATIONS	McAllister, Dr Addams S.	
1. Certification: Producer Contacts	*Martino, Robert A.	1923–33
2. Labeling: Consumer Contacts	McAllister, Dr Addams S.	
3. Directory of Specifications	*Ingels, Clarence W.	1928–33
4. Encyclopedia of Specifications	*Wardlaw, George A.	1930–33
XIII. TRADE STANDARDS	Fairchild, Ihler J.	1922–45
1. Wood Products, Paper, Rubber, etc.	*Steidle, Harry H.	1928–38
2. Metal Products	Fairchild, Ihler J.	
3. Textiles and Garments	Fairchild, Ihler J.	
4. Ceramic Products and Cement	Wray, George W.	

---

*Murray, to Warner Co., Pittsburgh, as Director of Research, 1930; died 1960.
*Colwell, to President's Emergency Committee for Employment, 1931.
*Dunn, to Department of Interior, 1933.
*Galt, resigned 1933.
*Taylor, to Federal Housing Administration, 1934.
*Riggleman, to National Recovery Administration, 1933.
*Wheeler, to Federal Emergency Administration, 1933.
*Martino, to National Recovery Administration, 1933; returned briefly to NBS in 1940.
*Ingels, to Navy Department, 1933.
*Wardlaw, to Navy Department, 1933
*Steidle, to private industry, 1938.

ADMINISTRATIVE, SCIENTIFIC, AND TECHNICAL STAFF CHIEFS

as of November 15, 1934

DIRECTOR	**Briggs, Dr Lyman J.**	
Assistant to the Director	Hubbard, Henry D.	1901–38
ASSISTANT DIRECTORS		
Assistant Director for Research and Testing	Crittenden, Dr Eugene C.	
Assistant Director for Commercial Standardization	McAllister, Dr Addams S.	
I. ELECTRICAL	Crittenden, Dr Eugene C.	
1. Resistance Measurements	Wenner, Dr Frank	
2. Inductance and Capacitance	Curtis, Dr Harvey L.	
3. Electrical Instruments	*Brooks, Dr Herbert B.	
4. Magnetic Measurements	Sanford, Raymond L.	
5. Photometry	Meyer, Dr J. Franklin	
6. Radio	Dellinger, Dr J. Howard	
7. Underground Corrosion	Logan, Kirk H.	
8. Electrochemistry	Vinal, Dr George W.	
9. Telephone Standards	Wolff, Dr Frank A.	
II. WEIGHTS AND MEASURES	*Holbrook, Fay S., and Bearce, Henry W.	
1. Length	Judson, Dr Lewis V.	
2. Mass	Pienkowsky, Dr Arthur T.	
3. Time	Gould, Ralph E.	
4. Capacity and Density	Peffer, Elmer L.	
5. Gas Measuring Instruments	Bean, Howard S.	
6. Thermal Expansivity, Dental Materials	Souder, Dr Wilmer	
7. Weights and Measures Laws and Administration	Smith, Ralph W.	
8. Railroad Scales and Test Cars	Holbrook, Fay S.	
9. Gage Standardization	Miller, David R.	
III. HEAT AND POWER	Dickinson, Dr Hobart C.	
1. Thermometry	Busse, Miss Johanna	
2. Pyrometry	Wensel, Dr Henry T.	
3. Heat Measurements	Mueller, Eugene F.	

*Brooks retired Jan. 31, 1939.
*Holbrook, died Feb. 4, 1940.

Division / Section	Chief	Years
III. HEAT AND POWER—Continued		
4. Heat Transfer	VanDusen, Dr Milton S.	
5. Cryogenic Laboratory	Brickwedde, Dr Ferdinand G.	
6. Fire Resistance	Ingberg, Simon H.	
7. Automotive Power Plant	Cummings, Herbert K.	
8. Lubrication and Liquid Fuels	Bridgeman, Dr Oscar C.	1927–45
IV. OPTICS	Skinner, Dr Clarence A.	
1. Spectroscopy	Meggers, Dr William F.	
2. Polarimetry	Bates, Frederick J.	
3. Colorimetry	Gibson, Dr Kasson S.	1916–55
4. Optical Instruments	Gardner, Dr Irvine C.	
5. Radiometry	Coblentz, Dr William W.	
6. Atomic Physics, Radium, X-Ray	Mohler, Dr Fred L.	
7. Photographic Technology	Davis, Raymond	
8. Interferometry	Peters, Chauncey G.	
V. CHEMISTRY	*Walker, Dr Percy H.	
0. Physico-chemical Research	Smith, Dr Edgar R.	1926–57
1. Paints, Varnishes, etc.	Hickson, Eugene F.	1918–50
2. Detergents, Cement, etc.	Smither, Frederick W.	
3. Organic Chemistry	Waters, Campbell E.	
4. Metal and Ore Analysis, Standard Samples	Lundell, Dr Gustave E. F.	
5. Reagents and Platinum Metals	Wichers, Dr Edward	
6. Electrochemistry (Plating)	Blum, Dr William	
7. Gas Chemistry	Weaver, Elmer R.	
VI. MECHANICS AND SOUND	Briggs, Dr Lyman J.	
1. Engineering Instruments and Mechanical Applicances	Stutz, Walter F.	
2. Sound	Heyl, Dr Paul R.	
3. Aeronautical Instruments	Brombacher, Dr William G.	
4. Aerodynamical Physics	Dryden, Dr Hugh L.	
5. Engineering Mechanics	Whittemore, Herbert L.	
6. Hydraulic Laboratory	Eaton, Herbert N.	
VII. ORGANIC AND FIBROUS MATERIALS	Emley, Warren E.	
1. Rubber	McPherson, Dr Archibald T.	
2. Textiles	Appel, William D.	
3. Paper	Scribner, Bourdon W.	
4. Leather	Bowker, Roy C.	
5. Testing and Specifications	Wormeley, Philip L.	
6. Industrial Utilization of Farm Wastes	Acree, Dr Solomon F.	1927–45

*Walker, retired, August 1937; consulting chemist to National Lead Co. subsidiary, 1937.

Division / Section	Chief	Years
VIII. METALLURGY	Rawdon, Dr Herbert S.	
1. Optical Metallurgy	McAdam, Dr Dunlop, J. Jr.	1930–48
2. Thermal Metallurgy	*Jordan, Louis	
3. Mechanical Metallurgy	Swanger, William H.	
4. Chemical Metallurgy	Thompson, Dr John G.	1921–24, 1930–56
5. Experimental Foundry	Saeger, Charles M., Jr.	
IX. CLAY AND SILICATE PRODUCTS	Bates, Phaon H.	
1. Whiteware	Geller, Roman F.	
2. Glass	Finn, Alfred N.	
3. Refractories	Heindl, Raymond A.	
4. Enameled Metals	Harrison, William N.	
5. Heavy Clay Products	Stull, Ray T.	
6. Cement and Concreting Materials	Tucker, John Jr.	
7. Masonry Construction	Parsons, Douglas E.	
8. Lime and Gypsum	Wells, Dr Lansing S.	1930–54
9. Stone	Kessler, Daniel W.	
X. SIMPLIFIED PRACTICE	Ely, Edwin W.	
1. Wood, Textiles, Paper	Schuster, George	
2. Metal Products and Construction Materials	Schuster, George	
3. Containers and Miscellaneous Products	Braithwaite, William E.	
4. Handling Equipment and Ceramics	Ely, Edwin W.	
XI. TRADE STANDARDS	Fairchild, Ihler J.	
1. Wood, Wood Products, Oils, etc.	Fairchild, Ihler J.	
2. Metal Products	Fairchild, Ihler, J.	
3. Textiles and Garments	Ehrman, H. A.	
4. Ceramic and Cement Products	Reynolds, Floyd W.	1918–19, 1930–NRF
5. Chemical and Miscellaneous Products.	Reynolds, Floyd W.	
XII. CODES AND SPECIFICATIONS	McAllister, Dr Addams S.	
1. Safety Codes	Lloyd, Dr Morton G.	
2. Building Codes	Thompson, George N.	
3. Building Practice and Specifications	Phelan, Vincent B.	
4. Producer Contacts and Certification	Wray, George W.	
5. Consumer Contacts and Labeling	McAllister, Dr Addams S.	

*Jordan, to American Institute of Mining and Metallurgical Engineering, Jan. 25, 1936.

ADMINISTRATIVE, SCIENTIFIC, AND TECHNICAL STAFF CHIEFS

as of May 1, 1940

DIRECTOR	**Briggs, Dr Lyman J.**
Assistant to the Director	*Hubbard, Henry D.
ASSISTANT DIRECTORS	
Assistant Director for Research and Testing	Crittenden, Dr Eugene C.
Assistant Director for Commercial Standardization	*McAllister, Dr Addams S.
I. ELECTRICITY	Crittenden, Dr Eugene C.
1. Resistance Measurements	*Wenner, Dr Frank
2. Inductance and Capacitance	Curtis, Dr Harvey L.
3. Electrical Instruments	Silsbee, Dr Francis B.
4. Magnetic Measurements	Sanford, Raymond L.
5. Photometry	*Meyer, Dr J. Franklin
6. Radio	Dellinger, Dr J. Howard
7. Underground Corrosion	Logan, Kirk H.
9. Electrochemistry	Vinal, Dr George W.
10. Telephone Standards	*Wolff, Dr Frank A.
II. WEIGHTS AND MEASURES	Bearce, Henry W.
1. Length	Judson, Dr Lewis V.
2. Mass	*Pienkowsky, Dr Arthur T.
3. Time	Gould, Ralph E.
4. Capacity and Density	Peffer, Elmer L.
5. Gas Measuring Instruments	Bean, Howard S.
6. Thermal Expansion, Dental Research	Souder, Dr Wilmer
7. Weights and Measures Administration	Smith, Ralph W.
8. Large-capacity Scales	Smith, Ralph W.
9. Limit Gages	Miller, David R.

*Hubbard, retired Sept. 1, 1938; died 1945.
*McAllister, retired, Feb. 28, 1945.
*Wenner, retired, 1943.
*Meyer, retired, Jan. 31, 1941 (ill health).
*Wolff, retired, Apr. 30, 1941.
*Pienkowsky, retired, 1944, and joined staff of Torsion Balance Co.; died Dec. 31, 1960.

III. HEAT AND POWER	Dickinson, Dr Hobart C.	
1. Thermometry	Busse, Miss Johanna	
2. Pyrometry	*Wensel, Dr Henry T.	
3. Heat Measurements	*Mueller, Eugene F.	
4. Heat Transfer	VanDusen, Dr Milton S.	
5. Cryogenic Laboratory	Brickwedde, Dr Ferdinand G.	
6. Fire Resistance	Ingberg, Simon H.	
7. Automotive Power Plants	Cummings, Herbert K.	
8. Lubrication and Liquid Fuels	Bridgeman, Dr Oscar C.	
9. Aviation Engines and Accessories	*Peters, Melville F.	1922–43
IV. OPTICS	*Skinner, Dr Clarence A.	
1. Spectroscopy	Meggers, Dr William F.	
2. Polarimetry	Bates, Frederick J.	
3. Colorimetry and Spectrophotometry	Gibson, Dr Kasson S.	
4. Optical Instruments	Gardner, Dr Irvine C.	
5. Radiometry	*Coblentz, Dr William W.	
6. Atomic Physics, Radium, X-Rays	Mohler, Dr Fred L.	
7. Photographic Technology	Davis, Raymond	
8. Interferometry	Peters, Chauncey G.	
V. CHEMISTRY	Lundell, Dr Gustave E. F.	
1. Paints, Varnishes, etc.	Hickson, Eugene F.	
2. Detergents, Cement, etc.	Smither, Frederick W.	
3. Organic Chemistry	*Waters, Campbell C.	
4. Metal and Ore Analysis, Standard Samples	Bright, Harry A.	1913–60
5. Reagents and Platinum Metals	Wichers, Dr Edward	
6. Electrochemistry (Plating)	Blum, Dr William	
7. Gas Chemistry	Weaver, Elmer R.	
8. Physical Chemistry	Smith, Dr Edgar R.	
9. Thermochemistry and Constitution of Petroleum	Rossini, Dr Frederick D.	1928–50
VI. MECHANICS AND SOUND	Dryden, Dr Hugh L.	
1. Engineering Instruments	Stutz, Walter F.	
2. Sound	*Heyl, Dr Paul R.	
3. Aeronautical Instruments	Brombacher, Dr William G.	
4. Aerodynamics	Dryden, Dr Hugh L.	
5. Engineering Mechanics	Whittemore, Herbert L.	
6. Hydraulics	Eaton, Herbert N.	

*Wensel, to General Staff, USA (Manhattan Project) 1942; acting chief, heat and power division 1945; assistant to Director on atomic energy research, 1946.
*Mueller, retired, 1944.
*Peters, to Titeflex Metal Hose Co., 1943.
*Skinner, retired, Jan. 31, 1941; died 1961.
*Coblentz, retired Jan. 1, 1945; NBS consultant; died Sept. 15, 1962.
*Waters, retired, 1942.
*Heyl, retired, July 1, 1942; died 1961.

Division / Section	Chief	Years
VII. ORGANIC AND FIBROUS MATERIALS	*Emley, Warren E.	
1. Rubber	McPherson, Dr Archibald T.	
2. Textiles	Appel, William D.	
3. Paper	Scribner, Bourdon W.	
4. Leather	*Bowker, Roy C.	
5. Testing and Specifications	Wormeley, Philip L.	
6. Fiber Structure	Acree, Dr Solomon F.	
7. Organic Plastics	Kline, Dr Gordon M.	1929–63
VIII. METALLURGY	Rawdon, Dr Herbert S.	
1. Optical Metallurgy	Rawdon, Dr Herbert S.	
2. Thermal Metallurgy	McAdam, Dr Dunlop J., Jr.	
3. Mechanical Metallurgy	*Swanger, William S.	
4. Chemical Metallurgy	Thompson, Dr John G.	
5. Experimental Foundry	*Saeger, Charles M., Jr.	
IX. CLAY AND SILICATE PRODUCTS	Bates, Phaon H.	
1. Whiteware	Geller, Roman F.	
2. Glass	*Finn, Alfred N.	
3. Refractories	Heindl, Raymond A.	
4. Enameled Metals	Harrison, William N.	
5. Heavy Clay Products	*Stull, Ray T.	
6. Cement and Concreting Materials	Tucker, John Jr.	
7. Masonry Construction	Parsons, Douglas E.	
8. Lime and Gypsum	Wells, Dr Lansing S.	
9. Stone	Kessler, Daniel W.	
X. SIMPLIFIED PRACTICE	Ely, Edwin W.	
1. Wood, Textiles, Paper	Schuster, George	
2. Metal Products and Construction Materials	Schuster, George	
3. Containers and Miscellaneous Products	Braithwaite, William E.	
4. Materials Handling Equipment and Ceramics	Ely, Edwin W.	
XI. TRADE STANDARDS	Fairchild, Ihler J.	
1. Wood, Wood Products, etc.	Medley, James W.	1938–NRF
2. Metal Products	Fairchild, Ihler J.	
3. Textiles	Ehrman, H. A.	
4. Apparel	Gilbert, L. R.	
5. Petroleum, Chemicals, Rubber	Reynolds, Floyd W.	
6. Export Standards	*Countryman, Milton E.	1940–42

*Emley, retired, Oct. 1, 1943; to War Production Board, 1943.
*Bowker, to OSRD, 1943.
*Swanger, died Aug. 19, 1942.
*Saeger, retired, June 27, 1945.
*Finn, died Sept. 21, 1942.
*Stull, died Jan. 5, 1944.
*Countryman, to War Production Board, 1942.

XII. CODES AND SPECIFICATIONS	McAllister, Dr Addams S.	
1. Safety Codes	*Lloyd, Dr Morton G.	
2. Building Codes	Thompson, George N.	
3. Building Practices and Specifications	Phelan, Vincent B.	
4. Producer Contracts and Certification	Wray, George W.	
5. Consumer Contracts and Labeling	Martino, Robert A.	
FIELD STATIONS		
Allentown, Pa. (Cement and Concrete Materials)	Moyer, W. N.	
Riverside, Calif. (Cement and Concrete Materials)	Evans, D. N.	
San Francisco, Calif. (Cement and Concrete Materials)	Furlong, I.	
Denver, Colo. (Cement and Concrete Materials)	Cox, O. H.	
Seattle, Wash. (Cement and Concrete Materials)	Carlson, Elmer T.	1928–NRF
Clearing, Ill. (Large-capacity Scale Testing)	Richard, C. L.	
San Jose, Calif. (Cement and Concrete Materials)	Foster, Bruce E.	1935–NRF
Beltsville, Md. (Radio Transmitting Station)	George, William D.	1929–63
Meadows, Md. (Radio Sending Station)	*Kirby, Samuel S.	1926–41

*Lloyd, died Apr. 26, 1941.
*Kirby, died Jan. 26, 1941.

ADMINISTRATIVE, SCIENTIFIC, AND TECHNICAL STAFF CHIEFS

as of July 1, 1945

DIRECTOR	***Briggs, Dr Lyman J.**	
ASSISTANT DIRECTOR	Crittenden, Dr Eugene C.	
I. ELECTRICITY	Crittenden, Dr Eugene C. Silsbee, Dr Francis B. (Assistant)	
1. Resistance Measurements	Thomas, Dr James L.	1927–
2. Inductance and Capacitance	*Curtis, Dr Harvey L.	
3. Electrical Instruments	Silsbee, Dr Francis B.	
4. Magnetic Measurements	Sanford, Raymond L.	
5. Radio	*Dellinger, Dr J. Howard	
7. Underground Corrosion	*Logan, Kirk H.	
9. Electrochemistry	Vinal, Dr George W.	
II. WEIGHTS AND MEASURES	*Bearce, Henry W. Souder, Dr Wilmer (Assistant)	
1. Length	Judson, Dr Lewis V.	
2. Mass	McCurdy, Lloyd B.	
3. Time	*Gould, Ralph E.	
4. Capacity and Density	*Peffer, Elmer L.	
5. Gas Measuring Instruments	Bean, Howard S.	
6. Thermal Expansion; Dental Research	Souder, Dr Wilmer	
7. Weights and Measures Administration	Smith, Ralph W.	
8. Large-capacity Scales	Russell, H. Haig	1919–
9. Limit Gages	Miller, David R.	
III. HEAT AND POWER	*Dickinson, Dr Hobart C. Cragoe, Carl S. (Assistant)	1918–50
1. Thermometry	*Busse, Miss Johanna	

*Briggs, retired, Nov. 5, 1945; died Mar. 25, 1963.
*Curtis, to Ordnance Development Division, 1946; retired late that year.
*Dellinger, retired, Apr. 30, 1948; NBS consultant.
*Logan, to Cast Iron Pipe Research Association, 1944.
*Bearce, retired Sept. 30, 1945.
*Gould, retired, 1950.
*Peffer, died July 1948.
*Dickinson, retired Oct. 31, 1945; died Nov. 27, 1949.
*Cragoe, resigned 1950.
*Busse, Miss, retired, 1949.

Division / Section	Chief	Years
III. HEAT AND POWER—Continued		
2. Pyrometry	*VanDusen, Dr Milton S.	
3. Heat Measurements	Cragoe, Carl S.	
4. Heat Transfer	Dill, Richard S.	1928–57
5. Cryogenics	Brickwedde, Dr Ferdinand G.	
6. Fire Resistance	*Ingberg, Simon H.	
7. Automotive Power Plants	*Brooks, Donald B.	1922–24, 1927–49
8. Lubricants and Liquid Fuels	*Bridgeman, Dr Oscar C.	
9. Aircraft Engines	*Cummings, Herbert K.	
IV. OPTICS	*Bates, Frederick J. Gibson, Dr Kasson S. (Assistant)	
1. Spectroscopy	Meggers, Dr William F.	
2. Polarimetry	Bates, Frederick J.	
3. Photometry and Colorimetry	Gibson, Dr Kasson S.	
4. Optical Instruments	Gardner, Dr Irvine C.	
5. Radiometry	Humphreys, Dr Curtis J.	1928–53
6. Atomic Physics	Mohler, Dr Fred L.	
7. Photographic Technology	Davis, Raymond	
8. Interferometry	*Peters, Chauncey G.	
9. Radioactivity	Curtiss, Dr Leon F.	1926–61
10. X-Rays	Taylor, Dr Lauriston S.	1927–
V. CHEMISTRY	*Lundell, Dr Gustave E. F. Wichers, Dr Edward (Asst.)	
1. Paints, Varnishes, Bituminous Materials	Hickson, Eugene F.	
2. Detergents, Cements, Miscellaneous Materials	*Smither, FrederickW.	
3. Organic Chemistry	Smith, W. Harold	
4. Metal and Ore Analysis; Standard Samples	Bright, Harry A.	
5. Reagents and Platinum Metals	Gilchrist, Dr Raleigh	1918–62
6. Electrochemistry (Plating)	Blum, Dr William	
7. Gas Chemistry	Weaver, Elmer R.	
8. Physical Chemistry	Smith, Dr Edgar R.	
9. Thermochemistry	Rossini, Dr Frederick D.	
10. pH Standards	*Acree, Dr Solomon F.	

*VanDusen, retired, 1946.
*Ingberg, retired, July 1, 1947.
*Brooks, retired, 1949.
*Bridgeman, to Phillips Petroleum Co., 1945.
*Cummings, section discontinued; NBS consultant, 1948– .
*Bates, F. J., retired, Jan. 31, 1947.
*Peters, retired, 1949; died 1955.
*Lundell, retired, June 1948; NBS consultant, 1948–50; died June 8, 1950.
*Smither, retired, August 1946; died Mar. 8, 1961.
*Acree, retired, Dec. 31, 1945; died Oct. 23, 1957.

Division / Section	Chief	Years
VI. MECHANICS AND SOUND	*Dryden, Dr Hugh L.	
	*Tuckerman, Dr Louis B. (Assistant)	1919–49
1. Engineering Instruments	*Stutz, Walter F.	
2. Sound	Cook, Dr Richard K.	1935–
3. Aeronautical Instruments	Brombacher, Dr William G.	
4. Aerodynamics	Dryden, Dr Hugh L.	
5. Engineering Mechanics	*Whittemore, Herbert L.	
6. Hydraulics	Eaton, Herbert N.	
7. Special Projects	Eaton, Herbert N.	
VII. ORGANIC AND FIBROUS MATERIALS	McPherson, Dr Archibald T.	
	*Wormeley, Philip L. (Assistant)	
1. Rubber	Wood, Dr Lawrence A.	1935–
2. Textiles	Appel, William D.	
3. Paper	Scribner, Bourdon W.	
4. Leather	Wallace, Everett L.	
5. Testing and Specifications	Wormeley, Philip L.	
6. Organic Plastics	Kline, Dr Gordon M.	
VIII. METALLURGY	*Rawdon, Dr Herbert S.	
	Thompson, Dr John G. (Assistant)	
1. Optical Metallurgy	Rawdon, Dr Herbert S.	
2. Thermal Metallurgy	*McAdam, Dr Dunlop J. Jr.	
3. Mechanical Metallurgy	Roeser, William F.	1920–64
4. Chemical Metallurgy	Thompson, Dr John G.	
5. Experimental Foundry	Krynitsky, Alexander I.	1918–50
IX. CLAY AND SILICATE PRODUCTS	*Bates, Phaon H.	
	Parsons, Douglas E. (Asst.)	
1. Whiteware	Geller, Roman F.	
2. Glass	Hahner, Clarence H.	1929–
3. Refractories	Heindl, Raymond A.	
4. Enameled Metals	Harrison, William N.	
6. Cement and Concreting Materials.	*Tucker, John Jr.	

---

*Dryden, assistant director, NBS, January 1946; associate director, NBS, June 1946; to National Advisory Committee for Aeronautics as director of research, September 1947; deputy administrator, National Aeronautics and Space Administration, August 1958.

*Tuckerman, retired, Sept. 30, 1949.

*Stutz, retired, 1947.

*Whittemore, retired, Oct. 31, 1946.

*Wormeley, retired, Dec. 31, 1947.

*Rawdon, retired, Oct. 31, 1945.

*McAdam, retired, 1947; NBS consultant, 1948–

*Bates, P. H., retired, Sept. 15, 1945.

*Tucker, died, Nov. 20, 1949.

IX. CLAY AND SILICATE PRODUCTS—Continued		
7. Masonry Construction	Parsons, Douglas E.	
8. Lime and Gypsum	Wells, Dr Lansing S.	
9. Stone	Kessler, Daniel W.	
X. SIMPLIFIED PRACTICE	Ely, Edwin W. Schuster, George (Asst.)	
1. Wood, Textiles, Paper, Rubber	Schuster, George	
2. Metal and Mechanical Products.	Umhau, George E.	
3. Containers and Miscellaneous Products.	Braithwaite, William E.	
4. Materials Handling Equipment and Ceramics.	Ely, Edwin W.	
5. Electrical Products	*Tait, Andres C.	1942–50
6. Construction Materials	*Poiesz, Clemens J.	1942–49
7. Metal and Wood Working Tools.	Umhau, George E.	
XI. TRADE STANDARDS	*Fairchild, Ihler J. Reynolds, Foyd W. (Asst.)	
1. Wood, Wood Products, Paper	Medley, J. W.	
2. Metal Products	*Powell, Franklin E.	1943–50
3. Textiles	Ehrman, H. A.	
4. Apparel	Gilbert, L. R.	
5. Chemical and Miscellaneous Products	Reynolds, Floyd W.	
6. Export Standards	Barrett, Edward C.	1942–56
7. Petroleum and Rubber Products	*Gale, G. S.	1942–47
XII. CODES AND SPECIFICATIONS	Thompson, George N. *Dickinson, John A. (Asst.)	 1919–59
1. Safety Codes	Dickinson, John A.	
2. Building Codes	Thompson, George N.	
3. Building Practices and Specifications	*Phelan, Vincent B.	
4. Producer Contacts and Certification	*Booth, Sherman F.	1939–62
5. Consumer Contacts and Labeling	*Cooley, Paul A.	1943–47

*Tait, transferred to Treasury Department, 1950.
*Poiesz, to Bureau of Indian Affairs, 1949.
*Fairchild, retired, 1945; to Plumbing Fixtures Association.
*Powell, transferred to Defense Department, 1950.
*Gale, reduction in force, 1947.
*Dickinson, J. A., retired, Sept. 30, 1959.
*Phelan, retired, Aug. 31, 1950.
*Booth, retired, 1962.
*Cooley, to Commodity Standards Division, Department of Commerce, 1947; to Bureau of Foreign and Domestic Commerce, 1951.

ORDNANCE DEVELOPMENT	*Diamond, Harry	1927–48
Assistant	Astin, Dr Allen V.	1932–
Chief Engineer	Hinman, Wilbur S. Jr.	1928–53
1. Proof Operations	Godfrey, Theodore B.	1928–53
2. Analysis and Recording	*White, Dr Thomas N.	1942–46
3. Electronic Engineering	Page, Dr Chester H.	1941–
4. Mechanical Engineering	Rabinow, Jacob	1934–53
5. Production Engineering	*Brunetti, Dr Cledo	1941–49
6. Control Testing	*Heilprin, Dr Laurence B.	1941–51
7. Basic Engineering	*Miller, Dr Bertrand J.	1943–48
8. Special Projects	Silsbee, Dr Francis B.	
FIELD STATIONS		
Beltsville, Md. (Radio Transmitting Station).	George, William D.	
Sterling, Va. (Radio Receiving Station).	*Pineo, Victor C.	1942–57
Clearing, Ill. (Standardization of Test Weight Cars).	Russell, H. Haig	
Allentown, Pa. (Cement Testing and Inspection).	Moyer, W. N.	
San Jose, Calif. (Cement Testing and Inspection).	Foster, Bruce E.	
Riverside, Calif. (Cement Testing and Inspection).	Evans, D. N.	
Seattle, Wash. (Cement Testing and Inspection).	Winblade, F. N.	
Denver, Colo. (Cement and Concrete Materials Testing).	Cox, O. H.	
San Francisco, Calif. (Cement, Concrete and Miscellaneous Materials).	Bohn, Richard A.	1928–NRF

*Diamond, died, Mar. 21, 1948.
*White, to Strategic Air Command, 1946.
*Brunetti, to Stanford Research Institute as associate director, 1949.
*Heilprin, to Taut Engineering Co. as consultant physicist, 1951.
*Miller, to Zenith Radio Corp., June 1948.
*Pineo, to Lincoln Laboratory, M.I.T., 1957.

ADMINISTRATIVE, SCIENTIFIC, AND TECHNICAL STAFF CHIEFS

as of March 1, 1950

DIRECTOR	**Condon, Dr. Edward U.**	**1945–51**
ASSOCIATE DIRECTORS	*Crittenden, Dr Eugene C.	
	*Brode, Dr Wallace R.	1923–28, 1947–58
ASSISTANTS TO THE DIRECTOR	Vinogradoff, Dmitri I.	
	Golovin, Nicholas E.	1949–58
	Odishaw, Hugh	1946–59
OFFICE OF SCIENTIFIC PUBLICATIONS	Odishaw, Hugh	
OFFICE OF WEIGHTS AND MEASURES	*Smith, Ralph W.	
	Bussey, William S. (Assistant)	1948–
I. ELECTRICITY AND OPTICS	Silsbee, Dr Francis B.	
	Gibson, Dr Kasson S. (Assistant)	
1. Resistance Measurements	Thomas, Dr James L.	
2. Inductance and Capacitance	*Moon, Dr Charles	1923–53
3. Electrical Instruments	Defandorf, Dr Francis M.	1916–
4. Magnetic Measurements	*Sanford, Raymond L.	
5. Photometry and Colorimetry	Gibson, Dr Kasson S.	
6. Optical Instruments	Gardner, Dr Irvine C.	
7. Photographic Technology	Davis, Raymond	
8. Electrochemistry	*Vinal, Dr George W.	
II. METROLOGY	Souder, Dr Wilmer	
	*Miller, David R. (Assistant)	
1. Length	Judson, Dr Lewis V.	
2. Mass	Macurdy, Lloyd B.	

*Crittenden, retired, Dec. 31, 1950; died Mar. 8, 1956.
*Brode, at Ohio State University, professor of organic chemistry, 1928–47; guest worker 1958 to date.
*Smith, retired, Nov. 1, 1950; NBS consultant, 1950 to date.
*Moon, died Jan. 31, 1953.
*Sanford, retired, 1954; NBS consultant, 1954 to date.
*Vinal, retired, June 30, 1950.
*Miller, retired, 1952.

II. METROLOGY—Continued		
3. Time	*Bowman, Horace A.	1946–
4. Capacity, Density, Fluid Measures	Bean, Howard S.	
6. Thermal Expansion	*Hidnert, Dr Peter	1911–57
7. Dental Materials	Schoonover, Dr Irl C.	1928–
8. Scales	Russell, H. Haig	
9. Gages	Miller, David R.	
III. HEAT AND POWER	Brickwedde, Dr Ferdinand G.	
1. Temperature Measurements	*Wilson, Dr Raymond E.	1947–53
2. Thermodynamics	Brickwedde, Dr Ferdinand C.	
3. Cryogenics	Scott, Russell B.	1928–
4. Engines and Lubrication	*McKee, Samuel A.	1921–53
5. Engine Fuels	Howard, Dr Frank L.	1937–
6. Combustion	Fiock, Dr Ernest F.	1926–
IV. ATOMIC AND RADIATION PHYSICS	Huntoon, Dr Robert D.	1941–
Assistant	Taylor, Dr Lauriston S.	
Consultant on Radioactivity	Curtiss, Dr Leon F.	
Consultant on Stable Tracers	Mohler, Dr Fred L.	
AEC Coordinator	Huntoon, Dr Robert D.	
Atomic Physics Laboratory	Huntoon, Dr Robert D.	
1. Spectroscopy	Meggers, Dr William F.	
2. Radiometry	*Humphreys, Dr Curtis J.	
3. Mass Spectrometry	Mohler, Dr Fred L.	
4. Physical Electronics	*Bennett, Dr Willard H.	1946–50
5. Electron Physics	Marton, Dr Ladislaus L.	1946–
6. Atomic Physics	*Hipple, Dr John A.	1947–53
7. Neutron Measurements	Curtiss, Dr Leon F.	
Radiation Physics Laboratory	Taylor, Dr Lauriston S.	
8. Nuclear Physics	Fano, Dr Ugo	1946–
9. Radioactivity	Taylor, Dr Lauriston S.	
10. X Rays	Wyckoff, Dr Harold O.	1941–
11. Betatron	Koch, Dr Herman W.	1949–
12. Nucleonic Instrumentation	Wyckoff, Dr Harold O.	
13. Radiological Equipment	Smith, Dr Scott W.	1947–

---

*Bowman, attached to division 6, sec. 6, Mass and Scale, 1954.

*Hidnert, transferred to Office of Weights and Measures, 1954; retired, Mar. 31, 1957; died June 10, 1964.

*Wilson, to Emerson Research Laboratories as principal physicist, 1954.

*McKee, retired, 1953.

*Humphreys, transferred to Corona Laboratories, September 1951; to Naval Ordnance Laboratory, 1953.

*Bennett, resigned, September 1950.

*Hipple, to Mineral Industries Experiment Station, Pennsylvania State College as director, 1953.

Division / Section	Chief	Years
V. CHEMISTRY	Wichers, Dr Edward	
	*Blum, Dr William (Assistant)	
1. Paint, Varnish, Lacquers	*Hickson, Eugene F.	
2. Surface Chemistry	Hoffman, Dr James I.	1918–62
3. Organic Chemistry	Smith, W. Harold	
4. Analytical Chemistry	Bright, Harry A.	
5. Platinum Metals and Pure Substances	Gilchrist, Dr Raleigh	
6. Electrodeposition	Blum, Dr William	
7. Gas Chemistry and pH Standards	Weaver, Elmer R.	
8. Physical Chemistry	Smith, Dr Edgar R.	
9. Thermochemistry and Hydrocarbons	*Rossini, Dr Frederick D.	
10. Spectrochemistry	Scribner, Bourdon F.	1927–
VI. MECHANICS	Ramberg, Dr Walter	1931–59
1. Sound	Cook, Dr Richard K.	
2. Mechanical Instruments	*Brombacher, Dr William G.	
3. Aerodynamics	Schubauer, Dr Galen B.	1936–
4. Engineering Mechanics	Wilson, Bruce L.	1929–
5. Hydraulics	*Eaton, Herbert N.	
VII. ORGANIC AND FIBROUS MATERIALS	McPherson, Dr Archibald T.	
	Kline, Dr Gordon M. (Assistant)	
	*Simha, Dr Robert (Consultant)	1944–51
1. Rubber	Wood, Dr Lawrence A.	
2. Textiles	Appel, William D.	
3. Paper	*Scribner, Bourdon W.	
4. Leather	Wallace, Everett L.	
5. Testing and Specifications	Stiehler, Dr Robert D.	1946–
6. Organic Plastics	Kline, Dr Gordon M.	
VIII. METALLURGY	Thompson, Dr John G.	
	Roeser, William F. (Assistant)	
1. Optical Metallurgy	Ellinger, George A.	1929–
2. Thermal Metallurgy	Digges, Thomas G.	1920–62
3. Mechanical Metallurgy	Roeser, William F.	
4. Chemical Metallurgy	*Cleaves, Harold E.	1912–15, 1930–53

*Blum, retired, Jan. 1, 1952.
*Hickson, retired, 1950.
*Rossini, to Chairman, Department of Chemistry, Carnegie Institute of Technology, 1950.
*Brombacher, retired, 1954.
*Eaton, retired, Jan. 31, 1953; NBS consulting engineer, 1953 to date.
*Simha, to New York University, 1951; subsequently to University of Southern California.
*Scribner, died Mar. 5, 1952.
*Cleaves, retired, 1953.

Division / Section	Chief	Years
VIII. METALLURGY—Continued		
5. Experimental Foundry	*Krynitsky, Alexander I.	
6. Underground Corrosion	*Denison, Dr Irving A.	1929–53
IX. MINERAL PRODUCTS	Insley, Dr Herbert	1922–53
1. Porcelain and Pottery	Geller, Roman F.	
2. Glass	Hahner, Clarence H.	
3. Refractories	Heindl, Raymond A.	
4. Enameled Metals	Harrison, William N.	
5. Building Stone	*Kessler, Daniel W.	
6. Concreting Materials	Blaine, Raymond L.	1929–
7. Constitution and Microstructure	McMurdie, Howard F.	1928–
8. Chemistry of Mineral Products	*Wells, Dr Lansing S.	
X. BUILDING TECHNOLOGY	Parsons, Douglas E. Thompson, George N. (Assistant)	
1. Structural Engeering	Parsons, Douglas E.	
2. Fire Protection	*Mitchell, Nolan D.	1922–52
3. Heating and Air Conditioning	Dill, Richard S.	
4. Exterior and Interior Coverings	Snoke, Dr Hubert R.	1920–60
5. Codes and Specifications	Thompson, George N.	
XI. APPLIED MATHEMATICS	*Curtiss, Dr John H. Cannon, Dr Edward W. (Assistant)	1946–53 1946–
1. Numerical Analysis	*Rosser, Dr J. Barkley	1949–51
2. Computation Laboratory	Alt, Dr Franz L.	1948–
3. Statistical Engineering	Eisenhart, Dr Churchill	1946–
4. Machine Development	Cannon, Dr Edward W.	
XII. COMMODITY STANDARDS	*Ely, Edwin W. Reynolds, Floyd W. (Assistant)	
1. Metal and Ceramic Products	Schuster, George	
2. Textiles and Apparel	Ehrman, H. A.	
3. Mechanical Equipment	Medley, J. W.	
4. Packaging	Braithwaite, William E.	
5. Chemical Products	Reynolds, Floyd W.	

*Krynitsky, retired, 1950.

*Denison, to Diamond Ordnance Fuze Laboratories, 1953.

*Kessler, to Kessler Stone Research Laboratory as materials engineer, 1952; NBS consultant, 1952 to date.

*Wells, died 1954.

*Mitchell, retired, September 1952; NBS consultant, 1952 to date.

*Curtiss, assistant to Director, April 1946; National Applied Mathematics Laboratories, 1947; to Institute of Mathematical Science and adjunct professor of math, New York University, 1953.

*Rosser, to Army Ordnance, 1951.

*Ely, NBS liaison with Commodity Standards Division, Department of Commerce, 1947–50; transferred with division to Office of Technical Services, Department of Commerce, 1950.

Division / Section	Chief	Years
XIII. ELECTRONICS AND ORDNANCE	Astin, Dr Allen V.	
Assistant Chief for Ordnance	*Hinman, Wilbur S. Jr.	
Assistant Chief for Aerophysics	Skramstad, Dr Harold K.	1935–
Electronics Consultant	Huntoon, Dr Robert D.	
Electronics Consultant	Page, Dr Chester H.	
Electronics Standards Laboratory	(Vacant)	
1. Engineering Electronics	*Reid, J. Gilman Jr.	1937–54
2. Electron Tubes	White, Dr John E.	1946–
3. Electronic Computers	Alexander, Samuel N.	1946–
Ordnance Development Laboratory.	Hinman, Wilbur S. Jr.	
4. Ordnance Research	*Goldberg, Dr Harold	1947–
5. Ordnance Mechanics	*Rabinow, Jacob	
6. Ordnance Electronics	Guarino, P. Anthony	1948–
7. Ordnance Engineering	Domsitz, M. G.	1942–
8. Ordnance Tests	*Godfrey, Theodore B.	
Guidance Missile Laboratory	Lamm, Ralph A.	1947–
9. Missile Dynamics	Skramstad, Dr Harold K.	
10. Missile Intelligence	Atchison, Dr F. Stanley	1942–
11. Missile Engineering	Lamm, Ralph A.	
12. Missile Instrumentation	Wildhack, William A.	1935–
13. Technical Services	McLean, J. D.	
XIV. CENTRAL RADIO PROPAGATION LABORATORY	*Smith, Dr Newbern	1935–54
Assistant Chief	McNish, Alvin G.	1946–
Assistant Chief	Norton, Kenneth A.	1946–
Microwave Research Consultant	Carroll, T. J.	
Ionospheric Research Laboratory		
1. Upper Atmosphere Research	McNish, Alvin G.	
5. Ionospheric Research	Bateman, Ross	
7. Field Operations	Hutchison, H. P.	
Systems Research Laboratory		
3. Regular Propagation Services	Chadwick, Walter B.	
4. Frequency Utilization Research	Norton, Kenneth A.	
6. Tropospheric Propagation Research	Herbstreit, Jack W.	
Measurements Standards Laboratory		
8. High Frequency Standards	George, William D.	
9. Microwave Standards	*Lyons, Dr Harold A.	1941–55

*Hinman, to Diamond Ordnance Fuze Laboratories, September 1953.
*Reid, to private industry, January 1954.
*Goldberg, and most of the Ordnance Development and Guidance Missile staffs, transferred to Diamond Ordnance Fuze Laboratories, 1953.
*Rabinow, to Diamond Ordnance Fuze Laboratories, 1953.
*Godfrey, to Diamond Ordnance Fuze Laboratories as division chief, 1953.
*Smith, N., to full-time technical work, Aug. 29, 1953, Dr Brode replacing him as division chief; resigned 1954.
*Lyons, resigned, May 1951.

FIELD STATIONS

Brookline, Mass. (Electricity and Optics—Lamp Inspection)
Clearing, Ill. (Metrology—Master Scale Depot)
Allentown, Pa. (Mineral Products—Cement Testing and Inspection)
Riverside, Calif. (Mineral Products—Cement Testing and Inspection)
Permanente, Calif. (Mineral Products—Cement Testing and Inspection)
Seattle, Wash. (Mineral Products—Cement Testing and Inspection)
Denver, Colo. (Mineral Products—Cement and Concrete Materials)
San Francisco, Calif. (Mineral Products—Materials Testing Station)
Los Angeles, Calif. (Applied Mathematics—Institute for Numerical Analysis)
LaPlata, Md. (Electronics—Blossom Point Proving Ground)
Tuckerton, N.J. (Electronics—Warren Grove Test Field)
Anchorage, Alaska (Central Radio Propagation Laboratory—Radio Propagation Field Station)
Point Barrow, Alaska (Central Radio Propagation Laboratory—Radio Propagation Field Station)
Guam Island (Central Radio Propagation Laboratory—Radio Propagation Field Station)
Puunene Maui, Hawaii (Central Radio Propagation Laboratory—Radio Propagation Field Station)
Honolulu, Hawaii (Central Radio Propagation Laboratory—Radio Propagation Field Station)
Puerto Rico (Central Radio Propagation Laboratory—Radio Propagation Field Station)
Trinidad, British West Indies (Central Radio Propagation Laboratory—Radio Propagation Field Station)
Las Cruces, N. Mex. (Central Radio Propagation Laboratory—Radio Propagation Field Station)
Fort Belvoir, Va. (Central Radio Propagation Laboratory—Radio Propagation Field Station)
Sterling, Va. (Central Radio Propagation Laboratory—Radio Propagation Field Station)
Beltsville, Md. (Central Radio Propagation Laboratory—Radio Propagation Field Station)

ADMINISTRATIVE, SCIENTIFIC, AND TECHNICAL STAFF CHIEFS

as of October 1, 1954

DIRECTOR	**Astin, Dr Allen V.**	
Associate Director for Chemistry	*Brode, Dr Wallace R.	
Associate Director for Physics	Huntoon, Dr Robert D.	
Associate Director for Testing	McPherson, Dr Archibald T.	
Associate Director for Administration	*Golovin, Nicholas E.	
Consultants to the Director	Crittenden, Dr Eugene C.	
	Curtiss, Dr Leon F.	
	Page, Dr Chester H.	
	*Souder, Dr Wilmer	
	McNish, Alvin G.	
OFFICE OF SCIENTIFIC PUBLICATIONS	Brode, Dr Wallace R.	
OFFICE OF WEIGHTS AND MEASURES	Bussey, William S.	
Assistant	Jensen, Malcolm W.	1951–
Consultant	Smith, Ralph W.	
OFFICE OF BASIC INSTRUMENTATION	Wildhack, William A.	
I. ELECTRICITY AND ELECTRONICS	*Silsbee, Dr Francis B.	
	*Stansbury, Carroll (Assistant)	1948–59
1. Resistance and Reactance	Thomas, Dr James L.	
2. Electron Tubes	Marsden, Dr Charles P. Jr.	1949–
3. Electrical Instruments	Defandorf, Dr Francis M.	
4. Magnetic Measurements	Cooter, Irving L.	1930–
5. Process Technology	*Tuckerman, Lucien P.	1949–56

*Brode, Science Advisor to Secretary of State, 1958.
*Golovin, to White Sands Proving Ground as Chief Scientist, 1958.
*Souder, retired, 1954.
*Silsbee, retired, July 31, 1959; NBS consultant.
*Stansbury, retired for reasons of ill health, October 1958.
*Tuckerman, transferred to Diamond Ordnance Fuze Laboratory, July 1, 1956.

Division / Section	Chief	Dates
I. ELECTRICITY AND ELECTRONICS—Continued		
6. Engineering Electronics	*Selgin, Dr Paul J.	1947–55
7. Electronic Instrumentation	Stansbury, Carroll	
8. Electrochemistry	Hamer, Dr Walter J.	1935–
II. OPTICS AND METROLOGY	*Gardner, Dr Irvine C. *Gibson, Dr Kasson S. (Assistant)	
1. Photometry and Colorimetry	Gibson, Dr Kasson S.	
2. Optical Instruments	Washer, Dr Francis E.	1935–
3. Photographic Technology	*Davis, Raymond	
4. Length	*Judson, Dr Lewis V.	
5. Engineering Metrology	Fullmer, Irwin H.	1917–
III. HEAT AND POWER	*Brickwedde, Dr Ferdinand G.	
1. Temperature Measurements	Brickwedde, Dr Ferdinand G.	
2. Thermodynamics	Beckett, Dr Charles W.	1950–
3. Cryogenic Physics	Hudson, Dr Ralph P.	1951–
4. Engines and Lubrication	Swindells, James F.	1927–
5. Engine Fuels	Howard, Dr Frank L.	
6. Free Radicals Research (1956–59)	*Broida, Dr Herbert P.	1949–59
IV. ATOMIC AND RADIATION PHYSICS	Taylor, Dr Lauriston S.	
Atomic Physics Laboratory	(Vacant)	
1. Spectroscopy	*Meggers, Dr William F.	
2. Radiometry	Plyler, Dr Earle K.	1945–63
3. Mass Spectroscopy	Mohler, Dr Fred L.	
4. Solid State Physics	*Breckenridge, Dr Robert G.	1949–55
5. Electron Physics	Marton, Dr Ladislaus L.	
6. Atomic Physics	Branscomb, Dr Lewis M.	1951–
Radiation Physics Laboratory	Wyckoff, Dr Harold O.	
8. Nuclear Physics	Fano, Dr Ugo	
9. Radioactivity	Mann, Dr Wilfrid B.	
10. X Rays	Wyckoff, Dr Harold O.	
11. Betatron	Koch, Dr Herman W.	
12. Nucleonic Instrumentation	Costrell, Louis	1946–

---

*Selgin, resigned to take up private consultant work, continuing part-time work with NBS.
*Gardner, retired, July 8, 1959.
*Gibson, retired, January 1955.
*Davis, retired, April 1958; NBS consultant.
*Judson, transferred to Office of Weights and Measures, Mar. 22, 1959.
*Brickwedde, to Pennsylvania State University as dean of College of Chemistry and Physics, February 1957.
*Broida, succeeded by Dr Arnold M. Bass, July 1, 1959; program terminated Oct. 1, 1959; returned as senior research fellow 1961–62.
*Meggers, retired, July 31, 1958; NBS consultant.
*Plyler, retired, Oct. 7, 1963.
*Breckenridge, resigned, May 1, 1955.

IV. ATOMIC AND RADIATION PHYSICS—Continued		
13. Radiological Equipment	Smith, Dr Scott W.	
14. Radiation Instruments Branch, AEC	Butenhoff, Robert L.	
V. CHEMISTRY	Wichers, Dr Edward	
	Hoffman, Dr James I. (Assistant)	
1. Organic Coatings	Howard, Paul T.	1922–
2. SurfaceChemistry	Hoffman, Dr James I.	
3. Organic Chemistry	*Smith, W. Harold	
4. Analytical Chemistry	*Bright, Harry A.	
5. Inorganic Chemistry	Gilchrist, Dr Raleigh	
6. Electrodeposition	Brenner, Dr Abner	1930–
7. Gas Chemistry	*Weaver, Elmer R.	
8. Physical Chemistry	*Smith, Dr Edgar R	
9. Thermochemistry	Prosen, Edward J.	1936–
10. Spectrochemistry	Scribner, Bourdon F.	
11. Pure Substances	Saylor, Dr Charles P.	1931–
VI. MECHANICS	*Ramberg, Dr Walter	
	Souder, Dr Wilmer (Consultant)	
1. Sound	Cook, Dr Richard K.	
2. Mechanical Instruments	Lloyd, Edward C.	1954–
3. Fluid Mechanics	Schubauer, Dr Galen B.	
4. Engineering Mechanics	Wilson, Bruce L.	
6. Mass and Scale	Tate, Douglas R.	
7. Capacity, Density, and Fluid Meters	*Bean, Howard S.	
8. Combustion Controls	*Fiock, Dr Ernest F.	
VII. ORGANIC AND FIBROUS MATERIALS	Kline, Dr Gordon M.	
	*Appel, William D. (Assistant)	
1. Rubber	Wood, Dr Lawrence A.	
2. Textiles	Appel, William D.	
3. Paper	Hobbs, Dr Robert B.	1930–
4. Leather	*Wallace, Everett L.	
5. Testing and Specifications	Stiehler, Dr Robert D.	
6. Polymer Structure	Bekkedahl, Dr Norman P.	1931–

---

*Smith, W. H., retired, Feb. 1, 1957; NBS consultant; died Apr. 14, 1959.
*Bright, retired, Feb. 29, 1960; died May 22, 1961.
*Weaver, retired, May 31, 1957.
*Smith, E. R., retired, June 30, 1957.
*Ramberg, to U.S. Embassy in Rome, Department of State, as scientific officer, Mar. 1, 1959.
*Bean, retired, July 1, 1958.
*Fiock, to Rocket Fuels Division, Phillips Petroleum Co., Texas, as technical director, March 1956.
*Appel, retired, Jan. 31, 1959.
*Wallace, retired, Jan. 1, 1955.

Division / Section	Chief	Years
VII. ORGANIC AND FIBROUS MATERIALS—Continued		
7. Organic Plastics	Reinhart, Frank W.	1937–
8. Dental Research	Sweeney, William T.	1922–
VIII. METALLURGY	*Thompson, Dr John G.	
1. Thermal Metallurgy	Digges, Thomas G.	
2. Chemical Metallurgy	Wyman, Leroy L.	1953–
3. Mechanical Metallurgy	Bennett, John A.	1936–
4. Corrosion	Ellinger, George A.	
IX. MINERAL PRODUCTS	Schoonover, Dr Irl C. Hahner, Clarence H. (Assistant)	
1. Porcelain and Pottery	*Geller, Roman F.	
2. Glass	Hahner, Clarence H.	
3. Refractories	*Heindl, Raymond A.	
4. Enameled Metals	Harrison, William N.	
6. Concreting Materials	Blaine, Raymond L.	
7. Constitution and Microstructure	McMurdie, Howard F.	
X. BUILDING TECHNOLOGY	Parsons, Douglas E. *Thompson, George N. (Assistant) Roeser, William F. (Consultant) *McBurney, John W. (Consultant)	1935–56
1. Structural Engineering	Parsons, Douglas E.	
2. Fire Protection	Robertson, Dr Alexander F.	1950–
3. Heating and Air Conditioning	*Dill, Richard S.	
4. Floor, Roof, and Wall Coverings	*Snoke, Dr Hubert R.	
5. Codes and Specifications	Thompson, George N.	
XI. APPLIED MATHEMATICS	Alt, Dr Franz L. Cannon, Dr Edward W. (Assistant)	
1. Numerical Analysis	*Todd, John	1949–57
2. Computation Laboratory	*Abramowitz, Dr Milton	1942–58
3. Statistical Engineering	Eisenhart, Dr Churchill	
4. Mathematical Physics	Cannon, Dr Edward W.	

*Thompson, J. G., retired, February 1956.
*Geller, retired, December 1955; NBS consultant.
*Heindl, retired, July 1955; NBS consultant.
*Thompson, G. N., retired, June 30, 1955.
*McBurney, retired, May 1956.
*Dill, died 1957.
*Snoke, retired, July 31, 1960.
*Todd, to California Institute of Technology as professor of mathematics, September 1957.
*Abramowitz, died July 5, 1958.

Division	Name	Years
XII. DATA PROCESSING SYSTEMS	Alexander, Samuel N.	
1. Components and Techniques	Holt, A. W.	
2. Digital Circuitry and Devices	Elbourn, Robert D.	1947–
3. Digital Systems	Leiner, A. L.	
4. Analog Systems	Skramstad, Dr Harold K.	
80. BOULDER LABORATORIES		
Director	Brown, Dr Frederick W.	1954–
81. Cryogenic Engineering	Scott, Russell B.	
1. Cryogenic Equipment	Birmingham, Bascom W.	1951–
2. Cryogenic Processes	VanderArend, Peter C.	1951–
3. Properties of Materials	Reynolds, Martin M.	
4. Gas Liquefaction	Johnson, Victor J.	1950–
82. Radio Propagation Physics	Slutz, Dr Ralph J.	1949–
1. Upper Atmosphere Research	Gautier, Thomas N. Jr.	1942–
2. Ionospheric Research	Bateman, Ross	
3. Regular Propagation Services	Chadwick, Walter B.	
83. Radio Propagation Engineering	Norton, Kenneth A.	
4. Frequency Utilization Research	Norton, Kenneth A.	
6. Tropospheric Propagation Research	Herbstreit, Jack W.	1946–
84. Radio Standards	*Thomas, Dr Harold A.	1947–56
	*Lyons, Dr Harold (Assistant)	
High Frequency Standards Branch	George, William D.	
1. High Frequency Electrical Standards	Selby, Myron C.	1941–
2. Radio Broadcast Service	Morgan, Alvin H.	1946–
3. High Frequency Impedance Standard	(Vacant)	
Microwave Standards Branch	Lyons, Dr Harold	
6. Extreme High Frequency and Noise	Kerns, Dr David M.	1946–
7. Microwave Frequency and Spectroscopy	Birnbaum, George	1946–
8. Microwave Circuit Standard	Beatty, Robert W.	1944–

FIELD STATIONS

Brookline, Mass. (Optics and Metrology: Lamp Inspection)
Arcata, Calif. (Optics and Metrology: Visual Landing Aids)
Clearing, Ill. (Mechanics: NBS Master Track Scale Depot)
Allentown, Pa. (Mineral Products: Concreting Materials Section)
Denver, Colo. (Mineral Products: Concreting Materials Section)
San Francisco, Calif. (Mineral Products: Concreting Materials Section)

*Thomas, to John Jay Hopkins Laboratory for Pure and Applied Science (San Diego), General Dynamics Corporation, December 1956.
*Lyons, to staff of Microwave Laboratory, Hughes Aircraft Co., July 1955.

84. Radio Standards—Continued
  FIELD STATIONS—Continued
    Seattle, Wash. (Mineral Products: Concreting Materials Section)
    Kansas City, Mo. (Mineral Products: Concreting Materials Section)
    Anchorage, Alaska (Boulder: Radio Propagation Field Station)
    Point Barrow, Alaska (Boulder: Radio Propagation Field Station)
    Guam Island (Boulder: Radio Propagation Field Station)
    Puunene Maui, Hawaii (Boulder: Radio Propagation Field Station)
    Puerto Rico (Boulder: Radio Propagation Field Station)
    Bluie West-1, Greenland (Boulder: Radio Propagation Field Station)
    Panama Canal Zone (Boulder: Radio Propagation Field Station)
    Colorado Springs, Colo. (Boulder: Radio Propagation Field Station)
    Fort Belvoir, Va. (Boulder: Radio Propagation Field Station)
    Sterling, Va. (Boulder: Radio Propagation Laboratory)
    Beltsville, Md. (Boulder: Radio Transmitting Station)
    Front Royal, Va. (Boulder: Radio Noise Recording Station)

ADMINISTRATIVE, SCIENTIFIC, AND TECHNICAL STAFF CHIEFS

as of December 1, 1960

DIRECTOR	**Astin, Dr Allen V.**	
Deputy Director	Huntoon, Dr Robert D.	
Associate Director for Physics	Huntoon, Dr Robert D.	
Associate Director for Engineering	McPherson, Dr Archibald T.	
Associate Director for Chemistry	Wichers, Dr Edward	
	Souder, Dr Wilmer (Consultant)	
Associate Director for Planning	Schoonover, Dr Irl C.	
Associate Director for Administration	Walleigh, Robert S.	
Associate Director for Boulder Laboratories	Brown, Dr Frederick W.	
NBS Reactor Program	Muehlhause, Dr Carl O.	
Special Research Assistant to Director	Fano, Dr Ugo	
Special Development Assistant to Director	Wildhack, William A.	
Consultant to the Director	*Curtiss, Dr Leon F.	
	Schuler, Dr Kurt E.	1955–
Director Emeritus	Briggs, Dr Lyman J.	
OFFICE OF WEIGHTS AND MEASURES	Bussey, William A.	
Assistant	Jensen, Malcolm W.	
Consultant	Smith, Ralph W.	
OFFICE OF TECHNICAL INFORMATION	Tilley, William R.	1946–
Assistant	Gautier, William K.	1947–
I. ELECTRICITY	Page, Dr Chester H.	
1. Resistance and Reactance	Thomas, Dr James L.	
2. Electrochemistry	Hamer, Dr Walter J.	
3. Electrical Instruments	Defandorf, Dr Francis M.	
4. Magnetic Measurements	Cooter, Irving L.	
5. Dielectrics	Hoffman, Dr John D.	1942–
II. METROLOGY	McNish, Alvin G.	
	Judd, Dr Deane B. (Assistant)	1927–
1. Photometry and Colorimetry	Barbrow, Louis E.	1927–

*Curtiss, retired, June 30, 1961.

Division / Section	Chief	Years
II. METROLOGY—Continued		
2. Refractometry	Washer, Dr Francis E.	
3. Photographic Research	McCamy, Calvin S.	1952–
4. Length	*Page, Benjamin L.	1918–61
5. Engineering Metrology	Fullmer, Irwin H.	
6. Mass and Scale	Peiser, H. Steffen	1957–
7. Volumetry and Densimetry	Collett, Charles T.	1943–
III. HEAT	Herzfeld, Dr Charles M.	1955–
	Beckett, Dr Charles W. (Assistant)	1950–
1. Temperature Physics	Swindells, James F.	
2. Heat Measurements	Ginnings, Dr Defoe C.	1929–
3. Cryogenic Physics	Hudson, Dr Ralph P.	
7. Equation of State	Hilsenrath, Joseph	1948–
8. Statistical Physics	Green, Dr Melville S.	1954–
IV. RADIATION PHYSICS	Taylor, Dr Lauriston S.	
Scientific Assistant	Ney, Wilbert R.	
AEC Coordinator	Taylor, Dr Lauriston S.	
1. X Ray	Wyckoff, Dr Harold O.	
2. Radioactivity	Mann, Dr Wilfrid B.	
3. Radiation Theory	Spencer, Dr Lewis V.	
4. High Energy Radiation	Koch, Dr Herman W.	
5. Radiological Equipment	Smith, Dr Scott W.	
6. Nucleonic Instrumentation	Costrell, Louis	
7. Neutron Physics	Caswell, Dr Randall S.	1952–
V. ANALYTICAL AND INORGANIC CHEMISTRY	Schoonover, Dr Irl C.	
	Bates, Dr Roger G. (Assistant)	1939–
	Saylor, Dr Charles P. (Consultant)	
1. Pure Substances	*Howard, Dr Frank L.	1937–63
2. Spectrochemistry	Scribner, Bourdon F.	
3. Solution Chemistry	Bates, Dr Roger G.	
4. Analytical Chemistry	Hague, John L.	
5. Inorganic Chemistry	Gilchrist, Dr Raleigh	
VI. MECHANICS	Wilson, Bruce L.	
	Brombacher, Dr William G. (Consultant)	
	Frankland, Dr John M. (Consultant)	
	Lloyd, Edward C. (Consultant)	
1. Sound	Cook, Dr Richard K.	
2. Pressure and Vacuum	Johnson, Dr Daniel P.	1935–
3. Fluid Mechanics	Schubauer, Dr Galen B.	

*Page, retired, 1961.
*Howard, died Oct. 15, 1963.

Division / Section	Chief	Year
VI. MECHANICS—Continued		
4. Engineering Mechanics	Irwin, Lafayette K.	1949–
5. Rheology	Marvin, Dr Robert S.	1949–
8. Combustion Controls	Caldwell, Frank R.	1920–
VII. ORGANIC AND FIBROUS MATERIALS	Kline, Dr Gordon M.	
1. Rubber	Wood, Dr Lawrence A.	
2. Textiles	Schiefer, Dr Herbert F.	1929–
3. Paper	Hobbs, Dr Robert B.	
4. Leather	Kanagy, Dr Joseph R.	1930–
5. Testing and Specifications	Stiehler, Dr Robert D.	
6. Polymer Structure	Bekkedahl, Dr Norman P.	
7. Plastics	Reinhart, Dr Frank W.	
8. Dental Research	Sweeney, William T.	
VIII. METALLURGY	*Hoffman, Dr James I. *Digges, Thomas G. (Assistant)	
1. Thermal Metallurgy	Digges, Thomas G.	
2. Chemical Metallurgy	Wyman, Leroy L.	
3. Mechanical Metallurgy	Bennett, John A.	
4. Corrosion	Ellinger, George A.	
5. Metal Physics	Kushner, Dr Lawrence M.	1948–
6. Electrodeposition	Brenner, Dr Abner	
IX. MINERAL PRODUCTS	Franklin, Dr Allan D. Hahner, Clarence H. (Assistant) Geller, Roman F. (Consultant) Lippincott, Dr Ellis R. (Consultant)	1955–
1. Engineering Ceramics	Burdick, Milton D.	1931–
2. Glass	Hahner, Clarence H.	
3. Refractories	(Vacant)	
5. Crystal Growth	Ordway, Dr Frederick	1948–
7. Constitution and Microstructure	McMurdie, Howard F.	
X. BUILDING RESEARCH	Parsons, Douglas E. *Roeser, William F. (Consultant)	
1. Structural Engineering	Watstein, David	1930–
2. Fire Research	Robertson, Dr Alexander F.	
3. Mechanical Systems	Achenbach, Paul R.	1937–

*Hoffman, retired, 1962.
*Digges, retired, 1962.
*Roeser, died June 17, 1964.

Division / Section	Chief	Years
X. BUILDING RESEARCH—Continued		
4. Organic Building Materials	Walton, Dr William W.	1929–
5. Codes and Safety Standards	*Lloyd, Richard L.	1941–62
6. Heat Transfer	Robinson, Henry E.	1937–
7. Inorganic Building Materials	Blaine, Raymond L.	
9. Metallic Building Materials	Harrison, William N.	
XI. APPLIED MATHEMATICS	Cannon, Dr Edward W.	
	Alt, Dr Franz L. (Assistant)	
	Youden, Dr William J. (Consultant)	1948–
1. Numerical Analysis	Davis, Dr Philip J.	1952–
2. Computation	Mittleman, Dr Don I.	1951–
3. Statistical Engineering	Eisenhart, Dr Churchill	
4. Mathematical Physics	Pell, Dr William H.	1956–
5. Operations Research	Goldman, Dr Alan J.	1961–
XII. PROCESSING SYSTEMS	Alexander, Samuel N.	
	Skramstad, Dr Harold K. (Assistant)	
	Rafferty, John F. (SEAC)	
1. Components and Techniques	Elbourn, Robert D.	
2. Digital Circuitry	Greenwald, Sidney	1947–
3. Digital Systems	Alexander, Samuel N.	
4. Analog Systems	Skramstad, Dr Harold K.	
5. Applications Engineering	Glaser, Ezra	
XIII. ATOMIC PHYSICS	Branscomb, Dr Lewis M.	
	*Mohler, Dr Fred L. (Consultant)	
1. Spectroscopy	Kessler, Dr Karl G.	1948–
2. Radiometry	*Plyler, Dr Earle K.	
4. Solid State Physics	Frederikse, Dr Hans P. R.	1953–
5. Electron Physics	Marton, Dr Ladislaus L.	
6. Atomic Physics	Smith, Dr Stephen J.	1954–
XIV. INSTRUMENTATION	Montgomery, G. Franklin	1946–
1. Engineering Electronics	Shapiro, Gustave	1947–
2. Electron Devices	Marsden, Charles P.	
3. Electronic Instrumentation	Montgomery, G. Franklin	
4. Mechanical Instruments	Wexler, Arnold	1941–
5. Basic Instrumentation	Stern, Joshua	1951–
XV. PHYSICAL CHEMISTRY	Wallenstein, Dr Merrill B.	1953–55, 1959–
1. Thermochemistry	Prosen, Edward J.	
2. Surface Chemistry	(Vacant)	
3. Organic Chemistry	Isbell, Dr Horace S.	1927–

*Lloyd, to Underwriters' Laboratories, New York, 1962.
*Mohler, retired, 1960; NBS consultant.
*Plyler, retired, Oct. 8, 1963.

XV. PHYSICAL CHEMISTRY—Continued

4. Molecular Spectroscopy	Mann, Dr David E.	1951–
5. Molecular Kinetics	Ferguson, Dr Robert E.	1952–
6. Mass Spectroscopy	Dibeler, Dr Vernon H.	1942–
7. Molecular Structure and Radiation Chemistry	Buckley, Floyd	1943–

80. BOULDER LABORATORIES—

Director	Brown, Dr Frederick W.	
CRPL Liaison and Progress Development	Shapley, Alan H.	1947–
Mathematical-Analysis and Computation Facility Group	Sopka, Dr John J.	1959–
Consultant in Mathematical Physics	Brown, Edmund H.	1952–
Consultant in Statistics	Crow, Dr Edwin L.	
Consultant in Astrophysics	Thomas, Dr Richard N.	
Consultant in Radio Wave Propagation	Wait, Dr James R.	
81. Cryogenic Engineering	Scott, Russell B.	
	Birmingham, Bascom W. (Assistant)	
1. Cryogenic Equipment	Jacobs, Dr Robert B.	1951–
2. Cryogenic Processes	Birmingham, Bascom W.	
3. Properties of Materials	Corruccini, Dr Robert J.	1944–
4. Gas Liquefaction	Johnson, Victor J.	

CENTRAL RADIO PROPAGATION LABORATORY—BOULDER

82. Ionosphere Research and Propagation	Smith, Dr Earnest K. Jr.	1951–
	Gautier, Thomas N. Jr. (Assistant)	
	Bailey, Dana K. (Consultant)	1948–
1. LF and VLF Research	Jean, Arthur G. Jr	1949–
2. Ionosphere Research	Davies, Dr Kenneth	1958–
3. Prediction Services	Chadwick, Walter B.	
4. Sun-Earth Relationships	Knecht, Robert W.	1949–
5. Field Engineering	Sellery, Harry G.	1946–
6. Radio Warning Services	Lincoln, J. Virginia	1942–
83. Radio Propagation Engineering	Norton, Kenneth A.	
	Herbstreit, Jack W. (Assistant)	
	Florman, Edwin F. (Consultant)	1946–
1. Data Reduction Instrumentation	Johnson, Walter E.	1953–
4. Radio Noise	Crichlow, William Q.	1946–
5. Tropospheric Measurements	Peterson, Charles F.	1952–
6. Tropospheric Analysis	Rice, Philip L.	1949–

Division / Section	Chief	Year
83. Radio Propagation Engineering—Continued		
7. Propagation-Terrain Effects	Kirby, Robert S.	1947–
8. Radio-Meteorology	Bean, Bradford R.	1950–
9. Lower Atmosphere Physics	Thompson, Dr Moody C. Jr.	1947–
84. Radio Standards Laboratory	Richardson, Dr John M.	1952–
Assistant Chief for Radio Frequencies	George, William D.	
Assistant Chief for Microwave Frequencies	Kerns, Dr David M.	1946–
Assistant Chief for Technical Planning and Coordination	Wolzien, Eldred C.	
Consultant	Brown, W. W.	
Consultant	Wacker, Dr Paul F.	1944–
1. High Frequency Electrical Standards	Selby, Myron C.	1941–
2. Radio Broadcast Service	Morgan, Alvin H.	1946–
3. Radio and Microwave Materials	Dalke, John L.	1947–
4. Atomic Frequency and Time Interval Standards	Mockler, Dr Richard C.	1954–
5. Electronic Calibration Center	Lance, Harvey W.	1948–
7. Millimeter-Wave Research	Culshaw, Dr William	1956–
8. Microwave Circuit Standards	Beatty, Robert W.	
85. Radio Systems	Kirby, Richard C.	1948–
	Patterson, Donald W. (Assistant)	1958–
	Haydon, George W. (Consultant)	1959–
1. High Frequency and VHF Research	Silberstein, Richard	1941–
4. Modulation Research	Koch, J. Wesley	1957–
5. Antenna Research	Cottony, Herman V.	1941–
6. Navigation Systems	Hefley, Gifford	1949–
7. Space Telecommunications	Coombs, William C.	1959–
87. Upper Atmosphere and Space Physics	Little, Dr C. Gordon	1958–
	Gates, Dr David M. (Asst.)	1957–
	Slutz, Dr Ralph J. (Cons.)	
	Bailey, Dana K. (Cons.)	
1. Upper Atmosphere and Plasma Physics	Gallet, Roger M.	1955–
5. Ionosphere and Exosphere Scatter	Bowles, Dr Kenneth L.	1955–

87. Upper Atmosphere and Space Physics—Continued

7. Airglow and Aurora	Roach, Dr Franklin E.	1954–
8. Ionospheric Radio Astronomy	Lawrence, Robert S.	1948–

FIELD STATIONS, NBS

Anchorage, Alaska (Central Radio Propagation Laboratory)
Koloa, Kauai, Hawaii (Central Radio Propagation Laboratory)
Antarctica and Kolb Stations, Boulder (Central Radio Propagation Laboratory)
Barrow, Alaska (Central Radio Propagation Laboratory)
Lima, Peru (Central Radio Propagation Laboratory)
Douglas, Wyo. (Central Radio Propagation Laboratory)
Lafayette, Colo. (Central Radio Propagation Laboratory)
Colorado Springs, Colo. (Central Radio Propagation Laboratory)
Havana, Ill. (Central Radio Propagation Laboratory)
Fort Belvoir, Va. (Central Radio Propagation Laboratory)
Puunene, Maui, Hawaii (Central Radio Propagation Laboratory)
Rollinsville, Colo. (Central Radio Propagation Laboratory)
Puerto Rico (Central Radio Propagation Laboratory)
Front Royal, Va. (Central Radio Propagation Laboratory)
Schickley, Nebr. (Central Radio Propagation Laboratory)
Lanham, Md. (Radio Standards Laboratory)
Puuenene, Maui, Hawaii (Radio Standards Laboratory)
Brookline, Mass. (Metrology: Lamp Inspection)
Arcata, Calif. (Metrology: Visual Landing Aids Field Laboratory)
Clearing, Ill. (Metrology: Master Railway Track Scale Depot)
Allentown, Pa. (Building Technology: Concreting Materials Section)
Denver, Colo. (Building Technology: Concreting Materials Section)
San Francisco, Calif. (Building Technology: Concreting Materials Section)
Seattle, Wash. (Building Technology: Concreting Materials Section)

APPENDIX K

NBS Publications representing RESEARCH HIGHLIGHTS IN SCIENCE AND TECHNOLOGY, 1901–1951

Abbreviations

NBS PUBLICATIONS

S	Scientific Paper
T	Technologic Paper
RP	Research Paper
C	Circular
H	Handbook
M	Miscellaneous Publication
BMS	Building Materials and Structures Report
LC	Letter Circular
TNB	Technical News Bulletin

NON-NBS PUBLICATIONS

Am. Mach.	American Machinist
ASTM Bull.	American Society for Testing Materials Bulletin
Am. Soc. Testing Mater. Proc.	Proceedings of the American Society for Testing Materials
Anal. Chem.	Analytical Chemistry
Ann. N.Y. Acad. Sci.	Annals of the New York Academy of Sciences
Elec. Eng.	Electrical Engineering
Horological Inst. Am. J.	Horological Institute of America Journal
Ind. Eng. Chem.	Industrial and Engineering Chemistry
J. Am. Dental Assoc.	Journal of the American Dental Association
J. Am. Ceram. Soc.	Journal of the American Ceramic Society
J. Appl. Phys.	Journal of Applied Physics
J. Dental. Res.	Journal of Dental Research
J. Opt. Soc. Am.	Journal of the Optical Society of America
J. Wash. Acad. Sci.	Journal of the Washington Academy of Sciences
Mech. Eng.	Mechanical Engineering
Natl. Adv. Comm. Aeron. Tech. Note	National Advisory Committee for Aeronautics Technical Note
Natl. Adv. Comm. Aeron. Tech. Rep.	National Advisory Committee for Aeronautics Technical Report

Natl. Adv. Comm. Aeron. Rep.	National Advisory Committee for Aeronautics Report
Phys. Rev.	Physical Review
Proc. Am. Phil. Soc.	Proceedings of the American Philosophical Society
Proc. IRE	Proceedings of the Institute of Radio Engineers
Proc. Natl. Acad. Sci.	Proceedings of the National Academy of Sciences
Rev. Sci. Instr.	Review of Scientific Instruments
Scripta Math.	Scripta Mathematica
Trans. ASME	Transactions of the American Society of Mechanical Engineers
Trans. AIEE	Transactions of the American Institute of Electrical Engineers
Trans. Soc. Motion Picture Eng.	Transactions of the Society of Motion Picture Engineers

NATIONAL BUREAU OF STANDARDS

RESEARCH HIGHLIGHTS IN SCIENCE AND TECHNOLOGY—1901–1910

1. ELECTRICITY

Coffin, Construction and calculation of absolute standards of inductance (S29, 1906)

Brooks, The deflection potentiometer: a new p. for the measurement of emf and current (S33, 1906)

Austin, Detector for small alternating currents and electrical [radio] waves (S22, 1905)

Rosa & Dorsey, A new determination of the ratio of the electromagnetic to the electrostatic unit of electricity (S65 and S66, 1907)

Wolff, The principles involved in the selection and definition of the fundamental electrical units to be proposed for international adoption (S102, 1909)

Burrows, A new permeameter for determination of magnetic induction in straight bars (S117, 1909)

2. WEIGHTS & MEASURES

Osborne & Veazey, New methods for testing glass volumetric apparatus (S92, 1908)

——— Standard density and volumetric tables (C19, 1909)

3. HEAT & THERMOMETRY

Waidner & Burgess, Optical pyrometry (S8 and S11, 1904)

Burgess, Radiation from platinum at high temperatures (S24, 1905; S124, 1909)

Burgess, Melting points of the iron-group elements by a new radiation method (S62, 1907)

Wensel, Roeser, Barbrow & Caldwell, The Waidner-Burgess standard of light (Elec. World, 52, 625, 1908; RP325, 1931)

Burgess, The estimation of the temperature of copper by means of optical pyrometers (S121, 1909)

Buckingham, On the definition of the ideal gas (S136, 1910)

4. OPTICS

Nutting, Some new rectifying effects in conducting gases [Development with Sperling of the first neon sign tubing] (S6, 1904)

Coblentz, A vacuum radiomicrometer [A new form of radiometer] (S46, 1906)

Bates, A quartz compensating polariscope with adjusting sensibility (S86, 1908)

Nutting, The resolving power of objectives (S122, 1909)

5. CHEMISTRY

Stokes & Cain, On the colorimetric determination of iron with special reference to chemical reagents (S53, 1907)

Noyes, The atomic weight of hydrogen (S77, 1908)

Douty, Bursting strength. The conditions which influence this test of paper considered (Paper Trade J. 50, 271, 1910)

NATIONAL BUREAU OF STANDARDS

RESEARCH HIGHLIGHTS IN SCIENCE AND TECHNOLOGY—1911–1916

1. ELECTRICITY

Agnew, A study of the current transformer . . . [Pioneer analysis of the performance of current transformers] (S164, 1911)

Dellinger, High-frequency ammeters [Measurement of high-frequency radio current] (S206, 1914)

Vinal & Bates, Comparison of the silver and iodine voltameters and the determination of the value of the faraday [Precise determination of the faraday] (S218, 1914)

Curtis, Insulating properties of solid dielectrics (S234, 1915)

Rosa & McCollum, Electrolysis and its mitigation (T52, 1915; Logan, C450, 1945)

Kolster, A direct-reading instrument for measuring the logarithmic decrement and wave length of electromagnetic waves [The Kolster decremeter] (S235, 1915)

Brooks & Weaver, A variable self and mutual inductor (S290, 1917)

Rosa & Vinal, Summary of experiments on the silver voltameter . . . and proposed specifications (S285, 1916)

2. WEIGHTS & MEASURES

Gray, Hidnert & Souder, Development of precision micrometric thermal expansion equipment (J. Wash. Acad. Sci. 2, 248, 1912; S219, 1914; S276, 1916; S410, 1922; S524, 1926)

——— U.S. standard tables for petroleum oils (C57, 1916; C154, 1924; C410, 1936–37)

3. HEAT & THERMOMETRY

Waidner & Burgess, On the constancy of the sulphur boiling point (S149, 1911)

Buckingham & Dellinger, On the computation of the constant c_2 of Planck's equation by an extension of Paschen's method of equal ordinates (S162, 1911)

Harper, Thermometric lag (S185, 1912)

Burgess, A micropyrometer (S198, 1913)

Dickinson & Mueller, New calorimetric resistance thermometers (S200, 1913; Sligh, S407, 1922)

Dickinson, Harper & Osborne, Latent heat of fusion of ice (S209, 1914)

Burgess & Crowe, Critical ranges A2 and A3 of pure iron (S213, 1914; Thompson & Cleaves, RP1226, 1939)

Waidner & Mueller, Industrial gas calorimetry [First comprehensive study of methods of measuring heating value of gases] (T36, 1914)

Burgess & Foote, Characteristics of radiation pyrometers (S250, 1915)

Buckingham, Model experiments and the forms of empirical equations [in fluid mechanics] (Trans. ASME, 37, 263, 1915)

Dickinson, Combustion calorimetry and the heats of combustion of cane sugar, benzoic acid and naphthalene (S230, 1915)

Waidner, Dickinson, et al., Wheatstone bridges for resistance thermometry (S241, 1915; S288, 1917)

Foote & Fairchild, Luminosity of a black body and temperature (S270, 1916)

4. OPTICS

Coblentz, Measurements on standards of radiation in absolute value [Standards of radiant flux and thermal radiation] (S227, 1915; Coblentz and Stair, RP578, 1933)

Coblentz, A comparison of stellar radiometers and radiometric measurements on 110 stars [Use of vacuum thermopiles with calcium "getter" bulb] (S244, 1915)

Coblentz & Emerson, Studies of instruments for measuring radiant energy in absolute value: an absolute thermopile (S261, 1916)

Coblentz, Present status of the determination of the constant of total radiation from a black body [Use of filters in combination with thermopiles] (S262, 1915)

Bates & Jackson, Constants of the quartz-wedge saccharimeter and the specific rotation of sucrose (S268, 1916)

5. CHEMISTRY

McBride, Weaver, et al., Determination of sulphur in illuminating gas [Development of apparatus and methods of gas analysis] (T20, 1913; T110, 1918)

——— Standards for gas service [First compilation of rules and regulations relating to standards for gas service of public utilities] (C32, 1912; 4th ed., 1920)

——— Standard methods of gas testing [Fuel gas testing and performance testing of gas appliances] (C48, 1914; 2d ed., 1916)

NATIONAL BUREAU OF STANDARDS

RESEARCH HIGHLIGHTS IN SCIENCE AND TECHNOLOGY—1917–1919

1. ELECTRICITY

Kolster, The radio direction finder and its application to navigation (1917; S428, 1922)

Wenner, [Construction of a high precision bridge] . . . for the comparison of precision standard resistors (1918; RP1323, 1940)

Silsbee, Note on electrical conduction in metals at low temperatures [The Silsbee hypothesis, relating critical current and critical magnetic field in superconductors] (S307, 1918)

Lowell & Willoughby, Underwater antenna for submerged submarines (NBS Radio Laboratory Report, Nov 1918)

Ould, [Standard variable condenser for radio] (reported in C74, 2d ed., 1918)

2. WEIGHTS & MEASURES

Stillman, A portable cubic-foot standard for gas (T114, 1918)

Van Keuren, Manufacture of Hoke precision gages . . . (Mech. Eng. 41, 289, 1919; Am. Mach. 50, 625, 1919)

3. HEAT & THERMOMETRY

Osborne & Van Dusen, The specific heat of liquid ammonia (S313, 1918)

Mueller & Burgess, H. A., Standardization of the sulphur boiling point (S339, 1919)

4. OPTICS

Jackson, The saccharimetric normal weight and specific rotation of dextrose (S293, 1917)

——— Method for slip casting large refractory pots; war-time production of optical glass; design of new types of optical glass (1917–18; Gardner & Hahner, M194, 1949)

Coblentz & Kahler, Some optical and photoelectric properties of molybdenite (S338, 1918)

Coblentz, The spectrophotoelectric sensitivity of thalofide [New infrared detection devices] (S380 and S398, 1920)

Gibson, Photoelectric spectrophotometry by the null method [First photoelectric spectrophotometer] (S349, 1919)

Bates & Bearce, New Baumé scale for sugar solutions (T115, 1918)

5. CHEMISTRY

Edwards, A specific gravity balance for gases [First commercial specific gravity balance for gases] (T89, 1917)

Edwards, Effusion method of determining gas density [Instruments and method for determinating gas density] (T94, 1917)

Weaver & Weibel, New forms of instruments for showing the presence and amount of combustible gas in the air (S334, 1919)

8. METALLURGY

Merica, Waltenberg & Scott, The heat treatment of duralumin [First explanation of the phenomenon of age hardening of metals] (S347, 1919)

9. CLAY PRODUCTS

Silsbee, Honaman, et al., [Development of a new type of porcelain for aviation spark plugs] (Natl. Adm. Comm. Aeron. Rep. 53, 1919)

NATIONAL BUREAU OF STANDARDS

RESEARCH HIGHLIGHTS IN SCIENCE AND TECHNOLOGY—1920–1930

1. ELECTRICITY

Breit, High-frequency resistance of inductance coils (S430, 1922)

Lowell, An electron-tube amplifier using sixty-cycle alternating current to supply power for the filaments and plates [First a.c. radio set] (S450, 1922)

Dunmore & Engel, Directive radio transmission on a wavelength of 10 meters [First aural radio beacon] (S469, 1923)

Hund, Theory of determination of ultra-radio frequencies by standing waves on wires [Standard of wavelength] (S491, 1924)

——— Standard frequency and time interval broadcasts (no publ., 1925–1937)

Pratt & Diamond, Receiving sets for aircraft beacon and telephony [Development of stub antenna for aircraft] (RP19, 1928; Diamond & Davies RP313, 1931)

Dunmore, Design of tuned reed course indicators for aircraft radio beacon (RP28, 1928)

Wenner, A new seismometer . . . (RP66, 1929)

Diamond and Kear, A 12-course radio range for guiding aircraft . . . (RP154, 1930)

Diamond & Gardner, Engine ignition shielding for radio reception in aircraft (RP158, 1930)

Thomas, A new design of precision resistance standard (RP201, 1930)

Diamond & Dunmore, A radiobeacon and receiving system for blind landing of aircraft (RP238, 1930)

2. WEIGHTS & MEASURES

Souder & Peters, An investigation of the physical properties of dental materials [A new dental interferometer for measuring expansion of dental amalgams] (T157, 1920)

Danielson & Souder, The causes and control of fish scaling of enamels for sheet iron and steel (J. Am. Ceram. Soc. 4, 620, 1921)

Peters & Boyd, Interference methods for standardizing and testing precision gage blocks (S436, 1922)

——— Testing sieves by projection methods (LC72 and LC74, 1922; LC584, 1940)

Bearce, A fundamental basis for measurements of length (S535, 1926)

Bean, Buckingham & Murphy, Discharge coefficients of square-edged orifices for measuring the flow of air (RP49, 1929)

Bean, An apparatus and method for determining the compressibility of a gas and the correction for "supercompressibility" (RP170, 1930)

3. HEAT & POWER

——— Tables of thermodynamic properties of ammonia (C142, 1923)

Osborne, Stimson, Sligh & Cragoe, Specific heat of superheated ammonia vapor (S501, 1924)

Kanolt, Nonflammable liquids for cryostats (S520, 1925)

Burgess and Stimson, The International Temperature Scale (RP22, 1928; RP1962, 1948)

Osborne, Stimson & Fiock, A calorimetric determination of thermal properties of saturated water and steam from 0° to 270° C. (RP209, 1930)

4. OPTICS

Jackson & Silsbee, C. G., The solubility of dextrose in water (S437, 1922)

Meggers, Kiess & Stimson, Practical spectographic analysis (S444, 1922)

Gibson & Tyndall, The visibility of radiant energy (S475, 1923)

Judd, Contributions in colorimetry to the development of the ICI standard observer (1924; J. Opt. Soc. Am. 23, 359, 1933)

Gardner & Bennett, A modified Hartman test based on interference (J. Opt. Soc. Am. 11, 441, 1925)

Gardner & Case, Camera for photographing the interior of a rifle barrel (J. Opt. Soc. Am. 12, 159, 1926)

Jackson, C. G. Silsbee & Proffitt, The preparation of levulose (S519, 1925)

Peters & Phelps, Color [and color nomenclature] in the sugar industry (T338, 1926)

Gardner, Application of the algebraic aberration equations to optical design (S550, 1926)

Meggers & Burns, Hyperfine structures of lanthanum lines (J. Opt. Soc. Am. 14, 449, 1927)

Davis & Walters, Sensitometry of photographic emulsions and a survey of the characteristics of plates and films of American manufacture (S439, 1922)

Davis, A special camera for photographing cylindrical surfaces (S517, 1925)

Davis, Artificial sunlight for photographic sensitometry (Trans. Soc. Motion Picture Eng. 12, 225, 1928)

Taylor, Analysis of diaphragm system for the X-ray standard ionization chamber (RP119, 1929; Taylor & Singer RP211, 1930)

Taylor, The precise measurement of X-ray dosage [The first X-ray dosage standards] (RP56, 1929)

Mohler, Relative production of negative and positive ions by electron collisions (Phys. Rev. 26, 614, 1926)

Mohler & Boecker, Photo-ionization of caesium by line absorption (RP186, 1930)

5. CHEMISTRY

Holler, A method of studying electrode potentials and polarization ((S504, 1924; Darnielle, RP1336, 1940)

Palmer & Weaver, [First U.S. publication of] Thermal-conductivity method for the analysis of gases (T249, 1924)

Weaver, Relation between the heating value of gas and its usefulness to the customer (T290, 1925)

——— First industrial recording instrument based on thermal conductivity (constructed for Navy plant at Indian Head, Md., 1924 — no publ.)

Weaver, Eiseman & Shawn, [First program based on] A method for testing gas appliances to determine their safety from producing carbon monoxide (T304, 1926)

Swanger, [First analytical methods for] The analysis of dental gold alloys (S532, 1926)

Souder et al., [First standards and certification system for dental materials] (J. Dental Res. 7, 173, 1927; C433, 1942)

Coleman, Physical properties of dental materials [First accurate determination of casting shrinkage of dental inlay gold] (RP32, 1928)

Washburn, Bruun & Hicks, Apparatus and methods for the separation, identification, and determination of the chemical constituents of petroleum (RP45, 1929)

Washburn, On the determination of the empirical formula of a hydrocarbon (RP236, 1930)

6. ENGINEERING PHYSICS

Eckhardt, Karcher & Keiser, Electron tube drive for tuning forks (Phys. Rev. 17, 535, 1921)

Heyl & Briggs, The earth inductor compass (Proc. Am. Phil. Soc. 61, 15, 1922)

Tuckerman, [The Tuckerman optical strain gage] (Am. Soc. Testing Mater. Proc. 23, 602, 1923)

Heck, Eckhardt & Chrisler, Radio-acoustic method of position finding in hydrographic surveys (no publ., 1924)

Quayle, Spark photography and its application to some problems in ballistics [First spark shadow photographs of bullets in flight] (S508, 1924)

Zobel & Carroll, A hot-wire anemometer for measuring air flow through engine radiators (T287, 1925)

Briggs, Hull & Dryden, Aerodynamic characteristics of airfoils at high speeds (Natl. Adv. Comm. Aeron. Tech. Rep. 207, 1924; Natl. Adv. Comm. Aeron. Tech. Rep. 319, 1929; Natl. Adv. Comm. Aeron. Tech. Rep. 365, 1930)

Tuckerman, Keulegan & Eaton, A fabric tension meter for use on aircraft [for testing rigid airship envelopes] (T320, 1926)

Buckingham, Theory and . . . experiments on the transmission of sound through partition walls (S506, 1925)

Dryden, Heald, et al., Investigations in turbulence in wind tunnels (Natl. Adv. Comm. Aeron. Tech. Rep. 231, 1926; Natl. Adv. Comm. Aeron. Tech. Rep. 342, 1930, et seq.)

Whittemore, Petrenko, et al., Proving rings for calibrating testing machines (patents, 1926; C454, 1946)

Heyl, A redetermination of the constant of gravitation (RP256, 1930)

Tuckerman, Whittemore & Petrenko, A new dead-weight testing machine of 100,000 pounds capacity (RP147, 1930)

Dryden & Hill, [Studies of wind pressure on structures] (Proc. Natl. Acad. Sci., Nov 1930; RP301, 1931; RP545, 1933)

7. ENGINEERING, STRUCTURAL & MISC. MATERIALS

Holt & Wormeley, Dynamometer [equipment and] tests of automobile tires (T240, 1923)

Holt & Wormeley, [Equipment for] Endurance tests of tires (T318, 1926)

Holt, Wormeley, et al., The testing of rubber goods (C38, 5th ed., 1927)

Kline & Acree, Consumption of nitric acid in the oxidation of xylose (Ind. Eng. Chem. 22, 975, 1930)

Kline & Acree, A study of the method for titrating aldose sugars with standard iodine and alkali (RP247, 1930)

8. METALLURGY

Merica & Waltenberg, [Pioneer work on the] Malleability and metallography of nickel (T281, 1925)

French & Klopsch, Initial temperature and mass effects in quenching ,T295, 1925; French & Hamill, RP103, 1929)

French & Tucker, Flow in a low-carbon steel at various temperatures [Pioneer work on creep of metals at elevated temperatures] (T296, 1925; Geil & Carwile, RP2329, 1952)

Jordan & Eckman, Gases in metals [Pioneer work on the effects of oxygen and hydrogen on the properties and behavior of metals] (S514, 1925)

Herschman, Air-hardening rivet steels (T358, 1927)

Rawdon, [The prevention of corrosion in duralumin] Natl. Adv. Comm. Aeron. Tech. Note 284, 1928)

Saeger and Ash, [Practical methods of determining the quality of metals in the foundry] (LC252, 1928; RP399, 1932)

Logan, Soil-corrosion studies [First explanation of the mechanism of corrosion in soils] (RP95, 1929)

French & Digges, Turning with shallow cuts at high speeds [and method for testing high-speed tool steels] (RP120, 1929)

Freeman, Scherer & Rosenberg, Reliability of fusible tin boiler plugs in service [Cause and remedy for their failure in marine boilers] (RP129, 1930; see also Burgess & Merica, T53, 1914)

9. CERAMICS

Finn, Making the glass disk for a 70-inch telescope reflector [The first reflector this large made in the United States] (RP97, 1929)

NATIONAL BUREAU OF STANDARDS

RESEARCH HIGHLIGHTS IN SCIENCE AND TECHNOLOGY—1931–1940

1. ELECTRICAL

Sanford, A method for the standardization of permeameters at high magnetizing forces (RP279, 1931)

Kear & Wintermute, A simultaneous radiotelephone and visual range beacon for the airways (RP341, 1931)

Diamond, The cause and elimination of night effects in radio range-beacon reception (RP513, 1933)

Brooks, The standard-cell comparator [Design and construction of a specialized potentiometer for exact comparison of standard cells] (RP586, 1933)

Harris, A new cathode-ray oscillograph and its application to the study of power loss in dielectric materials (RP636, 1934)

Dunmore, Unicontrol radio receiver for ultra high frequencies, using concentric lines as interstage couplers (RP856, 1935)

Dellinger, Sudden disturbances of the ionosphere [Discovery of the Dellinger effect] (RP1016, 1937)

Curtis, Moon & Sparks, An absolute determination of the ohm (RP857, 1936; RP1137, 1938)

Brooks, Defandorf & Silsbee, An absolute electrometer for the measurement of high alternating voltages (RP1078, 1938)

Diamond, Hinman, Dunmore, et al., A method for the investigation of upper-air phenomena and its application to radio meteorography [The radiosonde] (RP1082, 1938; RP1329, 1940)

Dunmore, An electric hygrometer and its application to radio meteorography (RP1102, 1938; RP1265, 1939)

Astin, Measurement of relative and true power factors of air capacitors (RP1138, 1938)

George, Production of accurate one-second time intervals (RP1136, 1938)

Curtiss, Astin, et al., An improved radio meteorograph on the Olland principle (RP1169, 1939)

2. WEIGHTS & MEASURES

——— Design of flexible steel gages for control of mesh size of gill nets (LC372, 1933)

Peffer, Device for testing haemacytometers and other pipettes of small capacity [The Peffer pipette tester] (RP1019, 1937)

Knoop, Peters & Emerson, A sensitive pyramidal-diamond tool for indentation measurements [The Knoop hardness indenter] (RP1220, 1939)

3. HEAT & POWER

Roeser, Caldwell & Wensel, The freezing point of platinum (RP326, 1931)

Van Dusen & Shelton, Apparatus for measuring thermal conductivity of metals up to 600° C (RP668, 1934)

Wensel, Judd & Roeser, Establishment of a scale of color temperature (RP677, 1934)

Wensel, International Temperature Scale and some related physical constants (RP1189, 1939)

Osborne, Stimson & Ginnings, Thermal properties of saturated water and steam (RP1229, 1939)

4. OPTICS

Taylor, L. S., X-ray protection [The first X-ray protection code] (H15, 1931; H20, 1936, et seq.)

Davis & Gibson, Filters for the reproduction of sunlight and daylight and the determination of color temperature [International standards for converting artificial light to daylight quality and for determining color temperature] (M114, 1931)

Taylor, International comparison of X-ray standards (RP397, 1932)

Mohler, Collisions of the first and second kind in the positive column of a caesium discharge (RP485, 1932)

Boeckner & Mohler, Scattering of electrons by ions and the mobility of electrons in a caesium discharge (RP535, 1933)

Taylor, Radium protection [The first radium protection code] (H18, 1934; H23, 1938, et seq.)

Tilton & J. K. Taylor, Refractive index and dispersion of normal and heavy water (RP703, 1934)

Curtiss, Deflection of cosmic rays by a magnetic field (RP509, 1932)

Hoffman & Scribner, Purification of gallium by fractional crystallization of the metal (RP823, 1935)

Gardner, Design and construction of eclipse apparatus [Application of telephoto lenses to eclipse photography] (1936; reported in Nat. Geo. Soc. Solar Expedition Papers, No. 2, 1942, pp. 4, 95)

Gardner & Case, Precision camera for testing lenses (RP984, 1937)

Mohler, Cesium discharge under conditions of nearly complete ionization (RP1150, 1938)

Gardner, Relation of camera error to photogrammetric mapping (RP1177, 1939)

Saunders, Improved interferometric procedure with application to expansion measurements (RP1227, 1939)

Gibson & Haupt, Standardization of the luminous-transmission scale used in the specification of railroad signal glasses (RP1209, 1939)

Judd & Kelly, Method of designating colors [Development of the ISCC–NBS method of designating colors] (RP1239, 1939; C553, 1955)

Washer & Gardner, Studies of the resolving power of camera lenses (1939–1950; C428, 1940; RP1636, 1945; C533, 1953)

Scribner, Spectrographic detection of rare earths in plants (Proc. 6th Summer Conf. on Spectroscopy, 1939, pp. 10–13)

Curtiss, Astin, et al., Cosmic-ray observations in the stratosphere with high-speed counters (RP1254, 1939)

Judd, Hue, saturation, and lightness of surface colors with chromatic illumination (RP1285, 1940)

Carroll & Hubbard, The photographic emulsion . . . (RP340, 1931 . . . RP622, 1933)

5. CHEMISTRY

Smith, W. H., Saylor & Wing, The preparation and crystallization of pure ether-soluble rubber hydrocarbon (RP544, 1933)

Washburn, Standard states for bomb calorimetry (RP546, 1933)

Washburn, E. R. Smith & Frandsen, The isotopic fractionation of water (RP601, 1933)

Gilchrist, Methods for the separation of platinum, palladium, rhodium, and iridium [First systematic method of separating the platinum metals] (RP655, 1934)

Washburn, E. R. Smith & F. A. Smith, Fractionation of the isotopes of hydrogen and of oxygen in a commerical electrolyzer (RP729, 1934)

Hoffman, Preparation of pure gallium (RP734, 1934)

Brickwedde, Scott, & H. S. Taylor, The difference in vapor pressures of ortho- and paradeuterium (RP841, 1935)

Brenner, Magnetic method for measuring the thickness of nickel coatings on non-magnetic base metals [The Magnegage] (RP994, 1937)

Knowlton & Rossini, Method and apparatus for the rapid conversion of deuterium oxide into deuterium (RP1050, 1937)

Gilchrist, New procedure for the analysis of dental gold alloys (RP1103, 1938)

Wildhack & Goerke, Formulas for diaphragm and diaphragm capsules (Natl. Adv. Comm. Aeron. Tech. Note 738, 1939; Natl. Adv. Comm. Aeron. Tech. Note 876, 1942)

Thompson, Methods of measuring pH in alkaline cyanide plating baths (RP1291, 1940)

6. MECHANICS & SOUND

Lyon, Whittemore, et al., Strain measurement in reinforcement . . . [The Whittemore hand strain gage] (RP268, 1931)

Snyder, An automatic reverberation meter for the measurement of sound absorption (RP457, 1932)

Peterson & Womack [The aviation superheat meter] (Natl. Adv. Comm. Aeron. Tech. Rep. 606, 1937)

Cordero, A vibrometer for measuring amplitude in a single frequency (patent, 1934)

Heald, [Ground effect tests and air forces on automobiles] (RP748 and RP749, 1934)

Snyder, Recent sound-transmission measurements [Threshold standards for audiometry] (RP800, 1935)

Wright, [Pioneer hydraulic model studies] (RP907, 1936; Keulegan, RP1488, 1942)

Heyl & Cook, The value of gravity at Washington (RP946, 1936)

Briggs, [The flight performance of golf balls and baseballs] (TNB, No. 252, 1938; RP1624, 1945)

Keulegan & Beij, Studies of turbulent flow in pipes and open channels (RP965, 1937; RP1110, 1938; RP1151. 1938; RP1488, 1942)

Golden & Hunter, Backflow prevention in over-rim water supplies [Cross-connection flow in plumbing systems] (BMS28, 1939)

Greenspan, Approximation to a function of one variable from a set of its mean values [Method of measurement of strain at a point] (RP1235. 1939)

Keulegan & Patterson, Mathematical theory of irrotational translation waves [Research on the theory of wave motion] (RP1272, 1940; RP1544, 1943)

7. ORGANIC & FIBROUS MATERIALS

Schiefer & Best, Carpet wear testing machine (RP315, 1931)

Schiefer, The flexometer . . . for evaluating the flexural properties of cloth and similar materials (RP555, 1933)

Schiefer, The compressometer . . . for evaluating the thickness . . . and compressional resilience of textiles and similar materials (RP561, 1933)

Becker, Spectral reflectance of . . . abacá [manila rope] fiber (RP628, 1933)

Schiefer & Appel, Hosiery testing machine (RP679 and LC466, 1934)

Carson, A sensitive instrument for measuring the air permeability of paper and other sheet materials (RP681, 1934)

Bekkedahl, [Volume dilatometer for studying phase changes in liquids and solids] (RP717, 1934; RP2016, 1949)

Kline & Malmberg, Suitability of various plastics [especially cellulose acetate butyrate] for use in airplane dopes (RP1098, 1938)

Taylor, R. H., & Holt, Small inertia-type machine for testing brake lining (RP1297, 1940)

Launer, Apparatus for the study of the photochemistry of sheet materials (RP1300, 1940)

8. METALLURGY

Rosenberg & Jordan, Influence of oxide films on the wear of steels (RP708, 1934)

Buzzard & Wilson, Anodic coating of magnesium alloys [for aircraft use] (RP964, 1937)

Krynitsky & Saeger, Elastic properties of cast iron [Optical method for measuring deflection of cast iron bars under pressure] (RP1176, 1939)

9. CLAY & SILICATE PRODUCTS

Geller & Creamer, "Moisture expansion" of ceramic white ware [Discovery of effect of moisture expansion on crazing of glasses] (RP472, 1932)

Kessler & Sligh, Physical properties and weathering characteristics of slate (RP477, 1932)

Swenson, Wagner & Pigman, Effect of the granulometric composition of cement on the properties of pastes, mortars, and concretes [New method for determining fineness of Portland cement] (RP777, 1935)

Theuer, Effect of temperature on the stress-deformation of concrete [Sonic methods for measurement of modules of elasticity of concrete] (RP970, 1937)

Stull & Johnson, Relation between moisture content and flow-point pressure of plastic clay [First comprehensive study of cause of white-coat plaster failures] (RP1186, 1939)

NATIONAL BUREAU OF STANDARDS

RESEARCH HIGHLIGHTS IN SCIENCE AND TECHNOLOGY—1941–1945

1. ELECTRICITY

——— [Development of workable perchloric and fluoboric acid batteries] (1941; TNB 30, 76, 1946)

Astin, Radio reporters for proximity fuse testing [Telemetering from missiles in flight] (Classified NDRC Rep. A–53, 1942)

Hinman & Brunetti, Radio proximity fuze design (1941; RP1723, 1946)

Silsbee, Static electricity [Nature, origins, and mitigation of static electricity in industrial processes] (C438, 1942)

——— [Development of first guided missile, the BAT] (1944; TNB 31, 30, 1947)

——— Code for protection against lightning (H40, 1945)

Franklin, NBS casting resin for potting electronic circuitry (1945; TNB 31, 78, 1947)

2. WEIGHTS & MEASURES

Hidnert, Thermal expansion of electrolytic chromium [Explanation of cracking of chromium plating] (RP1361, 1941)

——— Absolute collimeter for testing range and height finders (no publ., 1942)

Schoonover & Dickson, [Development of mold lining material for processing resin dentures] (J. Am. Dental Assoc. 29, 1349, 1942)

Schoonover, Souder & Beall, [First explanation of delayed] Excessive expansion of dental amalgam (J. Am. Dental Assoc. 29, 1825, 1942)

——— [Development of] Elastic dental impression compounds with an alginate base (J. Am. Dental Assoc. 30, 565, 1943)

Peters, Nefflen & Harris, Diamond cutting by an electric arc (RP1657, 1945)

4. OPTICS

Scribner, Spark spectrographic analysis of commercial tin (RP1451, 1942)

Coblentz & Stair, A daily record of ultraviolet solar and sky radiation in Washington, 1941 to 1943 (RP1593, 1944)

Scribner & Mullin, Carrier-distillation method for spectrographic analysis and its application to the analysis of uranium-base materials (Manhattan Project Report A–2907, Sep 1945; RP1753, 1946)

Washer, Region of usable imagery in airplane-camera lenses (RP1636, 1945)

Gibson, Haupt & Keegan, Specification of railroad signal colors and glasses (RP1688, 1946)

Meggers, Microscopy, past, present, and future (J. Opt. Soc. Am. 36, 431, 1946)

5. CHEMISTRY

Branham, Shepherd & Schuhmann, Critical study of the determination of carbon monoxide by combustion over platinum . . . [First sensitive colorimetric indicator for carbon monoxide] (RP1396, 1941)

Mair, Glasgow & Rossini, Separation of hydrocarbons by azeotropic distillation (RP1402, 1941)

Gilchrist, Analytical separations by means of controlled hydrolytic precipitation (RP1519, 1943)

Flint, Clarke, et al., Extraction of alumina from clays and high-silica bauxites (RP1691, 1945–46; Hoffman, Leslie, et al., RP1756, 1946)

6. MECHANICS & SOUND

Hunter, Water-distributing systems for buildings (BMS79, 1941)

Heyl & Chrzanowski, A new determination of the constant of gravitation (RP1480, 1942)

Wildhack & Iberall, [Linear flowmeter for measuring oxygen regulator characteristics] (TNB 28, 68, 1944)

Cordero, Waterproof and shockproof standby compass (no publ., 1943)

Ramberg & Osgood, Description of stress-strain curves by three parameters (Natl. Adv. Comm. Aeron. Tech. Note 902, 1943)

McPherson, Adaptor for measuring principal strains with Tuckerman strain gage (Natl. Adv. Comm. Aeron. Tech. Note 898, 1943)

Keulegan, Laminar flow at the interface of two liquids [Research on density currents] (RP1591, 1944)

Brueggman, Mayer & Miller, Devices for testing thin sheet metals in compression tests (Natl. Adv. Comm. Aeron. Tech. Note 931, 1944; Natl. Adv. Comm. Aeron. Tech. Note 1022, 1946)

Tate, Solenoid compensating device for hardness testing machines (patent, 1944)

Womack & Orbach, [Carbon monoxide indicators for aircraft] (1941; TNB 30, 73, 1946)

Womack & Cordero, Yaw meter for aircraft (no publ., 1945)

Greenspan & Sweetman, A transfer strain gage for [measurement of] large strains (RP 1658, 1945)

Cook & Chrzanowski, Absorption and scattering by sound-absorbent cylinders [Acoustic impedance of the human ear] (RP1709, 1946)

Ramberg, Vacuum-tube acceleration pickup (RP1754, 1946)

Womack & Cordero [A portable wind speed and direction indicator] (TNB 31, 97, 1947)

7. ORGANIC & FIBROUS MATERIALS

Dreby, The planoflex . . . for evaluating the pliability of fabrics (RP1434, 1941)

Kline & Schiefer, An instrument for estimating tautness of doped fabrics on aircraft [Tautness meter] (Natl. Adv. Comm. Aeron. Tech. Note 729, 1942)

Schiefer, Mizell & Mosedale, [Thermal transmission apparatus for testing textiles] (RP1528, 1943)

Dreby, A friction meter for determining the coefficient of kinetic friction [in testing the smoothness] of fabrics (RP1562, 1943)

Kanagy, Charles, et al., [Prevention of mildew of leather] (RP1713, 1946)

——— Plastic housing for binoculars (TNB 28, 30, 1944)

Schiefer, Machines and methods for testing cordage fibers (RP1611, 1944)

——— Standard fading lamp (LC785, 1945)

8. METALLURGY

Ellinger, Bissell & Williams, [Development of] The tee-bend test to compare the welding quality of steels (RP1444, 1942)

9. CLAY & SILICATE PRODUCTS

Geller, A resistor furnace . . . [Development of ceramic oxide resistors for high-temperature furnaces] (RP1443, 1941)

Harrison & Moore, [Mechanism of] Weather resistance of porcelain-enameled iron structural units (RP1476, 1942)

Hoffman, J. I., Leslie, et al., Development of a hydrochloric acid process for the production of alumina from clay (RP1756, 1946)

Harrison, Moore & Richmond, Ceramic coatings for high-temperature protection of steel (RP1773, 1947)

NATIONAL BUREAU OF STANDARDS

RESEARCH HIGHLIGHTS IN SCIENCE AND TECHNOLOGY—1946–1951

1. ELECTRICITY & OPTICS

Washer & Scott, Influence of the atmosphere upon the precision of telescope pointing (RP1829, 1947)

Washer, Sources of error in and calibration of the f-number of photographic lenses (RP1927, 1948)

Gardner & Hahner, Research and development in applied optics and optical glass at the NBS (M194, 1949)

Washer & Case, Calibration of precision airplane mapping cameras (RP2108, 1950)

——— Electrochemical constants: a symposium (C524, 1953)

——— Optical image evaluation: a symposium (C526, 1954)

2. METROLOGY

Peters, Emerson, et al., Electrical methods for diamond-die production (RP1787, 1947)

Bowman, An automatic correction-computing chronograph [A method for making precision isochronism measurements] (Horological Inst. Am. J. 6, 13, 1951)

——— Frequency-monitoring device for interval timers (TNB 33, 99, 1949)

——— Gravity waves: a symposium (C521, 1952)

3. HEAT & POWER

Woolley, Scott & Brickwedde, Compilation of thermal properties of hydrogen in its various isotopic and ortho-para modifications (RP1932, 1948)

Scott, [New helium liquefier for studies in superconductivity] (TNB 33, 13, 1949)

——— Low-temperature physics: a symposium (C519, 1952)

——— Mechanical properties of metals at low temperatures: a symposium (C520, 1952)

——— Energy transfer in hot gases: a symposium (C523, 1954)

4. ATOMIC & RADIATION PHYSICS

Singer, Braestrup & Wyckoff, Absorption measurements for broad beams of 1- and 2-million-volt X-rays [Use of concrete as a high-energy radiation shield] (RP1735, 1946)

Meggers & Westfall, Lamps and wavelengths of mercury 198 [New standard of length, the Hg198 lamp] (TNB 31, 133, 1947; Sci. Mo. 68, 3, 1949; RP2091, 1950)

Marton & Belson, Tracer micrography [with radioactive isotopes] (Science, 106, 2742, 1947)

——— A non-magnetic radio-frequency mass spectrometer (TNB 32, 1, 1948)

Marton & Lachenbruch, Electron optical observation of magnetic fields [The electron optical shadow method for field mapping] (RP2033, 1949)

Curtiss & Carson, Reproducibility of photo-neutron standards (Phys. Rev. 76, 1412, 1949)

Hipple, Sommer & Thomas, A precise method of determining the faraday by magnetic resonance [The omegatron] Phys. Rev. 76, 1877, 1949)

Thomas, Driscoll & Hipple, Measurement of the proton moment in absolute units (Phys. Rev. 75, 902, 1949; RP2104, 1950)

Driscoll, Thomas & Hipple, The absolute value of the gyromagnetic ratio of the proton (Phys. Rev. 78, 339, 1950)

Huntoon & Fano, Atomic definition of primary standards (Nature, 166, 167, 1950)

——— Electron physics: a symposium (C527, 1954)

——— Mass spectroscopy in physics research: a symposium (C522, 1953)

5. CHEMISTRY

Shepherd, Analysis of a standard sample . . . [First nation-wide effort to standardize gas analysis] (RP1704, 1946)

Brenner & Riddell, Nickel plating on steel by chemical reduction (RP1725, 1946)

Rossini, Pitzer, et al., Tables of selected values of properties of hydrocarbons (C461, 1947)

Glasgow, Murphy, et al., Purification, purity, and freezing points of 31 hydrocarbons of the API–NBS series (RP1734, 1946)

Schwab & Wichers, [Benzoic acid cells as thermometric standard] (TNB 31, 116, 1947)

Brenner, Couch & Williams, Electrodeposition of alloys of phosphorus with nickel or cobalt (RP2061, 1950)

Scribner & Corliss, Emission spectrographic standards (Anal. Chem. 23, 1548, 1951)

——— Electrodeposition research: a symposium (C529, 1953)

6. MECHANICS

Carson & Worthington, Apparatus for determining water-vapor permeability of moisture barriers (C453, 1946)

Wildhack & Goalwin, [Compact liquid-to-gas oxygen converter] (TNB 33, 65, 1949)

Wexler, Divided flow, low-temperature humidity test apparatus [for radiosonde hygrometers] (TNB 32, 11, 1948; RP1894, 1948)

Levy, A. E. McPherson & Hobbs, Calibration of accelerometers [for aircraft] (RP1930, 1948)

Cordero, Johnson & Womack [Development of the Pfund sky compass] (TNB 33, 53, 1949)

Cordero, Stick-force indicator for aircraft (TNB 34, 6, 1950)

French, Stack venting of plumbing fixtures (BMS118, 1950)

——— Characteristics and application of resistance strain gages: a symposium (C528, 1954)

7. ORGANIC & FIBROUS MATERIALS

Schiefer, et al., Solution of problem of producing uniform abrasion and its application to the testing of textiles (RP1807, 1947; RP1988, 1949)

Holt, Knox & Roth, Strain test for rubber [Vulcanizates] (RP1907, 1948)

Axilrod, Thiebeau & Brenner, Variable-span flexure test jig for plastic specimens (ASTM Bull. 148, 96, 1947)

Hobbs, [Luggage testing and fatigue tester for luggage handles] (TNB 32, 134, 1948)

Hanks & Weissberg [The osmometer] (1948; RP2377, 1952)

Newman, Borysko & Swerdlow, Ultra-microtomy by a new method (RP2020, 1949)

O'Leary, et al., Paper from glass fibers (TNB 35, 177, 1951; TNB 39, 82, 1955)

——— Polymer degradation mechanism: a symposium (C525, 1953)

8. METALLURGY

Digges, Reinhart, et al., Influence of boron on some properties of experimental and commercial steels [Substitution of boron for carbon in hardening steels] (RP1815, 1947; RP1938, 1948)

Rosenberg & Darr, Stabilization of austenitic stainless steel [Prevention of corrosion in certain stainless steels] (RP1878, 1948)

9. MINERAL PRODUCTS

——— [Preparation of very thin] Ceramic dielectrics for electronic signal devices (TNB 33, 142, 1949)

Harrison, Moore & Richmond, Ceramic coatings for high-temperature protection of steel (RP 1773, 1947)

11. APPLIED MATHEMATICS

Lowan, The computation laboratory of the NBS [Mathematical tables program, 1930–1950] (Scripta Math. 15, 33, 1949)

13. ELECTRONICS & ORDNANCE DEVELOPMENT

Brunetti & Curtis, NBS printed circuit techniques (TNB 31, 1946; C468, 1947)

Rabinow, Magnetic fluid clutch (TNB 32, 54, 1948)

——— Computer development at the NBS [SEAC, SWAC, and DYSEAC] (C551, 1955)

14. CENTRAL RADIO PROPAGATION LABORATORY

——— Ionospheric radio propagation [Basic radio propagation predictions] (C462, 1947)

Husten & Lyons, Microwave frequency [measurements and standards] (Elec. Eng. 67, 436, 1948)

Kerns, Determination of efficiency of microwave bolometer mounts from impedance data (RP1995, 1949)

Lyons, et al., The atomic clock: an atomic standard of frequency and time (TNB 33, 17, 1949)

Lyons, Microwave spectroscopic frequency and time standards [The atomic clock] (Elec. Eng. 68, 251, 1949)

Birnbaum, A recording microwave refractometer (Rev. Sci. Instr. 21, 169, 1950)

Greene & Solow, Development of very-high-frequency field-intensity standards (RP2100, 1950)

Birnbaum, Kryder & Lyons, Microwave measurements of the dielectric properties of gases (J. Appl. Phys. 22, 95, 1951)

Selby, Radio-frequency micropotentiometer [and measurement of accurate rf microvoltages] (TNB 35, 33, 1951; Trans. AIEE 72, 158, 1953)

Huston, Improved NBS ammonia clock (Proc. IRE 39, 208, 1951)

Lyons, Spectral lines as frequency standards [NBS Model III of the ammonia clock] (Ann. N.Y. Acad. Sci. 55, 831, 1952)

LAND PURCHASES

for the National Bureau of Standards

U.S. DEPARTMENT OF COMMERCE

WASHINGTON, D.C.

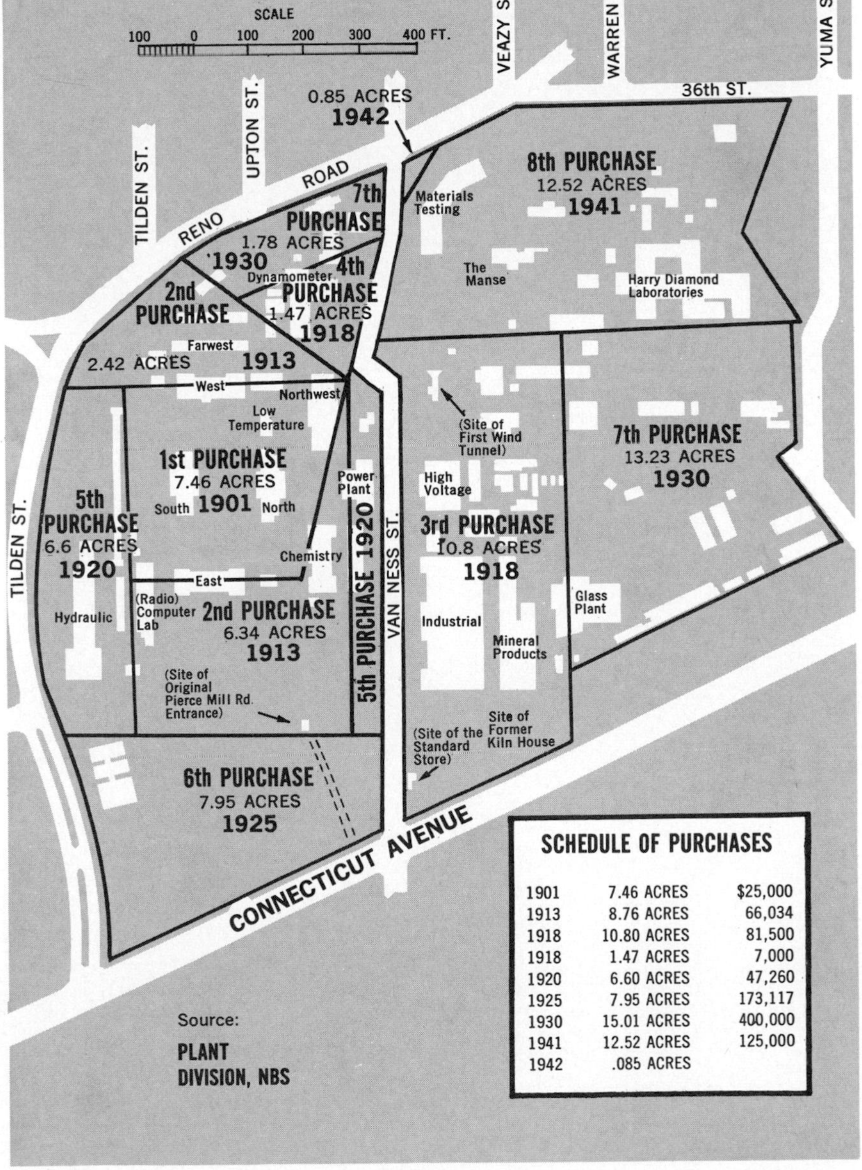

SCALE

100 0 100 200 300 400 FT.

VEAZY ST.
WARREN ST.
YUMA ST.
36th ST.
UPTON ST.
TILDEN ST.
RENO ROAD
0.85 ACRES 1942
8th PURCHASE 12.52 ACRES 1941
Materials Testing
The Manse
Harry Diamond Laboratories
7th PURCHASE 1.78 ACRES 1930
Dynamometer
4th PURCHASE 1.47 ACRES 1918
2nd PURCHASE 2.42 ACRES 1913
Farwest
West
Northwest
Low Temperature
1st PURCHASE 7.46 ACRES 1901
South
North
(Site of First Wind Tunnel)
7th PURCHASE 13.23 ACRES 1930
Power Plant
High Voltage
5th PURCHASE 6.6 ACRES 1920
3rd PURCHASE 10.8 ACRES 1918
Chemistry
East
TILDEN ST.
5th PURCHASE 1920
VAN NESS ST.
Glass Plant
Hydraulic
(Radio) Computer Lab
2nd PURCHASE 6.34 ACRES 1913
Industrial
Mineral Products
(Site of Original Pierce Mill Rd. Entrance)
Site of Former Kiln House
(Site of the Standard Store)
6th PURCHASE 7.95 ACRES 1925
CONNECTICUT AVENUE

SCHEDULE OF PURCHASES

Year	Acres	Cost
1901	7.46 ACRES	$25,000
1913	8.76 ACRES	66,034
1918	10.80 ACRES	81,500
1918	1.47 ACRES	7,000
1920	6.60 ACRES	47,260
1925	7.95 ACRES	173,117
1930	15.01 ACRES	400,000
1941	12.52 ACRES	125,000
1942	.085 ACRES	

Source:

PLANT DIVISION, NBS

APPENDIX M

SAMUEL WESLEY STRATTON

Founder and First Director of the National Bureau of Standards [1]

It is no exaggeration to say that Dr. Stratton's whole life was the National Bureau of Standards and that every formative influence in his early years was a preparation for his founding and direction of the Bureau. The Bureau is his monument, and the ideals of service that Stratton built into the edifice he raised in the age of commerce and industry survive intact into the present space age.

The name "Stratton" goes back to 12th-century Scotland, the surname of families who dwelt in a walled village by a paved road. The first Stratton on record in this country came from England in 1628. Dr. Stratton himself is believed to have descended from a Thomas Stratton who received a patent of land in Pittsylvania County, Va., in 1764. Thomas's great grandson Robertson Stratton moved from Virginia to Kentucky, where his fifth child, the father of Samuel Wesley Stratton, was born in 1832.

Upon the death of Robertson in 1832, his widow and children moved to Illinois. Dr. Stratton's father, Samuel, grew up in Litchfield, Ill., went into stock farming and later lumbering, and married a widow, Mrs. Mary Webster Philips. It was on the farm just outside Litchfield that Samuel Wesley was born on July 18, 1861.

Young Samuel Wesley grew up with little taste for farm life or for the stocks of Jersey cattle, Shetland ponies, Brahma chickens, and other new breeds of farm animals introduced into the State by his father as a result of periodic trips East and one voyage he made for new stock to England and the Channel Islands. Instead, he took an early interest in tinkering with the farm machinery, clocks, and other devices in the house, and in devising mechanical ways of taking the drudgery out of soapmaking, making apple butter, and similar farm chores. An annual treat was the stock show in St. Louis, 50 miles away, where his father exhibited his livestock and where young Samuel explored the exhibits of farm machinery, tools, and new mechanical inventions on display.

Determined on more education than provided by the district school and the high school in Litchfield, 2 miles away, Stratton sold a colt he had raised and announced his intention of going for a year to the Illinois Industrial University at Urbana, the future University of Illinois. In 1880 land-grant Illinois Industrial was almost 12 years old, a citadel of learning offering courses in "such branches of learning as are related to agriculture and the mechanic arts, and military studies, without excluding other scientific and practical studies."

The course Samuel Wesley set his heart on was that in "Machine shop practice," and he persuaded the registrar to let him take it in his freshman year. He was then 19,

[1] Except as otherwise noted, the present sketch is based on the manuscript fragment of a biography of Stratton written by Dr. Samuel C. Prescott of the Massachusetts Institute of Technology in 1933–34 and on the materials collected for that biography that now comprise the Stratton Papers in the Archives Library at M.I.T. The biographical fragment and other documents in that collection used in this sketch have been reproduced for the NBS Historical File.

Samuel W. Stratton at 21, probably early in his 3d year at Illinois Industrial University, about the time he entered the home of Dr. Peabody, president of the university.

Stratton as brevet captain, "Co. C., I.I.U. Battalion, Champagne, Ill., 2/25–84," as he wrote on the back of the picture. Fourteen years later, his fledgling moustache fully grown, he was in uniform again, serving under Commodore Remey during the Spanish-American War.

a stockily built boy of slightly less than average height, with gray-blue eyes and light brown hair, his serious face concealing a shyness that, except in the company of close friends, was to last all his life.

With little money from home, he found work in the college machine shops where he repaired farm machinery at 10 cents an hour. He also, with a wet-plate camera he had brought from home, took pictures of the buildings and classrooms for sale to students and visitors, and in the absence of satisfactory textbooks, began blueprinting the notes of professors at the university, at 2 cents a sheet. The notes, which he copied neatly from often illegible scrawls and then printed, sold well and enabled him to continue into his second year. That second year also he secured a room rent free in the chemical laboratory building in exchange for serving as fireman and janitor.

Stratton's last 2 years at the university were assured when the president and head of the department of mechanical engineering, Dr. Delim H. Peabody, offered him room, board, and a small salary in exchange for tending the farm and grounds of the president's house and acting as a sort of personal secretary. He became, a daughter of Dr. Peabody later recalled, a member of the family, and the training he received in the social graces, in household management, and in meeting and entertaining visitors and guests of the university was to prove almost the most valuable part of his college education.

It was about this time that he seems to have felt his youthful appearance belied his new responsibilities, for in his 22d year he began to grow the short, full mustache he wore the rest of his life.

Beginning in his second year, young Stratton took "Military," as required in State-supported universities, and demonstrated marked skill as a drillmaster. Of his other studies a contemporary was to say that his scholarship was fair but not brilliant, but "in some matters he did excel—shop work, draughtsmanship, and work in the physics laboratory * * * his work a model of neatness and accuracy."

Upon his graduation in 1884, Stratton received a completion certificate for his work in mathematics, physics, and mechanical engineering, his grades, according to the college record, consistently those expected of a "superior student"; a commission as brevet captain in the State military; and an invitation to return to the university as a member of the faculty. He presented his thesis, "The design of a heliostat," in 1886 and received his B.S. degree that year.

In his only extant autobiographical fragment, a four-page note on his military and naval service, Stratton said he once asked President Peabody why he been selected to teach at the university. The president replied that he had observed Stratton at drill and was impressed with the fact that he seemed to know how to get along with men. "I enjoyed the systematic way of doing things," Stratton commented, "and that experience, especially the discipline, has been of great value to me in most of the things I have been called upon to do later."

After a summer of engineering work in a Chicago factory, Stratton began instructing in mathematics and physics in the preparatory department of the university. He continued in the rank of instructor until 1889, when he was made assistant professor of physics. Upon his organization of a course in electrical engineering a year later, he occupied the chair of professor of physics and electrical engineering. In 1892, through a member of the faculty who preceded him, Stratton was called to the new University of Chicago as assistant professor of physics.[2]

The Ryerson Physical Laboratory at Chicago was under construction and Prof. Albert A. Michelson, brought from Clark University to head the new department, spent most of that year at the International Bureau of Weights and Measures outside Paris. There he demonstrated the practicability of a wavelength (light wave) standard, which was destined to replace the standard meter bar as the standard of length.

Stratton, as senior in Michelson's absence, therefore had the principal task of organizing the department and overseeing the construction and equipping of the new physics laboratory. He was then 26.

Stratton's 7 years under Michelson served him well, for the highly irascible master of the spectroscope and interferometer was a stickler for perfection and champion of the sixth decimal point. Disciplined in the measurement method of science, Michelson did not foresee its replacement by mathematical and theoretical physics, and like many of his scientific colleagues he continued to believe that the future of physics was strictly a matter of further precision and improved instrumentation.

---

[2] Stratton's salary of $2,000 was $500 less than that of Amos Alonzo Stagg (1862–1965), brought to the university that same year as athletic director and given the rank of associate professor. Time, Mar. 26, 1965, p. 45.

Sometime after settling into the routine of teaching and research with Michelson, Stratton was asked by Michelson, who had a strong interest in the Navy, to assist in organizing a volunteer naval militia at Chicago. A naval vessel on the Great Lakes was available for training in the operations of a warship, and Stratton accepted command of one of the four units constituting the naval militia battalion that was formed. At full strength his unit comprised a hundred men, consisting of trained engineers as officers and skilled artisans as crew.

At the outbreak of the war with Spain in the spring of 1898, Stratton was commissioned a lieutenant, put in charge of the battalion, expanded with additional volunteers to 705 men, and all were formally inducted into the U.S. Navy. The battalion was sent to Key West where it was distributed among the ships preparing to put to sea. Stratton saw most of his original unit detailed to the battleship *Oregon* when it arrived in late May after its famous 16,000-mile voyage around the Horn.

Many of his men saw action, but not Stratton. He had from the beginning of his naval service demonstrated marked executive ability and could not be spared. He was first attached to the naval base, then as watch and division officer on Commodore George C. Remey's flagship at the base, and finally attached to the battleship *Texas*, sister ship of the *Maine*, when she came north after the battle of Santiago. Mustered out in November 1898, Stratton kept up his naval connections, and from 1904 to 1912 held the rank of Commander in the District of Columbia Naval Militia. The Bureau laboratories were never to be without research projects for the Navy and he maintained a strong attachment to that service all his life.

His trip to the Nation's Capital late in 1898, to invite Admiral Dewey and Secretary of the Treasury Gage to give talks at the University of Chicago, led to Stratton's survey of the Office of Weights and Measures in the Coast Survey and the invitation to form and head the new National Bureau of Standards.[3]

---

[3] The originals of the Treasury Department appointment of Dr. Stratton as Inspector of Standards, effective date of oath Oct. 28, 1899, and the U.S. Civil Service certificate formally appointing him Inspector, dated Dec. 12, 1899, are in the Stratton Papers, MIT, Box 11.

A communication from Dr. Leonard B. Loeb, emeritus professor of physics, University of California, who studied and later taught under Michelson at Chicago, to Mrs. Dorothy Michelson Stevens, daughter of the great physicist, suggests that Michelson himself was very much interested in the position as Director of the new Bureau and, as plans for its establishment matured, hoped Stratton would make that known in Washington. Stratton had been Inspector of Standards for 6 months, working on the bill to be presented to Congress, when on Apr. 25, 1900, Michelson telegraphed Stratton asking him to return at once to Chicago, to help reorganize the local naval militia. Stratton, he said, was to be his chief of staff. (Telegram in Stratton Papers, MIT, copy in NBS Historical File.) But Stratton was now fully committed to his task in Washington.

One of Stratton's first duties upon becoming Director on Mar. 3, 1901, was to recommend to Secretary of the Treasury Lyman J. Gage suitable members for the Visiting Committee to the Bureau. A letter in April 1901 to Stratton from Dr. Henry S. Pritchett, former head of the Coast and Geodetic Survey who had recently become President of MIT, agreed with Stratton on the wisdom of asking Elihu Thomson, as well as Michelson, to join the Visiting Committee. "I think it wise to ask Michelson also as a member * * * because of his reputation and standing; no doubt we shall be able to keep him in good order." (Letter, Apr. 13, in Stratton Papers, Box 5.) The letter of invitation to Michelson was sent on June 6, 1901. No answer has been found. The letters

Prior to his appointment in March 1901 as the Bureau Director, Stratton lived at a boardinghouse at the corner of 18th and I Streets. Later that year he moved into an apartment in The Farragut, then nearing completion, a block away on 17th Street. His famous perfect and faithful maid Cordelia who came at this time was to run his bachelor household and delight his frequent dinner guests with her good cooking for the next 25 years in Washington and in Cambridge.

As Director of the Bureau, Dr. Stratton had considerable entertaining to do and learned to do it well. He streamed with charm and even his slight air of haughtiness was engaging. If he was somewhat formal and shy with strangers and acquaintances, with those who became friends he was wholly at ease, merry, and playful. He enjoyed most of all friends with large families, whose children he could spoil with presents and confections. They were sometimes unusual presents, such as the piglet he brought to one house, the great white goose he carried to another. As a treat for the Parris children on P Street, one of whom, Morris, was many years later to become his personal secretary and assistant at MIT, Stratton on one occasion secured the private car of the president of the Washington Railway & Electric Co. and for an afternoon and evening took them and a swarm of their friends on a picnic trip around the city and out into the suburbs.

Without a family, he made the Bureau family his own, presiding over their welfare, their education, and even their marriages, a number of which were held in his home at the Farragut. As the Bureau grew and the children of the staff members multiplied, Stratton began his custom of putting on elaborate Christmas parties and summer games and picnics for them. At the annual summer party in June, each child was weighed and measured and the new figures compared with those previously recorded. For their amusement he had swings erected on the Bureau lawn, brought up an organ grinder and monkey, a merry-go-round with a caliope, and hired a clown, and ponies to ride. There was a toy for each child, balloons were everywhere, and all the ice cream, lemonade, cake, and cookies the youngsters could eat. And to keep their parents happy out on Connecticut Avenue, Stratton held frequent receptions for their entertainment and arranged dances, lectures, and musicals, the latter often by members of the staff—events unheard of in a Government bureau before that time.[4]

He tried golf briefly and occasionally played tennis during his first years at the Bureau but never really cared for such organized exercise. The tennis ended when in 1905 Stratton and Louis A. Fischer, his chief of weights and measures, bought a 25-foot motor launch which they kept moored at a boat club on the Potomac. They spent many evenings and Sundays on the river, and made new friends along the waterway, among them James C. Courts, clerk of the Appropriations Committee, who became a great help to Stratton in getting Bureau bills through Congress. Not that he needed much help, for Stratton had a way with Congress, of interesting and exciting its committees in the research work of the Bureau, that was famous. As commander of the District Naval Militia, Stratton also had access to the monitor *Puritan* and a steam yacht, the

---

to those who were to form the first Visiting Committee, including both Thomson and Pritchett, were sent on June 18 (see ch. II, p. 61).

Mrs. Stevens, Michelson's daughter, presently engaged in writing a biography of her father, acknowledges that the introspective physicist, with his almost complete lack of interest in adminstration, would probably not have been happy as Director of the Bureau. But that his standing as a scientist and metrologist made him unquestionably the best qualified man in the Nation, and otherwise the obvious choice, for the position is beyond question.

[4] G. K. Burgess, "Dr. Samuel Wesley Stratton," The Tech Engineering News (MIT), 3, 146 (1922).

Scenes at the summer picnics that Dr. Stratton planned and presided over on the Bureau lawn between North and South buildings. Dr. Stratton appears in two of the scenes. The picture with the cameraman is dated 1922; the others are probably somewhat earlier.

Oneida, the latter a training ship whose crews on weekend outings and picnics frequently included some of Stratton's friends.

As Director of the Bureau and also a highly eligible bachelor, Stratton was in constant demand at official functions and private dinners. He was a frequent guest at the White House, beginning with the McKinleys. Later, the houseful of young Roosevelts became a recurring delight, as were his visits to the home of Commerce Secretary Hoover with its two enterprising youngsters. But his entertainment ranged far beyond official circles. For an inherently shy person Stratton had, Dr. Burgess was to say, "probably as wide an acquaintance among men of science, industry, engineering, and business as any single American."[5] Among his hundreds of acquaintances and friends, the two most intimate and longlasting were, not surprisingly, in the instrument industry, John Bashear, the great instrumentmaker, and Ambrose Swasey, manufacturer of machine tools and astronomical instruments, including the Lick, Naval Observatory, and Yerkes telescopes.

One chore that Dr. Stratton had all his professional life and could not evade was making speeches. Through the years he was called on more and more for talks and dedications and addresses, yet never learned to enjoy the prospect or effort. Even late in his career the thought of making an informal speech at the Bureau, on the occasion of its 25th anniversary, was daunting. As he wote to Dr. Burgess, "Of course, you know speaking is rather difficult for me."[6]

As the Bureau grew larger and the responsibilities greater, Dr. Stratton took less and less time off, until the yearly trips to Paris, mostly for meetings at the International Bureau of Weights and Measures, often became his only real vacation. It was during one of these Atlantic crossings shortly after World War I that he met Francis R. Hart of Boston, banker and member of the executive committee of the Massachusetts Institute of Techology, who is said to have submitted Stratton's name to the committee when that institution was looking for a new president.[7] He was invited to Cambridge in the spring of 1922 but deferred the decision to accept the office until he had discussed it with Secretary Hoover. Besides his concern for the Bureau, he had just bought an old house in Georgetown and was in the midst of remodeling it. Friends of 20 years were in Washington and its environs, and his roots were deep in the Bureau he had founded. But more visits to Cambridge followed, and on January 2, 1923, after receiving with the Hoovers at their annual New Year's day reception, Stratton arrived at the president's house on Charles River Road in Cambridge to stay.

Returning to the Bureau late in 1926 to take part in the celebration of its 25th anniversary, Stratton recalled as the greatest accomplishments of the Bureau under his direction, not its many achievements in science and technology, but its impact on American industry. Its most significant accomplishments for the advance of industry, promised when the Bureau was founded, were "the influence upon manufacturers, of the introduction of scientific methods of measurements and methods of research * * * [and] the training of men for industry."[8] They were also the objectives he had raised to new heights in his administration of MIT.

Dr. Stratton was summering at the home of friends in Manchester, Mass., in June 1927 when Gov. Alvan T. Fuller asked President Abbott Lawrence Lowell of Harvard University, Judge Robert A. Grant of the Probate Court of Suffolk County, and Dr.

---

[5] Ibid.

[6] Letter, Oct. 28, 1926 ("General Correspondence files of the Director, 1945–1955").

[7] Undocumented account in Prescott's manuscript. Hart may have been partly instrumental, but for a better documented account of the invitation, see ch. V, pp. 233–235.

[8] Speech, Dec. 4, 1926 (NBS Blue Folder Box 3, APW301c).

The Bureau of Standards Orchestra, fostered by Dr. Stratton to keep his staff happy, played at all social functions and from time to time attempted concerts.

Dr. Paul D. Foote, a regular member of the group, recalls "with embarrassment" that this picture was taken during the performance on the evening of April 17, 1918, when "the rendition of a quartet encore [of 'Moment Musicale'] failed to indicate sufficient coordination and practice."

Identified in the ensemble are Mr. and Mrs. W. F. G. Swann, C. G. Peters, P. D. Foote, H. F. Stimson, R. F. Jackson, W. F. Meggers F. L. Mohler, W. Skogland, L. E. Whittemore, J. H. Dellinger, O. Lytle, Miss G. Neidig, and P. McNicholas.

Stratton to serve on an advisory committee in the Governor's investigation of the Sacco-Vanzetti case.

Seven years before, in May 1920, Nicolo Sacco and Bartolomeo Vanzetti, one a shoe worker, the other a fish peddler, were arrested and subsequently charged with the murder of a shoe factory paymaster and his guard at South Braintree, near Boston. They bore the stigma of being unnaturalized foreigners, wartime draft dodgers, admitted anarchists and atheists. These crimes might have convicted them but in truth they were tried for murder and on July 14, 1921, found guilty.

Immediately after their arrest, Socialist and anarchist friends formed a Sacco-Vanzetti Defense Committee that was soon joined by a civil liberties committee and many of the dissident groups that flourished in the troubled years after the war. For 6 years the committee delayed execution of the sentence by successive motions for new trials, and created a worldwide cause célèbre in which law professors and students, lawyers, college professors, editors, journalists, preachers, poets, playwrights, publicists, authors, labor unions, church councils, the radical press, volunteer agitators, and simple citizens, labored in the atmosphere of the hysteria provoked by the case.

Two respites were granted by Governor Fuller after the sentence of execution, pronounced on April 9, 1927, was set. On June 1 the Governor appointed his advisory committee of three to make a final review of the evidence. Lowell, Grant, and Stratton studied the amassed records and held hearings and interviews with Judge Webster Thayer, the district attorney, the defense attorneys, the jury members, police, and many of the witnesses. A recommendation for commutation of the death sentence would have relieved them from the threats of violence and the abuse they were to suffer, but in their report to the Governor on July 27 they unanimously adjudged the trial fair and upheld the jury's verdict that the defendents were guilty beyond a reasonable doubt. Sacco and Vanzetti were executed on August 23, 1927.

It was a harrowing experience. Tempers were high and threatening letters bombarded the committee. An armed guard sat in Dr. Stratton's office at the State House and in his car wherever he went. At Manchester a policeman followed his car and another patroled his house at night. When the ordeal was over Stratton sailed for Europe under secrecy imposed by the uneasy steamship company. He spent the hours before sailing in the port captain's office and boarded the ship only at the last minute. His name was omitted from the passenger list. In London the American Embassy took over, and in that city and in Paris there were demonstrations, but Stratton was not recognized and he continued his tour without event.

Stratton's trips to Europe by then had become frequent, and besides visiting the friends he had everywhere, he spent much time in antique shops, collecting old silver in shops in Glasgow and at Mallets in Bath, rare china in Kings Street, London, old furniture in Rubgy, tapestries wherever they were to be found in France, and new pieces of china from the Sèvres factory outside Paris and in the Rive Gauche. No new or idle pastime, this connoisseurship was quite in keeping with his long years of interest in ceramics, in textiles, and metalworking.

His love of fine instruments and working with tools never diminished. As he had furnished a workshop next to his office at the Bureau, so one of the first things he set up in Cambridge was a nearly perfect shop, with great stores of material and extra tools, in the basement below his office at the Institute. Only slightly less complete was another shop downstairs in the president's house. His zeal for acquisition of "stock," as he called it, extended to his food supplies and linens for the house, to clothing and everything else that could be bought ahead.

He was as lavish, within his means, toward others as toward himself, and never made a visit without a shower of presents for his hosts and their children. After visiting the American consul and his wife in Dresden one summer he mailed them great hampers of food unobtainable in postwar Germany. To friends he visited on Norway's North Cape he sent two barrels of fruit. Besides his good company, he was always a welcome and useful guest, for he willingly mended toys and broken household machines brought to his attention.

A poor sleeper and avid reader from youth onward, Stratton carried books with him when he visited and collected them abroad. At home he kept his bedroom shelves filled with current scientific periodicals and books and often read from midnight to 3 or 4 in the morning.

In his 8 years at MIT he introduced at that institution many of the innovations he had set going at the Bureau, extending its research in engineering and industrial processes, in pure science, and expanding the Institute's work into new fields of applied science. Under him new laboratories and dormitories rose, lecturers were brought from the universities of Europe to make available the best research and teaching in science and technology abroad, and advisory committees of men eminent in professional or business life were appointed to counsel the departments of the Institute.

As at the Bureau, Stratton was everywhere overseeing, counseling, and directing the affairs of the Institute and the student body, and as his 70th birthday approached the effort became overtaxing. Acting on his suggestion, the corporation of MIT divided the heavy administrative responsibility in 1930, making Dr. Stratton chairman of the corporation. Dr. Karl T. Compton, who had been head of the physics department at Princeton, came to assume the presidency of the Institute.

Stratton's birthday on July 18, 1931, was celebrated by an avalanche of letters, almost 200 of them later mounted in a great gleaming leather birthday book. Beginning with a warm letter from Herbert and Lou Hoover, the book remains a remarkable index to the world circle of Stratton's friends and acquaintances.

Four months before his birthday, Stratton, still hale, in excellent health, and full of memories of his years at the Bureau, came as guest of honor to a party held in East building to celebrate the 30th anniversary of its founding. On the evening of October 18, 3 months after his birthday and a week after returning from England where he had attended the international Faraday celebration, he died suddenly of a coronary occlusion at his home in Beacon Street. He was dictating a tribute to Thomas Edison, whose death had occurred that same morning, when his own came.

Dr. Stratton's greatest achievement was in founding and establishing the National Bureau of Standards and gaining for it international respect and fame. It was a superlative feat and called for a high and specialized talent. Dr. Compton of the Institute spoke for all in paying tribute to those distinguishing traits of Dr. Stratton's that had served the Bureau and the Institute and marked the man: his fundamental kindness of character, his wholehearted absorption in his work, and the consistency of his life and thought in pursuit of his ideals and objectives. Unsympathetic perhaps and certainly impatient with people or things that ran contrary to his ideal, he gave the full measure of his support and force to that which advanced his ideal, first of the Bureau and later of the Institute. Few men's lives have been so consistent, straightforward, and unswerving in their devotion to public service as Stratton's, and with so complete an absence of self-interest.

The intense admiration that Dr. Stratton inspired in his friends led two of them to attempt his biography. Shortly after his death, Morris A. Parris, his personal secretary, and Prof. Samuel C, Prescott, his closest friend at the Institute, chairman of the Department of Biology and Public Health, and soon to become Dean of Science, began collecting records, reminiscences, and memoranda for the biography. The materials gathered over the next 3 years were to form the shelf of Stratton papers located in the Archives Library at MIT.

Several outlines of the proposed work and preliminary drafts of three chapters, through Stratton's early teaching career at Urbana, were completed when certain difficulties arose. Sufficient details and documents of Stratton's forebears could not be found and the early pages were thin. The complete absence of self-interest, and hence self-revelation, in Stratton's life and career gradually became evident. Then Parris left the Institute and Prescott assumed the additional duties of Dean of Science. But almost certainly the crowning difficulty, stifling further work on the biography, was the prospect of attempting to record the history of Stratton's directorship of the Bureau.[9]

Professor Prescott undoubtedly relinquished his project under the pressure of his administrative and teaching duties, but it is more than likely that he also came to realize that the heart of any possible biography of Dr. Stratton could not be a record of his life so much as a history, the history of his greatest single accomplishment, the National Bureau of Standards.

---

[9] The final correspondence in Prescott's search for biographical materials is that with Dr. Briggs of the Bureau in December 1934, which resulted in Prescott receiving nine items. These included copies of extracts from the report of the Electrical Conference of 1884, a chart of the funds and staff of the Bureau since its founding, the Bureau's brief biographical sketch of Dr. Stratton, and the program of the Bureau's farewell reception for him.

APPENDIX N

BOOKS by Staff Members of the National Bureau of Standards

1912–1960*

Alt, Franz L., Electronic digital computers: their use in science and engineering. New York: Academic Press, 1958, 336 p.

Bates, Roger Gordon, Electrometric pH determinations: theory and practice. New York: Wiley, 1954, 331 p.

Bichowsky, Francis Russell, Industrial research. Brooklyn, N.Y.: Chemical Publishing Co., 1942, 126 p.

Blum, William, and G. B. Hogaboom, Principles of electroplating and electroforming (electrotyping). New York: McGraw-Hill, 1924, 356 p.; 2d ed., 1930, 424 p.; 3d ed., 1949, 455 p.

Bogue, Robert Herman, The chemistry and technology of gelatin and glue. New York: McGraw-Hill, 1922, 644 p.

Bogue, Robert Herman, The chemistry of portland cement. New York: Reinhold, 1947, 572 p.; 2d ed., 1955, 793 p.

Brode, Wallace Reed, Chemical spectroscopy. New York: J. Wiley & Sons, 1939, 494 p.; 2d ed., 1943, 677 p.

Burgess, George Kimball, and H. LeChatelier, The measurement of high temperatures. 3d ed., rewritten and enlarged, New York: J. Wiley & Sons, 1912, 510 p.

Burgess, George Kimball, Die Messung hoher Temperaturen. Nach der dritten amerikanischen Auflage übersetzt und mit Ergänzungen versehen, von Prof. Dr. G. Leithauser. Berlin: J. Springer, 1913, 486 p.

Burgess, George Kimball, Precision machines and instruments for the measurement of length. Paper presented at the International Engineering Congress, Tokyo, 1930, 48 p., n.p., n.d.

Cleaves, Harold E., and J. G. Thompson, The metal-iron. New York & London: Published for the Engineering Foundation by McGraw-Hill, 1935, 574 p.

Coblentz, William Weber, From the life of a researcher. New York:

*Only books that had their inception or were largely or entirely written or revised while the author was a member of the staff, or were written in retirement, appear in this compilation. Books edited by Bureau members or to which Bureau members contributed, unless theirs was the major contribution, have been omitted.

Philosophical Library, 1951, 238 p.

Coblentz, William Weber, Investigations of infra-red spectra. Washington, D.C.: Carnegie Institution of Washington Publication Nos. 35, 65, 97, 1905–1908, 3 v.

Coblentz, William Weber, A physical study of the firefly. Washington, D.C.: Carnegie Institution of Washington Publication No. 164, 1912, 47 p.

Cohen, Louis, Formulae and tables for the calculation of alternating current problems. New York: McGraw-Hill, 1913, 282 p.

Cohen, Louis, Heaviside's electrical circuit theory, with an introduction by Prof. M. I. Pupin. New York: McGraw-Hill, 1928, 169 p.

Condon, Edward Uhler, and Hugh Odishaw, eds., Handbook of physics. New York: McGraw-Hill, 1958, 1,459 p.

Condon, Edward Uhler, and G. H. Shortley, The theory of atomic spectra. Reprint of 1935 ed. with corrections, Cambridge (England) University Press, 1951, 441 p.

Curtis, Harvey L., Electrical measurements: precise comparisons of standards and absolute determination of the units. New York & London: McGraw-Hill, 1937, 302 p.

Curtis, Harvey L., Recollections of a scientist: an autobiography. Privately printed at Bonn, Germany: L. Leopold Press, 1958, 128 p.

Curtiss, Leon Francis, An introduction to neutron physics. Princeton, N.J.: Van Nostrand, 1959, 380 p.

Dorsey, Noah Ernest, The physics of radioactivity. Baltimore, Md.: Williams & Wilkins, 1921, 223 p.

Dorsey, Noah Ernest, Properties of ordinary water-substance in all its phases: water-vapor, water, and all the ices. New York: Reinhold, 1940, 673 p.

Eaton, Herbert Nelson, K. H. Beij, and W. G. Brombacher, Aircraft instruments. New York: Ronald Press, 1926, 269 p.

Eisenhart, Churchill, and others, Techniques of statistical analysis. New York: McGraw-Hill, 1947, 473 p.

Fano, Ugo, and L. Fano, Basic physics of atoms and molecules. New York: Wiley, 1959, 414 p.

Fano, Ugo, and G. Racah, Irreducible tensorial sets. New York: Academic Press, 1959, 171 p.

Foote, Paul Darwin, and Fred L. Mohler, The origin of spectra. New York: Chemical Catalog Co., 1922, 250 p.

Gillett, Horace W., The behavior of engineering metals. New York: Wiley, 1951, 395 p.

Gillett, Horace W., An engineering approach to the selection, evaluation, and specification of metallic materials. Cleveland: Penton, 1944, 140 p.

Gillett, Horace W., and E. L. Mack, Molybdenum, cerium and related alloy steels. New York: Chemical Catalog Co., 1925, 299 p.

Hamer, Walter Jay, The structure of electrolytic solutions. New York: Wiley, 1959, 441 p.

Harriman, Norman Follett, Principles of scientific purchasing. New York: McGraw-Hill, 1928, 301 p.

Harriman, Norman Follett, Standards and standardization. New York: McGraw-Hill, 1928, 265 p.

Harris, Forest K., Electrical measurements. New York: Wiley, 1952, 784 p.

Hersey, Mayo Dyer, On the laws of lubrication of journal bearings. New York: n.p., 1915, 37 p.

Hersey, Mayo Dyer, Theory of lubrication. New York: Wiley; London: Chapman & Hull, 1936, 152 p.

Heyl, Paul Renno, The common sense of the theory of relativity. Baltimore: Williams & Wilkins, 1924, 44 p.

Heyl, Paul Renno, Electronics. Indianapolis: P. R. Mallory, 1943, 5 parts, n.p.

Heyl, Paul Renno, The fundamental concepts of physics in the light of modern discovery. Baltimore: Williams & Wilkins, 1926, 112 p.

Heyl, Paul Renno, The philosophy of a scientific man. New York: Vanguard Press, 1933, 182 p.

Hillebrand, William Francis, and G. E. F. Lundell, Applied inorganic analysis, with special reference to the analysis of metals, minerals and rocks. New York: Wiley, 1929, 929 p.; 2d ed., revised by Lundell, H. A. Bright, and J. I. Hoffman, 1953, 1,034 p.

Hilsenrath, Joseph, M. Klein, and H. W. Woolley, Tables of thermodynamic properties of air. New York: Pergamon, 1960, 148 p.

Hilsenrath, Joseph, and G. G. Ziegler, Tables of Einstein functions: vibrational contributions to the thermodynamic functions. Washington, D.C., 1962, 258 p.

Hudson, Claude Silbert, The collected papers of C. S. Hudson [in sugar research]. New York: Academic Press, 1946, 2 v., n.p.

Hund, August, Frequency modulation. New York & London: McGraw-Hill, 1942, 375 p.

Hund, August, High-frequency measurements. New York & London: McGraw-Hill, 1933, 491 p.; 2d ed., 1951, 676 p.

Hund, August, Hochfrequenzmesstechnik: ihre wissenschaftlichen und practischen grundlagen. Berlin: J. Springer, 1922, 526 p.; 2 aufl., 1928.

Hund, August, Phenomena in high frequency systems. New York & London: McGraw-Hill, 1936, 642 p.

Hund, August, Short-wave radiation phenomena. New York: McGraw-Hill, 1952, 2 v.

Insley, Herbert, and V. D. Frechette, Microscopy of ceramics and cements, including glasses, slags and foundry sands. New York: Academic Press, 1955, 286 p.

Ives, Herbert Eugene, Airplane photography. Philadelphia & London: J. B. Lippincott, 1920, 422 p.

Jacobs, Donald Harry, Fundamentals of optical engineering. New York & London: McGraw-Hill, 1943, 487 p.

Judd, Deane Brewster, Color in business, science, and industry. New York: Wiley, 1952, 401 p.

Ledley, Robert Steven, Digital computer and control engineering. Written with the assistance of Louis S. Rotolo and James B. Wilson. New York: McGraw-Hill, 1960, 835 p.

Levin, Ernest M., with Howard F. McMurdie and F. P. Hall, Phase diagrams for ceramists. Columbus, Ohio: American Ceramic Society, 1956, 286 p.

Lundell, Gustave Ernst Frederick, James Irvin Hoffman, and Harry A. Bright, Chemical analysis of iron and steel. New York: Wiley, 1931, 641 p.

Lundell, Gustave Ernst Frederick, and James Irvin Hoffman, Outlines of methods of chemical analysis. New York: Wiley, 1938, 250 p.

Mann, Wilfrid Basil, The cyclotron. With a foreword by E. O. Lawrence. New York: Chemical Publishing Co., 1940; London: Methuen, 2d ed., 1945; London: Methuen, 3d ed., 1948, 92 p.

Meggers, William Frederick, and Bourdon F. Scribner, Index to the literature of spectrochemical analysis, 1920–37. Sponsored by Committee E–2 on Spectrographic Analysis of the American Society for Testing Materials. Philadelphia: American Society for Testing Materials, 1939, 59 p.; 2d ed., 1941, issued in 4 parts of a continuing series.

Nutting, Perley Gilman, Outlines of applied optics, Philadelphia: P. Blakiston's Son, 1912, 234 p.

Page, Chester Hall, The algebra of electronics. Princeton, N.J.: Van Nostrand, 1958, 258 p.

Page, Chester Hall, Physical mathematics. Princeton, N.J.: Van Nostrand, 1955, 329 p.

Phelan, Vincent B., The American home book of repairs: the care and repair of the home. Garden City, N.Y.: Doubleday, Doran, 1931, 306 p.

Rawdon, Henry S., Protective metallic coatings. American Chemical Society Monograph Series, No. 403. New York: Chemical Catalog Co., 1938, 277 p.

Rossini, Frederick Dominic, Chemical thermodynamics. New York: Wiley, 1950, 514 p.

Rossini, Frederick Dominic, B. J. Mair, and A. J. Streiff, Hydrocarbons from petroleum: the fractionation, analysis, isolation, purification, and properties of petroleum hydrocarbons. An account of the work of American Petroleum Institute Research Project 6. American Chemical Society Monograph series, No. 121. New York: Reinhold, 1953, 556 p.

Rossini, Frederick Dominic, and others, Properties of titanium compounds and related substances. Washington, D.C.: Office of Naval Research, ONR Report ACR–17, 1956, 448 p.

Rossini, Frederick Dominic, and others, Selected values of physical and thermodynamic properties of hydrocarbons and related compounds, comprising the tables of American Petroleum Institute Research Project 44 as of December 31, 1952. Pittsburgh: Published for the American Petroleum Institute by the Carnegie Press, 1953, 1,050 p.

Rossini, Frederick Dominic, Thermodynamics and physics of matter. Vol. 1, High speed aerodynamics and jet propulsion. Princeton University Press, 1955, 812 p.

Ruark, Arthur Edward, and H. C. Urey, Atoms, molecules and quanta. International series in physics. New York: McGraw-Hill, 1930, 790 p.

Sasuly, Max, Trend analysis of statistics: theory and technique. Washington, D.C.: The Brookings Institute, 1934, 421 p.

Scott, Russell Burton, Cryogenic engineering. Prepared for the Atomic Energy Commission. Princeton, N.J.: Van Nostrand, 1959, 368 p.

Vinal, George Wood, Primary batteries. New York: Wiley, 1950, 336 p.

Vinal, George Wood, Storage batteries: a general treatise on the physics and chemistry of secondary batteries and their engineering applications. New York: Wiley, 1924, 402 p.; 2d ed., 1930, 427 p.; 3d ed., 1940, 464 p.; 4th ed., 1935, 446 p.

Whittemore, Herbert Lucius, Ideas on specifications. Columbia, Conn.: Columbia Graphs, 1952, 128 p.

Youden, William John, Statistical design: a collection by the editors of the bimonthly articles by Dr. W. J. Youden, National Bureau of Standards, during his 6 years (1954–59) as contributing editor for Industrial and Engineering Chemistry. Washington, D.C.: American Chemical Society, 1960, n.p.

Youden, William John, Statistical methods for chemists. New York: Wiley, 1951, 136 p.

APPENDIX O

BUILDINGS AND STRUCTURES of the National Bureau of Standards [1]

Washington, D.C.

Bldg. No.	Name	Year Built	Construction Cost	Estimated Replacement Cost—1947	Estimated Replacement Cost—1960
1	South	1905	$400,000 (Bldgs. 1 and 3)	$864,000	$1,620,000
3	North	1905–32 [2]		323,000	1,430,000
2	East	1914	430,000	767,000	1,906,000
4	West	1910	350,000	665,000	1,538,000
5	Chemistry	1918	386,000	750,000	1,932,000
6	Power Plant	1930	200,000	330,000	845,000
7	Northwest	1919	285,750	540,000	1,656,000
8	Dynamometer	1919–33	96,480	197,400	828,000
9	Hydraulic Lab.	1932	350,000	705,000	2,200,000
10	Radio (later Computer Lab.)	1919–42	200,000	300,000	825,000
11	Industrial	1920	1,090,000	1,600,000	5,636,000
12	High Voltage	1939	400,000	550,000	1,282,000
13	Materials Testing	1942	540,000	900,000	2,168,000
14	Kiln House (later Mineral Products)	1920	116,500	171,000	1,461,000
15	Glass Plant	1941	100,000	145,000	650,000
16	Service (later Electronics)	1942–45	70,000	100,000	855,900
17	The Manse	[3]	[3]	40,000	150,000
18	Low Temperature	1906	23,375	71,000	261,000
19	South Wind Tunnel	1918	16,440	31,500	60,000
20	Far West	1915–42	96,300	374,000	480,000
21	Utility (later Stucco)	1918–47	105,000	94,000	300,000
22	Sound	1921–44	[4]	63,000	120,000
23	Reverberation	1929	4,000	5,600	35,000
24	Meter Rating	1914	16,240	53,700	75,000
25	Lamp Test	1941–49	10,000	10,000	30,000
26	Telephone	1914–23–41	[4]	30,870	40,000
27	Chemistry Annex	1924–45–48	[4]	21,900	75,000
28	Scale House	1939	6,000	9,300	50,000
29	Utility (later Boiler Test)	1943	[4]	7,500	20,000
30	Sterrett House	[3]	[3]	7,500	35,000
31	Test Bungalow (later Plasma Res.)	1941	[4]	52,000	80,000
32	Fuel Synthesis #1 (later Surface Chem.)	1945	15,336	20,000	28,000

Footnotes at end of table.

Bldg. No.	Name	Year Built	Construction Cost	Estimated Replacement Cost—1947	Estimated Replacement Cost—1960
33	Fuel Synthesis #2	1943	(4)	4, 500	12, 000
34	Oil Storage	1925	(4)	11, 000	12, 800
35	Refrig. Plant	1925–45	(4)	14, 000	60, 000
36	Dynamometer Annex	1925–47	(4)	11, 500	65, 000
[5] 37	West Guard Office	1950	....	2, 000	10, 000
38	Plant Div. Storage (later Central Guard Office)	1929–52	4, 460	7, 100	10, 000
39	Plant Div. Storage	1933	(4)	....	....
40	Greenhouse	1946	1, 513	2, 200	10, 000
41	Radio Annex (later Microwave Spectroscopy)	1943	(4)	2, 200	9, 800
42	Utility Quonset	1943	4, 300	7, 500	75, 000
43	Utility Quonset	1943	4, 300	6, 250	75, 000
44	Central Guard Off.	1927	1, 500	1, 500	4, 000
45	Volatile Liquid Vault #1	1943	6, 520	8, 200	12, 500
46	Northwest Annex	1945	....	1, 260	....
47	East Guard Office	1942	....	(6)	....
48	Combustion Res.	....	(4)	(7)	....
49	Storage Battery	1943–44	(4)	27, 500	60, 000
50	Storage (later Corrosion Lab. Annex)	....	(4)	1, 000	3, 500
[8] 51	Construction Off.	1941	....	(7)	....
[8] 52	Supply Warehouse	1944	25, 219	34, 000	200, 000
[8] 53	Std. Sample Storage	1943	....	3, 750	25, 000
[8] 54	Shipping Warehouse	1943	....	3, 750	24, 000
[8] 55	Storage Warehouse #1	1942	....	18, 000	....
56	North Guard Off.	1942	....	(7)	....
57	Chemistry Storage	1944	(4)	(7)	....
58	Quartz Storage Ann.	1944	24, 974	(7)	....
59	Utility (later Ultra Centrifuge Lab.)	....	(4)	3, 900	6, 800
60	Volatile Liquid Vault #2	1944	....	7, 000	5, 000
61	Utility (later Mineral Products Shop)	1926	8, 000	13, 100	20, 000
62	Utility (later Heat Transfer Lab.)	1925	8, 000	10, 000	24, 000
63	Warehouse (later Plant Div. Shops)	1945	17, 000	17, 000	125, 000
64	Fire Resistance Lab #1	1929	111, 000	177, 000	97, 000
65	Fire Resistance Lab #2	1924–27–58	(4)	30, 500	80, 000
66	Paint Storage	....	(4)	1, 500	5, 000
67	Fire Resist. Lab #3	1943	(4)	12, 500	45, 000
68	Fire Resist. Lab #4	1930	(4)	20, 000	77, 000
69	Fire Resistance	1925–30	3, 800	(7)	....
70	Storage	....	1, 500	(7)	....
71	Storage	....	600	(7)	....

Footnotes at end of table.

Bldg. No.	Name	Year Built	Construction Cost	Estimated Replacement Cost—1947	Estimated Replacement Cost—1960
72	High Voltage Annex	1939	100, 000	155, 500	130, 000
73	North Wind Tunnel	1944	110, 000	142, 000	215, 000
74	Open Wind Tunnel	1923	20, 000	(7)	....
75	Storage (Bomb Shelter)	1942	1, 500	(7)	....
76	Hangar (later Supersonic Wind Tunnel)	1930	15, 000	24, 700	81, 000
77	Barracks	....	....	(7)	....
78	Canteen	....	....	2, 000	19, 000
79	Volatile Liquid Vault #3	1944	7, 000	9, 000	10, 000
80	Electronics Lab. Annex	1930–44	9, 500	22, 500	25, 000
81	Test Shed	....	....	(7)	....
82	Explosives Vault	....	....	600	800
[5] 83	Electronics Lab. (later Ordnance Hqs.)	1944–52	40, 141	52, 000	....
[5] 84	Electronic Tube Lab.	1944	20, 812	27, 000	....
[5] 85	Optical Test Lab.	....	(4)	21, 000	....
[5] 86	Test Shed	....	....	(7)	....
[5] 87	Alumina Res. Bldg.	(3)	(3)	15, 000	....
[5] 88	Explosive Components	1944–58	5, 195	6, 400	....
89	Grounds Maintenance	....	....	200	22, 650
90	Fire Prevention	....	....	400	3, 500
91	Utility Quonset #3	1944	....	15, 000	115, 000
[5] 92	Ordnance Laboratory	1939–43	513, 000	795, 000	....
93	Fire Resist. Lab. #5	1939	(4)	3, 000	15, 000
94	Hydrogenation Vault	1947	3, 300	4, 500	10, 000
95	Vibration Test	1946	2, 935	3, 700	75, 000
.....	Pipe Tunnels	....	....	194, 000	....
96	Combustion Research	1947	15, 722	17, 500	86, 000
97	Fire Resistance	1947	1, 000	(7)	....
98	Storage shed	....	400	(7)	....
99	Ordnance Refrigeration	....	....	....	....
100	Storage Warehouse #2	1948	19, 664	....	67, 000
101	Storage Warehouse #3	1948	19, 708	....	67, 000
102	Carpenter shop	1948	32, 798	....	85, 000
[5] 103	Ordnance Annex #1	1948	20, 000	....	....
104	Betatron	1949	282, 000	....	375, 000
[5] 105	Ordnance Annex #2	1949	6, 500	....	....
106	Battery Shelter	1949	2, 557	....	800
107	Labor Office	1949	7, 184	....	10, 000
108	Radio Systems Lab.	1949	20, 000	....	80, 000
111	Aggregate Storage	1951	5, 000	....	15, 000
[5] 112	Air Gun Bldg.	1951–58	32, 000	....	....
[5] 113	Refrigeration	1951	6, 800	....	....
114	Ordnance Rd. Guard Office	1950	2, 000	....	4, 000
115	Acoustics Lab.	1950	19, 300	....	35, 000

Footnotes at end of table.

Bldg. No.	Name	Year Built	Construction Cost	Estimated Replacement Cost—1947	Estimated Replacement Cost—1960
[5] 116	Ordnance Plating Shop	1950	5, 000	....	....
118	Timber Storage	1951	5, 000	....	45, 000
119	Sand Bins	1950	2, 000	....	9, 500
120	Tire Test	1952	20, 000	....	175, 000
121	Polymer Lab.	1952	22, 000	....	95, 000
122	Gamma Ray Lab.	1953	55, 000	....	85, 000
[5] 123	DOFL Storage	1956–58	....	....	....
124	High Pressure Test	1956	13, 485	....	20, 000
[5] 126	Fuze Laboratory	1957	....	....	....
127	Pneumatics Annex	1958	1, 500	....	6, 000
129	Tempo A	1957	8, 000	....	14, 000
130	Tempo B	....	200	....	1, 000
[5] 132	New Guard Hq.	1957	24, 761	....	....
[5] 133	Regional Training Center	1959	50, 209	....	....
[5] 134	Industrial Engineering Laboratory	1959	40, 800	....	....
[5] 135	Radioactive Material Storage	1959	16, 990	....	....
136	Plasma Power Supply	1961	10, 495	....	....
137	Gas Viscosity Lab.	1955	14, 156	....	18, 000
138	Gas Cylinder Storage	1961	5, 529	....	....

[1] Based on Public Buildings Administration (FWA) appraisal dated July 11, 1947, correlated with Public Buildings Administration survey data of Oct. 1, 1948; NBS Plant Division inventory of 1960; and addenda supplied by Plant Division, January 1963 (NBS Historical File). Note.—Original construction costs in the chart are in some instances higher than those reported in the history since they include special facilities, equipment, structural changes, and other costs above the original appropriation.

[2] Second date indicates major modification or addition to the structure. The additional story on North Building, for example, cost $138,687.

[3] Acquired with land.

[4] Experimental structure, erected with research project funds.

[5] Occupied by Diamond Ordnance Fuze Laboratories (DOFL), 1953.

[6] Razed 1948.

[7] Razed.

[8] Erected by Reconstruction Finance Corporation and transferred to NBS.

[Brady, Robert A.,] *Industrial Standardization* (1929)—p. 260.
Burchard, John E., (ed.), *Rockets, Guns and Targets* (OSRD, 1948)—p. 416.
Bureau of the Census, *Historical Statistics of the United States, Colonial Times to 1957* (1960)—p. 8.
Directorate of Tube Alloys (Great Britain), *Statements Relating to the Atomic Bomb* (1945)—p. 379.
Dorsey, N. Ernest, *Physics of Radioactivity* (1921)—p. 144.
Gilchrist, H. L., *A Comparative Study of World War Casualties from Gas and Other Weapons* (1931)—p. 203.
Federated American Engineering Societies, *Waste in Industry* (1921)—p. 253.
Harriman, Norman F., *Standards and Standardization* (1928)—p. 254.
Hart, A.B., and William Schuyler (eds.), *The American Year Book, 1929* (1930)—p. 222.
[Hinman, Wilbur S., Jr.] *The radio proximity fuzes for bombs, rockets, and mortars* (1945)—p. 389.
Irving, James R., *The Scientific Instrument Industry* (1959)—p. 269.
Morey, George W., *The Properties of Glass* (1938)—p. 187.
National Industrial Conference Board, *The Metric versus the English System of Weights and Measures* (1921)—p. 212.
National Resources Committee, *Research—A National Resource* (1938)—p. 327.
National Science Foundation, *Federal Funds for Research, Development, and other Scientific Activities* (1964)—p. 505.
National Science Foundation, *Reviews of Data on Research and Development* (1963)—p. 505.
Newman, James R., (ed.), *What Is Science?* (1961)—p. 357.
Newman, James R., and Byron S. Miller, *The Control of Atomic Energy* (1948)—p. 438.
Noyes, William A., Jr., (ed.), *Chemistry* (OSRD, 1948)—p. 423.
Office of Naval Research, *A Survey of Automatic Digital Computers* (1953)—p. 456.
Owen, Catherine, *Ten Dollars Enough: Keeping House Well on Ten Dollars a Week* (1887)—p. 8.
Price, Don K., *Government and Science: Their Dynamic Relation in American Government* (1954)—p. 430.
Reck, Dickson, (ed.), *National Standards in a Modern Economy* (1956)—p. 254.
Ryan, John A., *A Living Wage* (1906)—p. 8.
Schlink, Frederick J., and Stuart Chase, *Getting Your Money's Worth: a Study in the Waste of the Consumer's Dollar* (1927)—p. 305.
Scholes, Samuel R., *Modern Glass Practice* (1946)—p. 187.
Science Advisory Board, *Report, 1933–1934* (1934)—p. 321.
Science Advisory Board, *Report, 1934–1935* (1935)—p. 324.
Scientific Research Board, *Science and Public Policy. II. The Federal Research Program* (1947)—p. 441.
Smith, F. Langford, *The Radiotron Designer's Handbook* (3d ed., 1940)—p. 197.
Stewart, Irvin, *Organizing Scientific Research for War* (OSRD, 1948)—p. 368.
Suits, C. G., G. R. Harrison, and L. Jordan (eds.), *Applied Physics, Electronics, Optics, Metallurgy* (OSRD, 1948)—p. 403.
White, Frederick A., *American Industrial Research Laboratories* (1961)—p. 275.
White, Frederick A., *Scientific Apparatus* (1960)—p. 269.
Woodworth, Joseph V., *American Tool Making and Interchangeable Manufacturing* (1911)—p. 77.
Woodworth, Joseph V., *Gages and Gaging Systems* (1908)—p. 200.
Zeuner, Frederick E., *Dating the Past: an Introduction to Geochronology* (1952)—p. 470.

Biographies, Autobiographies, and Memoirs: Ten former members of the Bureau are the subjects of essays in the *Biographical Memoirs* series of the National Academy of Sciences: Lyman J. Briggs, George K. Burgess, William W. Coblentz, William F. Hillebrand, Claude S. Hudson, Herbert E. Ives, Paul D. Merica, Edward B. Rosa, Samuel W. Stratton, and Edward W. Washburn. Invaluable collective biographical works have been the *Dictionary of American Biography*, with its supplements; the *Year book* of the American Philosophical Society series; and the successive editions of *American Men of Science.*

Besides the manuscript memoirs of Bureau staff members noted below in Unpublished Sources, two splendidly frank autobiographies are available in print, those of William W. Coblentz and Harvey L. Curtis. Although his recollections of the Bureau are brief, another former staff member, George C. Southworth, offers good background material in his published memoirs. Five Secretaries of Commerce have left memoirs with commentaries on their terms of office: William C. Redfield, Herbert C. Hoover, Daniel C. Roper, Jesse H. Jones, and Lewis L. Strauss. These and other biographical and autobiographical works providing primary sources for the history of the Bureau, with the page reference to their first citation in the text, are as follows:

Cajori, Florian, *The Chequered Career of Ferdinand Rudolph Hassler* (1929)—app. A.
Coblentz, William W., *From the Life of a Researcher* (1951)—p. 196.
Curtis, Harvey L., *Recollections of a Scientist: An Autobiography* (1958)—p. 101.
Eve, A. S., *Rutherford* (1939)—p. 139.
Farley, James A., *Jim Farley's Story* (1948)—p. 333.
Fessenden, Helen M., *Fessenden: Builder of Tomorrows* (1940)—p. 139.
Flexner, Abraham, *Henry S. Pritchett: A Biography* (1943)—p. 53.
Groves, Leslie R., *Now It Can Be Told* (1962)—p. 340.
Hassler, Ferdinand R., *Documents Related to the Construction of Standards of Weights and Measures . . .* (1835)—app. A.
Hoover, Herbert C., *The Memoirs of Herbert Hoover: The Cabinet and the Presidency, 1920–1933* (1952)—p. 229.
Hoover, Herbert C., *The Memoirs of Herbert Hoover: The Great Depression, 1929–1941* (1952)—p. 333.
Jones, Jesse H., *Fifty Billion Dollars: My Thirteen Years with the RCF, 1932–1945* (1951)—p. 408.
Lindbergh, Charles A., *The Spirit of St. Louis* (1954)—p. 284.
Lord, Russell, *The Wallaces of Iowa* (1947)—p. 446.
Lyons, Eugene, *Our Unknown Ex-President* (1948)—p. 229.
Millikan, Robert A., *The Autobiography of Robert A. Millikan* (1950)—p. 13.
Moley, Raymond, *27 Masters of Politics, in a Personal Perspective* (1949)—p. 446.
Pershing, John J., *My Experiences in the War* (1931)—p. 161.
Redfield, William C., *Glimpses of Our Government* (series in the Saturday Evening Post, May 1944)—p. 154.
Redfield, William C., *With Congress and Cabinet* (1924)—p. 160.
Roper, Daniel C., *Fifty Years of Public Life* (1941)—p. 319.

Schmidt, Karl M., *Henry A. Wallace: Quixotic Crusade, 1948,* (1960)—p. 446.
Southworth, George C., *Forty Years of Radio Research* (1962)—p. 144.
Strauss, Lewis S. *Men and Decisions* (1962)—p. 381.
Tully, Grace, *F.D.R.—My Boss* (1948)—p. 319.
Vanderlip, Frank A., *From Farm Boy to Financier* (1935)—p. 54.
Zschokke, Emil, *Memoirs of Ferdinand Rudolph Hassler* (1882)—app. A.

Periodicals and Newspapers: The periodical literature of science, social and political affairs, philosophy, and current events that has been consulted is so extensive that reference can only be made to its direct citation in the history. Singled out, however, must be the magazine *Science,* scarcely a single issue of which since its founding in 1883 has not had a reference to weights, measures, or standards, and which since 1900 has reported every event of note relating to individual members of the Bureau staff and to the affairs of the Bureau itself.

The New York *Times* and the Washington, D.C., newspapers have since the turn of the century, provided useful background details of NBS and Department of Commerce concerns, and with other newspaper accounts of Bureau events (many of them preserved in the NBS correspondence files in the National Archives) give useful sidelights on the scientific and social milieu of the Bureau.

UNPUBLISHED SOURCES

ARCHIVAL COLLECTIONS

The National Archives is the repository for the main body of NBS correspondence since the founding of the Bureau. Located in National Archives Record Group (NARG) 167, the correspondence for the years 1901–45 fills 512 consecutively numbered boxes, each box containing approximately a thousand document sheets, or more than half a million pages of document history. The first citation to these boxes appears on p. 5 of the history.

NARG 167 also includes the Blue Folder collection of Bureau correspondence (first cited on p. 40), comprising 87 boxes, for the years 1902–52. Containing correspondence about significant transactions of recurring interest and identified, for ready reference, by blue folders, these files have been kept until recently at the Bureau.

In contrast to the amount of material in these two correspondence files, of which full use was made, little that was pertinent to the history of the Bureau was found in the special collection in NARG 167 of 57 volumes of the correspondence of the Office of Standard Weights and Measures for the years 1830–1900. With a few exceptions (i.e., p. 30), other sources adequately covered this background material.

Seventeen other collections of NBS records in NARG 167, comprising a total of 1,703 boxes, volumes, and trays, and containing miscellaneous papers relating to weights and measures, manuscripts of research papers, computations, laboratory notebooks, and test records were surveyed for possible papers or marginalia of historical interest. The sampling indicated that the amount to be found would not justify the time required for a full search.

Much useful information was found in the General Records of the Department of Commerce, located in NARG 40, particularly the correspondence of the Office of the Secretary of Commerce (first cited on p. 135), that of the Secretary's Visiting Committee to the Bureau (p. 311), and in the general records of the Department of Commerce (p. 314).

Correspondence of the Secretary of the Treasury relating to the early history of the Bureau appears in NARG 56 (p. 61), of the Secretary of Agriculture in NARG 16 (p. 152), that of the Bureau of the Budget in NARG 51 (p. 307), and of the Office of Scientific Research and Development (OSRD) in NARG 227 (p. 369).

Employment records of former Bureau staff members were made available by official transcript from the Federal Records Center in St. Louis, Mo. Biographical files on former members, which also contain news releases on their careers, records of achievement, copies of their publications, and other memorabilia, were forwarded on loan from the Federal Records Center at Alexandria, Va.

One other archival collection, the Stratton Papers (p. 49), comprising more than 25 boxes of materials, is located in the Archives Library at the Massachusetts Institute of Technology. The preservation and availability of these Papers made possible the biographical sketch of Dr. Stratton in the appendix of the history.

DIRECTOR'S FILES

A recent assembly of correspondence and other materials, long maintained in the Office of the Director, is that temporarily designated "General Correspondence Files of the Director, 1945–55" (first cited on p. 62). The dates are misleading, since the material includes correspondence of as long ago as 1902 and as recently as 1960.

Much of this material comprises NBS policy memoranda, correspondence of recurring interest and importance, and papers of historical concern. The equivalent of almost 30 National Archives boxes, it is presently being organized in the NBS Office of Records Management for transfer to the National Archives.

Other Bureau correspondence to which I have had access, and similar in nature to the "General Corespondence," is that currently maintained in the Office of the Director and so designated where cited in the history.

NBS HISTORICAL FILE

The assemblage of historical documents and other materials by members of the Bureau staff beginning in 1956 and extended by the author and his assistants during the course of research for the history forms the basis for the NBS Historical File. It will be maintained provisionally in the NBS Library at Gaithersburg.

Of special interest in the File are the brief manuscript memoirs by N. Ernest Dorsey (p. 65) and Hobart C. Dickinson (p. 240), and the manuscript memoir-histories of Elmer R. Weaver (p. 114), Raleigh Gilchrist (p. 175), J. Howard Dellinger (p. 292), William W. Coblentz (p. 338), and Galen B. Schubauer (p. 376).

Besides two extended historical accounts of Bureau administration and operations prepared by the individual section and division chiefs in 1949 and again in 1961, the NBS Historical File also contains the records of more than fifty personal interviews or conversations which I held with former and present members of the staff. My correspondence with other than Bureau members that is cited in the history will also be found in this File.

Letters and documents reproduced from the Stratton Papers at MIT, with other Stratton materials collected at the Bureau, have been designated in the NBS Historical File as the NBS Stratton Papers. Similar collections of materials not available in archival records have been tentatively set up and designated by reason of their principal source as the Briggs Papers, Condon Papers, Gilchrist Papers, Crittenden Papers (scarce publications and personal correspondence he preserved), Lowell Papers (relating to NBS patent history), and Silsbee Papers (largely concerning electrical matters).

INDEX

Note: Only those members of the Bureau staff mentioned in the text or singled out in the footnotes are indexed. Authors of NBS publications in the footnotes are not indexed, nor are the names of division and section chiefs from 1901 to 1960, listed in Appendix J.

A

B

D

E

H

I

N

O

Q

R

S

T

U

V

W

X

Y

Z

☆ U.S. GOVERNMENT PRINTING OFFICE : 1974 O—534-543

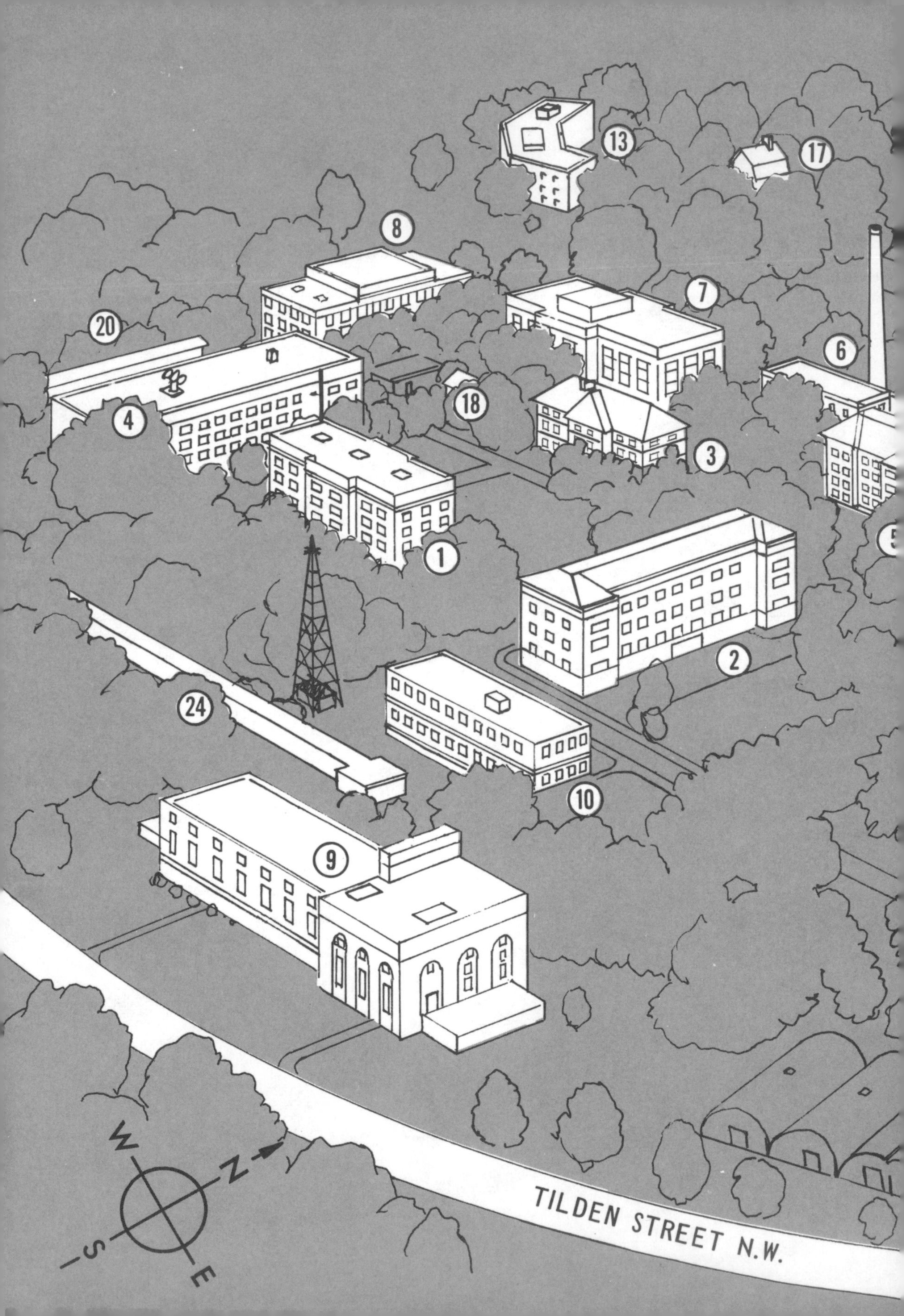
13
17
8
7
20
6
4
18
3
1
5
2
24
10
9
W
N
S
E
TILDEN STREET N.W.